GROUNDWORKS 7

Geotextiles and geomembranes 8–11
Ground reinforcement and erosion control 12–27
Green roof systems 28–30
Retaining walls, piles and anchors 31–43
Hydroseeding 44–45
Knotweed management 46
Landscape services 47–52

DRAINAGE 53

Interceptors, pipes and component chambers . 54–57
Headwalls and flow control 58–61
Stormwater management 62–66
Geocomposite drains 67–68
Permeable paving systems 68–77
Channel drainage systems 78–84

PAVEMENTS 85

Kerbs, edgings and tactile paving 86–91
Resin bound pavements 92–101
In-situ decorative concrete 103
Concrete flag and block paving 104–116
Porcelain tiles 117–118
Natural stone specialists 119–129
Footpath and landscape aggregates 130
Surfacing ancillaries 131–136
Decks, boardwalks and metal gratings 137–155
Bridges for foot and light vehicular traffic ... 156–158

FENCING 159

Mesh, grating and louvred fences 160–172
Vertical bar and ornamental railings 173–180
High security fencing 181–187
Composite panel fencing 188
Recycled plastic fencing 189–190
Timber fencing and slatted screens 190–192
Acoustic barriers and green screens 193–198

TRAFFIC 199

Gates and access control systems 200–215
Safety barriers and guardrails 216–220
Traffic calming, speed and flow control ... 221–224
Bollards, parking and utility posts 225–240
Cycle shelters and stands 241–252
Signage and waymarking 253–267
Pathway illumination 268–270

AMENITIES 271

Road, street and amenity lighting 272–276
Co-ordinated street furniture 277–313
Seats and benches 314–345
Litter bins and recycling units 346–359
Planters and planting systems 360–383
Shelters, canopies and walkways 384–395
Plant housing and storage compounds 395–400
Amenity and leisure buildings 401–403

FEATURES 405

Bespoke timberwork 406–407
Recycled plastic engineered profiles 408
Architectural cast stone 409
Bespoke metalwork 410–423
Public art and sculpture 424–440
Outdoor clocks 441
Landscape ornament 442–443
Fountains and water displays 444–449
Swimming pools and spas 450

RECREATION 451

Playground equipment 452–477
Outdoor games and fitness 478–481
Safer surfacing 482–487
Sports surfaces and equipment 488–496
Sports fencing 497–503
Sports shelters 504

SOFTSCAPE 505

Irrigation 506
Cultivated landscape and sports turf 507–512
Grass seed specialists 513–516
Wildflowers 517–519
Mulches and root barriers 520
Tree care and protection 521–529
Arboricultural services 530–532
Trees, hedging and topiary 533–543
Shrubs 544–545
Herbaceous perennials 546–548
Aquatic plants 549
Hardy exotics 550

ADVERTISERS 551

Contact details for featured companies ... 552

Acrylic coatings, sport and play 482
Admixtures, concrete 103
Adventure playgrounds 452–471
Aerators 506
Aggregates, granite 120
Aggregates, landscape/footpath 130
Air domes for sports facilities 504
Air spade root investigation 532
Airfield ground reinforcement 23
All-weather sports surfaces 488–492
Aluminium benches 324–339
Aluminium edge restraints 90–91
Amenity buildings 401–403
Amenity grass seed 513–516
Amenity lighting 272–276
Amenity turf 507–512
Anchors, earth 43
Anchors, tree root 527
Anti-carbonation coatings 135
Anti-chewing gum coatings 135
Anti-climb fences 160, 162, 164, 167
Anti-intruder fencing 182–187
Anti-ram-raid bollards 232–236
Anti-skateboard studs 132
Anti-slip decking 137–150
Anti-slip flooring
gratings and planks 153–155
panels and inserts 136
Anti-social studs 132
Anti-terrorist barriers & gates 200–211
Aquatic plants 549
Arboricultural services 530–532
Architectural cast stone 409
Architectural concrete 103
Architectural lighting 272–276
Architectural metalwork 410–423
Architectural railings 173–180
Architectural signs 256, 258, 261, 266
Armillary sphere sundials 442
Artificial grass edging systems 88
Artificial grass safer surfacing 482–486
Artificial sports pitches 488–492
Artwork ....
artist blacksmiths 419–423
ceramic artists 438–440
mosaic artists 438–440
muralists 438
sculptors 425–435

Asphalt edge restraints ... 88-90
Athletics track surfaces ... 489
Automatic gates & barriers ... 200-215
Automatic rising bollards ... 204-213

B

Backflow control ... 60
Balconies, metal ... 412
Balconies, hardwood ... 407
Ball courts ... 479
Balustrades
architectural cast stone ... 409
timber decks and boardwalks ... 137-150
Bandstands ... 415, 419
Barrier planters ... 360-372
Barrier planting baskets ... 372
Barriers
access control ... 200-215
acoustic ... 193-198
high visibility ... 217
pedestrian guardrails ... 218-219
post & rail ... 216-219
Basketball hoops ... 480
Bedding mortars ... 133-134
Benches ... 313-343
Bi-parting gates ... 201-215
Biaxial geogrids ... 15-20
Bicycle parking ... 241-252
Bin stores ... 396-398
Bins ... 346-359
Block paving
collections ... 112-116
permeable systems ... 75-77
Block paving accessories
kerb sets ... 112-116
metal edge restraints ... 88-90
sub-base drainage ... 68
Boardwalk construction ... 47
Boardwalks ... 137-150
Bollards ... 225-240
Bollards, high visibility ... 217, 276
Bollards, illuminated ... 268-270
Border edging systems ... 88-91
Boulder fountains ... 449
Boulders ... 126
Bound and bonded surfacing ... 92-101
Boundary fence walls ... 188
Bowling surfaces, synthetic grass ... 488-492
Box head trees ... 536
Bridges ... 156-158
Bronze conservation ... 413
Buildings, leisure & amenity ... 401-403
Bus shelters ... 384-393, 407, 416
Bus stop kerbs ... 86

Butyl rubber liners ... 11
Bypass oil separators ... 54

C

Cabinets, equipment ... 396
Calisthenics street workouts ... 481
Canopies
bespoke metalwork ... 415, 416
covered walkways ... 384-395
cycle shelters ... 241-252
entrance ... 384-395
timber bespoke ... 406-407
Cantilevered gates ... 201-215
Car park barriers ... 201-215
Car park lighting ... 272-276
Car park reinforcement ... 13-26
Carborundum paving inserts ... 136
Cascade water features ... 446
Cast iron benches ... 313-338
Cast stone, architectural ... 409
Cast-on-site concrete paving ... 21
Catchpits ... 56
Cellular confinement ... 12-13, 31, 35
Cellular porous pavers ... 68-72
Cellular stormwater storage ... 63-65
Ceramic artists ... 440
Channel drainage ... 241-252
combined kerb systems ... 78, 80
grating and slot systems ... 78-83
illuminated channels ... 78
Cigarette bins ... 346-359
Cleaning, stone paving ... 134
Climbing frames and walls ... 454-476
Climbing nets ... 456, 458, 467
Clocks & clock towers ... 441
Closeboard fencing,
recycled plastic ... 189-190
Co-ordinated street furniture ... 277-313
Cobblestones ... 126
Coconut fibre logs ... 26
Coir logs ... 26
Coir reinforcing fabrics ... 26-27
Coloured pavements
concrete ... 103
resin bound ... 92-101
Columns, cast stone ... 409
Combined kerb & drainage ... 84, 78, 80
Compaction bins ... 350
Component chambers ... 55-57
Composite decking ... 146-150
Composite panel fencing ... 188
Compounds, cycle parking ... 242-252
Compounds and utility stores ... 395-400
Concrete admixtures & stains ... 103

Concrete benches ... 320-340
Concrete block paving ... 112-116
Concrete flood defence walls ... 38
Concrete grass paving blocks ... 14, 21
Concrete kerbs & edgings ... 86
Concrete mattresses ... 14
Concrete paving flags ... 104-111
Concrete piles ... 42
Concrete retaining wall blocks ... 32-38
Concrete revetments ... 14
Coniferous trees ... 533-543
Containment kerbs ... 86
Continuous slot drainage systems ... 78-83
Contract growing, trees ... 533-543
Contractors, landscape ... 48-52
Copings, stone ... 128
Copings, cast stone ... 409
Corner protection hoops ... 217
Corporate branding signs ... 254-266
Corrugated tank liners ... 11
Corten steel edging ... 88, 91
Corten steel seating ... 318, 326, 336, 338
Courtyard gates ... 191
Covered walkways ... 385-393
Crash rated gates & barriers ... 200-215
Crib retaining walls ... 37-41
Cricket pavilions ... 401
Cricket wickets and cages ... 496
Cricket wickets, synthetic grass ... 488-492
Culvert head wall reinforcement ... 13
Culvert header beams ... 58
Cycle bridges ... 156-158
Cycle shelters and stands ... 241-252

D

Deciduous trees ... 533-543
Decking
metal gratings ... 153-155
timber, composite, plastic ... 137-150
fastening systems ... 151
pedestal supports ... 152
slip-resistant inserts ... 136
Decorative aggregates ... 130
Decorative bound surfacing ... 92-101
Decorative concrete effects ... 103
Decorative railings ... 173-180
Demarcation studs ... 132
Design and build contractors ... 48-52
Desilting services ... 47
Digital signage ... 256
Digital signs ... 253-267
Dimensional building stone ... 122-127
Directory signs ... 395-400
Display cases ... 253-267

Dog waste bins ... 346, 352, 356, 358, 359
Domes, sports shelters ... 504
Domestic channel drainage ... 79-82
Drainage
cellular paving ... 68-72
channels ... 78-83
combined kerb ... 84
drain guards ... 10
geocomposites ... 67-68
green roofs ... 68
headwalls ... 58-59
pipes, large diameter ... 55
pipes, component chambers ... 56-57
sports pitches ... 493-494
stormwater ... 62-66
structural ... 67-68
turf ... 67-68
Dredging services ... 47
Driving range shelters ... 504

E

Earth anchors ... 43
Earth reinforcement ... 13-26
Earth retaining walls ... 31-41
Edge restraints ... 88-91
Electric fencing ... 185-187
Embankment reinforcement
biodegradable ... 26-27
gabions ... 37-38
headwalls ... 58-59
non-degradable ... 12-26
retaining walls ... 31-41
Emergency vehicle access lanes ... 19-25
Energy distribution towers ... 239
Energy saving coatings ... 135
Entrance canopies ... 385, 386, 391, 393
Entrance gates ... 200-215
Entrance signs ... 258-267
EPDM liners ... 11
Equestrian arena sands ... 495
Equestrian surfaces ... 18
Equipment stores ... 395-400
Erosion control
biodegradable ... 26-27
gabions ... 37-38
headwalls ... 58-59
hydraulic seeding ... 44-45
non-degradable ... 12-26
Evergreen trees ... 533-543
Exhibitions ... 556
Expanded metal mesh fencing ... 166
Exposed aggregate, in-situ concrete ... 103
Extensive green roofs ... 28-30

F

Fabric canopies 390-395
Fabricated metalwork 410-419
Featherboard fencing 191
Feathered trees 534-543
Feature stones 126
Feeder posts 238-240
Fencing
  composite panel 188
  high security 181-187
  mesh, grating and louvred 160-172
  noise barriers 193-198
  railings 172-180
  recycled plastic 189-190
  sports 497-503
  timber 190-192
Fertilisers 514
Fibre-reinforced rootzone mixes 22, 25
Fibreglass planters ... 360, 362, 364, 379
Filter chambers 56
Fine fescue grass seed mixtures .. 515-516
Fingerposts 253-267
Finials, cast stone 409
Fire access roads 19-25
Fitness trails & equipment 456-478
Fixings & fasteners 151
Flags
  concrete 104-111
  natural stone 119-129
Flap valves 60, 56
Flexible bollards 236
Flexible retaining wall systems 31, 35
Flexible sheet membranes 11
Flowerbed edging systems 88
Football pitches, synthetic grass .. 488-491
Footbridges 410-416
Footpath and landscape aggregates 130
Footpath edging 88-91
Footpath reinforcement 12-26
Forestry mulching 531
Fountain & water display experts .. 444-448
Fountains, cast stone 443

G

Gabion fill materials 120
Gabion furniture 341

Gabion walls 37-38
Garages 401
Garden arches, bespoke 410-417
Garden design and construction 48-52
Garden irrigation 506
Garden ornament 443
Garden rings 88
Garden screens, timber 190-192
Garden seating 329-334
Gate valves 56
Gatehouses 396
Gates
  access control 200-215
  bespoke metalwork 410-423
Geocells, ground reinforcement 12-13
Geocells, stormwater management .. 63-65
Geocomposite drains 67-68
Geocomposite roof drains 15-20
Geogrids 11
Geomembranes 8-10
Geotextiles 11
Glacial boulders 126
Glass bound surfacing 96
Gneiss cladding 127
Goal ends 496, 480, 454, 456, 464
Golf bunker and green sands 495
Golf course irrigation 506
Golf course turf 508-510
Granite aggregates 120
Granite benches 313-343
Granite kerbs 86, 124, 127, 128
Granite paving 119, 124, 127
Granite, quarried products 120
Granite setts 127
Granite steps 127
Grass and wildflower seeding 44-45
Grass edging 88-91
Grass reinforcement
  grids and meshes 15-25
  rootzone mixes 22, 25, 26
Grass seed mixtures 513-516
Grassmats, play areas 482
Grate drainage systems 78-80
Grating fences 162
Grating flooring 153-155
Gravel surfacing
  aggregates 130
  cellular paving 69-71
  edge restraints 88-91
  resin bound and bonded ... 73-74, 92-101
Gravity retaining walls 33-39
Green roofs
  products and systems 28-30
  drainage 68
  hydroseeding 44

Green wall planter systems 376
Grit bins 346
Gritstone blocks 126
Ground anchors 43
Ground concrete paving 104-109
Ground cover plants 546
Ground reinforcement
  biodegradable 26-27
  non-degradable 12-26
Grounds maintenance services 48-52
Grouts and mortars 133-134
Guardrails, pedestrian 218-219
Guying for trees 521-529

H

Handrails
  illuminated 219
  protective 216-220
  wrought iron 419
Hanging baskets 372
Hard landscaping contractors 48-52
Hardy exotics 58-59
Headwalls 530
Hedge moving 533-543
Hedging 153
Heel-proof gratings 153
Heel-proof grilles 132
Height restrictors 208, 214, 215
Herbaceous perennials 547-548
High containment kerbs 86
High-capacity drainage systems 78-82
High-flow drainage ditch
  reinforcement 12, 26
High-security fencing systems 182-187
Highway parapets, hardwood 220
Hinged gates 203-204
Hockey pitches
  all weather 488-492
  bespoke timber 406-407
  fencing systems 497-503
Housings, utility / industrial 395-400
Hydroseeding 44-45

I

Illuminated benches 330, 340
Illuminated bollards 268-270
Illuminated handrails 219
Impact absorbing play surfacing 482-487
In-ground power units 238-240
Inclusive play 452-477
Instant hedging 533, 542
Intensive green roofs 28-30
Interceptors 54
Interpretation signs 253-265
Invasive non-native weed control 46

J

Japanese knotweed management 46
Jardinieres 142-143
Jetties 142-143
Jointing mortars 133-134
Jute erosion control products 26, 45

K

Kerbs
  block paving 112-116
  combined drainage 84
  concrete 86-87
  high containment 86
  natural stone 86-87, 119-129
  protective bollards 230
  rising road blockers 200-215
Kinetic sculptures 428, 431
Kiosks 396
Knotweed management 46, 520

L

Lake construction 47
Lake desilting 47
Lake liners 11
Landscape edging 88-91
Landscape irrigation 506
Landscape ornament 442-443
Landscape services 442-443
Landscape structures
  design, build, maintenance 48-52
  bespoke timber 406-407
Large format concrete paving 104, 109
Lawn edging systems 507-512
Lawn turf 88-91
Lectern signs 254-265
LED lighting 272-276
Leisure and amenity buildings 401-403
Letter carvers 436-437
Lift-assist manhole covers 131
Lighting
  pathway and signs 268-270
  road, street and amenity 272-276
Limestone benches 129
Limestone paving 119, 122, 124, 127, 129
Linear drainage systems 80
Litter bin stores 396-398
Litter bins 346-359
Living acoustic barriers 193-198

Irrigation
  landscaping, sportsfields 506
  urban trees 522-527

Living walls, slatted timber screens 192
Load support, geocells 13
Lockers, cycle parking 246-252
Long jump run-ups and pits 496
Louvred fencing, metal 160
Louvred fencing, timber 190-192
Low level protection rails 217
Low vibration piling 42

M

Machine-laid paving 112, 116
Manhole covers
  lift assist 131
  solid top 131
Map boards 258
Marginal plants, aquatic 549
Marine walling 34
Marking paint 132
Masonry protective coatings 135
Matting, biodegradable 26-27
Mechanical earth anchoring 43
Mesh
  erosion control 15-25
  floor gratings 153
  perimeter fencing 160-177
  sports fencing 497-503
Metal floor gratings 153-155
Metal grating fencing 160-177
Metalwork, specialist fabricators 410-419
Metalwork, artist blacksmiths 420-423
Metalwork, plant supports 416
Mild steel railings 173-180
Millstone fountains 449
Mobility scooter charging stations 395
Modular buildings 401-403
Modular planting systems 360-383
Modular play systems 452-477
Monolith signs 253-267
Monumental stone 120
Mooring bollards 235
Mortars, early trafficking 133
Mortars, pavement construction 134
Mosaics artists 438-440
Mountain bike trail construction 494
MUGA fencing 497-502
MUGA shelters 504
MUGA surfacing 488-491
Mulch mats, erosion control 26-27
Mulches, rubber surfacing 520
Multi-sport goals 478
Multi-stem trees 533-536
Murals 438
Musical play 464, 466, 475

N

Natural aggregates 130
Natural play 456, 458, 468, 469, 470, 477
Natural sports pitches 493-494
Natural stone
  cleaning and protection 134
  kerbs 86-87, 124, 127, 128
  paving, walling, feature stone 119-129
  seating 324, 343
Natural stone specialists 119-129
Natural swimming pond construction 49
Netball court surfacing systems 491
Noise barriers 193-198
Noise bund reinforcement 13-14
Non-woven geotextiles 9
Noticeboards 254-265
Nurseries
  aquatic plants 549
  perennials, ground cover plants 547-548
  shrubs 543-545
  trees, hedging, topiary 533-543

O

Oak benches 313, 335, 343
Oak-framed buildings 401
Open mesh floor gratings 153
Orientation signs 253-264
Orifice plates 56, 63
Ornamental cast stone 409, 443
Outdoor games and fitness 478-481
Outdoor gyms 481, 464
Outdoor musical play 464, 466, 475
Outdoor porcelain floor tiles 117-118
Outdoor seating 313-343
Overflow car parks 18-26

P

Paints, road marking 132
Palisade fencing, recycled plastic 189-190
Palisade fencing, steel 181, 184, 187
Palisades, recycled plastic 408
Parapet screening, cast stone 409
Park benches 313-343
Parking barriers 200-215
Parking posts 228
Parking, cycle 241-252
Parkour systems 479
PAS 68 rated products
  bollards 232, 235
  gates, barriers, blockers 204-211
  planters 378
Passenger shelters 384-393

Pathway edging systems 88-91
Pathway lights 268-270
Paved drainage systems 80
Paver slot gratings 78-83
Paving
  cleaning and protection 134
  concrete block 112-116
  concrete flags 104-111
  granite 119, 124, 127
  green roof overlays 30
  limestone 119, 122, 124, 127, 129
  porcelain 117-118
  porphyry 119, 124, 127
  quartzite 119, 124, 127
  sandstone 119-128
  travertine 127
  whin stone 119, 128
  Yorkstone 119, 124, 127
Paving accessories
  cleaning and protection 134
  edge restraints 88-91
  in-ground power units 238-240
  manhole covers, lift assist 131
  mortars 133-134
  pedestal supports 152
  ventilation access grilles 132
Pebbles 126
Pedestal decking supports 152
Pedestrian crossing studs 132
Pedestrian guardrails 218-219
Pedestrian turnstiles 204, 208, 209, 210, 211
Penstocks 60, 56
Percussion driven earth anchors 43
Perennial mats for green roofs 29
Perforated plank flooring 153-155
Pergolas 406-407
Perimeter fencing
  mesh, grating and louvred 160-172
  railings 173-180
  high security systems 181-187
  composite panel 188
  recycled plastic 189-190
  timber 190-192
  noise barriers 193-198
  sports 497-503
Permeable load supporting surfaces 13-24
Permeable paving
  cellular 68-72
  concrete block 75-77
  resin-bound 73-74
Permeable tree pit surfacing 528
Picket fencing, recycled plastic 189-190
Picnic tables 344-345, 320-341
Piling & ground engineering services 42
Pillar clocks 441

Pipe drain inlet units 59
Pipes, large diameter 55
Planks, metal grating 154
Plant housing/storage compounds 395-400
Plant housings 398-400
Planters, plant support systems 360-383
Planters, cast stone 443
Planters, raised terraces 360-383
Planters, roof gardens 360-383
Plastic benches & picnic tables 332
Plastic fencing 189-190
Play boulders 126
Play houses 460
Play logs 470
Play trees 470
Playground timbers 477
Playgrounds
  equipment 452-477
  railings 175-180
  surfacing 482-487
Pond construction 47
Pond desilting 47
Pond inlet headwalls 58-59
Pond liners 11
Pontoons 142-143
Pool houses 401
Porcelain tiles 117-118
Porphyry paving 119, 124, 127
Post & panel signs 258
Post & protective guardrail 216-220
Post & rail, recycled plastic 189-190
Poster cases 254-258
Potable water liners 11
Power supply bollards 238-240
Pre-seeded erosion control mats 27
Prefabricated buildings 401-403
Priming mortars 133-134
Projecting clocks 441
Protective coatings, paving 134
Public art
  architectural metalwork 410-423
  sculptors 424-435
  letter carvers 436-437
  ceramic & mosaic artists 438-440
Public seating 313-343
Public transport kerbs 86

Q

Quartzite paving 119, 124, 127
Quayside posts 216

R

Railings
  architectural
  guardrails and handrails 216-220
  mild steel 173-180
  spectator 497-503
  wrought iron 419
Ram-raid bollards 204-213
Ramps, traffic calming 221-224
Rebound fencing 497-502
Reclaimed stone 126-128
Reconstituted stone paving 111
Recycled plastic
  benches & picnic tables 332
  decks and boardwalks 142-143
  engineered profiles 408
  fencing 189-190
  sleepers and edgings 90
Recycling bins 346-359
Reflective acoustic barriers 193-195
Reflective bollards 276
Reinforced concrete paving 104, 111
Reinforced earth retaining walls 31-41
Reinforced grassed surfaces 18-25
Reinforced natural grass rootzones 25
Reinforced sports turf 26
Reinforced turf 26
Removable bollards 225-236
Reproduction stone flags 111
Resin bound surfacing
  bound and bonded 92-99
  permeable 73-74
  tree pit surfacing 528-529, 73-74
Restraints, landscape edging 88-91
Retail branding signs 256-266
Retaining walls 31-41
Retractable barriers 208
Retractable power units 240
Revetments, concrete 14
Rigid mesh fencing 164-171
Rising arm barriers 208-215
Riven concrete paving 104, 108, 111
River inlet headwalls 58-59
Riverbank erosion control 26
River inlet headwalls 58-59
Road and street lighting 272-276
Road blockers 204, 208, 210
Road drainage solutions 84
Road studs and markings 132

S

Roadside seeding 44-45
Rock armour 120
Roof gardens planters 360-381
Root barriers 520
Rootball fixing systems 527
Rope play 452, 460, 464, 467, 471, 477
Rounded glacial boulders 11
Rubber liners 482, 520
Rubber mulches 126
Rubber safety surfacing 482, 487
Rugby pitches, all-weather 489, 491

Safer surfacing 482-487
Sand play 458-460
Sand slitting 494
Sandstone paving 122-128
Sandstone paving flags & setts .. 119-128
Scottish whin stone 128
Sculptors 425-435
Sculpture
  sculptors 425-435
  metalworkers 410, 413-414, 420-423
  restoration services 413-419
Sculpture commissioning 424
Sea wall revetments 47
Seating / planter units 362-382
Seats and benches 313-343
Security fencing 160-187
Sediment entrapment matting 10
Sedum mats & trays, green roofs ... 29-30
Sedum matting, ground cover 546
Seed mixtures, grass 513-516
Seed mixtures, wildflowers ... 513-514, 519
Seeded blankets, erosion control 27
Seeding, hydraulic 44-45
Self-binding gravels 126
Self-drilling wood screws 151
Self-watering hanging baskets 372
Self-watering planters .. 372, 373, 383
Semi-mature tree transplanting .. 530-532
Semi-mature tree supply 533-543
Sensory play 462-475
Setts
  concrete 112, 116
  natural stone 124-128
Sheffield cycle stands 242-252
Shelters & covered walkways 384-395
Shelters, cycle parking 241-252
Shock-absorbent safety surfacing 487
Show home gardens 50
Shrubs, specimen 543-545
Shrubs, direct seeding 44
Sign lighting 276

Signage and waymarking 253-267
Silt fences 10, 27
Silt traps 56
Silver-grey granite 120
Skate parks 456, 464, 479, 481
Slate paving 119, 124, 126, 127
Slatted timber garden screens 192
Slides, playground 454-476
Sliding gates 200-211
Slip-resistant decking 144-150
Slip-resistant panels, treads, nosings ... 136
Slip-resistant gratings and planks .. 153-155
Slope reinforcement
  non-degradable 12-26
  biodegradable 26-27
  headwalls 58-59
  retaining walls 31-41
Slot drains 78-83
Small element paving 104-111
Smoking shelters 391-393
Smooth ground paving 104, 109
Soft landscaping contractors 48-52
Soil nail walls 42
Solar powered signs 258
Solid bar railings 176
Sound absorbent barriers 193
Sound sculptures, play 466
Spas 450
Specimen shrubs 543-545
Specimen trees 533-543
Spectator railings 499-502
Speed cushions 222
Speed gates 201-210
Speed ramps 221-224
Speed restrictors 224
Sports pitches and facilities
  court marking 496
  drainage 493-494
  equipment 496
  fencing 497-503
  grass seed mixtures 513-516
  irrigation 506
  natural pitch construction 493-494
  pavilions 493-494
  sands 495
  self binding aggregates 130
  shelters 504
  synthetic surfaces 488-492
  turf 508-512
Spring riders 456, 458
Stain removal, paving 134
Stainless steel edge restraints 90-91
Stainless steel seating 313-325
Stains, concrete colouring 103
Stair treads & planks 136

anti-slip treads & nosings 136
metal gratings and planks 153-154
Statues, cast stone 443
Steel landscape edging 88-91
Steel palisade fencing 181, 184
Steel piles 42
Steel railings 173-180
Steel tennis nets 478
Steps
cast stone 409
metal gratings and planks 153-154
slip-resistant inserts 136
stone 124-127
Stone benches 127-129
Stone carvers 436-437
Stone mastic asphalts 120
Stone piers 128
Stone quarries, granite 120-121
Stop logs 60
Storage compounds 396-400
Stormwater management
cellular water storage systems 62-66
drainage ditch channel lining 12, 21
headwalls and outfalls 58-59
high capacity drainage channels 78-82
penstocks and valves 60-61
pipes, large diameter 55
vortex flow control 56, 61-66
Street furniture
benches 313-343
bollards 225-240
co-ordinated 277-313
cycle parking 241-252
lighting 272-276
litter bins 346-359
planters 360-383
shelters 384-395
waymarking 253-267
Street lighting 272-276
Structural drainage 68
Structural tree soil 523-524
Studs for roads and pavements 132
Sub-base aggregates 120
Sub-base stabilisation 13
Subsoil drainage systems 55-57
Subsoil revegetation 44-45
Subsurface drainage 67
SUDS
cellular paving systems 68-72
permeable block paving 75-77
porous resin-bound surfacing 73-74
stormwater management 55-66
Sundials 442-443
Surface drainage 54-84
Swale inlet headwalls 58

Swimming pools and spas 450
Swing barriers & gates 208-215
Swings, play equipment 452-475
Symbols for road marking 132
Synthetic sports surfaces 488-492
cricket 488, 490-492
football 488-492
hockey 488-492
multi-sport 488-492
netball 491
tennis 489-492
Synthetic grass, safer surfacing 482-487

T
Table tennis 478, 481
Tactile panels, anti-slip 136
Tactile paving 87
Tactile stone paving, blister 87
Tactile stone paving, corduroy 87
Telescopic bollards 202-213
Telescopic sliding gates 202
Temporary access roads 13-20
Tennis courts
fencing systems 497-500
synthetic surfaces 489-492
Tensile fabric structures 394
Textured concrete paving 104, 107, 108
Textured kerbs 86-87
Themed play units 456
Thermoplastic road markings 132
Threshold drainage 79
Throwing cages 496
Tiered planters 373
Tiles, ground reinforcement 13-23
Tiles, porcelain 117-118
Tiles, safer surfacing 482-487
Timber decking 138-150
Timber fasteners 151
Timber fencing 190-192
Timber garden screens 190-192
Timber gates 191
Timber retaining walls 37-41
Timber seating 313-343
Timber, bespoke structures 406-407
Tongue & groove plastic fencing 189
Topiary 534-540
Topsoil revegetation 44-45
Tracked gates 200-215
Traffic calming and safety products
bollards 225-240
calming systems 222
cushions & ramps 221-224
direction restrictors 221
flow plates 221-224

road studs and markings 132
temporary islands 222
Trampolines 456, 458, 467
Transparent acoustic barriers 194
Transport shelters 388
Travertine paving 127
Tree and shrub supply and planting 541
Tree and vegetation clearance 531
Tree houses 464-471
Tree planters 360-380
Trees – nursery stock 533-543
Trees – planting products and systems
anchors 527
grilles & guards 525-528
irrigation systems 522-527
root barriers 520
soil 523-524
soil support systems 521-524
tree pit surfacing 528, 529
Trees – root protection
air spade root investigation 532
geocells 12, 13, 20
root bridges 521
soil support systems 521-524
Trees – services
direct seeding 44-45
moving large trees 530-531
supply and planting 530-531, 541-542
stump removal 531
tree surgery 531
Tree seats 314-336
Trellis panels, timber 191
Trim trails 458, 460, 478
Trolley shelters 391-393, 407
Troughs, planting 366-373
Turf growers 507-512
Turf irrigation 506
Turf rootzone mixes 22, 25, 26
Turf, soil-less 26
Turnstiles 204, 208, 209, 210, 211

U
Underground waste systems 351
Underground water tanks 11
Uniaxial geogrids 15
Urban furniture 277-313
Utility supply bollards 239-240

V
Vegetated acoustic barriers 193-196
Vegetated environmental bags 35
Vegetated retaining walls 31, 34, 35, 37
Vehicle parapets, hardwood 220
Venetian fencing 191

Ventilation access grilles 132
Verge stabilisation 18-24
Vertical bar fencing 175-178
Vertical green wall planters 376
Vortex flow control chambers 56
Vortex flow control, stormwater 61
Vortex separators 62-66

W
Waiting shelters 388-393
Walkways, covered 385-393
Walkways, decks & boardwalks 137-150
Walkways, metalwork (bespoke) 416, 423
Walling stone 122-128
Warm mix asphalt 120
Waste bins 346-359
Waste stream enclosures 395
Water backflow control 60
Water margin erosion protection 26
Water play 460-468
Water storage tanks 11
Water features & fountains 444-448, 417
Watercourse construction and
maintenance services 47
Waterproofing coatings 135
Wayfinding signs 253-267
Weathervanes 422
Welded mesh fencing
general purpose 162-172
high security 182-187
Wet pour safer surfacing 482-486
Wetland erosion control 26
Wetland habitat construction 47
Wetland plants & planting services 549
Wheelchair accessible play eqpt 454-475
Wheeled bin enclosures 395
Whin stone 128
Wildflowers
mats for green roofs 29
hydraulic seeding 44-45
seed mixtures 513-514, 519
turf 518
Willow walls 193
Wind pipes 475
Wind sculptures 422
Wingwalls 58
Woven geotextiles 8
Wrought iron metalwork 419

YZ
Yorkstone paving 119, 124, 127
Youth shelters 390
Zoological fencing systems 171

GROUNDWORKS

Geotextiles, geomembranes and environmental barriers

Geotextiles: woven geotextiles for road construction, soil reinforcement and critical filter demands; non-woven abrasion resistant and UV stabilised geotextiles.

Silt fences, drain guards and dewatering bags for run off pollution control.

Geomembranes and flexible sheet membranes for lakes, ponds, reservoirs, canals, slurry pits, settlement lagoons and water storage tanks.

8-11

Ground reinforcement and erosion control

- Non-degradables
Soil reinforcement, earth retention, pathway reinforcement, tree root protection. Geocells, geogrids, geocomposites, paving fabrics, geomats, revetments, meshes, cellular paving for grasses and gravels, reinforced turf and grass rootzone mixtures.

- Biodegradables
Mats, blankets and meshes for the protection of exposed soils on slopes and embankments in pre-seeded and non-seeded forms. Biodegradable mulch and weed suppression mats. Coir fibre logs, coconut fibre biorolls and filter blankets for bank protection and erosion control in waterways and wetlands.

12-27

Green roof systems

Products and services for extensive and intensive green roofs including:
- drainage layers, edging profiles, overlay paving systems and substrates
- wildflower, sedum and perennial mats.

28-30

Retaining structures

Gravity and reinforced soil walls in solid and cellular precast concrete, timber and recycled plastic. Gabion baskets for retaining walls and architectural cladding.

Geosynthetic retention solutions for steep slopes and vegetated walls.

31-41

Piling systems and earth anchors

Piling systems for foundations; earth anchors and soil nails for ground reinforcement and embankment stabilisation.

42-43

Hydroseeding

Hydroseeding services for land reinstatement, highway embankments, landfill sites, green roofs and residential housing developments on brownfield sites.

44-45

Knotweed management

Japanese knotweed control and eradication services for civil and commercial projects.

46

Lakes and watercourses

Specialists in installing anti-erosion, geomembrane and revetment products, piling and water control structures for lakes, ponds, watercourses and wetland habitats.

47

Landscape services

Specialists in hard and soft landscaping for clients in the public, commercial, industrial and leisure sectors.

48-52

EXTERNAL WORKS ONLINE

For detailed information supported by case studies, downloads and tools to help you make faster and better decisions ...

☞ www.externalworks.co.uk

TenCate Geolon® PP100s in prefabricated panels — Wood Wharf

TenCate Geolon® PP60 for wind farm access tracks – Calder Water

TenCate Geolon® PET 600 and 300 as a solution for a load transfer platform

TenCate Geolon® PET 1500 in prefabricated panels for installing below water for breakwater on marine days

TenCate Geosynthetics (UK) Ltd

Woven geotextiles

TenCate Geosynthetics delivers turnkey system solutions for the road and railway constructions, retaining structures, hydraulic constructions, embankments, tunnel construction, pipeline construction, landfill, and shoreline protection and marine structure construction markets.

Geotextiles for road constructions

TenCate Geolon® PP series are woven fabrics, made of polypropylene tape and split fibre yarns, developed and manufactured mainly for usage as separator and reinforcement geosynthetic in road constructions. They are also available with woven-in loops and long life additives for under water applications.

Typical applications:
* Subgrade stabilisation and reinforcement.
* Working platforms.
* Temporary haul roads.
* Wind farm access roads.

Geotextiles for soil reinforcement

TenCate Geolon® PET are woven geosynthetics for soil reinforcement made of 100% high tenacity polyester yarns, available in tensile strengths up to 2500 kN/m.

Typical applications:
* Basal reinforcement for embankments on soft ground.
* Embankments on piles (load transfer platform).
* Embankments over voids.

All are covered by BS8006.

Geotextiles for critical filter demands

TenCate Geolon® PE filter fabrics are woven geotextiles made from high density polyethylene monofilament and tape yarns.

These fabrics are UV-stabilised and specially designed to meet the most critical filter demands. They are also available with woven-in loops for underwater applications.

TENCATE
materials that make a difference

Contact

Carol Watkins, Telford
t: 01952 588066
f: 01952 588466
Service.uk@tencate.com

Scott Harvey, UK Sales Manager
t: 07940 738184
s.harvey@tencate.com

Sarah Nabbs, Area Sales M62 and North England
t: 07787 513393
s.nabbs@tencate.com

Simon McMail, Area Sales SW and Wales
t: 07958 027327
s.mcmail@tencate.com

David Dutton, Area Sales London, SE and East Midlands
t: 07990 935338
d.dutton@tencate.com

Web

www.tencate.com
www.geotube.com

Address

TenCate Geosynthetics (UK) Ltd
PO Box 773
Telford TF7 9FE

Accreditation

ISO 9001
ISO 14001

Operational area

Worldwide

Additional entries

Non-woven geotextiles ▶ 9
Reinforcement and erosion control ▶ 15

materials that make a difference

Contact
Carol Watkins, Telford
t: 01952 588066
f: 01952 588466
Service.uk@tencate.com

Scott Harvey, UK Sales Manager
t: 07940 738184
s.harvey@tencate.com

Sarah Nabbs, Area Sales M62 and
North England
t: 07787 513393
s.nabbs@tencate.com

Simon McMail, Area Sales SW
and Wales
t: 07958 027327
s.mcmail@tencate.com

David Dutton, Area Sales London,
SE and East Midlands
t: 07990 935338
d.dutton@tencate.com

Web
www.tencate.com
www.geotube.com

Address
TenCate Geosynthetics (UK) Ltd
PO Box 773
Telford TF7 9FE

Accreditation
ISO 9001
ISO 14001

Operational area
Worldwide

Additional entries
Woven geotextiles ▶ 8
Reinforcement and erosion control ▶ 15

TenCate Geosynthetics (UK) Ltd

Non-woven geotextiles

TenCate Geosynthetics delivers turnkey system solutions for the road and railway constructions, retaining structures, hydraulic constructions, embankments, tunnel construction, pipeline construction, landfill, and shoreline protection and marine structure construction markets.

UV-stabilised geotextiles

TenCate Polyfelt® TS and P geotextiles are mechanically bonded continuous-filament non-wovens manufactured from UV-stabilised polypropylene. Mechanical properties guarantee strong resistance to installation damage, excellent hydraulic properties and long-term performance.
Typical applications:

• Separation for infrastructure projects.
• Filter drain wraps.
• Membrane protection.
• Filtration for rock armour or rip rap layers.
• Horse ménage and gallops.

Geocomposite filter fabrics

TenCate Polyfelt® F filter fabrics are geocomposites, consisting of two layers of mechanically bonded continuous-filament non-woven made from 100% UV-stabilised polypropylene. One filament layer is designed as a filter, the other as a protection layer preventing mechanical damage to the filter. The optimised opening size and number of constrictions ensure excellent long-term filter performance.
Typical applications:

• Filtration for rock armour or rip rap layers.
• Separation within high permeability soils.

Abrasion-resistant geotextiles

TenCate Bidim® AR is a mechanically bonded continuous-filament non-woven with an enhanced abrasion resistance. TenCate Bidim® AR combines the benefits of conventional non-woven geotextiles with an improved resistance to abrasion stresses. It was developed for railway construction where the high mechanical stresses imposed by the ballast require special attention.

TenCate Polyfelt® demonstrating energy absorption

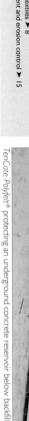

TenCate Polyfelt® protecting an underground concrete reservoir below backfill

TenCate Polyfelt® being used as a filter layer below rock armour

TenCate Bidim® AR abrasion-resistant geotextile

Ultra Drain Guard – emptying trapped sediment

Ultra Drain Guard for road gully silt protection

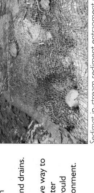

Sedimat in-stream sediment entrapment mats

Sedimat for disturbed sediment pollution control

Terrastop Premium – trapped silt on forestry project

Hy-Tex (UK) Ltd

Silt and run-off pollution control

Hy-Tex offers a range of products for silt management and run-off pollution control.

• Drain guards

Ultra Drain Guards are designed to remove oil and sediment pollution from surface water running into gully drains from construction sites, farms and industrial estates.

• In-stream sediment entrapment matting

Sedimat™ biodegradable disturbed sediment entrapment matting is used in waterways during in-stream construction such as pipe laying or dredging projects. It traps disturbed sediment to prevent pollution of aquatic habitats downstream.

• Silt fences

Terrastop™ Premium is a special, high-quality, permeable filter fabric that can be installed as an entrenched vertical entrapment fence. Applications include building areas, haul roads, spoil heaps and quarries where silt-laden stormwater run-off and site debris can contaminate land, watercourses, lakes and drains.

• Dewatering bags

Ultra Dewatering Bags provide an effective way to collect harmful sediments from dirty water pumped out of excavation works that would otherwise pollute the surrounding environment.

Contact
David Poole/Ryan Markham
t: 01233 720097
f: 01233 720098
sales@hy-tex.co.uk

Web
www.hy-tex.co.uk

Address
Hy-Tex (UK) Ltd
Aldington Mill, Mill Lane
Aldington
Ashford TN25 7AJ

Accreditation
ISO 9001

Affiliations
BALI

Additional entries
Biodegradables ➤ 26
Vertical green wall planters ➤ 376
Root barriers ➤ 520

Terrastop Premium silt fence – construction project

Ultra Dewatering Bag in use near lake

Terrastop Premium silt fence – Scottish Hydro

Ultra Dewatering Bag – construction site

Ultra Dewatering Bag – building site pollution control

Terrastop Premium silt fence controls run-off pollution

Ultra Dewatering Bag – preparing for use

☐ ☐ ☐ **For detailed information on featured products and services** ⌕ **www.externalworks.co.uk**

Russetts Developments Ltd
Flexible sheet membranes

For more than 25 years, Russetts Developments Ltd (RDL) has specialised in the fabrication of flexible sheet membranes for the containment of a variety of liquids, including aggressive chemicals and potable water.

• Geomembranes

Butyl rubber and *Epalyn*® EPDM are suitable for tailored liners, garden ponds, small lakes and reservoirs.

Butyl rubber and *Flagon GeoP/AT* are suitable for both WRc and DWI water storage tanks.

Flagon GeoP is supplied for the storage of oils and chemicals.

Polypropylene membranes are available for larger lagoons and reservoirs, as well as chemical containment.

Flexible PVC sheeting can be supplied for lining garden ponds.

• Applications

Applications range from small, tailor-made ornamental ponds to large slurry lagoons, reservoirs and water storage tanks.

Linings with WRc and DWI approval can be supplied, along with membranes for oil and chemical storage.

Contact
Steve Nunn
t: 0870 770 2800
f: 0870 770 2801
info@russetts.co.uk

Web
www.russetts.co.uk

Address
Russetts Developments Ltd
27-29 Burners Lane
Kiln Farm
Milton Keynes MK11 3HA

0.75mm EPDM rubber liner – Leatherhead

Buscot Park – lined with 1.2mm *Flagon TPO*

1.0mm EPDM rubber liners – Queensferry

Buscot Park – established

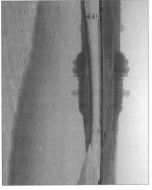

One of three 7000m² slurry lagoons in Cornwall

Easifit corrugated tank liner arrangement

Tank lined with 1.5mm *Flagon GeoP/AT* membrane

One of four 1.2mm TPO liners at a golf club in Kent

Completed lake at a golf club in Kent

1.5mm *Flagon GeoP* liner, underground water tank

Geoweb® – load support for driveway, Ripon

Geoweb® and Rock Rolls for channel protection

Geoweb® secured by Atra® Tendon Clips – for steeper slope protection applications

Geoweb® – load support for port road, Dublin

Geoweb® – tree root protection

![Greenfix logo]

Greenfix
Soil Stabilisation and
Erosion Control Specialists

Contact
t: 01608 666027
f: 01642 618525
info@greenfix.co.uk

Web
www.greenfix.co.uk

Address
Greenfix Soil Stabilisation & Erosion Control Ltd
Old Manor Farm Yard
Beckford Road
Ashton under Hill
Evesham WR11 7SU

Accreditation
Network Rail PADS Approval
ISO 9001:2008
CE certification
CPD certification
BSI approved

Additional entries
Erosion control mats and blankets ➤ 27
Earth retention structures ➤ 35

Greenfix Soil Stabilisation & Erosion Control Ltd

Geoweb® cellular confinement

Greenfix provides innovative, sustainable solutions to challenging soil stabilisation problems and turf protection requirements with the Geoweb® cellular confinement system.

• Load support

Geoweb® can be used for load support where soil stability is a problem. It is easy to deploy, making it economical for roads and tracks in difficult-to-access locations. Access roads made with Geoweb® can support heavy plant and vehicles, reducing ongoing costs in quarry, forestry, wind farm, agricultural and similar applications. It can reduce required stone depth by up to 50%. Geoweb® panels are joined with Atra® Keys, which makes an installation up to 3 times stronger than using staples and can contribute to the quick completion of projects.

• Tree root protection

Geoweb® distributes loads laterally, reducing soil compaction and its effects. If construction equipment, vehicles or pedestrian traffic pass over a tree's Critical Root Zone, soil compaction can damage near-surface roots and endanger the structural integrity or the life of the tree.

• Slope and channel protection

Geoweb® cellular confinement can be used for for slopes and embankments of all types. Benefits include long-term vegetated sustainability, reinforcement of the upper soil layer and resistance to erosive conditions and sliding forces. Atra® Tendon Clips are load transfer devices that transfer slope gravity forces from the Geoweb® cell wall to the tendon.

Accreditation

Geoweb® complies with the Arboricultural Method Statement as outined in BS 5837:2012, the Town and Country Planning Act 1990 and Arboricutural Practice Note 12 (APN12). It is used as the control measure for BS 5837:2012.

Design services

Greenfix engineers are able to design site-specific solutions for tree root protection.

Geoweb® panels connected with Atra Keys

Atra® Key for connecting Geoweb® panels

TERRAM

Geosynthetics you can trust

Contact
t: 01621 874200
f: 01621 874299
info@terram.com

Web
www.terram.com

Address
Fiberweb Geosynthetics Ltd
Blackwater Trading Estate
The Causeway
Maldon CM9 4GG

Accreditation
ISO 9001:2008
Investors in People

Additional entries
GrassProtecta reinforcement mesh ▶ 18
Porous paving for reinforcement ▶ 19
Porous paving for SUDS ▶ 72

Terram
Geocells

The Terram *Cellular Confinement System*, or *Geocell*, uses a three-dimensional geotextile honeycomb structure to provide soil stabilisation. The system confines the fill material within strong and flexible geotextile cells. This restricts down-slope migration in slopes, provides an even load distribution on paved and unpaved areas, and provides a stable base over soft subgrades.

• Soil reinforcement

Geocells provide a cost-effective alternative to conventional earth retention structures, owing to their flexibility and suitability for use with a wide range of infill materials and foundation soils. Typical soil reinforcement applications include steepened embankments, dams and flood defence bunds, retention bunds, green walls, culvert head walls and sound barriers.

• Ground stabilisation

Geocells reinforce unbound granular layers in roads and other trafficked areas, such as car parks, railways, airports and docks. They are used for site compounds, pile cap reinforcement, stabilised drainage layers, permeable load supporting surfaces, permanent way ballast stabilisation, and sub-base stabilisation for block paving, green access roads, temporary car parks, and permanent and temporary access roads.

• Load support

Geocells provide a stable base for paved surfaces and surface stabilisation for unpaved areas. When filled with sands or granular fills, their cellular structure performs as a semi-rigid slab. They distribute loads laterally, stabilising base materials, reducing sub grade contact pressures and minimising surface rutting. They prevent lateral displacement of infill and reduce vertical deflections, even on low-strength sub grades.

• Tree root protection

Geocells can also protect tree roots during hard landscaping and construction. Such products are recommended for no-dig tree root protection by BS 5837:1991 and the Arboricultural Advisory and Information Service's *Arboricultural Practice Note 12: Driveways Close to Trees* (APN12).

Composition and manufacture

Geocells are made from a strong, permeable geotextile, which restricts the movement of fill material while allowing the free movement of water and nutrients to create healthy soil. They are not prone to the cracking, spalling, splintering or corrosion that can affect concrete, steel and timber based reinforcement systems.

Sitework

Geocells are easy to handle and install, low maintenance, economical and strong. They allow the overall construction depth of ground stabilisation works to be reduced. This in turn saves on materials and excavation costs, and provides safe working platforms.

Geocell soil retention application

Geocell being filled with aggregate

Geocell embankment reinforcement – Monmouth

Geocell installation

Geocell for ground stabilisation

Geocell soil retention

Geocell installation for soil reinforcement

Permeable load-bearing access road

RPC Environmental

Armorflex closed-cell concrete block revetment system – Korean War Memorial, Wisconsin, USA

Armorloc concrete block revetment system

Armorflex open-cell block revetment installation

Dycel – marine installation

Dytap – slope paving

Ankalok revetment – balancing lake

Grasscel cellular paving

Erosion control systems

RPC Environmental manufactures and supplies concrete revetment/paving systems comprising either solid or cellular blocks. The blocks are supplied palletised for hand laying, or as articulated mattresses for machine installation. Mattresses are sized to suit particular applications.

• Revetment systems

Armorloc is a machine-made concrete block revetment system that is used for tough erosion control problems. Its rugged composition means it will withstand weather and remain durable over time.

Armorflex is a flexible, interlocking matrix of concrete blocks of uniform size and weight. They are connected by a series of cables which pass longitudinally through preformed ducts in each unit. They are available in closed-cell and open-cell blocks.

Dytap is a solid interlocking unit with a smooth masonry or natural stone facing. It is available in a variety of thicknesses for different applications. *Dycel* is a cellular or solid interlocking unit that is usually supplied in factory-assembled mattress format. The cellular format allows for the creation of a green landscape, and also enables the designer to use specified grasses to anchor the blocks.

Ankalok is an interlocking unit, that, when laid, forms pockets for planting. It is particularly suitable for irregular shaped areas.

• Erosion control paving

Grasscel is especially suitable for applications where a durable surface is required and where there is a need for the paving to blend in with the surrounding landscape. It is available in a choice of colours.

• Acoustic barriers

Planta is an environmentally friendly sound barrier system, that requires a minimum of space and is easy to install.

Contact

Sales
t: 01824 709102
f: 01824 709105
contracts@rpcltd.co.uk

Web
www.rpcltd.co.uk

Address
RPC Environmental
Quarryfields
Ruthin
Denbighshire LL15 2UG

Additional entries
Retaining structures ➤ 38
Decorative paving flags and kerbs ➤ 107

❒ ❒ ❒ ❒ For detailed information on featured products and services ☞ www.externalworks.co.uk

TenCate Geotube® used for marine erosion control

![TENCATE logo]
TENCATE
materials that make a difference

Contact
Carol Watkins, Telford
t: 01952 588066
f: 01952 588466
Service.uk@tencate.com

Scott Harvey, UK Sales Manager
t: 07940 738184
s.harvey@tencate.com

Sarah Nabbs, Area Sales M62 and
North England
t: 07787 513393
s.nabbs@tencate.com

Simon McMail, Area Sales SW
and Wales
t: 07958 027327
s.mcmail@tencate.com

David Dutton, Area Sales London,
SE and East Midlands
t: 07990 935338
d.dutton@tencate.com

Web
www.tencate.com
www.geotube.com

Address
TenCate Geosynthetics (UK) Ltd
PO Box 773, Telford TF7 9FE

Accreditation
ISO 9001, ISO 14001

Operational area
Worldwide

Additional entries
Woven geotextiles ► 8
Non-woven geotextiles ► 9

TenCate Geosynthetics (UK) Ltd

Reinforcement and erosion control

TenCate Geosynthetics is a market leader in delivering bespoke geosynthetic solutions.

- **Uniaxial and biaxial geogrids**

TenCate Miragrid® GX products are knitted geogrids made from high-tenacity polyester yarns which are covered with a black polymeric coating, providing high tensile strength with low creep characteristics. Tensile strengths, both uniaxial and biaxial, range from 20 to 600kn. Applications include subgrade stabilisation, strengthened embankments, veneer stability, working platforms and basal reinforcement.

- **Reinforced geocomposites**

TenCate Rock® PEC is a geocomposite consisting of continuous filament non-woven, reinforced by high-tenacity polyester yarns.
It is available in a wide range of tensile strengths, uniaxial and biaxial, from 35 up to 230kn.
Applications include embankment strengthening, subgrade stabilisation, and working platforms.

- **Paving fabrics**

TenCate Polyfelt® PGM paving fabrics are mechanically bonded, continuous-filament, polypropylene non-wovens with optimum bitumen retention capacity.
Its use retards reflective cracking of repaired asphalt road surfaces by a combination of the functions stress relief, sealing, and uniform bonding between the layers.
Installation is available through approved installer Asphalt Grid Systems in Sheffield.

- **Erosion protection systems**

TenCate Geotube® is used for erosion protection for marine structures or large-scale dewatering applications.
TenCate Robulon PET is used for high strength erosion matting for veneer stability on long slopes on top of membranes.
TenCate Accorder is a new patented product manufactured from non-woven products to provide stabilisation, separation and filtration on low bearing capacity soils.

TenCate Polyfelt Rock® PEC used in environbund

TenCate Miragrid® used to strengthen embankment

TenCate Accorder used to stabilise road foundation

TenCate Robulon PET high-strength erosion matting for veneer stability on long slopes

TenCate Polyfelt PGM G on airport taxiway increasing the maintenance lifecycle of highways

TenCate Miragrid® is flexible and easy to use

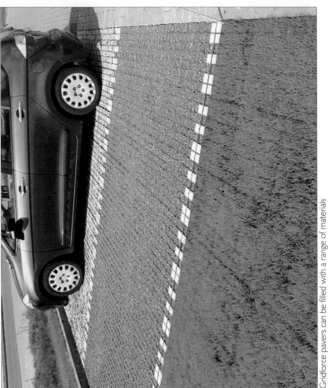

Gridforce pavers are suitable for permanent or temporary parking applications

Gridforce pavers can be filled with a range of materials

![gridforce logo]

Gridforce

Ground reinforcement

Gridforce offers a unique plastic paver system made from 100% recycled LDPE, which provides effective surface drainage and ground reinforcement. It is suitable for temporary or permanent use and provides a firm surface that will not sink, rut or shift. The pavers are cost effective compared to impermeable surfaces and their interlocking design makes installation easy. The system meets current SuDS legislation and has a 10-year guarantee.

• Applications

Hard landscaping applications include SuDS, car parks, ground reinforcement, industrial hardstanding, access routes, helipads, construction sites and domestic driveways. Soft landscaping applications include lawn and slope reinforcement, events grounds, caravan sites, golf courses and ground stabilisation. The *Gridforce Park* range can be used for instant grass reinforcement by being inverted and pressed into existing grass without the conventional dig out and build-up of sub-base.

• Sustainable Urban Drainage Systems

Pavers are fully compliant for use in SuDS to provide on-site infiltration of rainwater or stormwater, eliminating the need for drainage pipework. By returning the stormwater to the water table, pressure on the sewers is relieved.

Contact

Sales
t: 0115 965 7303
f: 0115 965 5151
sales@gridforce.co.uk

Web
www.gridforce.co.uk

Address
Gridforce
Industrial Estate South
Park Road
Calverton
Nottingham NG14 6BP

Operational area
Worldwide

Country of manufacture
England

Additional entries
Surface drainage ➤ 70

Heavy-duty interlocking paver

Gridforce pavers have heavy loading capability

Instant grassed access road

Pavers are fully Part M compliant

Gridforce pavers reinforcing grassed area in car park

Gridforce parking area used as a water run-off for impermeable tarmac

Gridforce pavers filled with aggregate in parking area

Completed parking area filled with aggregate and marked for parking

Terram

GrassProtecta reinforcement mesh

GrassProtecta is a heavy-duty polyethylene mesh that reinforces grassed surfaces prone to wear and smearing, such as permanent car parking and heavily used pedestrian areas.

Technical data

GrassProtecta's oscillated mesh structure provides a high level of traction and slip resistance, and is available in three thicknesses: Heavy 14.5mm, Medium 13mm, and Lite 10mm.

It provides reinforcement up to 8 tonnes per static axle load on firm ground, which makes it suitable for applications ranging from overflow car parks and light-aircraft taxiways to caravan sites, equestrian surfaces and verge stabilisation.

Installation and maintenance

GrassProtecta mesh is simple to install. The sward grows through the mesh apertures and knits with the filaments to create a strong, discreetly reinforced surface capable of withstanding vehicle loads, limiting damage and helping to reduce compaction by reducing direct contact with the soil surface. It can also be installed onto newly landscaped areas and seeded as required. Newly installed areas should be left untrafficked until the sward and the mesh have knitted – normally after a few weeks during the growing season, or a few months out of season.

TERRAM
Geosynthetics you can trust

Contact
t: 01621 874200
f: 01621 874299
info@terram.com

Web
www.terram.com

Address
Fiberweb Geosynthetics Ltd
Blackwater Trading Estate
The Causeway
Maldon CM9 4GG

Accreditation
ISO 9001:2008
Investors in People

Additional entries
Geocells ➤ 13
Porous paving for reinforcement ➤ 19
Porous paving for SUDS ➤ 72

GrassProtecta™ is laid directly onto existing grassed surfaces

GrassProtecta™ days after installation

GrassProtecta™ two weeks after installation

GrassProtecta™ installed on level free-draining grass

Grass quickly grows through the mesh

Rolls laid onto existing grass

Reinforced grass car park using *GrassProtecta*™

For detailed information on featured products and services ➘ www.externalworks.co.uk

Truckpave™ with grass for bus access roads

Truckpave™ interlocking grids

![TERRAM logo]
TERRAM
Geosynthetics you can trust

Contact
t: 01621 874200
f: 01621 874299
info@terram.com

Web
www.terram.com

Address
Fiberweb Geosynthetics Ltd
Blackwater Trading Estate
The Causeway
Maldon CM9 4GG

Accreditation
ISO 9001:2008
Investors in People

Additional entries
Geocells ▶ 13
GrassProtecta reinforcement mesh ▶ 18
Porous paving for SUDS ▶ 72

Terram

Porous paving for reinforcement

Under the Terram brand, Fiberweb
Geosynthetics Ltd offers reinforcement products
for lightweight occasional use up to regular heavy
traffic on grass or gravel surfaces.

• **BodPave™ 85 porous pavers**
BodPave™ 85 cellular, interlocking, porous pavers
are designed for natural grass reinforcement,
ground stabilisation and gravel retention.
Aimed at regularly trafficked surfaces, they suit
emergency vehicle and HGV access lanes,
car/coach parks, driveways, aviation applications,
pedestrian areas and disabled access paths.
BodPave™ 85 pavers have ground spikes that
resist lateral movement and castellated cells with
unique water retention chambers that enhance
traction and lateral root growth, promote
optimum nutrients/water uptake and protect
roots. The open-cell structure provides high
surface water infiltration and suits SUDS profiles.

• **Truckpave™ permeable pavers**
Truckpave™ is a heavy-duty plastic paver
developed specially for lorry access roads and
service yards, as well as road-widening schemes
and motorway emergency turning areas. Unlike
conventional concrete systems, *Truckpave™*
requires no specialist handling as each unit weighs
only 9kg. The system needs no steel
reinforcement and is flexible so will not crack or
overheat and conduct heat to grass.

Composition and manufacture
BodPave™ 85 is made from UV stabilised, 100%
recycled polyethylene. It is chemically inert,
non-toxic and load-bearing up to 400t/m². Units
are 500x500x50mm with a 35mm ground spike.
Truckpave™ pavers are made from recycled
plastic, which is harmless to plants and animals.
Each paver is 600x400x80mm.

Sitework
BodPave™ 85 is installed onto a firm, free-draining
base. Cells are filled with a root-zone blend for a
grassed finish or with an angular aggregate.
Truckpave™ can be supplied with design
assistance for individual projects.

BodPave™ 85 gravel filled porous paving grids

BodPave™ 85 typical construction profile

BODPAVE 85
with Grass or Gravel

Terram Geotextile
filter fabric
(e.g. T1000)

TensarTriAx™
TX160 geogrid
option

Subgrade soil

Dot reduced fines
Type 3 Sub-base

Terram Geotextile
filter fabric
Type 3 sub-base
option

Sand, Soil
Rootzone or
Gravel Bedding

Truckpave™ withstands heavy loads

Permeable gravel car park using BodPave™

BodPave™ 85 plastic pavers clip together

Truckpave™ permeable HGV paving

Truckpave™ access road

BodPave™ 85 is suitable for grass or gravel

CORE Landscape Products

Tree root protection and ground reinforcement

CORE Landscape Products supplies tree root protection systems, including biaxial geogrids and separation membranes. Each easy-to-install grid system creates a low-impact, porous wearing course suitable for all SUDS-compliant schemes. Advice on design and construction is also offered, with an optional independent warranty available.

• Temporary site access system

The temporary site access system can be installed in close proximity to mature trees. It provides access for heavy vehicles and construction traffic, preventing environmental impact on surrounding root systems. When construction is finished, the system is removed, leaving the area undisturbed.

• 'No dig' construction system

The 'no dig' system creates permanent sub-base confinement for access roads and driveways close to trees. Its 3-dimensional erosion barrier and structural bridge uniformly distributes loads to minimise traffic impact on surrounding trees.

• Gravel and grass reinforcement

Interlocking porous pavers for gravel stabilisation and grass reinforcement are available, for disabled access through to HGV traffic applications. They are approved to European standard DIN 14090 – Access for Fire Engines. Each been designed for a specific traffic load and site condition.

Contact
Manni Keates
t: 0800 118 2278
sales@corelp.co.uk

Web
www.corelp.co.uk

Address
CORE Landscape Products
Calves Lane Yard
Bellswood Lane
Iver SL0 0LU

Affiliations
BALI; CHAS; Constructionline; Exor;
OHIM Registered

Operational area
Worldwide

Additional entries
Porous gravel/resin bound surfacing ▶ 69

'No dig' construction build-up for APN12 applications

Temporary access tree root protector with infill

Temporary access system before gravel infill

Biaxial geogrid for CORE Tree Root Protector system

CORE Tree Root Protector accessories
CORE Commercial gravel stabiliser on gravel bedding layer

CORE Tree Root Protector confinement panels
CORE Commercial gravel stabiliser

CORE Drive domestic gravel stabiliser
CORE Grass reinforcement grid

Legend:
1. Existing Subsoil
2. Separation Membrane (CORE 1000)
3. Biaxial Geogrid (CORE 60)
4. CORE Tree Root Protector
5. Permeable Wearing Course

GrassConcrete

Grass Concrete Ltd
Grass pavers and erosion control

Grass Concrete Ltd produces a range of grass reinforcement systems for traffic and erosion control applications.

- **Grass pavers**

Grasscrete® is cast-on-site concrete paving that uses recycled plastic void formers. It is suitable for heavy-duty applications, such as fire access roads, parking areas, slope protection and erosion control.

Terratone is a new colour pigment that can be added to cast-in Grasscrete®. Colour options are granite, peat, earth brown and sand.

Grassblock® hydraulically pressed concrete grass paving blocks are available in a variety of depths, and incorporate interlocking lugs to increase resistance to displacement under load. Applications include parking areas, and embankment and slope protection works.

Grassroad® honeycomb plastic reinforcing pavers provide 95% grass cover. They are suitable for infrequently trafficked areas such as amenity sites and fire access roads.

Grasskerb® is a dry-fix edge kerb system. To form curves, the lattice base is clipped, which enables a wide variety of profiles to be formed. Grasskerb® 45 is suitable for lawn edges and Grasskerb® 60 can cater for block or slab paving.

Contact
Chris Daykin (sales)
Robert Howden OBE (technical)
t: 01924 379443
f: 01924 290289
cpd@grasscrete.com
reh@grasscrete.com

Web
www.grasscrete.com

Address
Grass Concrete Ltd
Duncan House
142 Thornes Lane
Thornes, Wakefield WF2 7RE

Affiliations
Mid-Yorkshire Chamber of Commerce

Additional entries
Overlay paving system for extensive or intensive
green roofs ▶ 30
Retaining walls ▶ 34

Grassblock® installation

Grasscrete® installation

Grasscrete® storm channel, Hong Kong

Grassroad® installation in progress

Grassroad® installation completed

Grasscrete® installations can be carried out worldwide, example shown: car parking, Kuwait

Grasscrete® for HGV use, Dulwich Recycling Centre

Grasscrete® used with asphalt, Farmleigh, Dublin

Mansfield Sand Company

Fibre-reinforced rootzones

Mansfield Sand provides a range of products for sports, landscaping, amenity and equestrian applications.

Fibreturf Rootzone Landscape is a fibre-reinforced rootzone that is used to create strong natural turf. It gives the appearance and benefits of natural turf but with additional durability, strength and drainage characteristics.

It is suitable for emergency vehicle access routes, grassed car parking areas, access roads and drives, landscaped areas, sports surfaces, airfields, pedestrian paths and recreational areas.

Composition and manufacture

Fibreturf Rootzone Landscape comprises silica sand, organic matter and 35mm long polypropylene fibres, which are blended to produce a homogeneous rootzone.

Sitework

Fibreturf Rootzone Landscape is supplied in bulk tippers and should be laid as the top 75–200mm, to produce a fibre reinforced or stabilised upper rootzone. The exact depth required depends on end use. A natural turf finish is then produced by either seeding directly into the rootzone or laying turf.

Contact

Louise Barrington-Earp
t: 01623 707555
f: 01623 707579
m: 07885 893607
louise.barrington-earp@mansfield-sand.co.uk

Web

www.mansfield-sand.co.uk

Address

Mansfield Sand Company
Two Oaks Quarry
Coxmoor Road
Kirkby in Ashfield
Mansfield NG18 5BW

Accreditation

ISO 9001

Reinforced *Fibreturf Rootzone Landscape* for fire access route

Fibreturf Rootzone Landscape for holiday park

Fibreturf Rootzone Landscape for airfield

Fibreturf Rootzone Landscape for car parking area

For detailed information on featured products and services ☞ www.externalworks.co.uk

PERFO

S2T Grass Reinforcement

Self-anchoring grass and ground reinforcement tiles

PERFO® is the self-anchoring ground reinforcement solution. The unique clip-together tile system can be compacted or rolled directly into grass to reinforce existing grass, or vibrated into crushed stone for permeable parking. Products include *PERFO-SD®* (standard), *PERFO-EQ®*, *PERFO-AK®* (anchor) and *PERFO-AK+®* reinforcement tiles.

Applications include parking, vehicle access, grass verges, paths, airfields and caravan parks.

Composition and manufacture

The recycled PE/PP tiles have excellent load-bearing and weight distribution properties. They are tested to withstand loads of over 60t/m². Installed loadings will, however, depend on site ground conditions. The tiles resist frost, acids, solvents, heat and UV, and do not rot.

Sitework

Unlike most reinforcement products, *PERFO®* can be compacted or rolled into unprepared even ground without excavation. Apart from a roller or rammer, no special tools or skills are needed. The patented 'barb' system makes fixing pegs unnecessary. Tiles can also be compacted into gravel with a sub-base for permeable parking.

Contact
Sales and technical
t: 01992 522797
f: 01992 878176
info@perfo.co.uk

Web
www.perfo.co.uk

Address
S2T Grass Reinforcement
125 High Road
North Weald
Epping CM16 6EA

Operational area
Worldwide

Country of manufacture
EU

PERFO-SD® — car park

PERFO® – park and sports area car park

PERFO-SD® – car park

PERFO-AK® installed in a crushed stone base

PERFO® is used extensively for airfields and helipads

PERFO-SD® path and verge reinforcement

PERFO-EQ® is ideal for temporary paths

PERFO® self-anchoring tiles being rolled into grass

PERFO-AK® Anchor tiles used for car parking

PERFO-EQ® is ideal for temporary paths

PERFO-AK® Anchor tiles used for permeable parking

Suregreen Ltd

Permeable grass and gravel ground reinforcement

Suregreen's grass, ground and gravel reinforcement products provide load-bearing, permeable paving solutions.

Products can be used as part of a source control layer within a SuDS design, where stormwater run-off is a consideration.

- **PP50 and PP4040 permeable pavers**
PP50 and PP40 permeable pavers are recycled plastic interlocking grids used to construct free-draining solutions. Applications include every day and overflow car parks, coach parks, fire access lanes, driveways, paths and disabled access. The open-cell structure is specially designed to work well with a grass or gravel finish, providing a stable and robust wearing surface.

- **GRI4 grass reinforcement mesh**
GRI4 grass reinforcement mesh is installed directly onto grass areas that are used as overflow car parks, paths, verges and lawns. Once installed, the grass grows quickly through the mesh. The grass roots intertwine with the mesh filaments creating a strong, reinforced invisible surface structure.

- **TRUCKGRID-Max permeable paving grids**
TRUCKGRID-Max permeable paving grids provide a wearing surface that can manage the pressures and tensions imposed by heavy weight vehicles.

The Professional Choice in Landscaping

Contact
Paul Munday, Technical Sales Manager
t: 01376 503869
m: 07703 784558
sales@sure-green.com

Web
www.sure-ground.com
www.sure-green.com

Address
Suregreen Ltd
2 Croft Way
Eastways Industrial Estate
Witham CM8 2FB

TRUCKGRID-Max in heavy vehicle unloading bay

PP40 installed in a large car park

PP40 installed in an access road

GRI4 installation enables cars to park on grass

GRI4 a few days after installation

PP40 installed in a courtyard

PP50 installed in a car park

abg | creative geosynthetic engineering

Contact
Jim Herbert
t: 01484 852096
info@abgltd.com

Web
www.abgltd.com/retaining-walls

Address
ABG Ltd
E7 Meltham Mills Road
Holmfirth HD9 4DS

Accreditation
ISO 9001:2000
Investors in People

Affiliations
BALI

Additional entries
Green and blue roofs ➤ 28
Webwall flexible retaining walls ➤ 31
Cellular SUDS paving ➤ 68
Geocomposite drainage ➤ 68

ABG Ltd

Reinforced natural grass rootzones

Advanced Turf® is a high-performance reinforced grass rootzone system.
Grass surfaces constructed using the system are compaction resistant, free draining and SuDS compliant. They are capable of sustaining heavy vehicle loadings in occasional use situations.
Typical applications include:
• Multi-use event areas.
• Emergency vehicle access roads.
• HGV access.
• Overspill car parks.
• Sports surfacing.
• Amenity areas.
• SuDS source control.

Composition
Advanced Turf® consists of a high-quality sandy soil rootzone into which thousands of playing card sized polypropylene *Netlon* plastic mesh elements are pre-blended.

Performance
Advanced Turf® is supported by over a decade of civil engineering and turf grass research.

Sitework
Advanced Turf® is delivered to site as a system comprising the composite mesh reinforced rootzone, selected turf and installation fertiliser.

Advanced Turf® system – Pottersfield

Advanced Turf® system – Oxford business park

Advanced Turf® system – Staleybridge events area

Advanced Turf® system supports heavy loads

Advanced Turf® – Bedford bypass bridge deck

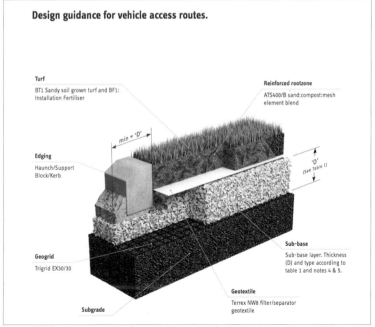

Design guidance for vehicle access routes.

Turf
BT1 Sandy soil grown turf and BF1: Installation Fertiliser

Reinforced rootzone
ATS400/B sand:compost:mesh element blend

Edging
Haunch/Support Block/Kerb

min = 'D'

'D' (See Table 1)

Geogrid
Trigrid EX30/30

Sub-base
Sub-base layer. Thickness (D) and type according to table 1 and notes 4 & 5.

Geotextile
Terrex NW8 filter/separator geotextile

Subgrade

Advanced Turf® systems are capable of sustaining heavy vehicle loadings in occassional use applications

Contact
Stephen Fell
t: 01904 448675
f: 01904 448713
lindum@turf.co.uk

Web
www.turf.co.uk

Address
Lindum
West Grange
Thorganby
York YO19 6DJ

Affiliations
British Association of Landcape Industries (BALI)
Sports Turf Research Institute (STRI)
Turfgrass Growers Association (TGA)

Additional entries
Green roofs ➤ 29
Cultivated turf ➤ 512
Wildflower turf ➤ 518

Lindum

Turf reinforcement

Grass specialist Lindum has developed a range of innovative products for turf reinforcement, erosion control and unusual landscape designs.
• **Reinforced turf: Lokturf**™
Lokturf™ is a 40mm-thick, reinforced, hard-wearing sports turf, grown in a polypropylene fibre-reinforced *Loksand* root-zone. *Lokturf*™ is instantly useable and provides strength and stability, and high wear resistance. It is ideal for vehicle access routes, overflow grass car parks, heavily used walkways, public squares and play areas. Example specifications are available.
• **Erosion control: Grassfelt**™
Grassfelt™ is a soil-less turf that provides erosion control and reinforcement. It comprises a mature grass grown on recycled felt. It is specifically designed to retain moisture. A reinforcing scrim is incorporated for additional strength.
The resulting flexible turf mat can be pegged into position and is extremely pliable, allowing it to lie close to unusual contours. *Grassfelt*™ achieves rapid rooting into the substrate beneath.
Grassfelt™ is available in different grades: *LT7* for landscape design; and *LT2* for low-maintenance areas, steep banks and drought-prone areas.
Grassfelt™ can be grown to order with other turf grades to match the landscape specification.

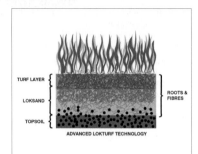

Lokturf™ technology for ground reinforcement

Lokturf™ overflow grass car park – Savil Gardens

Grassfelt™ sculptural mounds – M4 junction

Grassfelt™ embankment – Lincoln Castle

 HY-TEX logo

Contact
David Poole/Ryan Markham
t: 01233 720097
f: 01233 720098
sales@hy-tex.co.uk

Web
www.hy-tex.co.uk

Address
Hy-Tex (UK) Ltd
Aldington Mill, Mill Lane
Aldington
Ashford TN25 7AJ

Accreditation
ISO 9001

Affiliations
BALI

Additional entries
Silt and run-off pollution control ➤ 10
Vertical green wall planters ➤ 376
Root barriers ➤ 520

Hy-Tex (UK) Ltd

Biodegradables

Hy-Tex biodegradables are used for erosion control on embankments and water courses, and for natural weed suppression.
• **Water margin erosion protection**
CoirLog biodegradable, coconut fibre bio-roll erosion control substrates are designed to work with nature to protect and support banks and shorelines, and aid the restoration of vegetation in wetland environments. Applications include rivers, lakes, streams, canals and wetlands.
• **Erosion control meshes**
CoirMesh™ is an open weave, pure coconut erosion control mesh designed for use in areas where plants are slow to establish, and highly erosive environments. Applications include riverbanks and drainage channels.
Soil Saver™ biodegradable jute erosion control mesh blankets have an open weave. They are designed to protect seed and soil on bare surfaces that are vulnerable to erosion by wind, rain and water run-off.
• **Biodegradable weed control**
Ecotex MulchMat™ is a professional grade, biodegradable weed control fabric for planted areas. It has a dense, tightly bound, non-woven needlefelt construction with a heat fused underside for high strength and tear resistance.

CoirLog dense coconut fibre logs for water margins

CoirMesh™ flood alleviation channel lining

Soil Saver™ jute mesh slope erosion protection

Ecotex MulchMat™ fully biodegradable weed control

Greenfix
Soil Stabilisation and
Erosion Control Specialists

Contact
t: 01608 666027
f: 01642 618525
info@greenfix.co.uk

Web
www.greenfix.co.uk

Address
Greenfix Soil Stabilisation & Erosion Control Ltd
Old Manor Farm Yard
Beckford Road
Ashton under Hill
Evesham WR11 7SU

Accreditation
Network Rail PADS Approval (Geoweb)
ISO 9001:2008
CE certification
CPD Certification
BSI approved

Additional entries
Geoweb® cellular confinement ➤ 12
Earth retention structures ➤ 35

Covamat – quick establishment on rail embankment

Covamat pre-seeded matting – erosion protection

Bio Rolls and *Covamat* – new watercourse creation

Greenfix Soil Stabilisation & Erosion Control Ltd

Erosion control mats and blankets

Greenfix offers soil stabilisation products, ranging from pre-seeded erosion control blankets and permanent turf reinforcement mats to pavers for reinforcing grass or gravel surfaces.

• Pre-seeded erosion control mats
Covamat biodegradable pre-seeded mats provide a high level of soil and slope protection, ensuring seed retention on steep gradients. They are used where there are poor soil conditions. Manufactured from coir, straw or a mix of the two, they incorporate organic fertilisers and dry micro-organisms, which improve germination results. All seeded blankets can be offered with standard mixes, or a bespoke specified mix.

• Non-seeded blankets and meshes
Biodegradable erosion control mats can be offered without seeds. They are used for slope and embankment stabilisation applications where the establishment of planting it is not required.

• Organic Mulchmats
Mulchmats are used in applications where landscape planting is required, particularly on slopes. They provide mulching, moisture control, non-chemical weed control, soil erosion protection and soil temperature balance in a single operation. They are organic and typically last for 3 years.

• Silt fence
Silt Fence is a temporary sediment control material. It is used on construction sites to prevent sediment in stormwater run-off from polluting nearby watercourses.

• Permanent turf reinforcement mats
Permanent mats, made from synthetic materials, are available. They are used to reinforce the root and stem systems of vegetation that may be under high sheer stress. They are made from synthetic materials and provide effective erosion control and a high level of mulching.

• Permeable pavements
Permeable paving products are offered to aid the movement of stormwater through the surface.

Non-seeded embankment mat – Moreton In Marsh

Non-seeded *Rockmat* with anti-vermin mesh layer

Covamat Plus pre-seeded mat – channel protection

Seeded blankets after 6 months' establishment

Covamat Plus pre-seeded matting being installed

abg creative geosynthetic engineering

Contact

Matt Gledhill/Kirstin Forsythe
t: 01484 852096
buildings@abgltd.com

Web
www.abgltd.com/greenroofs

Address
ABG Ltd
E7 Meltham Mills Road
Holmfirth HD9 4DS

Accreditation
ISO 9001:2000
Investors in People

Affiliations
BALI

Additional entries
Reinforced natural grass rootzones ➤ 25
Webwall flexible retaining walls ➤ 31
Cellular SUDS paving ➤ 68
Geocomposite drainage ➤ 68

ABG Ltd

Green and blue roofs

ABG is a market leader in the design, installation and maintenance of green and blue roof systems. Finishes available include intensive, extensive and biodiverse for use in a range of roof and podium deck constructions.

• Blueroof water attenuation system
Blue roofs are explicitly designed to attenuate rainwater rather than drain it off as quickly as possible, as in traditional roof drainage design. ABG *blueroof* offers a new concept in the management of stormwater by collecting and retaining rainfall within the actual roof structure before discharging at a controlled rate. This is particularly beneficial where land take is tight, such as in urbanised areas, where installation of other attenuation techniques are not feasible.

Technical support

A full PI design service is available in-house. ABG works in conjunction with the project team to ensure that the right roof build up and finish is specified to create a green roof that meets the client's expectations.

Installation and maintenance

A full installation and on-going maintenance service is offered by Geogreen Solutions, ABG's in-house installation business.

ABG *Green Roof System* – Alder Hey Children's Hospital. Winner – Green Roof Project of the Year 2016.

Intensive roof – luxury hotel, Whitby

Extensive pitched roof – student halls, Oxford

Anchor points, reinforcement geogrids and geocellular technology were used to retain the growing media

Extensive roof – Center Parcs Woburn Forest

Blueroof installation – Kentish Town, London

Erosaweb was installed by ABG operatives Geogreen Solutions to retain growing media on the slopes

Contact
Stephen Fell
t: 01904 448675
f: 01904 448713
lindum@turf.co.uk

Web
www.lindumgreenroofs.co.uk
www.turf.co.uk

Address
Lindum
West Grange
Thorganby
York YO19 6DJ

Affiliations
British Association of Landcape Industries (BALI)
Sports Turf Research Institute (STRI)
Turfgrass Growers Association (TGA)

Additional entries
Turf reinforcement ➤ 26
Cultivated turf ➤ 512
Wildflower turf ➤ 518

Lindum

Green roofs

Lindum has developed a range of wildflower, sedum and grass mats that are designed to provide biodiverse, colourful and drought-tolerant vegetation that flourish in the conditions created on a green roof.

Sustainably grown in the UK, mats are supplied as a ready-to-roll-out instant vegetation layer.

• **Lindum SedumPlus™**
Lindum SedumPlus™ is a pure sedum mat, sown with sixteen varieties of sedum to combine drought-tolerance with extended interest and colour throughout the growing season.

• **Lindum Wildflower & Perennial Mat**
Lindum Wildflower & Perennial Mat is a ready established mix of drought-tolerant wildflowers, herbs, sedum and flowering perennials that will grow particularly well on green roofs and encourage biodiversity.
Lindum Low Maintenance Grass Mat is available.

• **Green roof packages**
Lindum can supply a complete green roof package containing growing medium, drainage layer and edging profile. All of Lindum's green roof components are manufactured in the UK.

Delivery
Options include flat-bed vehicles to allow direct crane up-lift. All materials are supplied on pallets.

Lindum SedumPlus™ on a development at High Street, Stratford

Lindum SedumPlus™ – flat roof extension

Lindum Wildflower & Perennial Mat – residential

Green roofs encourage biodiversity

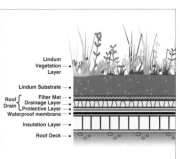
Profile of a Lindum green roof

Wildflower & Perennial Mat installation

Lindum SedumPlus™ – mixed use development

Green roofs reduce stormwater run-off

GrassConcrete

Contact
Chris Daykin (sales)
Robert Howden OBE (technical)
t: 01924 379443
f: 01924 290289
cpd@grasscrete.com
reh@grasscrete.com

Web
www.grasscrete.com

Address
Grass Concrete Ltd
Duncan House
142 Thornes Lane, Thornes
Wakefield WF2 7RE

Affiliations
Mid-Yorkshire Chamber of Commerce

Additional entries
Grass pavers and erosion control ➤ 21
Retaining walls ➤ 34

Grass Concrete Ltd

Overlay paving system for extensive or intensive green roofs

Grassroof® is an overlay paving system that can be applied to new or existing flat roof structures. When installed, it weighs as little as 17kg/m² for extensive roofs.
Grassroof® can be used as an extensive or simple-intensive paving layer, or as a base layer for intensive roof designs.

Composition and manufacture
The interlocking honeycomb units are manufactured from recycled polypropylene. These are fixed to the roof via a network of polypropylene leg supports, which create a drainage gap between the roof membrane and the underside of the paver.
The drainage gap can be formed as a clear waterway using the *GRF/2* variant. This incorporates a geotextile bonded to the underside, which permits moisture percolation but retains soil and roots.
Grassroof® can also be used with *Grasskerb®* dry-fix edge kerb units for rooftop planters.

Grassroof® – Dairsie, Fife, Scotland

Grassroof® GRF/2 unit installation

Grassroof® GRF/2 units with leg supports

Sedum-planted *Grassroof®* unit

gt specifier
Landscape Solutions

Contact
t: 01423 332114
info@gtspecifier.co.uk

Web
www.gtspecifier.co.uk

Address
Green-tech Ltd
Rabbit Hill Business Park, Great North Road,
Arkendale, Knaresborough HG5 0FF

Accreditation
ISO 9001:2008, ISO 14001:2004

Affiliations
BALI, APL, Constructionline, HTA

CPD
Introduction to green roof substrate and installation

Additional entries
Urban tree planting systems ➤ 524
Laser-cut tree grilles ➤ 525
Urban tree irrigation ➤ 525

gt Specifier

Green roofs

gt Specifier products for roof garden include:
• Substrates for intensive roof gardens
• Substrates for extensive roof gardens
• Sedum casettes, mats and blankets
• Low maintenance and wildflower turf
• Geocomposite roof drains with cuspated cores
Green-tree Intensive Roof Garden Substrate is lightweight in texture with good water holding capacity, ensuring healthy plants and trees.
Green-tree Extensive Roof Garden Substrate is rich in nutrients, ensuring quick plant establishment in harsh environments.

Green-tree Roof Garden Substrates have been installed on many projects across the UK

gtSedum Green Roof Cassettes – 8 sedum types

Green-tree Extensive Roof Garden Substrate

Green Roof Mix – sedums, herbs and wildflowers

abg creative geosynthetic engineering

Contact
Jim Herbert/Matt Gledhill
t: 01484 852096
info@abgltd.com

Web
www.abgltd.com/retaining-walls

Address
ABG Ltd
E7 Meltham Mills Road
Holmfirth HD9 4DS

Accreditation
ISO 9001:2000
Investors in People

Affiliations
BALI

Additional entries
Reinforced natural grass rootzones ➤ 25
Green and blue roofs ➤ 28
Cellular SUDS paving ➤ 68
Geocomposite drainage ➤ 68

ABG Ltd

Webwall – flexible retaining wall system using geocell technology

Webwall is a flexible retaining wall system that utilises geocell technology. Using *Webwall* green-faced walls allows near vertical faces to be built quickly and easily, with the added benefit of using site-won materials as fill.

The retaining wall structure is formed from horizontal layers filled, compacted and placed one on top of another. The front face of the structure can be filled with top soil then vegetated through seeding or planting to create a vegetated finish.

Webwall may be unreinforced for retained heights up to approximately 2m, or reinforced using geogrids to achieve greater heights.

Typical applications include noise barriers, retaining walls, steep slopes, blast bunds, anti-ram bunds and earth retaining walls.

Webwall cost advantages over other retaining wall systems include lower labour costs, fewer vehicular movements and reduced maintenance.

Composition

Webwall has a honeycomb structure of UV-stable polyethylene, securely interlocked at the joints.

Sitework

Webwall is supplied flat for expansion on site. Specialist installation is not required.

Webwall is a flexible retaining wall system using geocell technology. Site-won material can be used as fill.

Webwall reinforced soil wall – Ramsden Reservoir

Webwall is ideal for sites with weak foundation soils

Webwall – SuDS attenuation pond application

Webwall with vegetated finish on steep slope

Webwall allows near vertical faces to be built

Typical *Webwall* stacked installation

UV-stabilised HDPE honeycomb structure

acheson + glover

Contact
Sales
t: 0121 747 0202
specifications@ag.uk.com

Web
www.ag.uk.com

Address
Acheson & Glover Ltd
4 Marlin Office Village
1250 Chester Road
Castle Vale
Birmingham B35 7AZ

Accreditation
ISO 9001:2015
ISO 14001
OHSAS 18001:2007

Operational area
UK, Ireland

Additional entries
Concrete paving flag systems ➤ 106
Concrete block paving systems ➤ 116

Acheson + Glover Ltd
Concrete retaining walls

AG has been a leading manufacturer of hard landscaping and precast solutions for over 50 years and provides world-class products and innovative solutions to architects, specifiers, contractors and homeowners across the UK.

• **Anchor Landmark®**
Anchor Landmark® is a positive mechanical connection, dry-build retaining wall system with a 'riven stone' face. It offers high performance under extreme loading conditions.

• **Anchor Diamond®**
Anchor Diamond® is a mortarless, pinless retaining wall system with a patented rear alignment lip. It has a natural textured finish and is available in three colours and four profiles.

• **Anchor Vertica®**
Anchor Vertica® walling is designed for steep, sloping hillsides and other traditionally difficult installation areas. It is available in a straight or stonecut finish with a variety of warm earth tone colours.

• **Anchor Bayfield®**
Anchor Bayfield® is a versatile dry-build walling system with a patented rear alignment lip. It has a rough hewn weathered texture and is available in three colours and three profiles.

• **Anchor Regal Stone®**
Anchor Regal Stone® is ideal for non-engineered walls in domestic schemes and is completely vertical when installed. It is available in three colours.

• **Recon™**
Recon™ is a high performance, large-format dry build solution. It has an attractive, natural weathered stone finish. *Recon™* features a unique tongue and groove locking system which permits walls as high as approximately 3.6m to be built without geosynthetic reinforcement.

Technical support
AG's Technical Department can provide support from specification advice and concept design through to developing fully indemnified engineered designs.

Anchor Diamond®

Anchor Landmark®

Anchor Bayfield®

Anchor Vertica®

Anderton
Solutions in Concrete

Contact
Sales
t: 01606 535300
f: 01606 75899
structural@andertonconcrete.co.uk

Web
www.andertonconcrete.co.uk

Address
Anderton Concrete Products
Units 1 & 2 Cosgrove Business Park
Anderton Wharf
Soot Hill
Anderton CW9 6AA

Accreditation
ISO 9001:2000
ISO 14001:2004
BBA certified

Anderton Concrete Products

Retaining wall systems

Anderton manufactures three innovative, mortar-free retaining wall systems, *Keystone*, *Slope-loc* and *Stepoc*.

• **Keystone retaining wall blocks**
Keystone is a segmental block retaining wall system for major landscaping, highways and rail projects. It is fast and simple to build, yet offers high levels of structural integrity.

• **Slope-loc slope blocks**
Slope-loc is a smaller unit that creates a slope rather than a wall and can be used for both commercial and domestic schemes. It can be built as either a gravity or reinforced earth wall.

• **Stepoc dry-build blocks**
Stepoc comprises highly engineered blocks that are built dry and filled with concrete to create walls with very high lateral strength. A direct replacement for shuttered concrete, it is ideal for use in a wide variety of retaining wall applications, including basements and swimming pools.
Stepoc has achieved the highest rating for a security barrier system under the SEAP (Security Equipment Assessment Panel) testing regime.

Keystone retaining wall, East London railway line

Keystone blocks with ground reinforcement grid

Keystone, Bus Rapid Transit Link, Sheffield

Stepoc, Sondes Place, Dorking

Rendered Stepoc retaining wall, garden landscaping

325mm Stepoc, Woodhouse Hotel

Slope-loc, Barratt Homes, Wyke

Slope-loc, University of St Mark & St John, Plymouth

GrassConcrete

Contact
Chris Daykin (sales)
Robert Howden OBE (technical)
t: 01924 379443
f: 01924 290289
cpd@grasscrete.com
reh@grasscrete.com

Web
www.grasscrete.com

Address
Grass Concrete Ltd
Duncan House
142 Thornes Lane
Thornes
Wakefield WF2 7RE

Affiliations
Mid-Yorkshire Chamber of Commerce

Additional entries
Grass pavers and erosion control ➤ 21
Overlay paving system for extensive or intensive
green roofs ➤ 30

Grass Concrete Ltd

Retaining walls

Grass Concrete Ltd produces the *Betoconcept®*
range of cellular and solid concrete retaining wall
blocks.
• **Retaining wall blocks**
Betoflor® cellular retaining wall blocks are used to
construct retaining walls up to 2.5m high. Blocks
incorporate interconnecting lugs on the
underside, which aid quick construction and help
to eliminate overturning. They are filled with
topsoil as each layer is added. This enables plants
and flowers to be grown in the wall.
Betoatlas® blocks are based on the *Betoflor®*
design but are suitable for retaining walls up to
10m high.
Betotitan® extends the range of planted retaining
walls to heights of up to 22m. Features such as
variable angles and face geometry can also be
utilised.
Leromur® precast concrete retaining wall blocks
have interlocking ribs on the top and underside of
the units. The blocks produce split-textured or
smooth-faced walls suitable for hard-wearing
applications, such as marine walling.

Composition and manufacture

All units are constructed from pressed and
vibrated concrete.

Curved *Betoatlas®* construction

9m high *Betoatlas®* construction

Curved retaining wall structure

Betoatlas® plantable earth retaining wall

Betoatlas® to university campus

Leromur® split stone face earth retaining wall

Greenfix

Soil Stabilisation and
Erosion Control Specialists

Contact
t: 01608 666027
f: 01642 618525
info@greenfix.co.uk

Web
www.greenfix.co.uk

Address
Greenfix Soil Stabilisation & Erosion Control Ltd
Old Manor Farm Yard
Beckford Road
Ashton under Hill
Evesham WR11 7SU

Accreditation
Network Rail PADS Approval (Geoweb)
ISO 9001:2008
CE certification
BSI approved

Additional entries
Geoweb® cellular confinement ➤ 12
Erosion control mats and blankets ➤ 27

Greenfix Soil Stabilisation & Erosion Control Ltd

Earth retention structures

Greenfix offers *Geoweb*® cellular confinement systems and *Envirolok* encapsulated soil bag systems for providing naturally attractive, vegetated earth retention structures.

• **Geoweb cellular confinement system**
Geoweb® cellular confinement systems are used to create retaining walls. They are suitable for challenging site conditions; are structurally stable; develop an attractive, naturally vegetated appearance; and reduce stormwater run-off to help meet sustainable building requirements. Typical applications include: steepened slopes, geocomposite retaining walls, gravity walls and multi-layered channel systems. They can be designed for various requirements, including a wide range of infill, backfill, groundwater and surcharge conditions.

Geoweb® is easy for contractors to use on site. The sections are compact, and are lighter and easier to handle on site compared with concrete block retaining wall systems. They are also suitable for difficult-to-access or remote locations. This speeds up installation and reduces worker down-time. *Geoweb*® enables the use of on-site materials to be used for infill, which also saves construction costs.

• **Envirolok vegetated environmental bags**
Envirolok is an ecologically advanced, vegetated bag system that provides immediate stabilisation and permanent erosion control. It can be used in water or on dry sites, including bioengineered shoreline protection schemes and retaining walls. The bags contain structural soils, which are connected with spikes.

Envirolok allows for near-vertical construction that can be contoured to the existing non-load bearing soils with the flexibility to adapt, unlike hard armoured systems.

Geoweb® earth retaining wall being installed

Geoweb® earth retaining wall several months after installation

Envirolok vegetated bag system installation

Envirolok used to create embankment

Envirolok earth retaining wall

MODULARWALLS

Contact
t: 0800 915 5429
info@modularwall.co.uk

Web
www.modularwall.co.uk

Address
Modular Wall Systems (UK) Ltd
Unit 2
Rugby Street
Hull HU3 4RB

Accreditation
ISO 9001:2008

Operational area
UK

Country of manufacture
UK

Additional entries
Boundary fence walls ➤ 188
Acoustic barriers ➤ 197

Modular Wall Systems (UK) Ltd

Retaining walls

TerraFirm™ retaining panels are composite, lightweight fibre-cement panels with internal strengthening ribs for soil retention.
They can be used with the company's boundary fence wall systems to create seamless solutions. Soil retention up to 750mm.
Systems are of modular construction, offering a cost-effective alternative to traditional block walls for residential or commercial applications.

Composition
TerraFirm™ retaining panels have an EPS core with reinforcement ribs and fibre-cement outer skins.

Dimensions
Panels are 2400mm long x 50 or 75mm thickness, produced in three standard heights: 600, 900 or 1200mm.

Finish
Panels can be finished in textured or acrylic paints of any colour.

Three *VogueWall™* bays with *TerraFirm™* retaining panel

GuardianWall™ with *TerraFirm™* retaining panel (retaining 750mm)

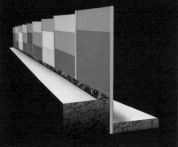

GuardianWall™ 750mm retaining wall for footpath

VogueWall™ with *TerraFirm™* retaining panel

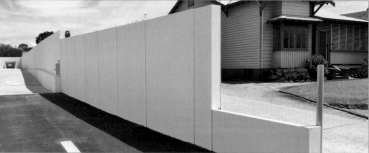

GuardianWall™ with *TerraFirm™* retaining panel (retaining 700mm)

Phi Group

Retaining structures

Phi Group specialises in the design, supply and installation of gravity retaining walls, reinforced soil and soil nailing facing systems. The company has expertise in designing and installing systems that meet site-specific engineering demands and satisfy environmental considerations.

• **Gravity retaining walls**

Crib, gabion and block gravity solutions include:
- *Permacrib* timber crib retaining walls.
- *Andacrib* concrete crib retaining walls.
- Gabion retaining walls and architectural cladding.
- L-shaped and 'lego' type block retaining walls.
- *Lockstone* modular block landscaping system.

• **Reinforced soil systems**

Reinforced soil solutions include:
- *Textomur* reinforced soil systems which are constructed using horizontal geogrids or geotextile layers with compacted infill material. The facing is steel mesh formwork backed with geosynthetics. Front slopes can be stone faced or vegetated for a green faced slope.
- Wraparound vegetated geogrid walls at 45°.
- Modular block or concrete panel vertical reinforced soil structures.
Soil panel facing systems, with soil or stone filled options, are also available.

Contact
Robert Torrington
t: 01242 707600
southern@phigroup.co.uk

Web
www.phigroup.co.uk

Address
Phi Group
Hadley House
Bayshill Road
Cheltenham GL50 3AW

Operational area
UK

Additional entries
Ground engineering ➤ 42

Andacrib modular concrete crib retaining wall system caters for applications with onerous loading conditions

Permacrib retaining wall – Interlink, Leicester

Titan modular concrete block earth retaining wall

Textomur stone faced wall – London 2012 Olympics

Gabion retaining walls

Two 70° *Textomur* walls with 6920m² face areas – new railhead to serve a Sainsbury's distribution centre

Textomur vegetated reinforced soil system

Gabion walls for architectural cladding

Contact
Sales
t: 01824 709102
f: 01824 709105
contracts@rpcltd.co.uk

Web
www.rpcltd.co.uk

Address
RPC Contracts
Quarryfields
Ruthin
Denbighshire LL15 2UG

Additional entries
Erosion control systems ➤ 14
Decorative paving flags and kerbs ➤ 107

RPC Contracts

Retaining structures

RPC Contracts designs, manufactures and installs a wide range of bespoke structures for earth retention, flood barrier, harbour and quay wall, and coastal and river defence applications.

• **Retaining walls**
Rocwall comprises precast concrete units with a cantilever design. The structure can be faced with a wide range of natural stone products or textured concrete finishes.
Kriblok is a gravity retaining wall with a crib structure. It comprises precast concrete components that can be landscaped to suit any environment.
Timbalok is technically the same as *Kriblok*, but uses stress-graded timber components (that are FSC certified) to achieve a more aesthetic appearance.
Chevloc is a modular, split-faced concrete block, available in a range of colours to suit a variety of applications.
Porcupine concrete retaining blocks weigh less than 20kg, and need no mortar and only a minimum of plant and machinery for installation.
• **Gabion baskets**
Gabion walling provides a cost-effective retaining wall or landscape feature, and can take a variety of stone filling materials to blend with its location.

Chevloc concrete retaining wall

Rocwall retaining wall

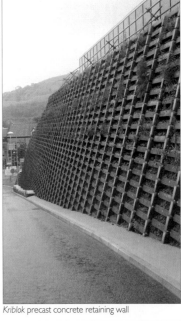
Kriblok precast concrete retaining wall

Timbalok timber retaining wall

Gabion baskets with buff walling stone

Coursed semi-dressed slate

Rocwall concrete flood defence wall faced with natural stone

Tobermore

WORLD CLASS PAVING & WALLING

Contact
Sales
t: 028 7964 2411
f: 028 7964 4145
sales@tobermore.co.uk

Web
www.tobermore.co.uk

Address
Tobermore
2 Lisnamuck Road
Magherafelt BT45 5QF

Accreditation
ISO 9001
ISO 14001

Operational area
UK, Ireland

Additional entries
Permeable concrete block paving ➤ 75
Concrete flag paving ➤ 108
Concrete block paving ➤ 114

Secura Grand retaining wall in Heather – Sainsbury's

Tobermore

Concrete retaining walls

Established in 1942, Tobermore is a leading manufacturer of walling and paving and supplies products for the commercial and domestic markets throughout the UK and Ireland.

• Secura retaining walls
Secura products are cost-effective for any type of retaining wall project, whether large or small. The products can be used to create interest through terraced landscaping as well as to make efficient use of land. They have an aged finish and are available in three colours. They are fast and easy to install using a mortar-free, dry process.

• Domestic applications
Secura Lite is used mainly in domestic situations. It is available in a combination of three block widths, which gives a random stone appearance. It has a traditional, aesthetic appearance, while being manufactured to modern production methods and technical requirements.

• Commercial applications
Secura Major and *Secura Grand* are designed for constructing larger, higher walls for expansive landscaping projects such as housing developments, roadworks and commercial landscaping projects.
Secura Major and *Secura Grand* can be used as gravity walling systems or combined with a geogrid to form reinforced soil walls for retaining structures.
Both ranges are available as single-face sized, dry-laid block systems with a split or aged finish.
Secura Grand is also available in an *Eco* version, with high rates of recycled content and a low carbon footprint.

Technical support

Tobermore's team of design and engineering specialists offers expert advice and support throughout the design and construction stages of *Secura* walling projects.

Secura Major in Slate – City Point, Cork

Secura Grand retaining wall in Slate – Denbigh School, Milton Keynes

Secura Lite retaining wall in Heather

Contact
Henry Blake
t: 0800 389 1420
f: 01349 864508
admin@woodblocx-landscaping.co.uk

Web
www.woodblocx-landscaping.co.uk

Address
WoodBlocX Landscaping Ltd
Munro Sawmills
Old Evanton Road
Dingwall IV15 9UN

Accreditation
CHAS, TRADA, BALI, FSC

CPD
Sustainable design with WoodBlocX

Country of manufacture
UK

Additional entries
Modular timber planters ➤ 382

WoodBlocX

Modular timber retaining walls

WoodBlocX manufactures a modular timber system that allows any size and shape of retaining wall, terrace or stepped structure to be built. *WoodBlocX* are lighter and easier to handle on site than timbers or railway sleepers.
A single wall will retain earth up to 1m in height, while multiple walls in a terraced design can retain higher sloping areas. WoodBlocX structures are inherently strong when built up, as they can withstand tension forces as well as compression. They have a 15 year guarantee.

Composition and manufacture

WoodBlocX are made from sustainably-sourced, FSC-accredited, treated Scots pine and are fitted together using recycled plastic dowels. WoodBlocX harvests and manufactures all of its own softwood, which allows full quality control throughout the production process.

Design services

A supply-only package includes free design and CAD production for any size of project.
A supply and project manage service includes the supervision of the client's labour and overseeing the construction process.
Full design and installation services include management of the project, which is built by one of WoodBlocX's own CHAS-registered teams.

WoodBlocX are built up to form a solid retaining structure that will not crack or distort

WoodBlocX can be used to make terraced walls

WoodBlocX are light and easy to handle on site

Multiple walls in a terraced design can incorporate steps and planters

WoodBlocX are fitted with recycled plastic dowels

WoodBlocX are light and easy to handle on site

Hahn Plastics Ltd

Ecocrib retaining wall system

Ecocrib is a BBA certified crib earth retaining wall system with a project lifespan of 120 years. Profiles are made from 100% recycled plastic, reducing the volume of plastic going to landfill. *Ecocrib* is strong, lightweight and durable. Finished walls have an attractive, brown timber-effect face that can be planted up if required.

Dimensions
Systems are designed to each specific job. Cross section: 125mm high x 50mm wide. Headers have a 12.5mm deep notch cut 50mm from each end to lock headers and stretchers.

Composition and manufacture
Ecocrib uses *hanit® Ultra Board* profiles which are strong, lightweight, weather resistant, chemically inert and maintenance-free. Components are moulded using 100% recycled polymers.

Installation
Ecocrib is quick and easy to install. It is built on a concrete foundation pad with perforated drainage pipe installed at the rear base of the slab.

Contact
t: 0161 850 1965
f: 0161 850 1975
sales@hahnplastics.co.uk

Web
www.hahnplastics.com

Address
Hahn Plastics Ltd
Old Pilkington Tiles Site
Rake Lane
Swinton
Manchester M27 8LJ

Affiliations
BALI

Additional entries
100% recycled plastic fencing ➤ 190
Recycled plastic palisade profiles ➤ 408

Ecocrib is made from *hanit®* 100% recycled plastic, a strong, lightweight, chemically inert material

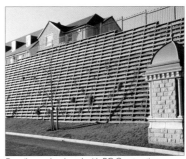

Ecocrib was developed with PC Construction

Ecocrib has an attractive timber-effect finish

M&M Timber Ltd

Unilog Pro retaining walls

M&M Timber is a leading supplier of landscaping timbers, with over 30 years' experience in sourcing, manufacturing and supplying timber products.
Unilog Pro landscaping timbers are used in a diverse range of landscaping applications including earth retaining walls, palisading, raised plant beds, border edging and pathways.
Unilog Pro is manufactured from specially selected pine timbers which are pressure-treated with *Tanalith E* wood preservative for durability and long service life.
The timbers, available in a variety of lengths, provide a natural, sustainable, flexible and cost effective method of landscaping for all projects.
DuraSleeper timber is a range of sanded and rough cut sleepers to lengths of 3000mm offering an alternative natural option for retaining walls.

Accreditation
The WPA Benchmark Certificate, held by M&M Timber, provides 15 and 30 years desired service life warranties for *Unilog Pro*.

Services
M&M Timber provides a bespoke cut service for specific measurements to meet design requirements for landscaping projects.

Contact
Sales Team
t: 0333 003 5133
sales@mmtimber.co.uk

Web
www.mmtimber.co.uk

Address
M&M Timber Ltd
Hunt House Sawmills
Clows Top
Nr Kidderminster DY14 9HY

Affiliations
BALI

Additional entries
PlayGuard playground timber ➤ 477

Unilog Pro retaining wall and planter

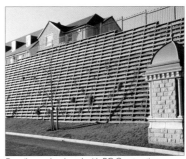
Unilog Pro retaining walls

Unilog Pro retaining wall

Unilog Pro retaining walls

Contact

Derek Taylor, Business Development Director

t: 024 7651 1266

derek.taylor@keller.co.uk

Web

www.keller.co.uk

Address

Keller
Oxford Road
Ryton-on-Dunsmore
Coventry CV8 3EG

Accreditation

ISO 9001
ISO 14001
OHSAS 18001

Affiliations

Federation of Piling Specialists

Additional entries

Retaining structures ➤ 37

Keller

Ground engineering

Keller provides innovative and cost effective solutions to foundation, stability and ground water problems.

Areas of expertise

Technologies and expert solutions are primarily provided in the following areas:

• Piling and earth retention.
• Ground improvement.
• Speciality grouting.
• Anchors, nails and mini piles.
• Instrumentation and monitoring.

Technical support

Keller is experienced in providing design and build solutions to meet project-specific geotechnical requirements.

With a wide range of techniques to draw on, Keller's strong UK engineering capability is backed by experience gained through technology transfer from operations in Europe, North America and Australia.

Operational area

Services are provided across the UK construction sector in infrastructure, industrial, commercial, residential and environmental projects.

Keller's *Continuous Flight Auger* (CFA) piling system is a quiet, low vibration solution for built-up areas

CFA low vibration piling is suitable for built-up areas

Vibro concrete piles for sites with very weak soils

High capacity anchors in lengths of up to 60m

High grade steel piles for *King* post wall

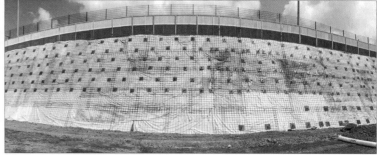

Soil nail walls for embankment stabilisation

EARTH ANCHORING SYSTEMS

Contact
Stewart MacArthur (North)
Tim Hall (South)
t: 01737 762300
f: 01737 773395
info@platipus-anchors.com

Web
www.platipus-anchors.com

Address
Platipus® Anchors Ltd
Kingsfield Business Centre
Philanthropic Road
Redhill RH1 4DP

Accreditation
ISO 9001:2008

Affiliations
British Geotechnical Association
International Geosynthetics Society

CPD
Earth anchoring systems for infrastructure
applications

Operational area
Worldwide

Country of manufacture
UK

Additional entries
Tree anchoring and irrigation ➤ 527

Earth anchors support slope at temporary works

Platipus® Anchors Ltd

Mechanical earth anchoring

Founded in 1983, Platipus® designs, manufactures
and supplies earth anchoring products and
systems for the civil engineering, construction and
landscaping industries.

Earth anchors

Platipus® Percussion Driven Earth Anchors (PDEA®)
are versatile products that can be rapidly
deployed in most displaceable ground conditions.
They create minimal disturbance of the soil
during installation, can be stressed to an exact
holding capacity and made fully operational
immediately. As a completely dry system, they
have minimal environmental impact.

• **Applications**
Applications include slope stabilisation, retaining
walls, bridge repair and construction, sheet piling,
gabion support, erosion control, pipeline
anchoring and guying of temporary and
permanent structures.

• **Product options**
Stealth Anchors are designed for lightweight
anchoring applications with typical loadings from
2.5 to 40kN.
Bat Anchors cater for higher loads with typical
loadings from 20 to 200kN. *Bat Anchors* are also
used to enhance anchoring in soft, cohesive soils.
Wire tendons and rods are available in a range of
sizes and materials to suit temporary (up to 5
year) through to permanent (120 year) design life.
Top fittings are available to suit most applications
and budgets, including near flush fitting load plates
for schemes where aesthetics are important.

Drainage

Plati-Drain® is an effective means of reducing pore
water pressure in clay slopes and behind retaining
walls. It can have a penetration of over 10m.
Systems constructed using *Plati-Drain®* and
Platipus® earth anchor systems provide dual
draining and restraining capability.

Composition and manufacture

Platipus® Percussion Driven Earth Anchors (PDEA®)
components are made in a range of materials
including aluminium alloy, hard anodised
aluminium alloy, galvanised spheroidal graphite
iron, stainless steel and aluminium bronze. Design
lives catered for range from 5 to 120 years.

Technical support

Design assistance including full indemnification,
technical presentations, site surveys and anchor
testing, on site training and demos are offered.
Anchor performance software is available online.

Installation

Hire equipment is available to install and proof
test systems. A supply and installation service is
offered through a network of approved installers.

Slope stabilsation on a main Norwich to London rail route

Platipus® Percussion Driven Earth Anchors (PDEA®) used for erosion control

Plati-Drain® used to strengthen embankment

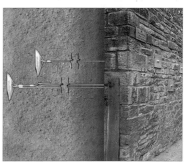

Platipus® anchors and Plati-Drain® support wall

Platipus® ARGS (anchored reinforced grid solution) used to improve flood defence

C·D·T·S

Contact
Iain Christison (South East)
t: 01954 232350
m: 07831 223484
iain@cdts.info

James Thomson (North West)
t: 01948 861088
m: 07831 593775
james@cdts.info

Web
www.cdts-ltd.co.uk

Address
Cambridge Direct Tree Seeding Ltd
Hilton House
37 Hilton Street
Over
Cambridge CB24 5PU

North West office
Cambridge Direct Tree Seeding Ltd
Allport Farm
Overton Common
Malpas SY14 7DG

Accreditation
BSI Kitemark™
Building Services Approved
CHAS
SMAS

Affiliations
British Association of Landscape Industries (BALI)
Constructionline

Operational area
UK

Cambridge Direct Tree Seeding Ltd

Hydroseeding

Established over 30 years ago as one of the first companies to offer hydroseeding, CDTS is recognised as a leading UK specialist seeding contractor. CDTS is able to offer a nationwide service with a full range of conventional seeding equipment and seven hydroseeding machines of various capacities. The company operates from offices in Cambridge and Cheshire, Gloucestershire and Scotland.

Areas of expertise

CDTS originates from a research background and specialises in establishing vegetation on hostile soils, utilising hydroseeding techniques.
A conventional seeding service is also offered.

Services

Correct specification is essential for predictable results – CDTS can provide a full service, from site assessment through to contract documentation, specification and programming. Services include hydroseeding, grass and wildflower seeding, direct seeding of trees and shrubs, and local seed collections using the company's brush seed harvester.
CDTS can provide aftercare, management advice and maintenance.

Seeding, Stonehenge

Hydroseeding, Northumberlandia earth sculpture

Hydroseeding on rails, Manchester Metro

Hydroseeding and soil restoration, Clyde wind farm

Stone raking

Hydroseeding with sedum on green roof, Center Parcs, Woburn

Green roof six months after hydroseeding

Conventional seeding for land reclamation

  For detailed information on featured products and services ☞ **www.externalworks.co.uk**

Contact
Franklyn Melville-Brown
t: 01453 511365
f: 01453 511364
info@hydroseeding.co.uk

Web
www.hydroseeding.co.uk

Address
RMB Hydroseeding
Lower Wick Farm
Lower Wick
Dursley GL11 6DD

Affiliations
BALI (British Association of Landscape Industries)
IECA (International Erosion Control Association)
IAHP (International Association of Hydroseeding Professionals)
ECTC (Erosion Control Technology Council)
Constructionline
Acclaim

RMB Hydroseeding

Hydroseeding

Specialists in hydroseeding with over 46 years' experience, RMB Hydroseeding has undertaken a wide range of projects across the UK and Ireland, from road and railway to land reclamation and major civil engineering schemes.

Composition and manufacture
Hydroseeding is the process of spraying a specially mixed slurry comprising of water, seed, woodfibre, fertiliser and eco-friendly binder in a single application. Hydroseeding is used when either the area is too large, inaccessible, or unsuitable for other conventional seeding methods.

Areas of expertise
For embankments prone to erosion, RMB Hydroseeding has developed a range of products, including *HBRS*, a biodegradable erosion control blanket that can be fitted prior to hydroseeding. Made from natural materials, it is the most aesthetically pleasing and environmentally friendly erosion control method available.

Services
RMB Hydroseeding's techniques cover a wide range of site requirements and conditions, and can be undertaken throughout the year. Design and maintenance services are also available.

Residential development – before hydroseeding

Residential development – after hydroseeding

Hydroseeding

Jute blankets help prevent erosion on embankments

Wildflower seeding – former steelworks, Ebbw Vale

New vegetation after hydroseeding

Example of soft engineering

Hydroseeding

Contact

Peter Whiteside (sales)
t: 01793 700100
enquiries@elcotenviro.com

Web
www.elcotenviro.com

Address
Elcot Environmental
Kingsdown Lane
Blunsdon
Swindon SN25 5DL

Accreditation
ISO 9001:2000
ISO 14001:2004
OHSAS 18001
CHAS Accredited
Safecontractor Approved
PCA accredited for knotweed management

Operational area
UK

Elcot Environmental

Japanese knotweed control

Elcot Environmental is a company with over 45 years' experience in landscape contracting and invasive weed control that has specialised in Japanese knotweed control since 1998.

• Japanese knotweed control
Elcot has unrivalled experience in providing and implementing cost-effective plans to control and eradicate knotweed in environments ranging from major development sites, to railway embankments, road verges and residential property. Services include initial site surveys and reports, knotweed treatment programmes, on site and offsite management of extracted materials, ongoing monitoring and treatment, and the provision of documentary and photographic evidence to legislative or other interested bodies. Contracts are undertaken for the building and civil engineering industries, as well as local and regional government bodies throughout the UK. Packages are specified to satisfy site conditions and client timescales at a fixed price for full knotweed eradication and management. Clients include Tesco, Vinci Construction, Scottish Power, Standard Life and Bellway Homes.

• Invasive non-native species control
Management plans are available for plants (excluding aquatics) listed on Schedule 9 or the Wildlife and Countryside Act.

Excavation of Japanese knotweed under a road, Watford General Hospital

Reconstructing levels with processed material, Cwmbran (approximately six weeks from start to handover)

Compaction of processed material, near Manchester

Checking knotweed three weeks after treatment

Bury cell, Highbridge Somerset

Bagged knotweed rhisome, Northampton

Contact
Richard Ward
t: 01277 890274
f: 01277 890322
richardward@hughpearl.co.uk

Web
www.hughpearl.co.uk

Address
Hugh Pearl (Land Drainage) Ltd
New Farm
Bobbingworth
Ongar CM5 0DJ

Accreditation
ISO 9001:2008, Constructionline, CHAS

Affiliations
Land Drainage Contractors Association; Institute of
Groundsmanship; RSPB; Essex Wildlife Trust

Additional entries
Natural sports field construction ➤ 494

Hugh Pearl (Land Drainage) Ltd

Lakes and watercourses

With 60 years' experience, Hugh Pearl offers a
high-quality service for the construction of lakes,
ponds, watercourses and wetland habitats.
Expertise is offered in installing anti-erosion,
geomembrane and revetment products, timber,
steel and plastic piling, and water control
structures. Clients include local authorities, the
Environment Agency, angling clubs, farm estates,
schools, colleges and private individuals.
Projects are carried out for wildlife organisations
within sites that are often ecologically,
environmentally or archeologically sensitive.

Lake desilting

Sea wall revetment

Boardwalk construction

Pond desilting

Wetland habitat creation

Contact

Andrew Baylis

t: 01474 569576

info@baylislandscapes.co.uk

Web

www.baylislandscapes.co.uk

Address

Baylis Landscape Contractors Ltd
Hartshill Nursery, Thong Lane
Shorne, Gravesend DA12 4AD

Accreditation

CHAS, Constructionline, Exor

Affiliations

British Association of Landscape Industries (BALI)

Operational area

London, South East England

Additional entries

Bespoke playgrounds ➤ 469

Baylis Landscape Contractors Ltd

Landscape services

Baylis Landscape Contractors specialises in landscaping for large-scale projects in the commercial, municipal and educational sectors. Located on the A2, near the M25/Dartford crossing, Baylis undertakes work throughout London and the South East.

With 48 years' experience, as well as a versatile and skilled management and workforce (100% CSCS qualified), the company can undertake complex, multi-faceted contracts. Acting as either a main or sub-contractor, Baylis provides a high-quality landscaping service at a reasonable cost. The company's Learning through Play section designs and constructs bespoke and innovative playground solutions for primary schools and nurseries. It won a BALI Landscape Award in 2013 for education-based projects.

Baylis's specialist divisions – Active Leisure Contracts and the Artificial Lawn Company – specialise in the construction of natural and synthetic sports surfaces and artificial grass for lawns and landscape use.

Accreditation

Baylis is a member of the British Association of Landscape Industries (BALI).

BALI award winner 2013

Learning through play design and build

Learning through play design and build

Quality hard landscaping

Polymeric rubber surfacing and sports fencing

Synthetic sports surface

Learning through play

Hard and soft landscape construction

Commercial and public contracts are undertaken

Contact

Joe Watson
t: 01285 654766
f: 01285 654499
j.watson@estatesandgardens.co.uk

Web
www.estatesandgardens.co.uk

Address
Cotswold Estates & Gardens Ltd
Baunton Lane
Cirencester GL7 7BG

Accreditation
Investors in People
CHAS; EXOR – Gold level
SMAS Verification; SAFEcontractor

Affiliations
BALI
Constructionline

Operational area
Gloucestershire, Wiltshire, Oxfordshire, South
Warwickshire, West Berkshire

Cotswold Estates & Gardens Ltd

Landscape services

Established in 1965, Cotswold Estates & Gardens Ltd, formerly known as Cotswold Estate Services, carries out hard and soft landscaping, as well as forestry and environmental work, for public, private and commercial clients.
Projects are undertaken up to £500k. Services include design, construction and ongoing maintenance throughout southern England. Cotswold Estates & Gardens also has experience as a principal contractor under CDM Regulations.

Projects

• Natural swimming pond – pumped circulation filters water through natural planting providing clear water with no harmful effects to wildlife.
• Garden design and construction on brownfield site – terracing, 60m rill cascades and planting.
• Private garden designed by Oliver Castledine – cruciform lily pond with glass spout waterfall, Cotswold stone steps with glass balustrade, paving, decking and soft landscaping.
• A419/A417 – native infrastructure planting with a subsequent ongoing maintenance contract using a specialist tractor for the banks.
• Private garden designed by TRees Associates – a sunken garden, terraces, parterre, Cotswold stone steps and retaining walls.

Natural swimming pond

Paved terrace with 60m long rill including cascades

Private garden designed by Oliver Castledine

A419/A417 – planting and maintenance

Private garden designed by TRees Associates

LAND DESIGN PARTNERSHIP
Design and Landscape Consultants

Contact
Robert Simmonds
t: 01622 820522
rob@ldp.uk.com

Web
www.ldp.uk.com

Address
The Land Design Partnership Ltd
Unit 1, Dairy Lane Farm
Chainhurst
Marden
Tonbridge TN12 9SS

Accreditation
CHAS
SMAS

Affiliations
BALI

Awards
BALI National Award Winner 2006
BALI National Award Winner 2008
BALI National Award Winner 2013

Operational area
London and the Home Counties

The Land Design Partnership

Landscape services

The Land Design Partnership (LDP) was formed in 1988 as a cutting edge design and build landscape business, operating at the prestige end of both the domestic and commercial markets.

Design services

LDP works across London and the South East with architects, designers and contractors.
In addition to landscape installations, LDP takes clients through the whole process from an initial consultation through to the final realisation.
Maintenance services are also available.

Domestic project with stone rill

BALI Principal Award winning garden – Canterbury

Sussex show home garden for Crest Nicholson

Sensory planting for a public courtyard

Kent show home garden for Crest Nicholson

Rookery Court Retirement Village – Marden

Contact
t: 01933 665151
enquiries@timotaylandscapes.co.uk

Web
www.timotaylandscapes.co.uk

Address
Timotay Landscapes Ltd
Crispin House
14 Hinwick Road
Wollaston NN29 7QT

Accreditation
ISO 9001
ISO 14001

Affiliations
Contractors Health & Safety Assessment Scheme
(CHAS)
British Association of Landscape Industries (BALI)
Association of Professional Landscapers (APL)

Awards
2011 Marshalls regional winners patio over 35 sqm
Design & Construction of a Play Garden 2008
Design & Construction of a Domestic Scheme 2001
Domestic Garden Planting Scheme 2001
Domestic Garden Design & Construction 2001

Operational area
UK

Additional entries
Playground equipment ➤ 462

Timotay Landscapes Ltd

Landscaping services

Established in 1985, Timotay Landscapes is an award-winning landscaping design and construction specialist.
The company's landscape designers, architects, horticulturists, manufacturing teams, installation teams and project managers work with clients to visualise and create bespoke outdoor spaces, from concept to completion.
Timotay Landscapes undertakes landscaping projects throughout the UK.

Landscaping of a garden, including a water feature

Services include driveways

Hard landscaping project includes paving, walling, planting schemes and a pergola

Concept drawing of garden project

Hard landscaping

Domestic garden project

East Midlands Landscaping Ltd

Soft landscaping services

Established in 1987, East Midlands Landscaping is a large commercial landscaping company based in Leicester, providing services to main contractors, house builders and housing associations.
East Midlands Landscaping specialises in soft landscaping, including initial site clearance, tree and shrub planting, bark mulching and top soiling, and can provide a landscape maintenance service. In partnership with its landscape design company, East Midlands is able to offer a comprehensive landscape design and build package.
Projects from £10,000–£500,000 are undertaken.

Contact
Jon King (Contracts Director)
t: 01455 850250
info@eastmidlandslandscaping.co.uk

Web
www.eastmidlandslandscaping.co.uk

Address
East Midlands Landscaping Ltd
The Knoll
Leicester Road
Earl Shilton
Leicester LE9 7TJ

Staff/turnover
£5m+

Affiliations
British Association of Landscape Industries (BALI)
– full contracting member

Accreditation
CHAS, SafeContractor, Constructionline,
SMAS Worksafe Contractor

Courtyard garden – East Village Marketing Suite, Stratford, London

Seeding works – solar farm, Measham

Planting scheme – new garden centre

Lace Market Square, Nottingham

Retail planting scheme – Morrisons, Wrexham

Commercial landscape design and build services

Public open space landscaping works – housing development

Landscaping – prestigious new college, Derby

Raised planter beds – Sue Ryder hospice garden

SURFACE WATER MANAGEMENT

Interceptors   54

Interceptors for surface water run-off filtration and oil retention.

Pipes and component chambers   55-57

Large diameter pipes for water management and large scale flood alleviation schemes. Large chamber components, flow control devices and separators.

Headwalls and outfalls   58-59

Headwalls and outfalls in precast concrete and GRC for connecting drainage pipework discharging into open watercourses such as rivers, streams, lakes, swales and ponds.

Flow control   60-61

Flow control devices for regulating water in surface, sewer and process applications including flap valves, penstocks, stop logs and vortex flow control.

Stormwater management   62-66

- Geocellular water storage with high void ratios for shallow or deep excavations. Load bearing modular solutions to retain, attenuate or infiltrate surface water.
- Vortex separators and flow control systems; surface water filtration.
- Integrated water management solutions for sustainable urban drainage systems.

Geocomposite and polymer drains   67-68

Geocomposite and polymer drainage systems to remove water from surface and sub-surface structures, embankments and grassed areas with low permeability.

Permeable paving systems   68-77

- Cellular permeable paving systems
  Cellular pavers and tiles for free-draining, reinforced, stabilised grass and gravel surfaces. Applications include industrial hardstandings, overground storm drains, car parking areas and emergency vehicle access routes.
- Porous resin-bound surfacing
  Resin-bound aggregate surfacing for use where an attractive permeable surface finish is required. Applications include walkways, communal access roads, car parks, driveways and tree pits.
- Permeable concrete block paving
  Concrete block paving designed to eliminate surface water run-off and improve water quality from hard landscaped areas. Used with the appropriate sub-base ancillaries, systems can be designed for the infiltration or harvesting of rainwater.

Channel drainage systems   78-84

- Linear channel drainage systems
  Slot and grate channel drainage systems in precast and polymer concrete, cast iron, stainless steel and stone for light- to heavy-duty highway and industrial applications.
- Combined kerb and drainage
  Systems in concrete, GRC and polymer concrete for high-capacity, integrated surface water management schemes.

EXTERNAL WORKS ONLINE

For detailed information supported by case studies, downloads and tools to help you make faster and better decisions ...
☞ www.externalworks.co.uk

Contact

Head office
t: 01462 816666
f: 01462 815895
technologies@aco.co.uk

Web
www.aco.co.uk

Address
ACO Water Management –
a division of ACO Technologies plc
ACO Business Park
Hitchin Road
Shefford SG17 5TE

Accreditation
ISO 9001: 2008
ISO 14001:2004

CPD
Accredited CPDs on surface water management

Additional entries
Stormwater control ➤ 63
Surface water management ➤ 78
Urban + Landscape drainage ➤ 79

ACO Water Management – a division of ACO Technologies

Interceptors

ACO Water Management recognises that protection of the environment is a crucial part of an integrated approach to modern surface water management and sustainable drainage systems (SuDS). Contamination of ground water and watercourses from hydrocarbons (petrol, diesel and engine oil) carried by surface water runoff poses serious threats to the environment. Two advanced systems are manufactured to address these challenges.

• Rainwater and surface water runoff filtration systems

ACO QuadraCeptor is a specialist rainwater and surface water runoff filtration system for the removal of sediment and harmful pollutants. ACO QuadraCeptor significantly improves water quality, removing pollutants before infiltration into the soil or discharge into water courses.

• Bypass and full retention oil separators

ACO Q-Ceptor oil separators are an innovative range of bypass and full retention separators. The high performance systems are fully compliant with BS EN 858:2002 parts 1 and 2 and exceed the requirements of the Environment Agency's PPG 3 guidelines.
ACO Q-Ceptors are available in a range of chamber sizes and flow rates for use in car parks, maintenance areas, and industrial and residential applications.
Manufactured from polyethylene, the innovative single chamber design of the ACO Q-Ceptor is very compact and robust offering significant advantages in installation and handling costs over traditional GRP products.
ACO Q-Ceptors are available in two performance classes as specified by BS EN 858-1:2002. Both Class 1 and Class 2 ACO Q-Ceptors are available as bypass or full retention separators.
ACO Water Management solutions address the four stages of Effective Water Management: Collect, Clean, Hold, Release.

ACO QuadraCeptor surface water runoff filtration

The four stages of Effective Water Management

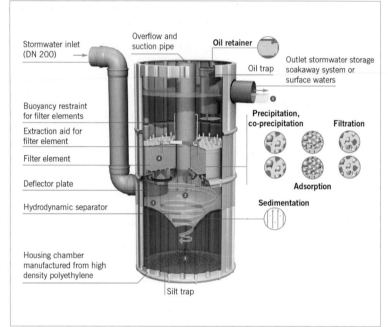

Stormwater inlet (DN 200)
Overflow and suction pipe
Oil retainer
Oil trap
Outlet stormwater storage soakaway system or surface waters
Buoyancy restraint for filter elements
Extraction aid for filter element
Filter element
Deflector plate
Hydrodynamic separator
Housing chamber manufactured from high density polyethylene
Silt trap
Precipitation, co-precipitation
Filtration
Adsorption
Sedimentation

ACO QuadraCeptor specialist rainwater and surface water runoff filtration system

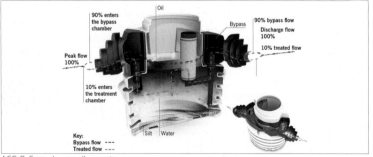

Oil
90% enters the bypass chamber
Bypass
90% bypass flow
Discharge flow 100%
10% treated flow
Peak flow 100%
10% enters the treatment chamber
Key:
Bypass flow ---
Treated flow ---
Silt | Water

ACO Q-Ceptor bypass oil separator

Oil
100% enters the treatment chamber
100% treated flow
Discharge flow 100%
Peak flow 100%
Key:
Treated flow ---
Silt | Water

ACO Q-Ceptor full retention oil separator

Contact
t: 01509 615100
f: 01509 610215
civils@polypipe.com

Web
www.polypipe.com

Address
Polypipe Civils (Head Office)
Charnwood Business Park
North Road
Loughborough LE11 1LE

Accreditation
BS EN ISO 9001:2015
BS EN ISO 14001:2004

Affiliations
British Water
British Plastics Federation
Plastic Pipes Group
Susdrain
The European Plastic Pipes and Fittings Association

Operational area
UK and Ireland

Additional entries
Component chambers ➤ 56
Permavoid ➤ 64
Polystorm ➤ 65

Polypipe Civils

Ridgistorm-XL

Ridgistorm-XL is a WRc approved engineered thermoplastic large diameter pipe system for use in a wide range of applications including surface water, foul water, combined sewers and large-scale flood alleviation schemes.

It is robust, reliable and long lasting, with a design life in excess of 100 years.

Ridgistorm-XL is designed to optimum stiffness classification, has excellent load bearing capability, delivers superior performance in areas of differential settlement and provides excellent resistance to sulphate and chemical attack.

Due to its longer lengths and lighter weight, *Ridgistorm-XL* can be 70% cheaper to transport than equivalent size concrete pipes and can be handled and stored more safely on-site.

Dimensions
Diameters 750–3000mm; pipe lengths 1.25–12m.

Applications
Ridgistorm-XL is a versatile and proven solution for applications ranging from pipelines for surface water drainage and foul sewer schemes, to attenuation structures, large diameter manholes and pre-fabricated component chambers.

Engineered designs
By analysing site conditions and installation parameters, Polypipe can create project-specific solutions with the appropriate profile strength and stiffness classifications, with pipe strength at varying stiffness classes between SN1–SN8.

Pipe profile design
Pipe profile designs can be adapted to optimise the strength of the system to site-specific requirements. This improves pipeline performance and provides a fully engineered solution.

Jointing options
Ridgistorm-XL can be manufactured to suit any jointing requirement on-site, including ring seals, electro-fusion welding, extrusion welding, flange connections and mechanical pipe couplings.

Ridgistorm-XL large diameter piping system

Ridgistorm-XL piping system – Doncaster iPort

Ridgistorm-XL installation – Manchester Airport

Ridgistorm-XL large diameter piping system – Strata Homes, Yorkshire

Contact
t: 01509 615100
f: 01509 610215
civils@polypipe.com

Web
www.polypipe.com

Address
Polypipe Civils (Head Office)
Charnwood Business Park
North Road
Loughborough LE11 1LE

Accreditation
BS EN ISO 9001:2015
BS EN ISO 14001:2004

Affiliations
British Water
British Plastics Federation
Plastic Pipes Group
Susdrain
The European Plastic Pipes and Fittings Association

Operational area
UK and Ireland

Additional entries
Ridgistorm-XL ➤ 55
Permavoid ➤ 64
Polystorm ➤ 65

Polypipe Civils

Component chambers

Polypipe's WRc approved large diameter component chambers are prefabricated using thermoplastic structured wall pipes for exceptional durability and superior performance. Structured wall chambers are fully-welded and watertight. They are strong but lighter in weight than concrete equivalents, minimising health and safety risks in handling and installation.
Systems are designed to precise project requirements and delivered directly to site ready to install as one-piece modular solutions.

Components and systems

RIDGISTORMCheck is designed for use where flows within a drainage system need to be limited or checked (eg prior to discharge from site).
RIDGISTORMAccess provides easy man-access for the maintenance of pipelines.
RIDGISTORMControl caters for drainage or sewer system designs where flow control devices are required.
RIDGISTORMSeparate chambers capture and separate out silt, particles and debris to protect downstream systems.
RIDGISTORM-X4 is a four-stage treatment device, used for the treatment of surface water run-off, providing high levels of contaminant removal, including hydrocarbons and heavy metals.

RIDGISTORMCheck vortex flow control chamber

RIDGISTORMCheck orifice plate flow control

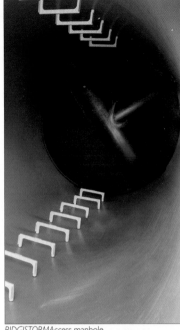

RIDGISTORMAccess manhole

RIDGISTORMControl flap valve

RIDGISTORMControl penstock

RIDGISTORMControl gate valve

RIDGISTORMSeparate basic silt trap

RIDGISTORMSeparate mini silt trap

RIDGISTORMSeparate advanced silt trap

RIDGISTORMSeparate catchpit

RIDGISTORMSeparate filter chamber

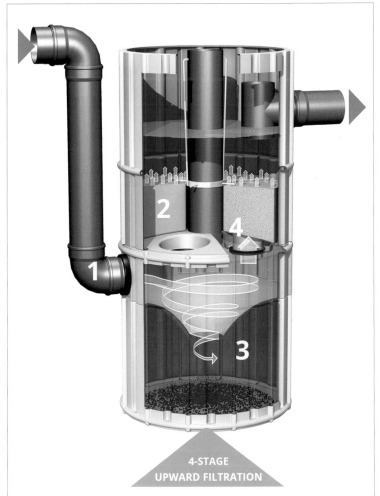

4-STAGE UPWARD FILTRATION

COMPONENT CHAMBER SIZES	
Diameter (mm)	Height (m)
750	<6
900	<6
1050	<6
1200	<6
1500	<6
1800	<6
2100	<6
2400	<6
2700	<6
3000	<6

Manufactured to exact depth requirements

1 **Sedimentation:** Water is induced into a radial flow within the dynamic separator at the base of the unit, promoting sedimentation of solid particles.

2 **Filtration:** Water flows up from the separator and through removable filter elements. The filter elements remain saturated, minimising the risk of the filter elements clogging.

3 **Chemical separation:** While passing through the filter unit, dissolved chemical pollutants are removed by a process of adsorption, absorption and precipitation.

4 **Oil retention:** Water is finally discharged via an oil trap assembly which is designed to retain free-floating oils in the event of a major spill.

RIDGISTORM-X4 four-stage treatment device for surface water run-off

Contact
t: 01603 488700
f: 01603 488598
sales@althon.co.uk

Web
www.althon.co.uk

Address
Althon Ltd
Vulcan Road South
Norwich NR6 6AF

Operational area
UK (headwalls)

Additional entries
Flow control ➤ 60
Channel drainage ➤ 82

Althon Ltd

Precast headwalls

Althon offers precast headwalls that are a cost-effective alternative to in-situ concrete structures for connecting pipework that discharges into open watercourses.

All drainage pipes discharging into open watercourses, such as swales, ditches, ponds and rivers, should be fitted with an appropriate headwall. Althon headwall units can be pre-fitted with a range of accessories such as flap valves, penstocks, Kee Klamp handrails and gratings, depending on requirements.

• **Sewers for Adoption headwalls**
Where a headwall is part of a Section 104 Agreement and the sewers are to be adopted once completed by the local water company, then the materials used and the installation must comply with the 'Sewers for Adoption' (SFA) guidelines. Althon offers SFA precast concrete headwalls to comply with these requirements.

• **Swale and pond inlets**
Althon's swale and pond inlet is a fibre-reinforced precast concrete open inlet that allows surface water run-off to enter SUDS features, or can act as an outlet or overflow. The profile of the inlet is 1:3 (18°), which should be the same as the surrounding ground, in accordance with guidelines for the construction and adoption of swales and ponds. A recess formed in either side keys the unit into the slope of the swale or pond and prevent it from slipping. It is designed to connect to 150, 225 or 300mm internal diameter twin-wall pipework with a stub that is cast into the unit. It is fitted with a hinged 25mm stainless steel grille.

• **Bespoke headwalls**
Althon is able to design and manufacture bespoke headwalls to suit site-specific circumstances. These can either be one-piece units, or sectional structures where the headwall must be very large. Bespoke headwalls can accommodate gratings, flap valves, trash screens and other security or flow control devices as well as health and safety essentials such as handrails, walkways and step ladders.

Bespoke precast wingwalls

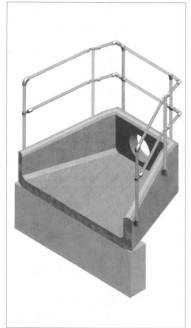
'Sewers for Adoption' headwall

Swale and pond inlet

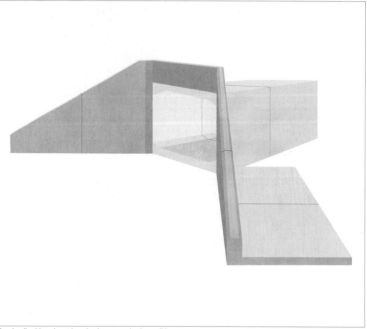
Headwall with culvert header beam and wingwall layout

BCM GRC Ltd

GRC headwalls/retaining structures

BCM GRC Ltd offers glass fibre reinforced concrete (GRC) headwalls, which ensure that the banks of rivers, streams or ponds are not eroded by discharged water. They can also be used as small retaining structures for carriageway lighting, utility boxes and other applications.

Headwalls are manufactured from high-strength, grade 18 GRC. Long-fibre GRC gives greater strength-to-weight ratios and resistance to damage, frost, chemical attack and road salts. All units are available with gratings if required.

Contact
Darin Ballington
t: 01948 665321
f: 01948 666381
info@bcmgrc.com

Web
www.bcmgrc.com

Address
BCM GRC Ltd
Unit 22
Civic Industrial Park
Whitchurch SY13 1TT

Accreditation
AMS – GRCA Approved Manufacturing Scheme

Affiliations
Glassfibre Reinforced Concrete Association (GRCA)
Concrete Society

Awards
GRCA Merit Award

Headwall unit used as a small retaining structure

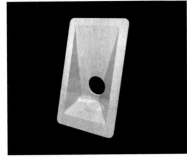
Large headwall

B900 headwall in situ

B300 headwall in situ

Retaining wall with pipe drain inlet unit and silt box

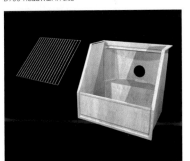
Pipe drain inlet units incorporate a silt box

B900 headwall unit awaiting dispatch from factory

Contact

t: 01603 488700
f: 01603 488598
sales@althon.co.uk

Web

www.althon.co.uk

Address

Althon Ltd
Vulcan Road South
Norwich NR6 6AF

Operational area

Worldwide (flow control/channel drainage)

Additional entries

Precast headwalls ➤ 58
Channel drainage ➤ 82

Flap valve

Headwall and penstock

Althon Ltd

Flow control

Althon offers flow control devices that can be used in surface, sewer and process water applications.

• Flap valves

Flap valves are a simple and effective way to prevent water backflow into a system. For heavier duty applications, 100–1500mm flaps are made with additional features such as welded stiffening ribs. They are manufactured in a combination of HDPE and 316 stainless steel, meaning they are lightweight and high in strength. They are easy to install, responsive and reliable.

• Penstocks

Medium-duty penstocks are a simple, effective way to prevent water backflow into a system. Designs have been developed to accommodate the majority of situations where a penstock is required. They are suitable for sealing pressures of 5mWC as standard, require virtually no maintenance, and are fast, safe and easy to install.

• Stop logs

Stop logs are used for the isolation and containment of water. They are lightweight and corrosion resistant, and are suitable for applications where standard single-piece stop gates would be too heavy to lift or where multiple door sections are called for. They are manufactured in the latest materials combined with aluminium or stainless steel, meaning that a solution can be provided for most water sewage and effluent treatment situations.

• Inline WaStop valves

WaStop valves can be installed inline between two pipes to prevent backflow. They are made from 304 or 316 stainless steel, or PVC tube, and incorporate a cone-shaped chloroprene membrane. The membrane allows water flow to pass in the desired direction, but when backflow occurs, the membrane fills, sealing the pipe. As the *WaStop* does not rely on gravity to close the membrane, it does not need to be fitted against a vertical headwall. They are suitable for pressures up to 8mWC.

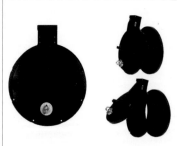

Flange-mounted flap valves

1600mm inline penstock

Contact

Hydro-Brake® hotline
t: 01275 337937
hydrobrake@hydro-int.com

Web
www.hydro-int.com

Address
Head Office
Hydro International
Shearwater House
Clevedon Hall Estate
Victoria Road
Clevedon BS21 7RD

t: 01275 878371
f: 01275 874979
enquiries@hydro-int.com

Accreditation
ISO 9001:2008
ISO 14001:2004
UVDB – Achilles

Affiliations
British Water
CIRIA
British Plastics Federation

Operational area
UK, Ireland, Europe

Additional entries
Stormwater treatment ➤ 62

Hydro International

Stormwater flow control

The *Hydro-Brake® Flow Control Series* can be used to manage surface water, watercourse and foul/combined sewer flows for sustainable urban drainage systems. They can be supplied pre-fitted in precast, reinforced concrete chambers for quick and easy installation on site.

• **Hydro-Brake® Optimum**
Hydro-Brake Optimum® vortex flow control manages low, moderate to high flow to deliver sustainable drainage from single sites to large networks. It provides customised water quantity management for surface, foul or combined water.

• **Hydro-Brake® Flood**
Hydro-Brake® Flood vortex flow control provides large-scale flood prevention at the watercourse level. Highly sustainable and precision-engineered, it prevents flooding by holding back excess water in temporary floor storage areas.

• **Hydro-Brake® Agile**
Hydro-Brake® Agile flow control reduces upstream storage and manages flood risk at sites with stringent discharge consents where space for on-site attenuation is a premium. Float-controlled, it achieves a constant rate of discharge and requires minimum upstream storage.

• **Hydro-Brake® Orifice**
Hydro-Brake® Orifice manages moderate flows, delivering sustainable drainage for developments.

Hydro-Brake® Optimum

Hydro-Brake® Flood

Hydro-Brake® Agile

Hydro-Brake® Orifice

The *Hydro-Brake® Flow Control Series*

Hydro-Brake® Flood installation

Completed *Hydro-Brake® Flood* installation – Northallerton

Hydro-Brake® Optimum installation – Dartford

Hydro-Brake® Flood installation – near Glasgow

Mounting and concrete chamber pre-fit options

Hydro-Brake® Optimum Design Tool

Contact
StormTrain® hotline
t: 01275 337955
stormtrain@hydro-int.com

Web
www.hydro-int.com

Address
Head Office
Hydro International
Shearwater House
Clevedon Hall Estate
Victoria Road
Clevedon BS21 7RD

t: 01275 878371
f: 01275 874979
enquiries@hydro-int.com

Accreditation
ISO 9001:2008
ISO 14001:2004
UVDB – Achilles

Affiliations
British Water
CIRIA
British Plastics Federation

Operational area
UK, Ireland, Europe

Additional entries
Stormwater flow control ➤ 61

Hydro International

Stormwater treatment

The *Hydro StormTrain® Series* from Hydro International provides surface water treatment in sustainable urban drainage systems (SuDS). The series comprises a range of surface water treatment devices, each delivering proven, measurable and repeatable surface water treatment performance. Each device can be used independently to meet the specific treatment needs of a site, or combined to form a management train.

• **First Defense® vortex separator**
First Defense® captures and retains stormwater sediment, litter and floatables in a unit that saves site space and adapts to smaller or logistically difficult site locations. This stormwater separator can work with single and multiple inlet pipes and inlet grates and is easily maintained from the surface by standard vacuum tanker.

• **Downstream Defender® advanced hydrodynamic vortex separator**
Downstream Defender® captures and retains sediment, oils and floatables from stormwater run-off over a wide range of flows in a small footprint. It is easily maintained from the surface by standard vacuum tanker.

• **Up-Flo™ Filter filtration system**
Up-Flo™ Filter captures sediment, oils, heavy metals and nutrients from stormwater in a reduced footprint. This advanced stormwater treatment solution combines sedimentation and screening with fluidised bed filtration to deliver exceptional surface water pollution removal.

• **Hydro Biocell™ biofiltration system**
Hydro Biocell™ removes sediment, trash, oil, dissolved metals and nutrients from surface runoff using the natural power of biofiltration. *Hydro Biocell™* uses soil and filter media to treat a range of coarse, fine and dissolved pollutants from surface runoff, even during high flows.

• **Surface Water Treatment Tool**
The *Surface Water Treatment Tool* can be used to develop scenarios and build example treatment trains, then calculate potential outcomes in terms of pollutant removal and costs.

First Defense®

Downstream Defender®

Up-Flo™ Filter

Hydro BioCell™

The *Hydro StormTrain® Series* of surface water treatment devices

The *Surface Water Treatment Tool*

Hydro BioCell™ installation – Glasgow

Downstream Defender® installation – Cambridge

Up-Flo™ Filter installation – Aberdeen

Hydro BioCell™ installation – Barry

Downstream Defender® installation – Hampshire

Contact

Head office
t: 01462 816666
f: 01462 815895
technologies@aco.co.uk

Web
www.aco.co.uk

Address
ACO Water Management –
a division of ACO Technologies plc
ACO Business Park
Hitchin Road
Shefford SG17 5TE

Accreditation
ISO 9001: 2008; ISO 14001:2004

CPD
Accredited CPDs on surface water management

Additional entries
Interceptors ➤ 54
Surface water management ➤ 78
Urban + Landscape drainage ➤ 79

ACO Water Management – a division of ACO Technologies

Stormwater control

ACO Water Management is an expert in water engineering, providing design solutions for stormwater management. ACO's approach to SuDS controls rainwater distribution from when it hits the ground until it re-enters the natural water environment, minimising environmental impact and maximising sustainability.

ACO Water Management solutions address the four stages of Effective Water Management: Collect, Clean, Hold, Release.

• Surface water infiltration and storage

ACO StormBrixx is a unique and patented plastic geocellular stormwater management system designed for surface water infiltration and storage. The versatility of the system means that it can be used in applications across all construction environments as a standalone solution or as part of an integrated sustainable urban drainage (SuDS) scheme.

ACO StormBrixx's unique pillar configuration gives a high void ratio of 95%. This minimises the excavation required to achieve a specified storage capacity, reduces the aggregate needed for backfilling, and improves the flow characteristics of runoff through the installed tank.

Delivery, site logistics and installation are all significantly simplified, as a result of the system's 'stackable' design.

The open cell structure provides simple access for remote CCTV and maintenance equipment to inspect all levels and areas of the system.

• Flow control and regulation

ACO Q-Brake Vortex is a horizontal vortex flow control system designed to regulate stormwater flows from 2–100 litres per second.

ACO Q-Plate regulates stormwater flows where a vortex flow control is not the most effective solution, or where flows are greater than 100 l/s. Both systems can be used in conjunction with retention and attenuation systems, such as *ACO StormBrixx*, as an integrated sustainable urban drainage (SuDS) scheme.

ACO StormBrixx installation – the unique pillar configuration gives a high void ratio of 95%

ACO StormBrixx stormwater management

ACO Q-Brake vortex flow control

ACO Q-Plate Orifice plates

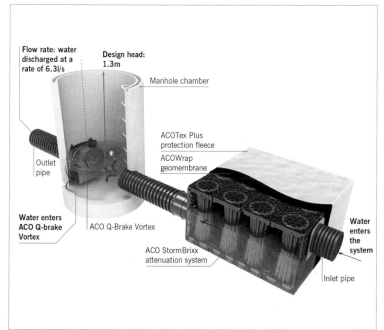

Flow rate: water discharged at a rate of 6.3l/s

Design head: 1.3m

Manhole chamber

ACOTex Plus protection fleece

ACOWrap geomembrane

Outlet pipe

Water enters ACO Q-brake Vortex

ACO Q-Brake Vortex

ACO StormBrixx attenuation system

Water enters the system

Inlet pipe

ACO Q-Brake Vortex flow control system and ACO StormBrixx attenuation system

Polypipe Civils

Permavoid

Permavoid is an engineered, geocellular water management system that meets the demands of current legislation and guidance for source control and surface water treatment.
The system comprises high-strength recycled polypropylene modular cells connected together using tapered ties to create a consistent structural raft of high compressive and tensile strength.
The geocellular structures have a void ratio up to 95%, greatly enhancing the site's attenuation capacity and reducing aggregate requirements in hydraulic pavements.

Applications

The *Permavoid* system is designed to be used in place of traditional aggregate sub-base for shallow applications. It provides a high strength, consistent structural raft in accordance with BS7533-13:2009 with all the benefits of a high voided modular geocellular structure.

• **Traffic loadings**
Permavoid can be installed beneath asphaltic, block-paved or concrete pavements for the full range of traffic conditions from domestic driveways to roads.

• **Problematic sites**
Minimising the need for excavation, *Permavoid* is ideal for sites with high water tables, shallow hard rock substrates or contaminated soil.

• **Multi-function and urban landscapes**
Permavoid supports Water Sensitive Urban Designs (WSUDs), particularly when incorporated into urban retrofitting applications.

Product options

Permavoid units are available in two depths, 85mm and 150mm. Units are stackable.
System components and accessories include: cell connectors, geotextiles for filtration and protection, geomembranes to form watertight tanks, drainage channels incorporating silt and oil interceptors, rainwater diffuser units, floating biomats, capillary cones for passive irrigation and absorbent foam for on-demand irrigation or check dam applications.

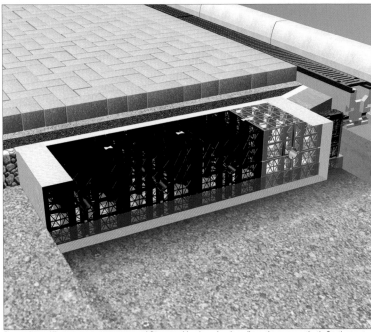

Permachannel linear treatment system and *Biomat* with a low density, oil treating, geosynthetic floating mat

Permavoid is designed to be used in place of traditional aggregate sub-base for shallow applications

Permavoid units are available in two depths, 85mm and 150mm

Contact
t: 01509 615100
f: 01509 610215
civils@polypipe.com

Web
www.polypipe.com

Address
Polypipe Civils (Head Office)
Charnwood Business Park
North Road
Loughborough LE11 1LE

Accreditation
BS EN ISO 9001:2015
BS EN ISO 14001:2004

Affiliations
British Water
British Plastics Federation
Plastic Pipes Group
Susdrain
The European Plastic Pipes and Fittings Association

Operational area
UK and Ireland

Additional entries
Ridgistorm-XL ➤ 55
Component chambers ➤ 56
Permavoid ➤ 64

Polystorm's rounded corners make it easy to handle

Polypipe Civils

Polystorm

The *Polystorm* geocellular range is designed to provide retention, attenuation or infiltration, primarily for deeper applications. It can accommodate a wide range of traffic loadings, from pedestrianised areas to large HGV parks.

Product options

There are four modular cells to choose from. *Polystorm R* is the standard cell for trafficked and loaded applications at greater depths including housing, commercial and infrastructure projects. It has a compressive strength of 61 tonnes/m². *Polystorm* is used for attenuation or infiltration under trafficked and loaded areas at greater depths. It has a compressive strength of 44 tonnes/m². *Polystorm Xtra* is designed for deeper burial depths and very heavily trafficked applications. It has a compressive strength of 83 tonnes/m². *Polystorm Lite* is designed for non-trafficked landscaped and pedestrianised areas. It has a compressive strength of 20 tonnes/m².

Access and maintenance

To complement the range of *Polystorm* modular cells, two options are available for access and maintenance purposes.
Polystorm Access provides a 1x0.5m vertical shaft within a *Polystorm* geocellular structure to enable surface access for remote camera inspection and maintenance activities such as flushing and rodding.
Polystorm Inspect provides a tunnel along the length of a fully installed *Polystorm* structure to enable access for lateral inspection and maintenance.

Accessories

Shear connectors, inspection and treatment modules, geotextiles, geomembranes, vents, upstream and downstream chambers complete the system.

Manufacture and composition

Polystorm, *Polystorm Xtra*, *Polystorm Inspect* and *Polystorm Access* are manufactured from virgin polypropylene. *Polystorm-R* and *Polystorm Lite* are manufactured from recycled polypropylene. All materials are 100% recyclable at the end of their usable life.

Performance

Up to 60 year design life. 95% void ratio for high water storage capacity and lower excavation and disposal costs. BBA approved for *Polystorm Lite*, *Polystorm-R* and *Polystorm*.

Sitework

Polystorm is a lightweight system that is safe and quick to install. Unique rounded corners make it easy to handle, reducing the risk of punctures to membranes.

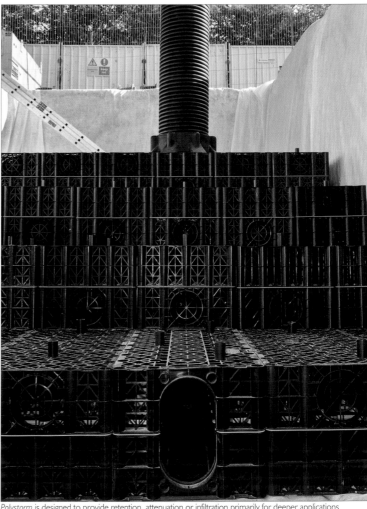
Polystorm is designed to provide retention, attenuation or infiltration primarily for deeper applications

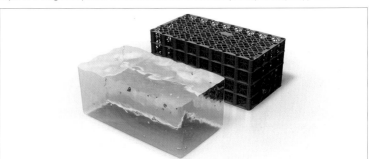
Polystorm has a 95% void ratio for high water storage capacity and lower excavation and disposal costs

Contact
t: 01934 751303
f: 01934 751304
info@sdslimited.com

Web
www.sdslimited.com

Address
SDS Limited
Clearwater House
Castlemills
Biddisham
Somerset BS26 2RE

Accreditation
ISO 9001
CHAS
Achilles UVDB

Affiliations
British Water
British Plastics Federation

Country of manufacture
UK

SDS Limited

Surface water management

SDS specialises in engineering innovative and cost-effective turnkey surface water management systems.

SDS's integrated water management system ensures that surface water run-off can be collected, treated, stored and released efficiently and sustainably, from the point at which rainfall first meets the ground to the point of its ultimate dispersal.

Technical support

The company provides a full service solution to support clients throughout the entire lifecycle of their installed water management systems. Services range from initial consultation, to design, manufacture and installation of systems, to ongoing maintenance.

Projects

• Stormwater treatment system – London Luton Airport expansion.
• Sustainable urban drainage system – new Volkswagen Financial Services (UK) headquarters, Milton Keynes.
• Sustainable urban drainage system – Newlands residential development, Berewood, Hampshire.
• Surface water management and sustainable drainage systems – Mill Hill East Primary School, London.

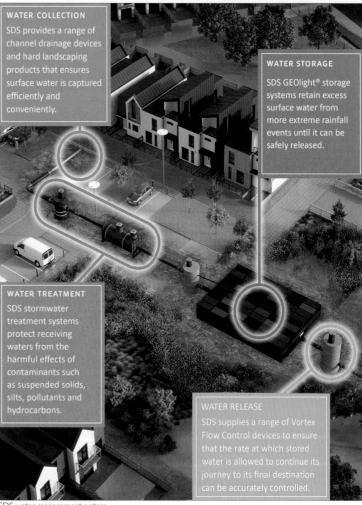

WATER COLLECTION
SDS provides a range of channel drainage devices and hard landscaping products that ensures surface water is captured efficiently and conveniently.

WATER STORAGE
SDS GEOlight® storage systems retain excess surface water from more extreme rainfall events until it can be safely released.

WATER TREATMENT
SDS stormwater treatment systems protect receiving waters from the harmful effects of contaminants such as suspended solids, silts, pollutants and hydrocarbons.

WATER RELEASE
SDS supplies a range of Vortex Flow Control devices to ensure that the rate at which stored water is allowed to continue its journey to its final destination can be accurately controlled.

Water treatement system installation – Luton Airport

GEOlight® installation

SDS water management system

Aqua-Swirl™ hydrodynamic vortex separator

Aqua-Filter™ water filtration unit

GEOlight® water storage system

GEOlight® water storage unit

HydroBlox Ltd

Surface and sub-surface drainage

HydroBlox Ltd provides surface and sub-surface drainage solutions using the civil engineering grade of *HydroPlanks™*.

HydroPlanks™ are a world first in water management, dramatically reducing ground disturbance, materials, labour and time. They provide cost-effective drainage solutions that require little to zero maintenance once installed.

• Applications

HydroPlanks™ are suitable for a wide range of surface and sub-surface drainage projects, including those located on sites with challenges such as limited space, slopes, low-permeability soils, regulations and failed drainage systems. They can also be used to meet rainwater harvesting and site runoff requirements.

• French and geocomposite drainage replacement and enhancement

HydroPlanks™ are rapidly deployed as a primary system to entirely replace costly traditional french and geocomposite drainage systems without using aggregates and geotextiles that are susceptible to clogging and require maintenance. *HydroPlanks™* can be retrofitted to existing systems that have failed in order to rehabilitate aggregate permeability, longitudinal flow and enhance whole life performance.

Manufacture and composition

HydroPlanks™ are manufactured from recycled mixed polymer plastics. Sustainability benefits include a significant reduction in the need for quarried aggregates and earth removal, reducing vehicle movements and construction costs.

Installation and maintenance

HydroBlox solutions provide design flexibility, all supported by UKAS and ISO accredited technical and hydraulic performance information. *HydroPlanks™* can be installed at surface and/or sub-surface levels, and are compatible with the majority of permeable capping options and other water management products. Little to zero maintenance is required once installed.

Contact
Carl Hopkins/Patrick O'Neil
t: 020 3189 1468
sales@hydrobloxinternational.co.uk

Web
www.hydrobloxinternational.co.uk

Address
HydroBlox Ltd
Franklin House
4 Victoria Avenue
Harrogate HG1 1EL

Operational area
Worldwide

HydroBlox® high permeability and hydraulic pressure alleviation. Made from 100% recycled thermoplastics.

HydroBlox® green site installation

HydroBlox® solar park installation

HydroBlox® sub-surface drainage vertical wall

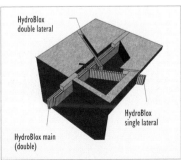
HydroBlox® flexible installation options

HydroPlanks™ rapid land drainage installation

HydroPlanks™ connect easily

ABG Ltd

Geocomposite drainage

ABG is a market leader with 25 years experience is the design, development and manufacture of high performance geosynthetics for use in a wide range of civil engineering, environmental and building projects.

- **Structural drainage**

Deckdrain is designed to relieve external water pressure from vertical and horizontal buried structures. It provides high flow capacity and protection in waterproofing applications.

- **Block paving drainage**

Deckdrain can also be used to collect and remove seepage water from the sand course beneath block paving, preventing saturation of the sand and settlement of the block paving.

- **Green roofs**

Roofdrain is used in green roof constructions to retain water for plant irrigation during dry spells and allow free drainage during wet periods.

- **Sports pitch drainage**

Turfdrain is a preformed drainage system suitable for the efficient drainage of existing and new grass playing surfaces and amenity areas.

Composition and manufacture

ABG geocomposites consist of an HDPE cuspated core bonded to a geotextile filter fabric.

Contact
Jim Herbert/Matt Gledhill
t: 01484 852096
info@abgltd.com

Web
www.abgltd.com

Address
ABG Ltd
E7 Meltham Mills Road
Holmfirth HD9 4DS

Accreditation
ISO 9001:2000, Investors in People

Affiliations
BALI

Additional entries
Reinforced natural grass rootzones ➤ 25
Green and blue roofs ➤ 28
Webwall flexible retaining walls ➤ 31
Cellular SUDS paving ➤ 68

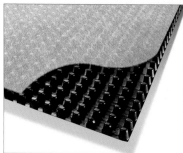
Deckdrain composition

Typical roof drainage with *Deckdrain*

Deckdrain in podium deck build up

Turfdrain installation

ABG Ltd

Cellular SUDS paving

ABG offers high-performance geosynthetic systems for a wide range of SUDS applications.

- **Sudspave cellular paving**

Sudspave cellular paving is suitable for trafficked and landscaped areas where a reinforced grass surface is required. Typical applications include car parks, emergency accessways, maintenance routes, cycle paths, pedestrian and disabled access. It is available in depths of 30mm for gravel fill, or 40mm for grass and gravel surfacing.

- **Truckcell cellular paving**

Truckcell cellular paving is suitable for trafficked and landscaped areas where a confined, free-draining grass surface is required and where high vehicle loads are expected. Typical applications include coach and truck parks, and emergency access and maintenance routes. It is available in depths of 80 or 100mm with an anti-skid finish, both of which can be filled with either gravel or a suitable media to support grass growth.

Design services

A full PI design service is available in-house.

Installation and maintenance

A full installation and on-going maintenance service is offered by Geogreen Solutions, ABG's in-house installation business.

Contact
Jim Herbert/Phil Allen
t: 01484 852096
suds@abgltd.com

Web
www.abgltd.com/suds

Address
ABG Ltd
E7 Meltham Mills Road
Holmfirth HD9 4DS

Accreditation
ISO 9001:2000, Investors in People

Affiliations
BALI

Additional entries
Reinforced natural grass rootzones ➤ 25
Green and blue roofs ➤ 28
Webwall flexible retaining walls ➤ 31
Geocomposite drainage ➤ 68

Truckcell installation – M1, Leicestershire

Sudspave installation – Park & Ride, Dublin

Gravel access and parking – Derby University

Grassed taxiway for light aircraft

Contact
Manni Keates
t: 0800 118 2278
sales@corelp.co.uk

Web
www.corelp.co.uk

Address
CORE Landscape Products
Calves Lane Yard
Bellswood Lane
Iver SL0 0LU

Affiliations
BALI; CHAS; Constructionline; Exor;
OHIM Registered

Operational area
Worldwide

Additional entries
Tree root protection and ground reinforcement
➤ 20

CORE Landscape Products

Porous gravel/resin bound surfacing

CORE Landscape Products supplies gravel stabilisation and grass reinforcement grids that can be used as a porous wearing course or as the base layer for the *CORE* bound resin surface.

• Gravel stabilisation/grass reinforcement
Interlocking porous pavers are available for gravel stabilisation and grass reinforcement. Each easy-to-install grid system creates a low-impact, porous wearing course suitable for all SUDS-compliant schemes. They are suitable for applications ranging from disabled access through to HGV traffic and are approved to European standard DIN 14090 – Access for Fire Engines. Each grid has been designed and manufactured for a specific traffic load and site condition.

• Porous resin bound system
CORE Bound comprises a 2-layer design consisting of a plastic honeycomb base that provides strength and durability, topped with a dried aggregate set in resin. A choice of aggregates is available. The system can be used for pathways and driveways.
The combination of 2 layers creates a strong surface that is aesthetically pleasing, 100% porous and wheelchair accessible.
CORE Bound can be laid without the need for a pre-existing hard surface, unlike traditional resin bound installations.

CORE Commercial gravel stabiliser on gravel bedding layer for SUDS-compliant scheme

DN 14090 approved for fire services access

CORE Commercial gravel stabiliser for car park

CORE Bound resin surfacing system – Four Freedoms Park, NYC

CORE Grass reinforcement grid

CORE Drive domestic grade gravel stabiliser

CORE Bound porous resin bound system – gravel grid with resin bound surface layer

CORE Drive domestic gravel stabiliser for driveways and pathways

Contact
Sales
t: 0115 965 7303
f: 0115 965 5151
sales@gridforce.co.uk

Web
www.gridforce.co.uk

Address
Gridforce
Industrial Estate South
Park Road
Calverton
Nottingham NG14 6BP

Operational area
Worldwide

Country of manufacture
England

Additional entries
Ground reinforcement ➤ 16

Gridforce

Surface drainage

Gridforce offers a plastic paver system made from 100% recycled LDPE, which provides effective surface drainage and ground reinforcement. It is suitable for temporary or permanent use and provides a firm surface that will not sink, rut or shift. The pavers are cost effective compared to impermeable surfaces and their interlocking design makes installation easy. The system meets current SuDS legislation and has a 10-year guarantee.

• Applications
Hard landscaping applications include SuDS, car parks, ground reinforcement, industrial hardstanding, access routes, helipads, construction sites and domestic driveways. Soft landscaping applications include lawn and slope reinforcement, events grounds, caravan sites, golf courses and ground stabilisation. The *Gridforce Park* range can be used for instant grass reinforcement by being inverted and pressed into existing grass without the conventional dig out and build-up of sub-base.

• Sustainable Urban Drainage Systems
Pavers are fully compliant for use in SuDS to provide on-site infiltration of rainwater or stormwater, eliminating the need for drainage pipework. By returning the stormwater to the water table, pressure on the sewers is relieved.

For drainage applications, Gridforce tiles can be filled with stone or other aggregates

Gridforce pavers reinforcing grassed area in car park

Lorry using completed access road filled with aggregate

Gridforce pavers provide a firm, stable surface

Completed parking area

Contact

Craig Woolley – North, Midlands,
Eastern England and Scotland
t: 01484 860044
craig@hrlonline.co.uk

Andy Clark – London and South
England
t: 01932 862473
sales@landscaping.co.uk

Web
www.hrlonline.co.uk

Address
Hardscape Resourcing Limited
Westleigh Hall, Wakefield Road
Denby Dale, Huddersfield HD8 8QJ

Additional entries
Landscape edgings and perimeters ➤ 90
Gravel stabilisation grids for naturally permeable
paving ➤ 101
Decorative in situ concrete pavements ➤ 103

Hardscape Resourcing Limited

Permeable paving in grass and gravel

HRL's grass and gravel grids provide free draining,
reinforced surfaces. Systems are fully interlocking
for optimum stability and performance.
  • **Grass grids**
StableGRASS MAXI is produced in large panels,
providing greater lateral stability and much faster
installation times than standard panels. Panels are
1200x800x38mm as standard, with a 50mm
depth to order for heavier duty uses.
StableGRASS 38 is a well-proven, traditional grass
paver designed for light- to medium-duty
applications. Panels are 500x500x38mm deep.
StableGRASS cells are designed for minimal
restriction for root development. Both products
are available in green or black.
  • **Gravel grids**
StablePAVE PRO is a translucent white gravel
stabilisation grid that is buried and invisible after
installation. Panels are 1180x944x32mm deep
with a solid, perforated base that prevents
rutting, sinking and gravel migration. It is suitable
for all appropriate vehicular and pedestrian uses.

Composition and manufacture

Products are manufactured from recycled raw
materials, are UV-stable and chemically inert.
Recyclable in themselves, they provide a
BREEAM and SuDS friendly option.

StableGRASS MAXI – 1200x800mm panels with enhanced lateral stabilty, fast to install, ideal for large areas

StableGRASS – stabilised reinforcement for grass

StableGRASS – black

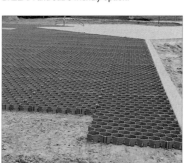

StableGRASS – does not restrict root development

StableGRASS MAXI is quick to install

StablePAVE PRO – heavy-duty porous paving

StableGRASS – provides a free draining, reinforced surface for vehicle access

StablePAVE PRO – illustrated cross-section

Reinforced gravel – no sinking, rutting or migration

TERRAM
Geosynthetics you can trust

Contact
t: 01621 874200
f: 01621 874299
info@terram.com

Web
www.terram.com

Address
Fiberweb Geosynthetics Ltd
Blackwater Trading Estate
The Causeway
Maldon CM9 4GG

Accreditation
ISO 9001:2008
Investors in People

Additional entries
Geocells ➤ 13
GrassProtecta reinforcement mesh ➤ 18
Porous paving for reinforcement ➤ 19

Terram

Porous paving for SUDS

Under the Terram brand, Fiberweb Geosynthetics Ltd offers reinforcement products for lightweight occasional use up to regular heavy traffic on grass or gravel surfaces.

• **BodPave™ 85 porous pavers**
BodPave™ 85 cellular, interlocking, porous pavers are designed for natural grass reinforcement, ground stabilisation and gravel retention. Aimed at regularly trafficked surfaces, they suit emergency vehicle and HGV access lanes, car/coach parks, driveways, aviation applications, pedestrian areas and disabled access paths. *BodPave™ 85* pavers have ground spikes that resist lateral movement and castellated cells with unique water retention chambers that enhance traction and lateral root growth, promote optimum nutrients/water uptake and protect roots. The open-cell structure provides high surface water infiltration and suits SUDS profiles.

• **Truckpave™ permeable pavers**
Truckpave™ is a heavy-duty plastic paver developed specially for lorry access roads and service yards, as well as road-widening schemes and motorway emergency turning areas. Unlike conventional concrete systems, *Truckpave™* requires no specialist handling as each unit weighs only 9kg. The system needs no steel reinforcement and is flexible so will not crack or overheat and conduct heat to grass.

Composition and manufacture

BodPave™ 85 is made from UV stabilised, 100% recycled polyethylene. It is chemically inert, non-toxic and load-bearing up to 400t/m². Units are 500x500x50mm with a 35mm ground spike. *Truckpave™* pavers are made from recycled plastic, which is harmless to plants and animals. Each paver is 600x400x80mm.

Sitework

BodPave™ 85 is installed onto a firm, free-draining base. Cells are filled with a root-zone blend for a grassed finish or with an angular aggregate. *Truckpave™* can be supplied with design assistance for individual projects.

Gravel filled porous paving grids

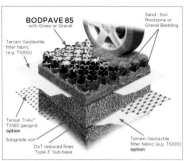
BodPave™ 85 typical construction profile

BodPave™ 85 plastic pavers clip together

Truckpave™ heavy-duty permeable pavers

BodPave™ 85 grass surface with parking markers

Truckpave™ grassed access road

Truckpave™ heavy load-bearing access roads

Truckpave™ interlocking pavers

Gravel filled *Truckpave™* surface

Truckpave™ is suitable for industrial yards

A member of the **TERRACO** group

Contact
Tim Hopkins
t: 01825 761333
sales@addagrip.co.uk

Web
www.addagrip.co.uk

Address
Addagrip Terraco Ltd
Addagrip House
Bell Lane Industrial Estate
Uckfield TN22 1QL

Affiliations
British Association of Landscape Industries (BALI)
English Historic Towns Forum

Country of manufacture
UK

Additional entries
Resin bound porous surfacing ➤ 92
Addastone resin bonded decorative surfacing ➤ 93

Addagrip Terraco Ltd

Resin bound SUDS porous surfacing

Addagrip formulates and produces high-quality, SUDS porous, resin-based surfacing systems.

• **Addaset resin bound surfacing**
Addaset provides smooth, hard-wearing and low-maintenance surfacing. Owing to its porous nature, it is especially suitable for SUDS applications. It is seamless, flexible and resistant to cracking, and can be applied onto an asphalt or concrete base. *Addaset* is BBA certified.

• **Addabound resin bound surfacing**
Addabound provides smooth, porous, hard-wearing and low-maintenance surfacing. It incorporates a minimum of 25% recycled material. *Addabound* is BBA certified.

• **Terrabound resin bound surfacing**
Terrabound provides smooth, hard-wearing and porous surfacing based on a select blend of natural aggregates. *Terrabound* is BBA certified.

• **Terrabase Rustic bound surfacing**
Terrabase Rustic is an innovative, patented, 'no-dig' resin bound porous sytem that can be applied onto a compacted MOT Type 3 or similar. No asphalt or concrete is required.

• **Addastone TP tree pit surfacing**
Addastone TP provides an attractive porous paving surface using natural or recycled aggregates. Its open texture enables tree roots to access air, and allows for water penetration.

Terrabase Rustic – Broad Walk, Royal Botanic Gardens, Kew

Terrabound – Abbotsford House, Scotland

Addabound – UEA, Norwich

Terrabound – Hampton Court Magic Garden

Addastone TP tree pit – London

Terrabase Rustic – Exeter flood defence

Terrabase Rustic – Melior St Garden, London

Addaset – residential driveway project

Contact
t: 01985 841180
mail@sureset.co.uk

Web
www.sureset.co.uk

Address
SureSet UK Ltd
32 Deverill Road Trading Est, Sutton Veny BA12 7BZ

Accreditation
CHAS; CPD Certified; ISO 9001; ISO 14001

Affiliations
Builders and Contractors Guild; English Historic Towns Forum; British Association of Landscape Industries (BALI); Building Register; Landscape Institute; Confederation of Construction Specialists; The Guild of Builders and Contractors Considerate Contractors Scheme

Additional entries
Spectrum glass bound surfacing ➤ 96
SureSet permeable bound surfacing ➤ 97
Permeable tree pit surfacing ➤ 528

SureSet resin bound paving is permeable

SureSet UK Ltd

Surface drainage

SureSet, established in 1997, is a specialist manufacturer, installer and supplier of permeable resin bound paving.

SureSet resin bound paving is a fully permeable product that can be used in SuDS (Sustainable Drainage System) schemes.

SuDS schemes consist of drainage systems that are designed to alleviate the affects of flooding.

• **SureSet resin bound surface drainage**

SureSet permeable paving allows water to permeate through the surface, preventing standing water and largely eliminating surface water run-off. SuDS schemes reduce the risk of flooding, create flourishing and ecologically diverse environments and reduce the flow of surface water run-off to sewers.

Specifying *SureSet* in a planning application demonstrates the implementation of a more sustainable approach than traditional drainage systems. It has been used on communal access roads, parking areas, planted tree trenches and tree pits in urban areas.

• **SureCell® honeycomb units**

SureCell® interlocking honeycomb units are used for permeable surfacing applications that require a 'no-dig' construction method, such as near the roots of protected trees.

The system provides a strong and stable permeable surface that is suitable for vehicular and foot traffic. It gives a base for small areas of surfacing and is strong, with high load-bearing capacity. Its durability is covered by SureSet's 18-year guarantee.

It is eco-friendly, being fully permeable, filtering clean water back into the natural water table.

Installation and maintenance

• **SureSet resin bound surface drainage**

SureSet resin bound surfacing can be used to overlay worn surfaces or installed as a surface course in new construction projects. For maximum permeability, a porous base should also be used.

• **SureCell® honeycomb units**

SureCell® is laid directly onto an existing sub-grade with a geotextile fabric, then infilled with 6–10mm gravel. For straight driveways, a double layer of *SureCell®* is required. The *SureCell®* units are clipped together by hand, making sure each one is fully connected with its neighbour.

SureCell® is faster, cheaper and easier to install than most traditional systems.

It is installed by hand by SureSet's expert team. Little to no noise pollution is created during installation and there is no need for heavy machinery.

Technical support
Specification advice and BIM files are available.

SureCell® is clipped together by hand

SureCell® installed on a permeable base

SureCell® is in-filled with crushed loose gravel (4/10mm)

SureCell® provides a strong, stable, permeable surface that is suitable for vehicular and foot traffic

Tobermore
WORLD CLASS PAVING & WALLING

Contact
Sales
t: 028 7964 2411
f: 028 7964 4145
sales@tobermore.co.uk

Web
www.tobermore.co.uk

Address
Tobermore
2 Lisnamuck Road
Magherafelt BT45 5QF

Accreditation
ISO 9001, ISO 14001

Operational area
UK, Ireland

Additional entries
Concrete retaining walls ➤ 39
Concrete flag paving ➤ 108
Concrete block paving ➤ 114

Tobermore

Permeable concrete block paving

Established in 1942, Tobermore is a leading manufacturer of paving and walling and supplies products for the commercial and domestic markets throughout the UK and Ireland.

• Hydropave permeable paving range
Tobermore manufactures the *Hydropave* range of permeable paving products. The range is as versatile as Tobermore's standard concrete block paving, but allows the creation of hard landscaping features that reduce the risk of flooding and pollution from surface water run-off. A number of *Hydropave* products can be machine laid, reducing labour costs.

• Eco permeable paving range
Tobermore also offers a range of *Eco* products, manufactured with the aesthetic and practical benefits of the standard product range, but with high rates of recycled content and a low carbon footprint.

Hydropave Fusion (Silver) and *Hydropave Sienna Duo* (Silver) – Queen Elizabeth University Hospital, Glasgow

Hydropave Pedesta in Charcoal and Natural

Hydropave Shannon Duo in Bracken

Hydropave Tegula Duo in Bracken

Hydropave 240 permeable block paving in Heather – York University

Additional entries

Linear drainage systems ➤ 80
Combined kerb & drainage systems ➤ 84
Kerb systems ➤ 86
Concrete paving systems ➤ 104
Concrete block paving and setts ➤ 112
Natural stone ➤ 124
Traffic calming systems ➤ 222

Marshalls plc

Priora permeable block paving

Marshalls *Priora* is the UK's best-selling permeable paving system. It eliminates surface water run-off, alleviates flood risk and improves water quality, providing biodiversity benefits to the local area. In addition, field tests in 2014 have proven that the patented nibs on the edge of each block create 40% more interlock than British Standard blocks. This provides a structurally superior surface that can take heavy loads moving at speeds in excess of 30mph. *Priora* sub-bases are also now shallower than the British Standard, saving time and money. *Priora* comes in a range of aesthetic finishes, including new flag-sized options.

• **Sub-base ancillaries**

Priora blocks are underpinned by a suite of sub-base ancillaries, which can be specified as required.

Priora 20mm sub-base and 6mm laying course aggregate give a higher void ratio and structural integrity than specified in the British Standard.

MG15 Grid stabilises the sub-base aggregate, improving CBR by 1%.

MM380 Membrane is used for the tanking of Type C permeable paved systems.

MT120 Textile is used to improve the quality of water that falls from the sub-base.

La Linia Priora – Corby Railway Station

La Linia Priora

Mistral Priora – East Sussex University

Priora in Natural – Cowbridge

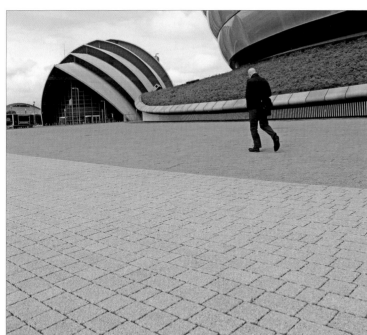

Mistral Priora in Silver Grey and Charcoal – SSE Hydro Arena, Glasgow

MG15 Grid installation

Priora sub-base design

MT120 filtration geotextile installation

MM380 tanking membrane installation

Mistral Priora – London

La Linia Priora – Oldham

Contact
Head office
t: 01462 816666
f: 01462 815895
technologies@aco.co.uk

Web
www.aco.co.uk

Address
ACO Water Management –
a division of ACO Technologies plc
ACO Business Park
Hitchin Road, Shefford SG17 5TE

Accreditation
ISO 9001: 2008; ISO 14001:2004

CPD
Accredited CPDs on surface water management

Additional entries
Interceptors ➤ 54
Stormwater control ➤ 63
Urban + Landscape drainage ➤ 79

ACO Water Management –
a division of ACO Technologies

Surface water management

ACO Water Management is an innovative supplier of surface water management products and support services that provide architects, specifiers and engineers with a complete package of integrated systems for use on all civil engineering projects.

ACO Water Management solutions address the four stages of Effective Water Management: Collect, Clean, Hold, Release.

• **Medium- to heavy-duty channel drainage**
ACO MultiDrain™ MD is a general-purpose drainage system available in a range of channel widths and constant, shallow or sloping depths.
ACO S Range is a heavy-duty channel drainage system with cast-in, ductile-iron edge rails.
ACO MultiDrain™ Monoblock PD100D is a tough, one-piece channel drainage system that is designed for medium-duty applications.
ACO RoadDrain® is a one-piece channel drainage system for use in high-speed, medium- to heavy-duty road and warehouse applications.

• **Channel drainage lighting systems**
ACO LightPoint can enhance and add definition to public and private areas, while providing an economical solution for surface water drainage.

• **High-capacity drainage systems**
ACO Qmax® is a continuous slot drainage system for high-capacity storage.
All of the above products feature in ACO's Surface + Grating Visualiser, an easy-to-use software program that visualises how ACO's range of grating designs could look in projects (www.aco.co.uk/gratingvisualiser/).

• **Combined kerb and drainage systems**
ACO KerbDrain® is an award-winning, one-piece combined kerb and drainage system for highways, car parks, and commercial and urban landscaping.

ACO RoadDrain® channel drainage system

ACO MultiDrain™ MD general-purpose channel drainage

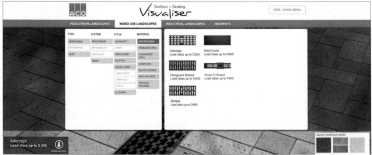

ACO Visualiser software program for visualising grating designs – www.aco.co.uk/gratingvisualiser/

ACO Qmax® continuous slot drainage system

ACO KerbDrain® combined drainage system

Contact

Head office
t: 01462 816666
f: 01462 815895
technologies@aco.co.uk

Web
www.aco.co.uk

Address
ACO Water Management –
a division of ACO Technologies plc
ACO Business Park
Hitchin Road
Shefford SG17 5TE

Accreditation
ISO 9001: 2008
ISO 14001:2004

CPD
Accredited CPDs on surface water management

Additional entries
Interceptors ➤ 54
Stormwater control ➤ 63
Surface water management ➤ 78

ACO Water Management – a division of ACO Technologies

Urban + Landscape drainage

ACO Water Management's *Urban + Landscape* range is tailored to the demands of domestic applications, providing a complete surface drainage solution for driveways, patios, level doorway thresholds, landscaped areas and permeable ground reinforcement.

• Domestic channel drainage

HexDrain® and *RainDrain®* channels are designed for a range of domestic applications including patios and garage thresholds.

ACO's 'Complete the Look' gratings for driveways and patios are available in six modern finishes: polished stainless steel; anthracite; black plastic; stainless steel wedge wire grating; galvanised steel; and cast iron.

HexDrain® B 125 and *RainDrain® B 125* channels are designed for driveways and small, private car park applications.

• Domestic slot drainage

HexDrain Brickslot and *RainDrain Brickslot B 125* are designed for domestic projects where discrete channel drainage is required in paving and threshold drainage applications.

• Threshold drainage

StepDrain is a slimline, unobtrusive level threshold drainage system, fitted with stainless steel *Heelguard™* grating.

DoorwayDrain provides unobtrusive, high-quality level threshold drainage.

DrainMat performs the function of traditional matwells, but eliminates the risk of water ponding at domestic entrances.

Systems are compliant with Part M and Section 4 Building Regulations.

• Landscaping systems

GroundGuard is an award-winning tile for lightweight, permeable ground reinforcement systems used for grass or gravel stabilisation.

ACO HexDrain® – high quality, high strength, light-duty channel drainage system with *Heelguard™* grating

ACO RainDrain® B 125 driveway channel drainage

ACO StepDrain – slimline level threshold drainage

ACO RainDrain® channel drainage

ACO HexDrain® Brickslot discreet channel drainage

ACO GroundGuard ground reinforcement

Marshalls

Creating Better Spaces

Contact
t: 0870 444 6217
f: 0870 442 7725
esi.marshalls@web-response.co.uk

Web
www.marshalls.co.uk/commercial

Address
Marshalls plc
Landscape House
Premier Way
Lowfields Business Park
Elland
West Yorkshire HX5 9HT

Additional entries
Priora permeable block paving ➤ 76
Combined kerb & drainage systems ➤ 84
Kerb systems ➤ 86
Concrete paving systems ➤ 104
Concrete block paving and setts ➤ 112
Natural stone ➤ 124
Traffic calming systems ➤ 222

Marshalls plc

Linear drainage systems

Marshalls' linear drainage systems combine robust, high-performance concrete channels with a variety of tops. The range covers any capacity requirement or loading application.

• Slot systems

Drexus Slot Drain is a highly effective, discreet linear drainage system that creates an almost invisible, trafficable, surface water drainage system. It can be used with premium concrete flags, blocks or natural stone paving.

• Paved systems

Max-E Channel is a high-capacity system that is compatible with the *Beany Block®* combined kerb and drainage system, allowing for continuity of flow between kerb and slot units.

Drexus Pave Drain is a concrete drainage channel that is available with a concrete or natural stone top with an aesthetic that complements Marshalls' most popular paving. It is a trafficable unit suitable for any public realm development.

Drexus XL is a recycled polyethylene (PE) high-capacity channel, ideally suited for high-capacity, heavy-duty projects. The system is designed to offer attenuation and storage facilities but also to achieve sufficient flow velocities at low gradient to ensure channels require minimal maintenance.

• Grated systems

Birco is available in five ranges, all of which feature constant and in-built fall channels. Sizes range from low- to high-capacity, catering for loadings from A15 to F900 with the appropriate gratings.

Traffic Drain is a medium-capacity heavy duty system that complements the *Mini Beany®* range. It provides continuity of flow between kerb and grate unit, can withstand fast-moving vehicles and is suitable for heavy-loading highway applications.

Max-E Channel and *Traffic Drain* systems are available with gratings.

Technical support

Marshalls offers a free drainage design service, frequently partnering clients from the early stages of a project to develop the optimal solution.

Birco 100 low-capacity linear drainage system with cast iron slot grate

Birco 150 low-capacity linear drainage system with cast iron slot grate

Birco 300, cast iron slot grate, high-capacity system

Birco Shallow is ideal for shallow excavations

Birco 200 medium-capacity linear drainage system with cast iron slot grate

Drexus Slot Drain discreet low capacity linear drainage system – ideal for natural stone landscapes

Drexus Pave Drain in Yorkstone – Holborn

Drexus 100 low-capacity linear drainage system – load classes B125 to D400 with cast iron grates

Max-E Channel heavy-duty linear drainage system; high-capacity for loadings up to F900

Drexus XL recycled polyethylene (PE) high-capacity channel

Traffic Drain heavy-duty linear drainage system, medium-capacity for loadings up to F900

Althon Ltd

Channel drainage

Althon offers channel drainage systems for applications ranging from domestic to heavy-duty industrial use and airports.

• Concrete slot drainage channel
Althon concrete slot drainage channels are manufactured in sections up to 4m long for fast on-site installation. Options are available for D400 or F900 load classes making these ideal for draining large, heavily trafficked areas such as industrial estates, ports, airports and motorways.

• High-capacity drainage channels
Althon's high-capacity channel drainage system is manufactured in glass reinforced concrete (GRC) in 150–600mm widths. Lid units are available for residential, car park and heavy industrial use. The channels enable long uninterrupted runs to be installed without the need for intermediate outfalls and offer considerable reductions in secondary pipework requirements. The largest channel has a capacity of 412L/m.

• BGZ heavy-duty concrete channels
Althon *BGZ* concrete drainage channels are available in internal widths up to 500mm. They have been developed for areas where high acceleration, braking forces or torque could occur, and have very high load-bearing capabilities, with gratings that can withstand up to load class F900. Mesh, slotted and solid gratings are available.

• BGZ-F shallow concrete drainage channel
Althon *BGZ-F* concrete channels are suitable for applications up to E600 load class. They are available in widths from 100–300mm, but are much shallower than standard drainage channels of this size. A range of ductile iron, galvanised and stainless steel gratings is available.

• Facade slot drainage channel
Slot drains are available in galvanised or stainless steel. These slim channels are a discreet method of draining hardstandings or landscaped areas. The stainless steel option is also suitable for internal drainage applications such as food processing plants and areas where chemicals may be present in the run-off.

Contact
t: 01603 488700
f: 01603 488598
sales@althon.co.uk

Web
www.althon.co.uk

Address
Althon Ltd
Vulcan Road South
Norwich NR6 6AF

Operational area
Worldwide (channel drainage/flow control)

Additional entries
Precast headwalls ➤ 58
Flow control ➤ 60

Althon concrete slot drain – airport installation

Concrete slot drain installation

BGZ ductile iron bar grille

BGZ-S heavy-duty drainage channel

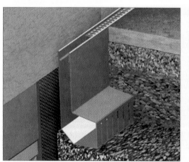
Slot drainage channel

High-capacity channel installation

component
developments

Contact
James Russell
t: 01952 588488
info@componentdevelopments.com

Web
www.componentdevelopments.com

Address
Component Developments
Halesfield 10
Telford TF7 4QP

Accreditation
ISO 9001:2008 Quality Assurance
ISO 14001:2004 Environmental Management
OHSAS 18001:2007 Occupational Health & Safety

Operational area
Worldwide

Country of manufacture
UK

Component Developments

Channel and slot drainage

Component Developments designs, manufactures and supplies stainless steel building products, including drainage, access and surface protection for interior and exterior use.

• Channel drains
A standard range of stainless steel channel drains has been developed to meet common drainage requirements. All products can be adapted to suit specific needs, including custom lengths, widths and depths.

• Slot drains
A slot drain system has been designed to provide discreet, effective drainage. It maximises flow capacity while minimising the profile visible at ground level to fit within the surrounding area.

Design services
A full service is available for completely bespoke products designed to suit specific requirements.

Technical support
Component Developments offers guidance and support, the design stage through to the completion and hand-over of the project. The company is able to help specifiers overcome common on-site problems relating to drainage and surface protection.

Facade drainage for roof terrace, Ropemaker Place

Channel drainage for pedestrian area

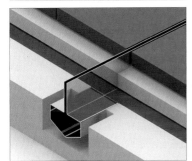

Type 3603 slot drain

Type 6081 channel drain

Type 3604 slot drain

Slot and channel drain range

Channel drain

Marshalls

Creating Better Spaces

Contact
t: 0870 444 6217
f: 0870 442 7725
esi.marshalls@web-response.co.uk

Web
www.marshalls.co.uk/commercial

Address
Marshalls plc
Landscape House
Premier Way
Lowfields Business Park
Elland HX5 9HT

Additional entries
Priora permeable block paving ➤ 76
Linear drainage systems ➤ 80
Kerb systems ➤ 86
Concrete paving systems ➤ 104
Concrete block paving and setts ➤ 112
Natural stone ➤ 124
Traffic calming systems ➤ 222

Marshalls plc

Combined kerb & drainage systems

Marshalls' *Beany* system is a trusted, reliable and highly effective road drainage solution. It has the advantages of a combined kerb and drainage system and the benefits of a high-quality, robust concrete product.

• **Beany Block® high-capacity system**
Beany Block® is a high-capacity combined kerb and drainage system that has been on the market for over 30 years. It provides a flexible, cost-effective solution to highway drainage requirements. When installed, it is strong enough to withstand loadings imposed by both road and construction traffic.

• **Mini Beany® medium-capacity system**
Mini Beany® is a combined kerb and drainage system evolved from *Beany Block®*. Its flow rates and robust concrete construction are suited to medium-capacity road drainage requirements.

• **Mono Beany® compact system**
Mono Beany® is a low- to medium-capacity, one-piece combined kerb and drainage system. It is simple and straightforward to design, set out and install. It comprises high-strength *M-Tech* concrete cast around a plastic core, giving good strength, aesthetics and hydraulic flow rates.

Technical support

Engineers can order Marshalls' *Drainage Design Guide* or use a free, no-obligation design service.

Conservation Mini Beany® – Bedford

Beany Block® – Glasgow

Mono Beany® – A21, East Sussex

Beany Block® – Newcastle

Mono Beany® – A259

PAVEMENTS

Kerbs and landscape edgings   86-91

Concrete and natural stone kerbs in standard and proprietary designs for pedestrian pavements, vehicle containment and landscape applications.

Tactile paving in natural stone.

Edge restraint systems in aluminium, steel, stainless steel and plastic to demarcate hard landscaped surfaces, lawns and planted areas.

Resin bound and bonded pavements   92-101

Resin bound and bonded decorative surfacing using natural stone, pigmented or recycled glass aggregates for car parks, access roads, driveways, courtyards, pavements and pathways. Grid pavers for bound surfacing systems.

Concrete pavements   103-116

Admixtures, colours and finishes for decorative, in-situ concrete pavements.

Concrete paving flags in smooth, textured, exposed aggregate and reproduction stone finishes for commercial, light vehicular and residential applications. Small element, plank, standard and large format paving flags.

Concrete block paving in rectangular, shaped and sett formats for pedestrian areas, driveways, access roads, car parks and industrial hardstandings.

Porcelain tiles   117-118

Natural stone specialists   119-129

Natural stone quarried in the UK and supplied from around the world. Granite, sandstone, porphyry, limestone, slate, whinstone and quartzite. Paving flags, setts, kerbs, walling, cladding, feature stones, boulders, aggregates and rock armour.

Footpath and decorative aggregates   130

Footpath gravels and decorative aggregates for landscape applications.

Surfacing ancillaries   131-136

Access covers and power unit pavers; road studs and markings; specialist pavement mortars; cleaning materials, anti-graffiti and protective coatings; anti-slip coatings, inserts and strips.

Decks and boardwalks   137-152

Decks and boardwalks in timber and recycled plastic for domestic, commercial, roof garden and rural applications. Fasteners for decks and timberwork.

Pedestal support systems for decks and raised pavements.

Metal gratings and planks   153-155

Metal floor gratings and planks for walkways, stairs, decks and balconies.

Bridges   156-158

Bridges for pedestrian, cyclist, equestrian and light vehicular use.

EXTERNAL WORKS ONLINE

For detailed information supported by case studies, downloads and tools to help you make faster and better decisions ...
☞ www.externalworks.co.uk

Marshalls

Creating Better Spaces

Contact
t: 0870 444 6217
f: 0870 442 7725
esi.marshalls@web-response.co.uk

Web
www.marshalls.co.uk/commercial

Address
Marshalls plc
Landscape House
Premier Way
Lowfields Business Park
Elland HX5 9HT

Additional entries
Priora permeable block paving ➤ 76
Linear drainage systems ➤ 80
Combined kerb & drainage systems ➤ 84
Concrete paving systems ➤ 104
Concrete block paving and setts ➤ 112
Natural stone ➤ 124
Traffic calming systems ➤ 222

Conservation Textured Kerb

Marshalls plc

Kerb systems

Marshalls' kerb range includes textured concrete and natural stone products, specialist kerbs for public transport and large goods vehicles, and a full range of British Standard kerbs and ancillaries. Marshalls kerbs are used to define boundaries for vehicular users, pedestrians and cyclists, promoting road safety and helping create safer communities for the benefit of everyone.

• **Textured concrete kerbs**
Marshalls textured concrete kerbs have high-quality, textured finishes with strong aesthetic appeal. They are durable units able to withstand heavy impact. Designs are offered in a wider square contemporary profile to complement Marshalls' paving ranges.

• **Granite kerbs**
Granite kerbs are available in rectangular or bullnosed sections with flamed or fine picked finishes. Drop and radius kerbs can be provided.

• **High containment kerbs**
Titan Kerb is a high containment kerb system that safely demarcates routes for large goods vehicles. Designed to redirect errant traffic to its intended path, *Titan Kerb* provides a passive traffic control system to protect vulnerable installations and pedestrians.

• **Bus stop kerbs**
Bus Stop Kerb is a smooth, angled faced kerb with the option of channel usage that is designed to enable safe access to public transport vehicles.

• **British Standard kerbs**
The *Standard Kerb* range includes the popular half-battered kerb profile, which has a face that is slightly battered back to allow traffic to run close to it. Bullnosed and 45° splay profiles are also available. A full range of ancillaries includes transitions, droppers, centre stones, angles, quadrants and radius kerbs.

Composition and manufacture

Marshalls concrete kerbs are hydraulically wet-pressed, offering excellent consistency and performance during installation and throughout the life of the pavement.

British Standard concrete kerb

Charnwood Textured Kerb

Saxon Concrete Kerb includes Yorkstone aggregate

Conservation Textured Kerb

Natural stone granite kerb

Titan Kerb – high containment kerb system

Contact
Julian Pomery
t: 01489 789444
sales@pomery.co.uk

Web
www.pomery.co.uk

Address
Pomery Natural Stone Ltd
Little Heathers
Outlands Lane
Curdridge SO30 2HD

Operational area
UK, Ireland

Additional entries
Tactile paving, natural stone ➤ 87
Natural stone specialists ➤ 127
Natural stone seating ➤ 343

Pomery Natural Stone Ltd

Natural stone kerbs

Pomery Natural Stone Ltd supplies stone for paving, traffic calming and landscape design, as well as internal and building applications.
Kerbs can be supplied in gauged lengths or in variable 800–1100mm lengths, which ensures less wastage. Straight and radius kerbs, as well as quadrants, transitions and specials are available. The standard finish is fine-picked to BS EN 1343 with a square edge. Flamed or more textured finishes, and bullnose or chamfered edges are available to order.

150x300mm section radius kerb

Kerbing – Aldershot War Memorial

Kerbs in gauged or variable 800–1100mm lengths

Natural stone steps

Traditional fair picked finish

Contact
Julian Pomery
t: 01489 789444
sales@pomery.co.uk

Web
www.pomery.co.uk

Address
Pomery Natural Stone Ltd
Little Heathers
Outlands Lane
Curdridge SO30 2HD

Operational area
UK, Ireland

Additional entries
Natural stone kerbs ➤ 87
Natural stone specialists ➤ 127
Natural stone seating ➤ 343

Pomery Natural Stone Ltd

Tactile paving, natural stone

Pomery Natural Stone Ltd was formed in 1996 to provide high-quality materials and support to the building industry.
The company produces tactile corduroy and blister paving to bespoke client requirements. Stones available include granite, Yorkstone, porphyry, limestone, slate, quartzite, travertine and Canadian hard limestone.
Sawn paving, setts, cubes, kerbs and specials are also offered in a variety of finishes for pedestrian schemes, traffic calming and landscape design.

Tactile corduroy stone paving in silver grey granite

Buff Yorkstone – Golden Jubillee Bridges, London

Donegall Quay, Belfast (Contractor: Marmic)

Tactile blister stone paving

Tactile stone units co-ordinate with setts and paving

THE EDGING COMPANY

Contact
Aubrey Watson (sales)
t: 01453 731717
info@everedge.co.uk

Simon Arrowsmith (technical)
t: 01939 291110
simonarrowsmith1@btinternet.com

Web
www.everedge.co.uk

Address
Head Office
EverEdge®
PO Box 333
Market Drayton TF9 4WL

Sales Office
EverEdge®
PO Box 9
Stroud GL6 8HA

t: 01453 731717

Operational area
UK, Europe, North America, Australia, New Zealand

Country of manufacture
UK

EverEdge®

Steel landscape edging

EverEdge® manufactures and supplies an extensive range of high quality landscape edging suitable for public and private sector use. Applications include business parks, private residences, commercial buildings, parks and public spaces.

- **EverEdge® steel landscape edging**
EverEdge® edging is available in different heights, lengths, thicknesses and finishes. It can be easily curved or bent to virtually any angle to provide a permanent edge that is suitable for most landscape applications. *EverEdge®* edging is frequently used to create well-defined and maintenance-free lawn borders, driveways, paths and flowerbeds.

- **EverEdge® Atlas edging system**
EverEdge® Atlas edging is designed to be used exclusively with artificial grass. *EverEdge® Atlas* allows installers to attach the artificial carpet to the edging, ensuring a permanent fixture for artificial lawns. The edging remains durable and flexible providing installers with limitless design possibilities.

- **EverEdge® Halestem edging system**
EverEdge® Halestem is designed specifically for use with tarmac/asphalt, resin bonded surfaces, blocks, paving and driveways. The *Halestem* range offers a versatile solution for straight lines, or curves, where an L-shape edge is required.

- **EverEdge® Garden Rings**
EverEdge® Garden Rings are pre-curved to allow a perfect circle to be installed quickly and easily. Available in depths of 75 or 125mm, the 1.6mm thick *Garden Ring* ranges from 600–1500mm in diameter.

- **EverEdge® Planter**
EverEdge® Planter is a bespoke product that is manufactured in mild, galvanised, powder-coated and corten steel. Entirely customisable, the *EverEdge® Planter* can be as small or as large as the project requires.

- **EverEdge® Custom**
EverEdge® Custom is a made-to-order service that allows client-specified products to be manufactured to meet project requirements.

EverEdge® installation diagram

EverEdge® Atlas is for use with artificial grass

EverEdge® Halestem installation diagram

EverEdge® Planter

EverEdge® Custom

EverEdge® ProEdge

EverEdge® Titan

EverEdge® Custom

EverEdge® Garden Ring

EverEdge® Halestem

EverEdge® Planter

Contact

Craig Woolley
t: 01484 860044
craig@hrlonline.co.uk

Web
www.hrlonline.co.uk

Address
Hardscape Resourcing Limited
Westleigh Hall
Wakefield Road
Denby Dale
Huddersfield HD8 8QJ

Additional entries
Permeable paving in grass and gravel ➤ 71
Gravel stabilisation grids for naturally permeable paving ➤ 101
Decorative in situ concrete pavements ➤ 103

Hardscape Resourcing Limited

Landscape edgings and perimeters

HRL edge restraints provide secure, unobtrusive, straight and curved landscape edging solutions.

• **Secure structural aluminium edging**
StableEDGE flexible aluminium edge restraints offer a secure structural edging for straight lines and curves. Typical applications include edge support for pavers, asphalt, resin bound, poured rubber and stabilised gravel construction. Fast and simple to install, they are supplied in 2.438m lengths and eight depths from 18 to 150mm.

• **Landscape border edging**
HRL aluminium landscape border edgings offer a flexible, discreet edging detail for borders and lawns where simple segregation is required. Suitable for both straight and curved applications, they are available at 10 or 14cm depths.

• **Custom-made stainless steel edging**
Stainless steel edgings are made-to-order to the required size and length. Typical applications include upstands for raised beds and visual containment of planting.

• **Recycled plastic kerbs and borders**
Recycled plastic edgings and beams for straight length use include: round top edging with end connectors in 50x260x2500mm lengths; 'U' profile 16x24cm edging block, with hidden connectors in 1.5 and 3.0m lengths; and recycled plastic sleepers up to 3.0m long.

StableEDGE – aluminium edge restraints provide flexible, structural edging for straight lines or curves

Landscape border edging – 10 or 14cm deep

StableEDGE – separation line

StableEDGE – block paving restraint

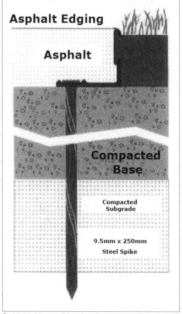

StableEDGE – traditional make-up

Recycled plastic sleepers – 4 profiles, up to 3m long

Recycled roll-top plastic edging – 50x260x2500mm

StableEDGE – asphalt restraint

Kinley K

INSPIRED PLACES MADE POSSIBLE

Contact
t: 01580 830688
sales@kinley.co.uk

Web
www.kinley.co.uk

Address
Kinley Systems Ltd
Northpoint
Compass Park
Staplecross TN32 5BS

Operational area
UK, Europe

Additional entries
Decking and paving ➤ 147
Perimeta planter systems ➤ 383

Kinley Systems Ltd

Landscape edging: ExcelEdge®

Kinley Systems manufactures *ExcelEdge®* edge restraints, which are flexible, robust, and durable. Applications include municipal parks, public open spaces, business parks, school paths, playgrounds and private estates. Where viable, Kinley uses recycled materials and manufactures in the UK.
- **AluExcel aluminium hard landscape edging**
AluExcel® is available in nine heights from 18 to 150mm. It is suitable for most hard landscape applications, forming smooth sinuous curves or straight lines. The aluminium is 100% recyclable.
- **Borderline steel lawn edging**
Borderline® is available in a range of heights, thicknesses and finishes. It is competitively priced and simple to install.
- **HiGrade heavy-duty steel edging**
HiGrade comes in 3m lengths, in 3, 6, 8 or 10mm thicknesses. It is offered in galvanised, corten or stainless steel, or powder-coated. It is strong, aesthetic and durable, and can be used for any kind of landscape layout.
- **AllEdge Premium aluminium edging**
AllEdge Premium is suitable for soft landscape areas. It is flexible and can be used to create curved designs. Its unique sliding plate and fixing detail make it quick to install.

Bespoke edging

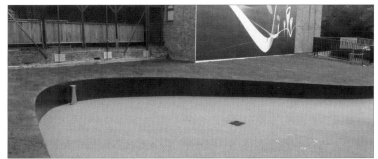
Bespoke edging – Serpentine Sackler Gallery, London

Installation – Serpentine Sackler Gallery, London

AluExcel® edging between paving and gravel

AllEdge Premium aluminium edging

AluExcel® aluminium edging

Borderline® steel edging

A member of the TERRACO group

Contact
Tim Hopkins
t: 01825 761333
sales@addagrip.co.uk

Web
www.addagrip.co.uk

Address
Addagrip Terraco Ltd
Addagrip House
Bell Lane Industrial Estate
Uckfield TN22 1QL

Affiliations
British Association of Landscape Industries (BALI)
English Historic Towns Forum

Country of manufacture
UK

Additional entries
Resin bound SUDS porous surfacing ➤ 73
Addastone resin bonded decorative surfacing ➤ 93

Addagrip Terraco Ltd

Resin bound porous surfacing

Addagrip formulates and manufactures high-quality, SUDS porous, resin-based surfacing systems for residential and commercial projects. *Addaset*, *Addabound* and *Terrabound* resin bound systems are suitable for a range of projects including car parks, access roads, driveways, paths, patios, courtyards, school playgrounds and swimming pool surrounds.

• **Addaset resin bound surfacing**
Addaset provides smooth, hard-wearing and low-maintenance surfacing. Owing to its porous nature, it is especially suitable for SUDS applications. It is seamless, flexible and resistant to cracking, and can be applied onto an asphalt or concrete base. *Addaset* is BBA certified.

• **Addabound resin bound surfacing**
Addabound provides smooth, porous, hard-wearing and low-maintenance surfacing. It incorporates a minimum of 25% recycled material. *Addabound* is BBA certified.

• **Terrabound resin bound surfacing**
Terrabound provides smooth, hard-wearing and porous surfacing based on a select blend of natural aggregates. *Terrabound* is BBA certified.

• **Terrabase Rustic bound surfacing**
Terrabase Rustic is an innovative, patented, 'no-dig' resin bound porous sytem that can be applied onto a compacted MOT Type 3 or similar. No asphalt or concrete is required.

• **Addacolor resin bound surfacing**
Addacolor coloured resin bound surfacing is suitable for projects requiring designs and logos. Any RAL colour can be matched.

• **Addastone TP tree pit surfacing**
Addastone TP provides an attractive porous paving surface using natural or recycled aggregates. Its open texture enables tree roots to access air, and allows for water penetration.

Terrabase Rustic – Broad Walk, Royal Botanic Gardens, Kew

Terrabound – Horatio's Garden, Scotland

Addacolor – 'Love Your Garden' TV show

Addacolor – Portobello School, Scotland

Addaset – driveway, West Sussex

Addabound – Culinary Institute of America

Terrabound – Hengistbury Head

Terrabound – David Wilson Homes

Addastone TP tree pit – London

A member of the **TERRACO** group

Contact
Tim Hopkins
t: 01825 761333
sales@addagrip.co.uk

Web
www.addagrip.co.uk

Address
Addagrip Terraco Ltd
Addagrip House
Bell Lane Industrial Estate
Uckfield TN22 1QL

Affiliations
British Association of Landscape Industries (BALI)
English Historic Towns Forum

Country of manufacture
UK

Additional entries
Resin bound SUDS porous surfacing ➤ 73
Resin bound porous surfacing ➤ 92

Addagrip Terraco Ltd

Addastone resin bonded decorative surfacing

Addagrip formulates and manufactures the *Addastone* two-part resin bonded surfacing system. It is designed to bond natural aggregates to a macadam or concrete base.
The finish provides an attractive, hard-wearing and low-maintenance surface for pedestrian and vehicular areas where a textured aggregate appearance is desired.
Addastone is suitable for car parks, access roads, driveways, courtyards, pathways and patios. It provides the traditional appearance of aggregate without the associated maintenance issues of loose gravel surfacing.
Addastone is available in a range of natural aggregate finishes.

Projects
• Dún Laoghaire People's Park, Ireland.
• Littlehampton seafront.
• Wembley Arena, London.
• Durham University.
• Walsall Arboretum.
• Bexhill seafront.
• Olympic Park.
• Lee Valley White Water Centre.

Addastone – Lee Valley White Water Centre

Addastone – Littlehampton seafront

Addastone – Wembley

Addastone – Bexhill seafront

Addastone – Durham University

Addastone – Olympic Park

Addastone – Walsall Arboretum

Addastone – Dún Laoghaire People's Park, Ireland

Contact
Mark Stott
m: 07584 311266
t: 01594 826768
f: 01594 826948
mark@bituchem.com

Web
www.bituchem.com

Address
Bituchem Asphalt Ltd
Laymore Road
Forest Vale Industrial Estate
Cinderford GL14 2YH

Accreditation
ISO 9001:2008
National Highway Sector Scheme 14
ISO 14001:2004
BS OHSAS 18001:2007

Affiliations
Road Surface Treatment Association
Institute of Asphalt Technology
Road Emulsion Association

Bituchem Asphalt Ltd

Natural and coloured macadam surfaces: Natratex, Colourtex

Natratex and *Colourtex* surfacing offers a cost-effective, resin-bound alternative to block paving, surface dressing and other hard landscaping surfaces. Using traditional techniques, the material can be machine- or hand-laid throughout the year. *Natratex* and *Colourtex* are used in various locations, including highways, schools and colleges, heritage sites, parks and footpaths, as well as commercial and domestic premises.

Composition and manufacture

Natratex combines a specially formulated, translucent, resin-based binder with natural aggregates to produce a durable, heritage-style surface course. *Colourtex* uses a pigmented resin-based binder and complementary aggregates that provide an aesthetic appearance. It is especially suitable for demarcation and delineation uses on highways, leisure developments and car parks. Both products can be designed to meet various on-site requirements.

Finish and appearance

Natratex is non-pigmented and draws its colours from the coarse and fine aggregates used. *Colourtex* is offered in primary colours, such as green, yellow, red and blue, and bespoke colours.

6mm *Natratex* on footpath – Hertfordshire University

6mm *Natratex* – Hertfordshire University

6mm *Natratex Cotswold* – Blandford, Dorset

Royal College Street, London

6mm *Natratex Cotswold* – Brincliffe Gardens, Sheffield

Winchester Park & Ride

6mm *Natratex* – Hampshire

10mm heavy-duty buff – Woodford Bridge Road, London Borough of Redbridge

Queen Street, Oxford

10mm heavy-duty buff on highway

Cavendish Square

Peckham Square

Milton Keynes

Lower Grosvenor Gardens, Victoria

Spectrum
from SureSet

Contact
t: 01985 841180
mail@sureset.co.uk

Web
www.sureset.co.uk

Address
SureSet UK Ltd
32 Deverill Road Trading Est, Sutton Veny BA12 7BZ

Accreditation
CHAS; CPD Certified; ISO 9001; ISO 14001

Affiliations
Builders and Contractors Guild; English Historic
Towns Forum; British Association of Landscape
Industries (BALI); Building Register; Landscape
Institute; Confederation of Construction Specialists;
The Guild of Builders and Contractors;
Considerate Contractors Scheme

Additional entries
Surface drainage ➤ 74
SureSet permeable bound surfacing ➤ 97
Permeable tree pit surfacing ➤ 528

SureSet UK Ltd
Spectrum glass bound surfacing

SureSet, established in 1997, is a specialist manufacturer, installer and supplier of permeable resin bound paving.
Spectrum permeable resin bound paving incorporates 3 or 6mm recycled glass that is coloured and batched in-house by SureSet. It is suitable for public areas, playgrounds, entrance areas and pathways. The range of colours available offers design flexibility, making it suitable for demarcation, logos and vibrant eye-catching designs. From artwork, SureSet can create stencils and colour matches for approval.

• Guarantee
SureSet installations are offered with an 18-year guarantee that protects against loose stone, cracking, oil damage, UV degradation, colour change, frost damage and workmanship.

Finish and appearance
Spectrum incorporates coloured glass that is available in almost any colour.

Installation and maintenance
Spectrum permeable paving is mixed cold on site and installed by skilled tradesmen. Full technical advice and specifications are available.
It is virtually maintenance free requiring only an occasional brush or power-wash.

Spectrum permeable resin bound paving incorporates 3 or 6mm recycled glass aggregate

Spectrum can be specified in bespoke colours

Spectrum is available in virtually any colour

Spectrum permeable resin bound paving

Spectrum is suited to creating bespoke motifs

Spectrum can be used to recreate client designs

Bespoke beach design for garden/patio

Contact
t: 01985 841180
mail@sureset.co.uk

Web
www.sureset.co.uk

Address
32 Deverill Road Trading Estate
Sutton Veny BA12 7BZ

Accreditation
CHAS; CPD Certified; ISO 9001; ISO 14001

Affiliations
Builders and Contractors Guild; English Historic
Towns Forum; British Association of Landscape
Industries (BALI); Building Register; Landscape
Institute; Confederation of Construction Specialists;
The Guild of Builders and Contractors
Considerate Contractors Scheme

Additional entries
Surface drainage ➤ 74
Spectrum glass bound surfacing ➤ 96
Permeable tree pit surfacing ➤ 528

SureSet UK Ltd

SureSet permeable bound surfacing

SureSet, established in 1997, is a specialist
manufacturer, installer and supplier of permeable
resin bound paving.

• **SureSet resin bound paving**
SureSet resin bound paving provides a durable,
low maintenance, eco-friendly and safe surface.
It is colour consistent and UV stable and is
suitable for public areas, playgrounds, car parks,
entrance areas and pathways.
SureSet is available in a 3, 6 or 10mm aggregate,
and its permeability eliminates standing water,
meaning that surfaces can be safely used
immediately after wet weather.
SureSet's environmental credentials include its
suitability for Sustainable Urban Drainage Systems
(SUDS) and its laying method, which is a low-
energy cold-applied process.
It is also available in a sealed finish for internal use.

• **Guarantee**
SureSet comes with an 18-year guarantee against
stone loss, inherent failure, and all workmanship.

Installation and maintenance
SureSet permeable paving is mixed cold on site
and installed by skilled tradesmen.

Technical support
Full technical advice, specifications and BIM files
are available.

Applications include town centres, playgrounds, pool surrounds and patios

SureSet is suitable for car parks

SureSet is suitable for cycle paths

SureSet is suitable for public realm

SureSet gives a colour-consistent, UV-stable surface

SureSet is suitable for driveways, gardens and patios

SureSet permeable paving is mixed cold on site and installed by skilled tradesmen

Bespoke logos and motifs in virtually any colour

Clearstone® is UV-stable and colour-consistent

Clearstone Paving Ltd

Resin-bound surfacing

Clearstone Paving Ltd designs and installs resin-bound UV-stable surfacing. The company offers a personal service from the conception of a design through to installation. Applications include driveways, walkways, terraces and car parks in domestic, commercial or public spaces. Any style, including traditional, heritage, creative or ultra-modern can be accommodated and a bespoke colour-matching service is offered.

• **Clearstone® resin-bound surfacing**
Clearstone® resin-bound surfacing comprises a blend of naturally sourced aggregates and recycled materials in UV-stable resin. It is available in a wide choice of colours and textures. Its porosity allows water to filter back to the water table, which can help a project meet SuDS requirements whereby the pollution caused by surface water run-off must be minimised. A resin-bound surface can also provide acoustic properties, mitigating the impact of sound for those living nearby or visiting a landscaped area. It is durable; resistant to weeds, staining and cracking; and is buggy- and wheelchair-friendly.

• **PrismStone® surfacing**
PrismStone® is a smooth porous surfacing used to reproduce bespoke logos, designs, patterns, motifs, numbers, letters or any decorative feature for playgrounds, pool surrounds and town centres. *PrismStone®* comprises decorative powder-coloured quartz aggregates, which are available in various shades ranging from subtle pastels to bright primary hues.

Installation and maintenance

Clearstone® and *PrismStone®* resin-bound surfaces can be laid on existing concrete or asphalt, or installed as a new surfacing course in new construction projects. They are cold-mixed on site and hand-trowelled to a seamless, smooth surface. They can be laid in curves or angles to a depth of 15 to 18mm.

Clearstone offers a year-round installation service and has installed thousands of square metres of resin-bound surfacing. By formulating and installing its own products, and through a background in landscape design and build, the company has built a reputation for high-quality craftsmanship.

Clearstone® surfaces can be power-washed, are easy to maintain and long lasting.

Technical support

Clearstone offers a single point of responsibility from design through to the completion of a project, with the technical knowledge and experience to control the whole process. The team can advise on site preparation, aftercare and maintenance. It can provide specifications for the design loading, whether foot traffic, domestic vehicles, or car park or access road traffic.

Clearstone® resin-bound surfacing is suitable for roadways and car parks – Berkeley Homes, The Ashmiles

PrismStone® is suitable for decorative features

Clearstone® for driveways, patios and garden paths

Clearstone® is suitable for public areas and footpaths – Middle Temple Gardens, Embankment, London

Contact
Adrian Smallridget
t: 023 9220 0606
mail@meonuk.com

Clinton Humphris
t: 028 3085 0049
mail@meonireland.com

Matthew Hadden – Head of Sales
t: 023 9220 0606
matthew@meonuk.com

Web
www.meonuk.com

Address
Meon Ltd
Railside
Northarbour Spur
Portsmouth PO6 3TU

Operational area
UK, Ireland

Additional entries
DekorGrip Rubber Mulch ➤ 520
DekorGrip Tree Surround surfacing ➤ 529

Meon Ltd

DekorGrip Resin Bound surfacing

Meon's *DekorGrip* material provides a decorative, wearing, durable, anti-slip surface for use on park footpaths, drives, walkways and courtyards. *DekorGrip Resin Bound* is an encapsulated natural aggregate surface with a smooth troweled finish. It is also a permeable solution demonstrating a sustainable approach to water conservation and is fully SuDS-compliant.

As *DekorGrip* is a free-flowing material almost any shape, style or design possible. It is available in a range of colours and blends and Meon can pigment the aggregate to match customers' unique requirements.

Installation and maintenance
DekorGrip Resin Bound is simple to lay and can be installed over existing surfaces including asphalt, concrete, timber and steel. Surfaces are easily brushed clean and can be pressure washed.

Sitework
Meon offers on-site support for *DekorGrip Resin Bound* and personally supports all projects with brochures and samples and users are fully trained to appropriate levels. Application assistance and aftersales service are also provided.
DekorGrip is guaranteed when installed by approved contractors.

DekorGrip Resin Bound – Hampshire Terrace, Portsmouth

DekorGrip Resin Bound – Lidl HQ

DekorGrip Resin Bound – distillery

DekorGrip Resin Bound surfacing – Bow roundabout, London

DekorGrip Resin Bound – Horsham

DekorGrip Resin Bound – Oracle Shopping Centre

Innovators in surface treatments

Contact
Lee Banner
t: 01925 752165
f: 01925 757098
Lee.Banner@rms-ltd.com

Web
www.rms-ltd.com

Address
Road Maintenance Services Ltd
Mowpen Brow
High Legh
Knutsford WA16 6PB

Accreditation
ISO 9001:2008
ISO14001:2004
OHSAS 18001
CHAS
Constructionline
HAPAS
National Highway Sector Scheme No 13

Road Maintenance Services Ltd

Impressions natural surfaces

Road Maintenance Services (RMS) has extensive experience as a contractor in providing specialist decorative finishes.

High-quality binder systems provide a durable treatment as an alternative to asphalt, brick paviors, paving slabs and concrete.

Depending on site requirements, *Impressions Bindcoat* or *Impressions Bondcoat* is specified to achieve the desired finish.

Various coloured chippings ensure a decorative surface appearance to suit all applications.

Surfacing for Heritage Lottery funded projects

Surfacing for prestige development

Surfacing for pathways

Surfacing for parks and gardens

Surfacing for public spaces

Surfacing for cycleways

Surfacing for environmental improvement projects

Surfacing for driveways

Contact
Craig Woolley – North, Midlands, Eastern England and Scotland
t: 01484 860044
craig@hrlonline.co.uk

Andy Clark – London and South England
t: 01932 862473
sales@landscaping.co.uk

Web
www.hrlonline.co.uk

Address
Hardscape Resourcing Limited
Westleigh Hall, Wakefield Road
Denby Dale, Huddersfield HD8 8QJ

Additional entries
Permeable paving in grass and gravel ➤ 71
Landscape edgings and perimeters ➤ 90
Decorative in situ concrete pavements ➤ 103

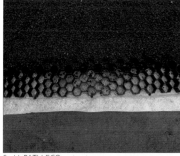
StablePATH ECO – structure

Hardscape Resourcing Limited

Gravel stabilisation grids for naturally permeable paving

HRL offers permeable reinforced gravel stabilisation honeycombs for applications ranging from simple pathways to intensely trafficked communal access areas.
• **StablePAVE PRO heavy-duty surfaces**
StablePAVE PRO is a robust, interlocking honeycomb panel with a solid, perforated base, designed to handle frequent vehicular and pedestrian use. It provides substantial lateral load resistance and compressive strength for heavier vehicular applications such as commercial car parking, equestrian and leisure facilities.
• **StablePAVE 30/40 medium-duty surfaces**
StablePAVE 30 and *StablePAVE 40* offer a very cost-effective medium-duty gravel paving solution for residential and light traffic use. Produced at 1200x800mm in two depths, the translucent white panels have a weed-suppressant membrane attached to the base. They are fast and easy to install.
• **StablePATH ECO Black light-duty surfaces**
StablePATH ECO Black is used mainly for pathway, garden and communal social areas. Produced in the same size as *StablePAVE TRADE 30* with a weed-suppressant membrane attached to the base, the black coloured panels offer a lower cost without compromise on performance.

Composition and manufacture
Products are manufactured from specially selected recycled raw material. They are UV-stable and fully recyclable, so significantly contribute to BREEAM and SUDS content.

Dimensions
StablePAVE PRO: 1180x944x32mm deep – Translucent White.
StablePAVE TRADE 30: 1200x800x30mm deep – Translucent White.
StablePAVE TRADE 40: 1200x800x40mm deep – Translucent White.
StablePATH ECO Black: 1200x800x30mm deep – Black.

StablePAVE 40 – residential application

No sinking, spreading, rutting or gravel migration

StablePAVE PRO – heavy-duty for permeable commercial car park

StablePATH ECO Black – heritage application

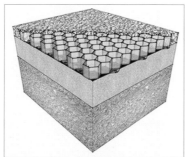
Honeycomb structure creating a free-draining path

StablePAVE PRO withstands loads to 280 tonnes/m²

StablePAVE PRO honeycomb structure

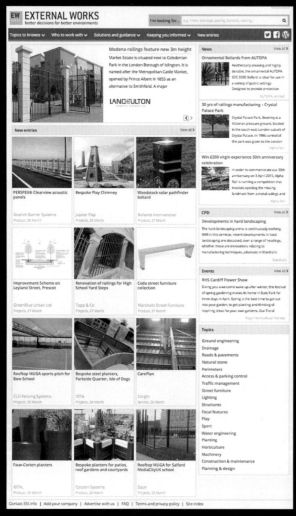

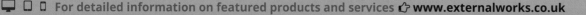

Contact
Craig Woolley
t: 01484 863880
sales@colchem.co.uk

Web
www.colchem.co.uk

Address
HRL Ventraco Limited
Westleigh Hall
Wakefield Road
Denby Dale
Huddersfield HD8 8QJ

Additional entries

Permeable paving in grass and gravel ➤ 71
Landscape edgings and perimeters ➤ 90
Gravel stabilisation grids for naturally permeable
paving ➤ 101

Integral colour, light broom finish

HRL Ventraco Limited

Decorative in situ concrete pavements

HRL Ventraco produces and distributes colour additives, surface treatments and decorative stains for in situ concrete pavements and hard-standings. The product portfolio gives designers and contractors a flexible, cost effective means to create strong, durable and attractive concrete pavements that are easy to maintain.

- **Integral colour addition**

Ferrotone Classic Landscape Colours are available in 9 earth tone and 3 intense shades. The colours are non-fading and UV-resistant, with consistency ensured by pre-dosed packaging to suit prescribed mix designs. Many architectural finishes can be applied for enhanced interest including smooth trowel, broom and band, surface etching, surface texturing and decoration.

- **Exposed aggregate finishes**

Whispercast topping screeds bring the beauty of natural aggregate into the equation. They offer a low risk, pre-packaged method of finish, which can be installed as a bonded screed or laid monolithically onto a base slab.

The bonded screed method can also be used with old or existing concrete pavements.

Two colour ranges are offered: *Sasso Italia*, based on Italian marble aggregates; and *Sasso Celtica*, based on Scottish granites and quartz. Controlled depth of exposure through self-neutralising surface retarders, ensures consistency of finish.

- **Decorative concrete stains**

Sienna and *Sorrento* decorative stains offer post-finishing decoration for concrete surfaces. Suitable for use as a single application or in conjunction with integral colour or exposed aggregate surfaces, the stains provide a wide colour palette for the creation of unique effects.

- **Protecting architectural concrete**

The *Colchem* range provides solutions for most requirements extending from basic dirt and stain resistance to enhanced freeze/thaw performance, anti-graffiti coatings, dust proofing, surface hardening, and improved abrasion resistance.

Suitable for roads and pathways

Whispercast exposed aggregate

Exposed aggregate reveal

Detail broom and band

Integral colour and decorative stains

Ferrotone colours, textures and stains

MicroETCH finish

MicroETCH finish is available in various colours

Decorative stain

Creating Better Spaces

Contact
t: 0870 444 6217
f: 0870 442 7725
esi.marshalls@web-response.co.uk

Web
www.marshalls.co.uk/commercial

Address
Marshalls plc
Landscape House
Premier Way
Lowfields Business Park
Elland HX5 9HT

Additional entries
Priora permeable block paving ➤ 76
Linear drainage systems ➤ 80
Combined kerb & drainage systems ➤ 84
Kerb systems ➤ 86
Concrete block paving and setts ➤ 112
Natural stone ➤ 124
Traffic calming systems ➤ 222

Marshalls plc

Concrete paving systems

Marshalls' commercial concrete paving range provides solutions for contemporary and traditional schemes. The paving range gives designers the opportunity to create beautiful landscapes to frame buildings and enhance public realm spaces.

A variety of ethically sourced aggregates and high-performance concrete mixes are used in a range of highly durable, aesthetically pleasing products. Paving designs include textured, smooth ground, skimmed, riven, leather effect and standard pimple finishes in a wide range of colours.

A variety of plan sizes and thicknesses is manufactured to give design freedom and to cater for required loading requirements.

Special products include permeable flag paving, step treds and units, fibre-reinforced paving, marker blocks, platform copings, tactile paving, bollard surround paving, large format 1m² paving, and paving with high recycled content.

Technical support

Marshalls 360 offers expert design and technical support to guarantee long-term, optimum engineering. An online Paving Design Tool can be used to create a bespoke sub-base design for selected products based on maximum loading requirements.

Celestia skimmed concrete flag paving

Kerigg flamed concrete paving

Rivero leather-effect concrete paving

Conservation skimmed concrete paving

Organa leather-effect concrete paving

Priora flag permeable paving, Natural and Charcoal

Saxon textured concrete paving – Salford University

Conservation textured in Silver Grey – Glasgow

Charnwood textured paving – Canary Wharf

Conservation smooth ground paving – Endike PS

Renaissance concrete flag with high recycled content

St George smooth ground paving, used internally and externally – Victoria Station, London

Acheson + Glover Ltd

Concrete paving flag systems

AG has been a leading manufacturer of hard landscaping and precast solutions for over 50 years. The company provides world-class products and innovative solutions to architects, specifiers, contractors and homeowners across the UK.

Product range

AG's flagstone range includes the expansive *TerraPave®* range of advanced granite flagstones, *Caliza®*, *Granaza*, *Canterra®*, *Manor Stone®*, *Pedra®*. An extensive range of tactile and deterrent flag products is also available.

Composition and manufacture

The company combines a heavy investment in R&D, state-of-the-art production machinery and bespoke finishing processes with a tradition of producing aesthetically excellent, high-performing products.
Flagstones are manufactured with materials from AG's own quarries, combined with the highest quality European aggregates and pigments.

Technical support

AG's Sales and Technical Departments can provide extensive support, including pre-sales specification advice and on-site technical support.

Contact
Sales
t: 0121 747 0202
specifications@ag.uk.com

Web
www.ag.uk.com

Address
Acheson + Glover Ltd
4 Marlin Office Village
1250 Chester Road
Castle Vale
Birmingham B35 7AZ

Accreditation
ISO 9001:2015
ISO 14001
OHSAS 18001:2007

Operational area
UK, Ireland

Additional entries
Concrete retaining walls ➤ 32
Concrete block paving systems ➤ 116

Caliza®

Canterra®

TerraPave®

Manor Stone®

Paving Solutions

Contact

Sales
t: 01824 702493
f: 01824 704527
enquiries@rpcltd.co.uk

Web

www.rpcltd.co.uk

Address

RPC Paving
Quarryfields
Ruthin
Denbighshire LL15 2UG

Additional entries
Erosion control systems ➤ 14
Retaining structures ➤ 38

RPC Paving

Decorative paving flags and kerbs

RPC Paving offers decorative paving flags and kerbs for domestic and commercial applications. They are available in a number of different finishes and colours.

Solo, *Saron*, *Brecon Black Fleck* and *Cambrian Eco* are textured concrete paving ranges manufactured using a Welsh aggregate.

In addition to decorative paving and kerbs, RPC Paving also offers British Standard paving, concrete block paving, concrete seating and utility products.

Solo paving in Buff and Charcoal – North Wales

Cambrian Eco paving in Buff and Natural – Rhyl

Paving installed on roof terraces

Solo paving in Charcoal – Runcorn

Brecon Black Fleck step inlay paving – Liverpool

Saron paving and seating – Colwyn Bay

![Tobermore logo]
Tobermore
WORLD CLASS PAVING & WALLING

Contact
Sales
t: 028 7964 2411
f: 028 7964 4145
sales@tobermore.co.uk

Web
www.tobermore.co.uk

Address
Tobermore
2 Lisnamuck Road
Magherafelt BT45 5QF

Accreditation
ISO 9001, ISO 14001

Operational area
UK, Ireland

Additional entries
Concrete retaining walls ➤ 39
Permeable concrete block paving ➤ 75
Concrete block paving ➤ 114

Tobermore

Concrete flag paving

Established in 1942, Tobermore is a leading manufacturer of paving and walling and supplies products for the commercial and domestic markets throughout the UK and Ireland.

• Concrete paving flag range

Tobermore produces one of the largest paving flag ranges available. The company manufactures a large number of flag styles, finishes and sizes, and offers many different solid and blended colour options. Paving flags are produced using modern manufacturing processes under ISO 9001 and ISO 14001 accreditation.

• Eco concrete paving flag range

In addition to its standard range of products, Tobermore offers a range of *Eco* products. These are manufactured with the same aesthetic and practical benefits as the standard products, but with high rates of recycled content and a low carbon footprint.

• Contemporary flags

Mayfair Flags are ideal for contemporary schemes as their sparkling natural granite aggregates, coarse surface finish and chamfered edge give a modern look.

Kensington Flags feature special colour blends that produce an eye-catching marbling effect.

• Traditional flags

Historic Flags provide the look and feel of traditional natural stone with similar hard-wearing characteristics. The fettled edges and riven face of *Historic Flags* add to their warmth and character.

Riven Flags resemble the rugged appearance of natural stone and feature a bevelled surface finish. Although *Riven Flags* are produced in a small, lightweight size, they have the strength and durability of machine pressed flags, and are economically priced.

Kensington Flag in Black and White

Mayfair Flags in Silver and *Shannon* in Charcoal

Riven Flags in Natural

Textured Flags in Buff – Tibshelf Community School

Historic Flags in Slate – Cutters Wharf, Belfast

Tactile Flags Hazard Warning in Buff

Contact
Richard Williams
t: 07890 585768
uk@urbastyle.com

Web
www.urbastyle.com

Address
URBASTYLE®
Severn House
Hazell Drive
Newport NP10 8FY

Additional entries
Architectural concrete bollards ➤ 237
Architectural concrete street furniture ➤ 312
Architectural concrete benches and seats ➤ 340
Architectural concrete planters ➤ 381

URBASTYLE®

Silkstone Fasonado paving

URBASTYLE's *Silkstone Fasonado* range provides large-dimension paving for areas subject to both pedestrian and vehicular traffic.
The large-perspective paving solutions are in keeping with the design accent favoured in modern urban and commercial developments. Paving panels with 'pop up' seats or planters are available on request.
In addition, *Fasonado Lite* tiles are available for surface cladding.

Finish and appearance
Silkstone Fasonado paving comes in three finishes – smooth trowelled and micro-etched, exposed aggregate, and polished – and in five colour combinations.
Fasonado Lite paving comes in a polished/brushed finish and in eight colour combinations.

Dimensions
Silkstone Fasonado tiles are available in sizes from 1.0x1.0m up to 3.0x1.5m and in thicknesses from 8 to 14cm.
Fasonado Lite tiles are 60x60cm and 2cm thick.

Fasonado – Smedenpoort, Bruges, Belgium

Silkstone Fasonado – Docks Bruxsel, Belgium

Silkstone Fasonado – Marcinelle-Charleroi, Belgium

Silkstone Fasonado – Den Haag, The Netherlands

Silkstone Fasonado – Portsmouth, UK

Fasonado – Hoveniersberg, University of Flanders　　*Silkstone Fasonado – Ingelmunster, Belgium*

Silkstone Fasonado – Leuven, Belgium

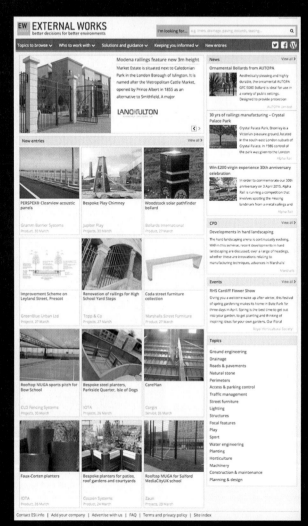

westminsterstone
A Tradition of Excellence

Contact
John Clifford
t: 01978 710685
ask@westminsterstone.com

Web
www.westminsterstone.com
www.pavingandflooring.com

Address
Westminster Stone Company Ltd
Shaw's Estate
Sodylt
Ellesmere SY12 9EL

Affiliations
British Association of Landscape Industries (BALI)

Operational area
Worldwide

Additional entries
National Trust Landscape Collection ➤ 111

Westminster Stone Co Ltd

Paving flags

Westminster Stone provides paving suitable for exterior and interior applications in architectural and landscape projects. As well as standard flags, the company can provide kerbstones, bullnose steps, gulleys and octagons. Products give an authentic finish in restoration projects, and add charm and maturity to new developments. Westminster Stone's products are used extensively in domestic landscape projects, but pubs, hotels and restaurants specify traditional flags for a traditional ambience.

Composition and manufacture
• **Reconstituted stone paving**
Products are made from high-specification fibre-reinforced reconstituted stone. They give the appearance of natural stone, while providing high levels of strength and durability.
• **Natural stone paving**
Flags, cobbles and setts are offered in limestone, sandstone, travertine, granite, slate and marble.

Finish and appearance
Flags are available in grey/green, weathered slate grey, Cotswold cream or Yorkshire buff/brown. *Old Provence* tiles are a terracotta colour. Natural stone is available in a variety of colours.

Lancashire Mill Flags

Livingstone Welsh Midnight Flags – Lymm

Old Provence random tiles

National Trust
Landscape
Collection
Inspired by tradition

Contact
John Clifford
t: 0844 815 6442 (local rate)
ask@westminsterstone.com

Web
www.nationaltrustpaving.com

Address
Westminster Stone Company Ltd
Shaw's Estate
Sodylt
Ellesmere SY12 9EL

Affiliations
British Association of Landscape Industries (BALI)
The National Trust

Operational area
Worldwide

Additional entries
Paving flags ➤ 111

Westminster Stone Co Ltd

National Trust Landscape Collection

The *National Trust Landscape Collection* is an award-winning collaboration between Westminster Stone and the National Trust. Launched in 2011, it comprises 4 ranges: *Cotswold Manor*, *Country House*, *Roman Villa* and *Kitchen Garden*. Paving, cobbles, tiles and gravels are designed to reflect the heritage of houses and gardens within the National Trust. They can also enhance contemporary landscapes.
Projects include gardens, pathways and drives. The products are also used by pubs and hotels.

Hidcote, Cotswold Manor range

Petworth flagstone and Tatton cobbles

Country House kerbstone

Cotswold Manor range

Marshalls

Creating Better Spaces

Contact
t: 0870 444 6217
f: 0870 442 7725
esi.marshalls@web-response.co.uk

Web
www.marshalls.co.uk/commercial

Address
Marshalls plc
Landscape House
Premier Way
Lowfields Business Park
Elland HX5 9HT

Additional entries
Priora permeable block paving ➤ 76
Linear drainage systems ➤ 80
Combined kerb & drainage systems ➤ 84
Kerb systems ➤ 86
Concrete paving systems ➤ 104
Natural stone ➤ 124
Traffic calming systems ➤ 222

Marshalls plc

Concrete block paving and setts

Marshalls concrete block paving (CBP) combines durable, load-bearing performance with attractive aesthetics. It has been proven in a wide range of applications over many years.

• **Concrete block paving designs**
A wide variety of shapes, colours, sizes and finishes gives designers the creative freedom to develop paving designs that stand out in contemporary or traditional settings.

• **Priora permeable block paving**
Block paving designs that include *Priora* are permeable paving blocks – they reduce the risk of flooding by eradicating surface water run-off at source. *Priora* permeable block pavers feature a patented enhanced interlock design that has been field tested and is proven to provide 40% more interlock than standard CBP, improving surface stability. This means that a Marshalls *Priora* surface offers additional benefits in terms of longevity and maintenance in addition to its performance in SuDS schemes.

• **Machine-lay block paving**
Marshalls offers many of its CBP options in a machine-lay format. This combination of product and plant is ideal for large projects as it improves health and safety on site and allows large areas to be laid up to three times quicker than traditional hand-lay methods.

Tegula in Traditional – Lutterworth

Myriad Priora in all colours – Midnight, Twilight, Morning Light, Moonlight

Mistral Priora in Silver Grey and Charcoal – Glasgow

Tegula in Traditional – Blackpool

Myriad paving multicoloured installation – a creative paving option for standout urban landscapes

La Linia in Light Granite, Anthracite Basalt and Blue – Corby

Metrolinia City in Silver Grey and City Charcoal Grey – Bolton

La Linia Priora in all colours – Anthracite Basalt, Grey Granite, Mid Grey Granite, Light Granite

Metropolitan in Natural – Coventry University

Blister concrete block paving in Yellow

Eskoo Six machine lay and *Max-E-Channel*

Marshalls Marker Blocks White Reflective and Black

Tobermore
WORLD CLASS PAVING & WALLING

Contact
Sales
t: 028 7964 2411
f: 028 7964 4145
sales@tobermore.co.uk

Web
www.tobermore.co.uk

Address
Tobermore
2 Lisnamuck Road
Magherafelt BT45 5QF

Accreditation
ISO 9001, ISO 14001

Operational area
UK, Ireland

Additional entries
Concrete retaining walls ➤ 39
Permeable concrete block paving ➤ 75
Concrete flag paving ➤ 108

Tobermore
Concrete block paving

Established in 1942, Tobermore is a leading manufacturer of paving and walling and supplies products for the commercial and domestic markets throughout the UK and Ireland.
• **Concrete block paving range**
Tobermore's versatile block paving range provides very high physical performance, is aesthetically pleasing, has reconstitution abilities and offers whole-life cost-effectiveness.
• **Eco block paving products**
Tobermore offers a special range of *Eco* products, which are manufactured with the aesthetic and practical benefits as the standard product range, but with high rates of recycled content and a low carbon footprint.

Finish and appearance
• **Hard-wearing surface**
Tobermore's block paving products have a special hard-wearing surface layer. The surface is made using high cement content, ensuring that it is extremely hard and durable. This improves the strength, durability and overall appearance of the products.
• **Strong colour blends**
Tobermore offers a variety of solid and blended colours. The surface layer of the products is produced with high pigment content, making the colours strong, deep and vibrant, and providing very good colour retention.
• **Significantly reduced efflorescence**
Efflorescence is one of the biggest problems encountered with concrete paving. The vapour curing processes used in Tobermore's manufacturing significantly reduce the occurrence of efflorescence.
• **Non-slip surface**
Block paving products have skid resistant and non-slip surfaces, making them suitable for trafficked and pedestrian areas in any type of application.

Sienna Duo paving in Graphite and Sandstone – Sir Chris Hoy Velodrome, Glasgow

Chieftain VS5 paving in Silver, *Manhattan* paving in Graphite, and *Country* kerb – Keady

Tegula Trio paving and *Kerbstone* in Bracken

Manhattan paving in Silver – Park Regis

Fusion paving in Silver, Mid Grey and Graphite – University of Lincoln

City Pave VS5 in Silver, Mid Grey and Charcoal – Camberwell Regeneration, Southwark

Shannon paving in Heather – Kirkcudbright Primary School

Fusion paving in Graphite, Mid Grey and Silver – Hurst Lane Place, Solihull

Acheson + Glover Ltd

Concrete block paving systems

AG has been a leading manufacturer of hard landscaping and precast solutions for over 50 years. The company provides world-class products and innovative solutions to architects, specifiers, contractors and homeowners across the UK.

Product range

AG's concrete block paving range includes *Magnum Stone®* large format paving, *Kin Stone®*, *Plaza*, *River Stone*, *Country Cobble®* rumbled paving, *Rectangular*, *Boulevard®*, *Xflo®* permeable paving. Setts, circles, mixed-size packs and machine-lay paving is also available.

Composition and manufacture

AG combines a heavy investment in R&D, state-of-the-art production machinery and bespoke finishing processes with a tradition of producing aesthetically excellent, high-performing products. Paving is manufactured with materials from AG's quarries, combined with the highest quality European aggregates and pigments.

Technical support

AG's Sales and Technical Departments can provide extensive support, including pre-sales specification advice and on-site technical support.

Contact
Sales
t: 0121 747 0202
specifications@ag.uk.com

Web
www.ag.uk.com

Address
Acheson + Glover Ltd
4 Marlin Office Village
1250 Chester Road
Castle Vale
Birmingham B35 7AZ

Accreditation
ISO 9001:2015
ISO 14001
OHSAS 18001:2007

Operational area
UK, Ireland

Additional entries
Concrete retaining walls ➤ 32
Concrete paving flag systems ➤ 106

Rectangular and River Stone

Kin Stone®

Country Cobble®

Plaza

Alfresco Floors Ltd

Outdoor floor tiles

Alfresco Floors has over 25 years experience in the design, supply and installation of hard landscaping across the UK.

Almost 100 different shapes and designs of slip-resistant Italian porcelain tiles are imported, specifically designed for outdoor use.

The double-depth tiles are 20mm thick and can withstand a one tonne load, even when installed as a raised floor. They are virtually maintenance-free compared to timber and are stronger than most stone alternatives.

Alfresco Floors is the exclusive UK importer of *Ebema* concrete paving products, a very design-conscious collection with two surfaces, Carreau and Rockstone, and is available in a large range of tile sizes up to 1200mm long and 80mm deep.

Finish and appearance

Porcelain products are impermeable to water and provide floors that are frost-, impact-, scratch, chemical spill-, slip-, and thermal expansion/contraction-resistant, as well as being fade- and fire-proof.

Installation

Alfresco Floors can supply just the tiles, tiles and *Buzon* pedestals, or a complete turnkey design and installation service.

Matching internal tiles can also be supplied.

Tiles are mould- and algae-resistant

Tiles can be used to create steps

Almost 100 shapes and designs are available

Ebema Carreau concrete paving

Service cables can run under the tiles

Ebema Rockstone concrete paving

Complementary designs can flow from inside to outside

Contact

Clare Morgan
t: 0845 606 0240
f: 01206 213229
info@globalstonepaving.co.uk

Web

www.globalstonepaving.co.uk

Address

Global Stone (Colchester) Ltd
Tey Gardens
Little Tey
Colchester CO6 1HX

Affiliations

BMF
BALI
NMBS

Global Stone (Colchester) Ltd

Porcelain paving tiles

Global Stone is one of the UK's leading suppliers of Italian porcelain paving tiles for pathways, patios, driveways, outdoor eating areas and swimming pool surrounds.

Global Stone's porcelain paving tiles regularly feature in medal winning show gardens.

Clients include architects, landscape architects, garden designers and builders.

Product range

Petrous is a collection of hard-wearing and stylish outdoor porcelain paving solutions in consistent colourways designed for modern day living.

There are 7 ranges, 37 colours and 11 standard sizes up to 600x1200mm.

All tiles are 20mm thickness.

Project packs, matching accessories and bespoke paving solutions are also available.

Technical properties

Porcelain paving is an extremely hard-wearing, slip-resistant product that is almost totally impervious to moisture.

It is scratch- and abrasion-resistant, not impacted by salts, oils, chemicals or extreme heat or cold. These properties result in a product that retains its colour and is very easy to maintain.

Petrous Premium Porcelain (Toscana Latte) – ideal for cooking areas and swimming pools

Petrous Premium Porcelain (Trento Sand)

Petrous Premium Porcelain (Smoke) – low maintenance non-slip surface for public spaces around ponds

Petrous Premium Porcelain (Trento Black)

Petrous Premium Porcelain (Oyster) – stain-resistant

Contact

Head Office (UK)
t: 01455 559474
f: 01455 554118
enquiries@bbsgraniteconcepts.com

Web
www.bbsnaturalstone.com

Address
BBS Granite Concepts Ltd
Kimcote House
Kimcote Court
Walton Road
Kimcote LE17 5RU

Affiliations
Ethical Trading Initiative (ETI)

Operational area
UK

Country of manufacture
China, Vietnam, Spain, Italy, Portugal, Scandinavia,
South America, UK

BBS Granite Concepts Ltd

Natural stone suppliers

BBS Granite Concepts' natural stone portfolio includes Caithness flagstone, granite, porphyry, sandstone, limestone and slate from around the world. Clay paving is also available.

The company provides stone samples and data sheets, as well as advice on laying, aspects of engineering and mortar options.

CAD technology is used to read and interpret architectural drawings.

BBS works with skilled craftsmen to engineer bespoke granite street furniture. Tactile paving and stone lettering services are also available.

Alta quartzite – Adams Place, Canary Wharf, London

Caithness stone and granite – Johnstone Town Hall

Mixed granite – Merthyr Tydfil Town Hall

Granite paving and planters – Westminster

Porphyry and granite – High Street, Kinross

Yorkstone and whinstone – St Salvator's Quad

Granite street furniture – Giant's Causeway, Regent's Place, London

Contact
Contact
t: 01326 375660
f: 01326 375167
colas.cornwall@colas.co.uk

Web
www.colas.co.uk

Address
Colas Ltd
Carnsew Quarry
Mabe
Penryn
Cornwall TR10 9DH

Operational area
UK

Country of manufacture
UK

Shipping via Falmouth Docks

Carnsew Quarry, Cornwall

Colas Ltd

Coarse grained, silver-grey granite products from Carnsew Quarry

Colas Ltd's Carnsew Quarry, the largest inland quarry in Cornwall, is located in the developing area between Redruth, Falmouth and Truro. The proximity of Falmouth docks enables crushed aggregates to be shipped throughout the UK and around the world. Customers include local authorities, builders merchants, and major and small works contractors.

• Dry stone granite products
The quarry is sited on the Carnmenellis intrusion and can produce a full range of coarse-grained silver-grey granite products.
Dry stone products for construction applications range from very large rock armour for coastal erosion protection to bulk fill, gabion fill and sub-base aggregates.
Select single-size aggregates are decorative silver-grey granite for landscape applications. They are available in 6, 10, 14 and 20mm sizes.
Monumental and architectural stone features can be produced by working collaboratively with a local stonemason, an example of which is shown.

• Asphalt
Carnsew Quarry has its own, on-site Amman asphalt plant from which coated macadams, asphalts and stone mastic asphalts are produced. Materials are manufactured to satisfy customer requirements and conform to relevant National and European standards and specifications.

• Asphalt alternatives
Colas is able to offer alternatives to conventional asphalt products, by incorporating recycled asphalt planings (RAP) back into the mix, replacing up to 20% of raw materials.
Colas also has the infrastructure to supply warm mix asphalt (WMA), allowing materials to be manufactured and installed at reduced temperatures with no impact on product quality.

• Shipping
Aggregates and fill materials can be shipped via Falmouth Docks in load sizes from 1600 to 8000 metric tonnes.

Technical support

The quarry's on-site technical department provides laboratory, design and testing services, enabling it to respond to customers' special requirements, and ensure material quality.
With the use of the Group's Technical Facilities for research and innovation, Colas is able to offer new products to meet all customer requirements and specifications.

Granite is produced at Carnsew Quarry in Cornwall

Select 14mm silver-grey granite aggregate

Coarse-grained granite

Colas SA CST Laboratory

Amman asphalt plant

Monumental stone, produced collaboratively with stonemason, to celebrate I.K. Brunel – Portsmouth

Dunhouse
NATURAL STONE

Contact
Paul Allison
t: 0845 456 3479
f: 01833 660748
paul@dunhouse.co.uk

Web
www.dunhouse.co.uk

Address
Dunhouse Quarry Co. Ltd
Dunhouse Quarry Works
Staindrop
Darlington DL2 3QU

enquiries@dunhouse.co.uk

Staff/turnover
45 people
£3–4m per year

Accreditation
Stone Federation Great Britain
Mineral Products Association (MPA)

Operational area
Worldwide

Dunhouse Quarry Co. Ltd

Natural stone suppliers

Dunhouse has over 75 years' experience in quarrying and supplying dimensional building stone. It draws on substantial reserves, quarrying 20,000 tonnes of stone annually, so the company is able to accommodate major construction projects, as well as any future extensions. Dunhouse currently operates nine quarries in the north of England and Scotland. A range of stone types is offered, including buff stone from Northumberland and Durham, Scottish red sandstone, and Weardale paving/walling stone. Sandstone and limestone are available for ashlar cladding, wallstone, paving and internal flooring.

Composition and manufacture

Dunhouse's factory at Staindrop is equipped to supply bespoke masonry requirements on any scale. Computer-controlled diamond circular saws, lathes and CNC profiling machinery ensure that natural stone keeps the tolerances required for modern design and construction. Hand-worked detailing can also be carried out on single items as well as larger scale ornate developments.

Technical support

Dunhouse offers design and technical services including acquisition of site details, production of CAD drawings, 3D stone detailing, production of full-size templates, and creation of pallet lists.

Dunhouse Buff sandstone – St Dunstans Court, London EC4

Cop Crag sandstone – Rutland Building, Edinburgh

Corsehill sandstone – Bridgewater Hall, Manchester

Dunhouse Buff sandstone – Clydesdale Bank

Catcastle Buff – Harvey Nichols store, Edinburgh

Cop Crag sandstone – Rutland Building, Edinburgh

Corsehill – Scottish National Portrait Gallery

Dunhouse Buff sandstone – Leith Street, Edinburgh

Carved stone – McEwan Hall restoration, Edinburgh

Dunhouse Buff – Tempietto – Settrington House

Cop Crag sandstone – Royal Vet School, Easter Bush Campus, Edinburgh

Raw block stored at Dunhouse Quarry

Catcastle Grey – Glasgow Sheriff Court

Dunhouse Blue – hard landscaping, Market Place, Bishop Auckland

Marshalls

Creating Better Spaces

Contact

t: 0870 444 6217
f: 0870 442 7725
esi.marshalls@web-response.co.uk

Web

www.marshalls.co.uk/commercial

Address

Marshalls plc
Landscape House
Premier Way
Lowfields Business Park
Elland HX5 9HT

Additional entries

Priora permeable block paving ➤ 76
Linear drainage systems ➤ 80
Combined kerb & drainage systems ➤ 84
Kerb systems ➤ 86
Concrete paving systems ➤ 104
Concrete block paving and setts ➤ 112
Traffic calming systems ➤ 222

Marshalls plc

Natural stone

With over 120 years' experience, Marshalls is the UK's leading supplier of natural stone paving for landscape works. Services include specialised masonry and expert drainage management, as well as bespoke street furniture solutions.

• **Yorkstone**

Marshalls quarries a wide range of Yorkstone for paving, setts, kerbs and specialist features. *Scoutmoor* is blue-grey to brown, *Moselden* is buff to grey, *Appleton* is blue-buff, *Cromwell* is buff, *Westmoor Crest* is blue-grey with some brown in a textured finish, and *Greenmoor Rustic* is blue-grey to ochre with a flame-textured top.

• **Cambrian sandstone**

Marshalls' Cambrian sandstone colours range from very light buff through beiges, greys, browns and reds, to black. *Hawk's View* is a grey to brown stone, supplied with a blasted finish, and is suitable for pedestrian or vehicular trafficking.

• **Granite**

Marshalls granites range from warm buffs, reds and pinks through to a wide variety of cooler greys and blacks. Available finishes are blasted, fine picked, flamed, honed and polished. Products include paving, setts, kerbs and special features.

• **Other stones**

Blue limestone, porphyry, slate, basalt and quartzite natural stone products are also supplied.

Moselden Yorkstone paving – One New Change

Stainless steel-inlaid granite paving – Williamson Sq.

Appleton flamed Yorkstone paving – Bradford Alhambra

Granite paving and cladding – Winnersh Triangle

Hawks View Cambrian sandstone – Liverpool Lime Street Station

Scoutmoor steps and cladding – Winnersh Triangle

Scoutmoor Yorkstone setts – Bristol Harbourside

Five colours of granite – Highcross Shopping Centre

Granite – Victoria Gate, Leeds

Masonry can be supplied in most stone types

IMAG Limited

Contact
Gordon Mitchell
t: 01260 278810
f: 01260 278331
imag.ltd@btconnect.com

Web
www.imag.co.uk

Address
IMAG Ltd
1 Fountain Street
Congleton
Cheshire CW12 4BE

Operational area
UK

IMAG Ltd

Natural stone suppliers

IMAG Ltd supplies natural and reclaimed stone sourced from both the UK and abroad.

• **Play boulders**
A range of natural materials is supplied for children's play areas throughout the UK.

• **Rounded glacial boulders**
Rounded glacial boulders are available from two principal sources: Welsh Glacial boulders come in mixed colours, and Scottish Highland in mixed colours including speckled black and white.

• **Large feature stones**
Other play boulders are supplied in gritstone and sandstone, principally coloured buff to buff grey and red/pink.

• **Other feature stones**
Glacial boulders and gritstone blocks are available for feature landscape work, along with Welsh slate boulders in sizes from $1/4$ tonne up to 20–25 tonnes.
A large range of decorative cobblestones and pebbles comes from sources throughout the UK. Three colours of slate mulch are supplied as an alternative to bark or loose chippings, which also help to stabilise soil.

• **Self-binding gravels**
Self-binding gravels are supplied in a variety of colours and materials for footpath car parks and sports pitches.

Rock on Top of Another Rock – Hyde Park

Gritstone water feature

Boulders – Birchwood Park, Warrington

Large boulders

Rock on Top of Another Rock – Hyde Park

Boulders – Birchwood Park, Warrington

Boulders – play area, Eaves Green, Chorley

Boulders – play area, Eaves Green, Chorley

Raisby Golden Gravel™ – The Mall, London

Contact

Julian Pomery
t: 01489 789444
sales@pomery.co.uk

Web
www.pomery.co.uk

Address
Pomery Natural Stone Ltd
Little Heathers
Outlands Lane
Curdridge SO30 2HD

Operational area
UK
Ireland

Additional entries
Natural stone kerbs ➤ 87
Tactile paving, natural stone ➤ 87
Natural stone seating ➤ 343

Pomery Natural Stone Ltd

Natural stone specialists

Pomery Natural Stone Ltd was formed in 1996 to provide high-quality materials and support to the building industry. Natural stone is supplied for external paving, internal flooring, pedestrianisation schemes, traffic calming, landscape design, cladding and building stone. Stones available include granite, Yorkstone, porphyry, limestone, slate, quartzite, travertine and Canadian hard limestone.
Sawn paving, cladding, setts and cubes, kerbs and specials are offered in a variety of finishes.

Granite seat – Chelsea Flower Show

Gneiss cladding, silver grey granite steps

Portland stone paving and dished channels

S76 grey granite – Titanic Memorial, Belfast

Vulcan Red granite planter and paving – Barking

Multi-coloured fine picked granite setts

Sandstone paving

Quartzite plank paving, granite paving and seating

Quartzite plank paving, granite and tactile paving

 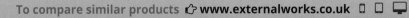

Contact

t: 01786 850400
f: 01786 850404
info@tradstocks.co.uk

Web
www.tradstocks.co.uk

Address
Tradstocks Thornhill
Dunaverig
Thornhill
Stirling FK8 3QW

Tradstocks Westwood
Five Sisters Business Park
Westwood
Livingston EH55 8PN

Affiliations
Stone Federation Great Britain

Operational area
UK

Tradstocks Ltd

Natural stone processor

Tradstocks is a leading processor of indigenous stone for paving and building, quarrying, cutting and hand-finishing standard and bespoke items for contemporary applications and historic sites.

• **Tradstocks Scottish Whinstone**
Scottish Whinstone is a hard, attractive, versatile quartz-dolerite material, used widely in Scotland for hundreds of years. It is generally dark grey with some light grey/red variation. It is suitable for kerbs, setts, channels, paving and walling, and is supplied in a range of sizes and finishes.

• **Walling and coping stone**
Ashlar, split face, coursed and random walling stone products are available in a wide variety of indigenous types with dressed cope to suit. They are often used in major flood alleviation projects.

• **Reclaimed materials**
Tradstocks also offers a range of reclaimed setts and kerbs from stock, subject to availability.

Projects

• Edinburgh Tram Network – Scottish whin kerbs, setts and station platforms.
• Kelso town centre – Scottish whin kerbs, edging, setts and bollards.
• River Ness flood prevention scheme – sandstone walling and copes.
• Galashiels Transport Interchange – Scottish whin walling, features and copes.
• Cromlix Hotel, Dunblane – sandstone paving, edging and bollards.
• Scottish National War Memorial, Edinburgh Castle – Scottish whin benches and plinths.
• 5 Lochs Project, Loch Lomond and The Trossachs National Park – walling, copes and kerbs.

Cullalo stone piers – Hopetoun House, Edinburgh

Gatehouse – Carrick Golf Course

Walling – Kinross, Perthshire

Flood prevention scheme – Braid Burn, Edinburgh

Scottish whin setts – Kelso town square

Threshold signage – Loch Lomond and Trossachs

Whin walling

Ornate fountain – Auchterarder, Perthshire

Scottish whin and Tradstocks pennant paving

Belgian Blue limestone paving with tumbled finish – Chatham Historic Dockyard

![Trans-European Stone logo](www.t-estone.co.uk)

Contact
Alan Gayle
t: 07939 801722
alan@t-estone.co.uk

Dirk Eeckhout
00 32 471 221 016
dirk@t-estone.co.uk

Web
www.t-estone.co.uk

Address
Trans-European Stone Ltd
4th Floor
Park House
22 Park Street
Croydon CR0 1YE

Operational area
UK

Country of manufacture
Belgium

Trans-European Stone Ltd

Natural stone supplier

Trans-European Stone supplies the construction industry with natural stone paving and street furniture.
The company is the UK commercial agent for Belgian Blue limestone from Pierre Bleue Belge, one of Europe's largest quarry operators.

Technical support

Trans-European Stone offers specification advice and technical support for Belgian Blue to architects, contractors and developers. Samples stocked in the UK are available on request.

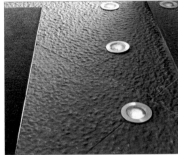
Belgian Blue limestone paving with spuntato finish

Belgian Blue paving – Mercer's Yard, London

Belgian Blue limestone table top with antique finish

Belgian Blue limestone external bench

Belgian Blue limestone paving with tumbled finish

Belgian Blue limestone external benches with frosted finish – University College London

Contact
Sales
t: 01629 636500
f: 01629 636425
sales@derbyaggs.com

Web
www.derbyshireaggregates.com

Addresses
Derbyshire Specialist Aggregates
Arbor Low Works
Long Rake
Youlgreave
Bakewell DE45 1JS

South Wales Depot
Wyndlam Close
Brackla Industrial Estate
Bridgend CF31 2AN

North Wales Depot
Port Penrhyn
Bangor LL57 4HN

Derbyshire Specialist Aggregates

Resin bound, bonded, decorative and landscape aggregates

Derbyshire Specialist Aggregates has supplied aggregate materials to trade and private customers throughout the world since 1984. The company holds decorative landscape, resin-bonded and dashing aggregates in stock, supplying the industrial, pre-cast concrete, filtration, and roofing sectors, as well aggregates and rock salt for adverse weather conditions.

• **Production and material selection**
Derbyshire Specialist Aggregates' investment in production facilities means that grades and mixes can be produced to meet exact specifications. Many products are washed and screened at least twice as part of the blending process to create the colours and textures available. Around 20,000 tonnes are held in stock, enabling instant availability and consistency of grade and colour.

• **Service and technical support**
The customer service and technical support team can advise on the best aggregate for the specification and can also provide quantity calculations. A bespoke matching service is also offered as well as site visits if required. Products can be supplied in handy sample boxes containing 18 different product types, or as a sample pallet.

Decorative landscaping

Resin bound aggregates

Resin bound tree pit

Decorative landscaping

Dashing

Contact
UK freefone: 0800 376 8377
t: +353 (0) 53 914 3216
f: +353 (0) 53 914 1802
info@kentstainless.com

Web
www.kentstainless.com

Address
Kent Stainless (Wexford) Ltd
Ardcavan
Wexford
Republic of Ireland

Accreditation
ISO 9001:2008
ISO 14001:2004
OHSAS 18001:2007

Country of manufacture
Republic of Ireland

Additional entries
Heelproof ventilation access grilles ➤ 132
In-ground units ➤ 239
Wayfinding signage ➤ 262
Planters ➤ 383

Kent Stainless (Wexford) Ltd

Lift-assist manholes

Kent Stainless is a specialist stainless steel fabricator that offers a variety of external lift-assist manholes for streetscapes and heavy loading areas.
• **Concrete/paving top manholes**
Concrete/paving top versions include *Kent Hinged Solo Paver*, *Kent Hinged Multi Paver*, and *Kent Paver Man Access*.
• **Solid top manholes**
Solid top versions include *Kent Hinged Solo Chequer*, *Kent Hinged Multi Chequer*, and *Kent Chequer Man Access*.
Kent's manholes can be used where it needs to be opened frequently; where a single operator may arrive on site and requires easy access; and where maintenance personnel may not have access to specialised lifting equipment.
The manholes are equipped with a robust stainless steel hinge; have keying-in mesh to allow block adhesion with epoxy mortar; and have Kent lift-assist mechanical struts to allow them to be opened with a force compliant with manual handling regulations.

Accreditation
Manholes are manufactured in accordance with BS EN 124 loading. Clients can opt for B125, C250 or D400 loading class.

Kent Hinged Multi Paver – St Barts Hospital, London

Kent Hinged Multi Chequer – Pfizer, Cork

Kent Hinged Solo Paver – Lusail City, Qatar

Kent Paver Man Access – Lusail City, Qatar

Kent Stainless (Wexford) Ltd

Heelproof ventilation access grilles

Kent Stainless is a specialist stainless steel fabricator that manufactures ventilation grilles for public realms projects and streetscapes.

Five different ventilation grilles are produced: the *Solo Vent Grille*, *Hinged Solo Vent Grille*, *Multi Vent Grille*, *Hinged Multi Vent Grille* and the *Man Access Vent Grille*. All ventilation grilles are manufactured in accordance with the FACTA standards. Any radius can be supplied.

Projects include variations of ventilation grilles for Lusail City, Qatar and Regents Place, London.

D400 Multi Vent Grille – Regents Place, London

Multi Vent Grille – Regents Place, London

Multi Vent Grille – Lusail City, Qatar

Contact
UK freefone: 0800 376 8377
t: +353 (0) 53 914 3216
f: +353 (0) 53 914 1802
info@kentstainless.com

Web
www.kentstainless.com

Address
Kent Stainless (Wexford) Ltd
Ardcavan
Wexford
Republic of Ireland

Accreditation
ISO 9001:2008, ISO 14001:2004,
OHSAS 18001:2007

Additional entries
Lift-assist manholes ➤ 131
In-ground units ➤ 239
Wayfinding signage ➤ 262
Planters ➤ 383

Sportsmark™ Group Ltd

Road studs and markings

Sportsmark™ Group provides reflective and non-reflective road studs, road marking paint and preformed road markings. The company also provides road and court marking services.

• **Pedestrian crossing studs**
100mm square pedestrian studs are available in plain and profiled 'as cast' aluminium, rough-ground stainless steel or polished stainless steel.

• **Demarcation studs**
Demarcation studs are produced in brass or stainless steel, with a high quality machine finish. These studs can be used to delineate walkways, parking bays and other areas.

• **Anti-social studs**
Also available in brass or stainless steel, anti-social studs have a protruding design and are used to discourage unwanted skateboarding and other activities that might be considered anti-social.

• **Road markings**
Preformed thermoplastic road markings are available in a wide range of colours. They are supplied in rolls of lines or sheets, or can be cut to make different shapes and symbols.

• **Marking paint**
Waterborne and solvent-based road marking paints are available, along with specialist paints for marking synthetic sports surfaces.

Brass demarcation studs

Aluminium road studs

Thermoplastic road marking being laid on a car park

Anti-social studs

Contact
Julie Brewster (sales)
t: 01635 867537
f: 01635 864588
julie@sportsmark.net

Mike Pocklington (technical)
t: 01635 867537
f: 01635 864588
mike@sportsmark.net

Web
www.sportsmark.net

Address
Sportsmark™ Group Ltd
18 St Georges Place
Semington
Trowbridge BA14 6GB

Additional entries
Sports equipment ➤ 496

Steintec®

Early trafficking mortars

Steintec® mortars have been developed to meet the requirements of pavement and carriageway construction where natural stone or concrete slabs, kerbs or setts are used. They are fully compliant with the performance criteria in BS 7533.

• **tuffset G early trafficking mortar**
tuffset G is a specialist mortar that allows early trafficking after three hours, while achieving full BS 7533 compliance. It can be used with *tuffgrit* aggregate for high-performance bedding with early strength gain, on its own as a high adhesive bond priming mortar, or as a low-shrinkage jointing slurry grout.

Projects

tuffset G products have been used in a number of high profile projects around the world.
• Hull – regeneration of the town ahead of its 2017 European City of Culture status.
• Doha, Qatar – stadia construction and preparations for FIFA World Cup 2022.
• London – The O2 Arena, The Shard, Blackfriars Bridge, One Tower Bridge and Ealing Broadway Shopping Centre. Where early heavy trafficking and time critical repairs were required, *tuffset G* kept traffic and people moving soon after installation.

Hull European City of Culture 2017, Britain's biggest paving project at 40,000m²

Blackfriars Bridge, London

Doha, Qatar

The Shard, London

Greenwich Market, London

Ealing Broadway Shopping Centre

One Tower Bridge, London

Steintec®

Specialist mortars for pavement construction

Steintec® mortars have been developed to meet the requirements of pavement and carriageway construction using all natural stone and concrete products, kerbs, setts and slabs.

All Steintec® mortars are fully compliant with the performance criteria stated in BS 7533.

• **tuffbed 2-pack bedding mortar**
tuffbed 2-pack is a high-performance bedding mortar that has a low carbon footprint, giving economy in both financial and ecological terms. It comprises a natural, polymer and additive-free 2-pack dry mortar, mixed with *tuffgrit* aggregate.

• **tuffbond high-adhesion priming mortar**
tuffbond high-adhesion priming mortar ensures that paving is properly bonded to a bedding layer beneath. It complies with all parts of BS 7533 for heavily trafficked pavement construction.

• **tufftop jointing mortar**
tufftop is a high-performance, free-flowing grout slurry suitable for natural stone and modular paving. It is quick to apply and easy to clean. Its natural ingredients prevent the shrinkage problems associated with polymer additives.

• **Other products**
WEISS® cleaning and protection products are suitable for natural stone and modular paving.

Three Quays, London

Broadgate Circle, London

Glasshouse Street, London

Longfield Avenue, Ealing Broadway

WEISS®

Paving cleaning and protection

WEISS® pavement cleaning and protection products are supplied by Steintec®. Products are economical, easy to apply and environmentally friendly, and can be used on all types of natural stone and modular paving.

• **Cleaning products**
The use of a pH neutral, biodegradable cleaning agent such as *WEISS® Grundreiniger*, facilitates gentle but effective cleaning while protecting the environment, reducing costs and extending the life of the pavement.

• **Protection products**
The application of a water-based penetrating impregnator protects the surface against staining by forming a transparent barrier beneath the pavement surface.

All types of natural stone and pre-cast concrete paving can be effectively protected using this system.

• **Applications**
Applications include pre-construction protection, post-construction cleaning, cement stain removal, long-term protection, colour enhancement, general cleaning, maintenance cleaning and protection, deep oil stain removal, biological stain removal and rust removal.

Cleaning and protection products for natural stone and modular paving

Contact
Joe Meanley
t: 01902 450950
f: 01902 451050
enquiries@hydronpc.co.uk

Web
www.hydronpc.co.uk

Address
Hydron Protective Coatings Ltd
Unit 7, Phoenix Road Industrial Estate
Phoenix Road
Wednesfield
Wolverhampton WV11 3PX

Accreditation
ISO 9001:2000
National Building Specification (NBS)

Affiliations
Anti-Graffiti Association (AGA)

Operational area
UK

Nu-Cryl® WRS Colour Enhancer

Hydron Protective Coatings

Protective coatings

Hydron manufactures and supplies high performance coating systems to major companies in all industries, and local and central government.

- **Anti-graffiti coatings**
Nu-Cryl® AG is a clear, hydrophobic anti-graffiti coating that provides protection against solvents, chemicals, grease, oil, dirt and weather damage. It does not noticeably change the appearance of the substrate and still allows it to breathe.
Nu-Guard® AG Clear is a one-coat, single pack external anti-graffiti coating. Graffiti is removed using only water.
Nu-Guard® AG Colour is a one-coat, single pack anti-graffiti coating that is available in any colour. Graffiti is removed using only water.

- **Floor coating**
Nu-Cryl® WRS EXTRA is an oil and water resistant coating for dense exterior floor surfaces such as pedestrian areas, car parks and stone paving. It is suitable for areas subjected to heavy wear. It resists oil penetration and creates a non-stick surface that enables the easy removal of gum.
Nu-Cryl® WRS Colour Enhancer is a water-based modified polysiloxane which provides oil and water repellent properties and lifts the true colour of the substrate.

- **Waterproofing coating**
Nu-Cryl® WRS is a super-hydrophobic water repellent treatment. It is suitable for porous walls and facades and prevents frost damage and organic growth. It also protects against soiling and the effects of acid rain.

- **Energy-saving coatings**
Nu-Guard® NRG internal and external energy-saving coatings minimise heat loss and reduce energy bills in domestic, commercial and industrial buildings. They are available in clear or coloured versions, and provide weather and stain resistance and water repellency.

- **Masonry/anti-carbonation coatings**
Nu-Guard® Anti-Carbonation Coating is a water-based paint that provides 10 years of weather resistance for general masonry and concrete surfaces. It protects against attack from carbon dioxide, airborne chlorides, acid rain and weathering, while maintaining breathability. It is available in clear or coloured versions.
Nu-Guard® Clear AC is a transparent anti-carbonation coating, based upon acrylic resins. It protects concrete and masonry against attack from carbon dioxide and airborne chlorides.
Nu-Guard® WB Masonry Coating is a durable, water-based coating for general exterior masonry surfaces. It is weather resistant and breathable, and prevents the build up of dirt, moss and algae.
Nu-Guard® SR Masonry Coating is a water-based silicone resin coating for protecting exterior masonry in harsh environments. It is hydrophobic and provides a decorative, weather-resistant barrier with self-cleaning properties.

Nu-Cryl® WRS – Napp Pharmaceuticals

Nu-Cryl® AG – Starbucks

Nu-Guard® SR masonry coating

Nu-Guard® NRG Colour energy-saving coating

Nu-Guard® AC – Civic Centre MSCP

Magma Safety Products Ltd

Anti-slip surfaces

Magma manufactures anti-slip flooring products.
Alispar™ high-visibility nosings and treads are
used for heavy foot traffic on external stairs.
Magmatac™ is a flexible, moulded tactile panel,
alerting visually impaired pedestrians to hazards.
It will bond to asphalt, concrete and steel.
Magma Safety Panels™ have a near-diamond hard
aggregate bonded into the wearing surface.
Decksafe® gives slip resistance to timber decking.
MagmaStrip™ are carborundum inserts for
pre-cast concrete, terrazzo and timber steps.
Custom-made products can also be provided.

Magma Safety Panels™ on a railway platform

Contact
Sales
t: 01223 836643
f: 01223 834648
info@magmasafety.co.uk

Web
www.magmasafety.co.uk

Address
Magma Safety Products Ltd
Unit 1, Sawston Park
London Road
Pampisford
Cambridge CB22 3EE

Affiliations
Link-up

Magmatac™ will mould to most surface undulations

MagmaStrip™ carborundum inserts in stone

Alispar™ on a railway footbridge

Magma Safety Panels™ on a disabled access ramp

MagmaStrip™ carborundum inserts between tiles

DeckSafe® makes timber decking slip resistant

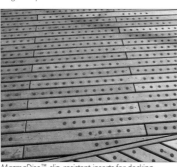

MagmaDisc™ slip-resistant inserts for decking

Alispar™ used for heavy foot traffic on external stairs

Magma Safety Panels™ on a cycleway

Contact
Wendy Sykes (sales)
Simon Newby (technical)
t: 01484 606416
f: 01484 608763
enquiries@ctsbridges.co.uk

Web
www.ctsbridges.co.uk

Address
CTS Bridges Ltd
Abbey Road, Shepley, Huddersfield HD8 8BX

Accreditation
ISO 9001:2008; Constructionline; FSC Chain of
Custody; CHAS

Affiliations
Register of Qualified Steelwork Contractors (RQSC)
Timber Research & Development Association
(TRADA)

Additional entries
Bridges ➤ 156

CTS Bridges Ltd

Decking and landscape structures

Over 25 years, CTS has built up expertise in the
design and manufacture of bespoke structures.
These range from very simple forms to highly
elaborate one-off designs.
Incorporating the company's *Hi-Grip Excel™*
non-slip decking into the structures means that
they are safe for use by the general public.
CTS offers a design, build and installation service
or can supply components for others to fit on
site. The company employs its own experienced
installation teams that operate nationwide.

Fishing platforms – Wixams

Curved boardwalk – Wixams

Timber steps – Kirkstall Brewery, Leeds

Hardwood *Hi-Grip Excel™* decking – Bradford

Bespoke spiral ramp – Savill Gardens

Hardwood boardwalk – Clapham Common

Hi-Grip Excel™ on bridge and walkway – Aberfeldy

Ekki hardwood boardwalk – Aberdeen

Hi-Grip Excel™ softwood non-slip decking

Hi-Grip Excel™ Ekki hardwood non-slip decking

Contact
t: 01283 722588
info@marleyeternit.co.uk

Web
www.marleyeternit.co.uk

Address
Marley Eternit Ltd
Lichfield Road
Branston
Burton-on-Trent DE14 3HD

Marley Eternit Ltd

Anti-slip timber deck boards: JB Antislip Plus® and JB CitiDeck®

Marley Eternit Ltd structural timber decking and associated products are designed for commercial and domestic applications.

JB Antislip Plus® maintains the natural beauty of a timber deck while providing a durable and slip-resistant surface. It provides enhanced grip where there is a high level of pedestrian traffic, making it suitable for all public access areas including decks, bridges and boardwalks.

JB CitiDeck® is a smooth deckboard with enhanced grip. It is particularly suited to urban environments and inclusive access. The smooth board gives a level surface for wheelchair users and the less able. It is also very easy to keep clean as it does not harbour dirt.

A step profile is available for use with *JB CitiDeck®* and *JB Antislip Plus®* boards. This has a wide yellow anti-slip strip for ease of visibility and secure footing.

Composition and manufacture

Deck boards are manufactured from selected joinery grade European Redwood.

JB Antislip Plus® incorporates resin-based aggregate inserts, injected into specially formed grooves in the deck board. Castellated or smooth profiles are available.

JB CitiDeck® uses a less abrasive grit for a more even surface.

JB Antislip Plus® and *JB CitiDeck®* are available with a choice of two or three inserts and in a variety of colours for highlighting changes in surface level.

• **Environmental considerations**
Deck boards are supplied with full chain of custody and are either FSC or PEFC accredited.

Finish and appearance

JB Antislip Plus® and *JB CitiDeck®* deck boards will season and mature to a silver grey colour.
All decking is given a preservative treatment. For Use Class 3, *MicroPro®*, a clear preservative treatment is used, while *Naturewood®* is used for Use Class 4. All decking has a 25 year guarantee.

Accreditation

Both *JB Antislip Plus®* and *JB CitiDeck®* have been independently tested by the Health & Safety Laboratory (HSL) using the Stanley Pendulum Test (the operation and calibration of which are described in BS 7976:2002-1–3) operated to the current issue of the UKSRG (UK Slip Resistance Group) guidelines (Issue 3, 2005). Both deck boards significantly exceed the minimum required classification for 'low potential for slip'.

Technical support

An experienced technical support team works with clients to discuss their requirements and help them find the best solution.

JB Antislip Plus® Smooth profile – Oxford Brookes

JB CitiDeck® on balconies

JB Antislip Plus® Castellated – BeWILDerwood Park

JB CitiDeck® on a roof terrace

JB CitiDeck® – Hilton Garden Inn

JB Antislip Plus® Castellated – Nutwell Boardwalk

JB Antislip Plus® Classic – Canary Wharf

Contact
t: 0151 495 3111 (Cheshire)
t: 020 8150 8055 (West London)
enquiries@silvatimber.co.uk

Web
www.silvatimber.co.uk

Address
Silva Timber Products Ltd
Unit 4, Albright Road
Widnes WA8 8FY

Unit 7, Skyport Drive
Skyport Trade Park
Harmondsworth UB7 0LB

Accreditation
FSC, PEFC

Affiliations
TRADA, Timber Decking & Cladding Association,
Timber Trade Federation, Cedar Shake & Shingle
Bureau

Additional entries
Timber fencing and screens ➤ 192

Silva Timber Products Ltd

Timber decking and cladding

Silva Timber is one of the UK's leading experts for specialist decking, and also offers cladding, fencing, slatted screens, woodcare and finishing. A variety of timber species is offered that vary in texture, grain patterns and colour palettes to suit individual tastes, including western red cedar, Siberian larch, ipé, yellow balau, and lesser known species such as mandioqueira.
Products are sourced from the world's most reputable primary sawmills, meaning that stock consistently exceeds grading rules. Silva only uses suppliers that conform to the strict environmental standards, sourcing timber harvested legally and sustainably from independently certified forests. The vast majority of the product range conforms to PEFC and FSC certification.

Technical support

Silva Timber provides landscape professionals with knowledgeable advice when they specify, so that clients get the best results from their projects. Articles and installation guides are also available on the company's website.

Projects

Traditional and contemporary projects have included commercial developments, residential properties, eco-tourism resorts, hotels, marinas and award-winning gardens.

Western red cedar decking

Siberian larch decking

Garapa decking

Mandioqueira decking

Western red cedar decking

Ipé decking

Western red shingles for garden building

Yellow balau decking

Slatted screen deck

Contact
Katherine Lorek-Wallace (Sales)
t: 0333 202 6800
f: 01773 533862
plaswoodsales@bpipoly.com

Web
www.plaswoodgroup.com

Address
BPI Recycled Products
College Road
Dumfries DG2 0BU

Accreditation
ISO 9001:2008
ISO 14001:2004
OHSAS 18001:2007

Affiliations
Constructionline

BPI Recycled Products

Plaswood boardwalks and decking

Plaswood recycled plastic lumber from BPI Recycled Products is suitable for use in structures such as boardwalks, decking and jetties that are located in wet and harsh environments. *Plaswood* will not rot, splinter, crack or degrade with age and, unlike conventional wooden decking, it requires no annual maintenance, staining or painting. *Plaswood* will not leach chemicals into the environment and can be used as an environmentally supportive direct substitute for wood, concrete or steel.
Plaswood is 100% recycled and fully recyclable.

Cyclepath boardwalk – Sandgrene

Plaswood boardwalk

Plaswood boardwalk – Aberdeenshire

Plaswood decking

Plaswood bridge

Plaswood boardwalk

Plaswood boardwalk – Sandgrene

Plaswood recycled plastic decking

QUALITY
RECYCLED PRODUCTS

Contact
Michael Janes (Sales)
t: 029 2086 4095
m: 07745 189022
mike@goplastic.co.uk

Sarah Mitchell
(Marketing and general enquiries)
t: 01920 469926
m: 07887 528434
sarah@goplastic.co.uk

Web
www.goplastic.co.uk

Address
GoPlastic Ltd
Waverley
40 St Martins Road
Caerphilly CF83 1EJ

Accreditation
Constructionline

CPD
The economic value of recycled products

Operational area
UK

Additional entries
Recycled plastic fencing ➤ 189
Recycled plastic bollards ➤ 234
Recycled plastic seating ➤ 332

GoPlastic Ltd

Recycled plastic profiles for decks, boardwalks, jetties and bridges

GoPlastic Ltd specialises in recycled plastic products made from *Govaplast®*, a high-quality, solid plastic profile that is graffiti and vandal resistant.
Govaplast® requires no maintenance or treatments, and will not crack, rot or shrink. It contains a UV stabiliser with an expected life span of 40+ years.

Govaplast® recycled plastic decking – The Rock Shopping Centre, Manchester

Govaplast® recycled plastic walkway

Boards can be laid either textured or smooth side up

Govaplast® recycled plastic bridge

Govaplast® decking and fencing

Govaplast® recycled plastic bridge

Govadeck® decking boards

Govadeck® decking boards

Contact
t: 0800 849 6339
f: 01992 561385
decking@hoppings.co.uk

Web
www.qualitydecking.co.uk

Address
Hoppings Softwood Products plc
The Woodyard
Epping Road
Epping CM16 6TT

Accreditation
FSC, PEFC, ISO 9001:2008

Affiliations
Timber Decking & Cladding Association
Wood Preservation Association
Timber Trade Federation

Additional entries
Anti-slip decking ➤ 145
Q-Garden treated pine screening ➤ 190

Hoppings Softwood Products

Q-Shades decking

Hoppings Softwood Products manufactures the *Q-Shades* colour-washed decking range. *Q-Shades* decking is pre-stained with a transparent colour wash prior to the application of a tanalith preservative treatment. The resultant shades allow the wood grain to show through and have long-term preservative protection built-in. *Q-Shades* decking is available in Pebble Grey or Autumn Brown, or in Black Peat to order. The standard *Q-Deck* 15-year warranty applies to *Q-Shades* decking.

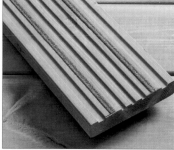
Q-Shades slip-resistant decking – Pebble Grey

Q-Shades decking – Pebble Grey

Q-Shades decking – Autumn Brown

Q-Shades slip-resistant decking – Autumn Brown

Q-Shades Canterbury decking – Pebble Grey

GRiP®
slip resistant decking

Contact
t: 0800 849 6339
f: 01992 561385
decking@hoppings.co.uk

Web
www.qualitydecking.co.uk

Address
Hoppings Softwood Products plc
The Woodyard
Epping Road
Epping CM16 6TT

Accreditation
FSC, PEFC, ISO 9001:2008

Affiliations
Timber Decking & Cladding Association
Wood Preservation Association
Timber Trade Federation
Wood for Good

Additional entries
Q-Shades decking ➤ 144
Q-Garden treated pine screening ➤ 190

Hoppings Softwood Products

Anti-slip decking

Q-Grip slip-resistant decking is available in a smooth *York* profile, grooved *Canterbury* profile, grooved *Bangkirai* hardwood profile, or can be created bespoke in different sizes or timber. The grooved *Canterbury* profile is also available pre-stained with a transparent colour wash, referred to as *Q-Shades Slip Resistant Canterbury* decking. Shades: Pebble Grey; Autumn Brown. *Q-Grip Strip* anti-slip decking inserts can be retrofitted to standard pressure-treated *Q-Deck York* and *Canterbury* decking, or within new grooves applied to existing decking.

Q-Grip Bangkirai Slip Resistant hardwood decking

Q-Grip strips in *Q-Deck York* decking

Q-Grip Bangkirai Slip Resistant hardwood decking

Bespoke *Q-Grip* – 2012 Olympic Park, London

Q-Shades Canterbury Slip Resistant decking – Autumn Brown

Q-Grip York slip-resistant decking

Q-Grip York slip-resistant decking

Q-Shades Canterbury Slip Resistant decking – Pebble Grey

Q-Shades Slip Resistant decking – Autumn Brown

Q-Shades Slip Resistant decking – Pebble Grey

Contact
Neale Brewster
t: 0330 119 3119
info@howarth-timber.co.uk

Web
www.howarth-timber.co.uk

Address
Howarth Timber Group Ltd
Prince Edward Works
Pontefract Lane
Cross Green
Leeds LS9 0RA

Accreditation
Chain of Custody (selected products)

Operational area
UK

Howarth Timber

Trex® Transcend composite decking

Trex® Transcend composite decking is used to create attractive, durable decks for residential and commercial applications. *Trex®* decking is a low maintenance system that will not fade, split or rot, and does not require oiling or painting.

Composition and manufacture
Composite boards are made using 95% recycled materials, including wood and plastic, that is bound and processed to resemble natural timber.

Finish
Decking has a high-definition satin finish with distinctive wood grain patterns in four rich earth tones.

Dimensions
Decking boards: 25mm thick x 140mm wide with the option of 3.66m or 4.88m lengths.
Fascias: 19mm x 286mm x 3.66m.
Balusters: 35mm x 35mm x 924mm.

Installation
Trex® decking is quick and simple to install. Grooved boards have a screwless finish giving a smooth and uninterrupted deck surface.

Warranties
- 25-year limited residential warranty.
- 10-year limited commercial warranty.

Trex® Transcend outdoor dining area in Island Mist

Trex® Transcend multi-level decking

Trex® Transcend decking in outdoor seating area

Trex® Transcend decking in Tiki Torch

Timber decking

Trex® Transcend multi-level decking

Kinley Systems Ltd

Decking and paving

Kinley Systems offers a range of composite decking and porcelain paving tiles.

• Terrafina decking boards

Terrafina decking boards are made from a wood polymer composite that provides long-lasting stability, durability and aesthetic appearance. The boards have a hard-wearing and contemporary finish and can resolve the maintenance and performance issues that are associated with natural timber.

The clip fitting design means that virtually no screws are required for installation.

Terrafina has good non-slip and non-combustible properties, making it ideal for use in schools, restaurants and other public areas, as well as leisure and residential developments.

The composite substructure of *Terrafina* provides a fixing system that requires virtually no screws. This makes the decking faster to install and virtually maintenance free.

As an almost inert product, the deck board will not split, warp, sustain the growth of algae, rot or need any extensive maintenance.

• Atria paving tiles

Atria porcelain paving tiles are suitable for external and internal use. Seven styles and a number of colour variations are available. As well as having attractive aesthetics, the external tiles achieve high anti-slip ratings, are frost resistant and easy to install.

Atria tiles are available in a 20mm thickness for external use and a 10mm thickness for internal use, allowing matching flooring on a balcony or terrace application to be created.

The *Atria* range includes a large number of accessory parts for step areas and edges.

• Support pedestals

Complementary adjustable pedestal systems, *VersiJack®* and *SpiraPave®*, can be used to provide adjustment from 12mm up to over 1m.

Terrafina decking – Dauntsey's School, Devizes

Terrafina decking – private residence, Hampshire

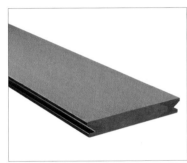
Terrafina Excel decking board

Atria paving tiles – Alwyns Terrace, Ireland

Terrafina Ultra decking board

Contact

t: 01580 830688
sales@kinley.co.uk

Web
www.kinley.co.uk

Address
Kinley Systems Ltd
Northpoint
Compass Park
Staplecross TN32 5BS

Operational area
UK, Europe

Additional entries
Landscape edging: ExcelEdge® ➤ 91
Perimeta planter systems ➤ 383

VersiJack® decking and paving support pedestal

Spirapave® decking and paving support pedestal

Atria tiles on *Spirapave®* supports

Atria paving tiles

![ROUND WOOD of Mayfield]

Contact
t: 01435 867072
f: 01435 864708
sales@roundwood.com

Web
www.roundwood.com

Address
Round Wood of Mayfield Ltd
Round Wood
Newick Lane
Mayfield
East Sussex TN20 6RG

Operational area
Europe

Additional entries
Oak-framed buildings ➤ 401

Round Wood of Mayfield Ltd

Hardwood timber decking

Round Wood of Mayfield specialises in high-quality, attractive hardwood decking boards. Several varieties are offered, along with a selection of fixings and accessories.

• Decking
Ipe, an extremely dense South American timber, is one of the toughest available for the production of garden decking boards. It can provide 100 years of use without treatment.
Balau is a durable hardwood native to Asia, where it is widely used in construction. Its light-to-mid brown and sandy red/orange colours have made it popular in the UK.
Oak decking blends into any English garden, and complements the oak-framed buildings that Round Wood also supplies. It provides many years of service and will weather gently.
Heveatech engineered hardwood decking boards are cut from FSC-certified rubber trees that have reached the end of their useful life. They are cut into thin layers, bonded under extreme compression and finished with a solid veneer.

• Fastenings and balustrade
Round Wood exclusively supplies *ArchiDeck* and *Sharkstooth* hidden fastenings in the UK.
Balau, ipe and oak hardwood decking components can be combined to provide a matching balustrade for garden decks.

Hardwood decking with rendered, raised beds

Slate pond in Balau deck

Raised deck in engineered *Heveatech* boards

Reeded decking in Balau tropical hardwood

Multi-level roof deck in Balau

Ipe hardwood deck, integrated lighting, steel seating

Contact
The Sales Team
t: 01254 685185
f: 01254 671237
sales@woodscape.co.uk

Web
www.woodscape.co.uk

Address
Woodscape Ltd
1 Sett End Road West
Shadsworth Business Park
Blackburn BB1 2QJ

Accreditation
ISO 9001:2008
FSC, PEFC and FPCC certification
Approved supplier to Tesco

Additional entries
Co-ordinated street furniture ➤ 304
Hardwood seating ➤ 342
Landscape structures ➤ 407

Woodscape Ltd

Hardwood decking, raised decks and boardwalks

Woodscape designs and manufactures decking, boardwalks and ramps in marine-grade, naturally durable hardwoods. Deck boards are available in grooved or planed profiles, typically measuring 25mm thick by 145mm wide in random lengths. Other profiles and dimensions can be produced, and carborundum inserts can be added to provide a slip-resistant surface.

Composition and manufacture
Woodscape's structures and bespoke designs can be supplied with FSC, PEFC or FPCC Chain of Custody certification.
150mm cross-sections have a life expectancy of more than 100 years in ground contact.

Design services
An in-house team offers a design and build service. They draw on years of experience of working with the world's most durable timbers to make striking timber engineered components.

Sitework
Most structures are supplied in kit form for on-site assembly, including pre-assembled hidden fix deck panels.

Hardwood timber raised boardwalk

Hardwood timber raised boardwalk

Hardwood timber decking

Marine-grade hardwood timber boardwalk

Marine-grade hardwood timber decking and handrail

Hardwood timber decking – Bicester designer outlet

Bespoke curved hardwood timber decking – private residential project, Alfreton, Hampshire

Contact
t: 01726 844616
info@gripsure.co.uk

Web
www.gripsure.co.uk

Address
Gripsure UK Ltd
Unit 2, Rockhill Business Park
Bugle
St Austell PL26 8RA

Affiliations
Timber Research and Development Association
(TRADA)
Timber Decking and Cladding Association (TDCA)

CPD
How to specify timber decking

Kevin Girdler
t: 01726 844616
kevin@gripsure.co.uk

Gripsure UK Ltd

Non-slip timber decking

Gripsure manufactures and supplies a wide range of slip-resistant decking boards. Products are suitable for many applications, including balconies, boardwalks, public decking areas and footbridges, or anywhere that safety is a priority.

Traditional timber decking is a popular choice for specifiers and landscapers due to its natural appearance, sustainability and design flexibility, but it can be dangerously slippery, especially in wet weather.

Decking is available in C16 or C24 visually graded boards and has a 10-year non-slip performance warranty.

Composition and manufacture

Gripsure decking is made from FSC® certified Vth's grade Scandinavian redwood pressure-treated to Use Class 3 as a minimum, with a 15 year 'in service' life. Non-slip inserts are formed by injecting liquid resin into the grooved surface of the timber deck board, and then dressing the resin with a highly abrasive-resistant aggregate.

Design services

Gripsure's innovative design and supply service enables it to offer non-slip solutions to any potential project that requires non-slip decking.

Gripsure Aquadeck® – Titanic Spa, W Yorkshire

Thermowood Ash boardwalk with non-slip strips

Gripsure Pro decking used for balconies

Contact
Mike Wilderink
t: 020 8977 0820
f: 020 8977 0825
sales@outdoordeck.co.uk

Web
www.outdoordeck.co.uk

Address
The Outdoor Deck Company
Unit 6, Teddington Business Park
Station Road
Teddington TW11 9BQ

Affiliations
Timber Research and Development Association
(TRADA)
Royal Institute of British Architects (RIBA)
National Building Specification (NBS)

Additional entries
Outdoor floor tiles ➤ 117
Paving support pedestals ➤ 152

The Outdoor Deck Company

Timber decking

The Outdoor Deck Company is one of the largest installers of timber decking in the UK.
• Softwood and hardwood decking
The company is the sole importer of the *DuraPine®* range of Grade 1 Southern Yellow pine DSS (dense select structural), and the *DuraDeck®* range of premium grade hardwoods.
Outdoor Deck can meet a full range of decking requirements, and can undertake associated timber engineering such as pergolas, gazebos, seating and fencing, as well as groundworks.

Composition and manufacture

DuraPine® timbers are Grade 1, and are pressure treated to 98% penetration levels, the highest available in the pine sector. All timbers are kiln-dried before and, more importantly, after treatment. This stabilises the timbers, and reduces shrinkage, warping and twisting.
DuraDeck® is a range of some of the best grade hardwoods available in the UK. Timbers are hand selected and graded, and kiln-dried.
Both *DuraPine®* and *DuraDeck®* are warranted against rot and insect decay for a minimum of 25 years, even in conditions with direct and permanent water and/or ground contact.

Children's play area – East Village, London

Completed commercial roof terrace – London

Wood composite decking with hidden fixings

FSC hardwood decking to large communal area

OSC Sales Ltd

Self-drilling screws

OSC fasteners are designed to make light work of time-consuming landscaping and building tasks.

• Self-drilling wood screws

Carpenters Mate® is the UK's original self-drilling wood screw. Strong and reliable, proven to stand the test of time even in the harshest of outdoor environments, the range includes carbon steel and stainless steel self-drilling screws for timber and composite decks and landscape structures.

• Hidden deck fastening system

CAMO is a hidden deck fastening system for fastening softwood, hardwood, composite and PVC hybrid decking. Finished decks are totally secure with no visible screw holes.

• Industrial strength wood fasteners

FastenMaster are precision-engineered industrial-strength fasteners for wooden and composite structures and decks. They are heat-treated and anti-corrosion coated for greater durability.

• Electrical fastening applications

Orbix self-drilling screws are designed for electrical applications, require no washers or pre-drilling and do not snag.

Procurement

Products can be purchased from the OSC website or through a UK-wide network of more than 800 distributors and merchants.

Contact

Enquiries and free samples
t: 0800 652 2203
f: 0845 241 9863
sales@oscsales.com

Web

www.oscsales.co.uk

Address

OSC Sales Ltd
The Forge
Wheelers Lane
Linton ME17 4BN

Carpenters Mate® coloured head screws

FastenMaster TrapEase II composite deck screws

CAMO hidden decking fastening system

Carpenters Mate® hex head screws

Self-drilling screws for landscape walls

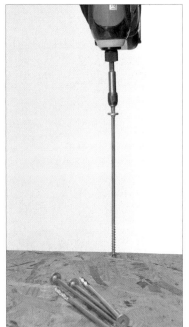

Carpenters Mate® flat head screws

Carpenters Mate® self-drilling screws

Orbix screws fastening metal cable tray

Contact

Mike Wilderink
t: 020 8614 0874
f: 020 8977 0825
sales@buzonuk.com

Web
www.buzonuk.com

Address
Buzon UK Ltd
Unit 6
Teddington Business Park
Station Road
Teddington TW11 9BQ

Affiliations
Royal Institute of British Architects (RIBA)
Timber Research and Development Association (TRADA)
National Building Specification (NBS)

Additional entries
Outdoor floor tiles ➤ 117
Timber decking ➤ 150

Buzon UK Ltd

Paving support pedestals

Buzon UK Ltd distributes the *Buzon* system of screwjack pedestals for constructing raised floors, external terraces and paved areas.
The system is used to support concrete and stone paving, as well as timber decking, industrial grating, temporary flooring and water features. All ranges have the same unique adjustment properties; each has substrate-specific benefits.
• **Design and cost performance benefits**
Benefits include: patented slope correction; superior drainage; speed of application; labour and material savings; ease of access; durability, stability and strength; flexible height and spacing; and ease of adjustment. Selected *DPH®* pedestals are fire-resistant.

Composition and manufacture

Buzon pedestals are made from 100% recycled materials in polypropylene, polyester fibre glass and clear polycarbonate, and have been tested to conform to safety, compression, traction and side-pull standards. Each pedestal is robust enough to support loads of over 1000kg.

Technical data

All *Buzon* pedestals comprise a round base on which a cylinder-type head is secured. By adjusting their positions, the required height can be fine-tuned to exact millimetre precision.

Adjustable pedestals ensure level surfaces at hotel

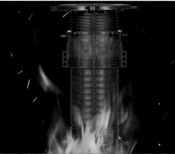
Selected *DPH®* pedestals are fire resistant

All services can be hidden, with easy access

Pedestal system supports concrete and stone paving

Four separation spacers give a joint between slabs

Contact

Sales and Technical Office
t: 0131 441 1255
f: 0131 441 4161
sales@langandfulton.co.uk

Web
www.langandfulton.co.uk

Address
Lang+Fulton
Unit 2b, Newbridge Industrial Estate
Newbridge, Edinburgh EH28 8PJ

Distribution
West Midlands

Accreditation
ISO 9001:2000

Additional entries
Louvred fences: Italia and Delta ➤ 160
Grating fences ➤ 162
Railings: Modena, Siena and Rimini ➤ 176
Gates ➤ 203
Bin stores, plant housings and compounds ➤ 398

Lang+Fulton

External floor gratings and treads

Lang+Fulton supplies high quality open mesh gratings, specialising in small heel-proof apertures and unique products for walkways, stairs, balconies, decking and ventilation.
- **Pressure-locked open mesh gratings**
Pressed (*PL*) and cross-pressed (*PLX* and *PLXE*) gratings are made entirely from flat bars. A wide range of apertures and bearing bars makes them suitable for all applications from pedestrian to extreme vehicle loading.
- **Stainless steel gratings**
Gratings can also be supplied in stainless steel.
- **Specialist gratings**
Barrot, designed for pedestrian comfort, has a wide bearing surface and anti-slip dimples.
Anti-Vertigo is a heel-proof, non-slip grating which is non-transparent. It is suitable for mezzanine or elevated floors and escape stairs.
- **Bespoke products**
All gratings are cut, shaped and framed to custom sizes, and supplied with fixings and supporting steelwork where required.

Finish and appearance
Products are hot-dip galvanised before optional polyester powder coating in any RAL colour.

Technical support
Lang+Fulton provides a full design service.

PL-55x11/40x2 pressed grating – Siemens Sustainable Cities Exhibition, The Crystal, London Docklands

PL-33x11/25x2 stair and DemiAlto balustrade

PLSS-33x33 stainless steel grating

Barrot grating manufactured from reversed U-profiles for pedestrian comfort – The Strand, London

PL-33x11/50x3 steel deck and post-free balustrade

Anti-Vertigo provides a total visual screen

PL-15x88/70x3 pressure locked grating – The Zig Zag Building, 70 Victoria St, London SW1

Contact
Peter Webster (UK sales and technical)
t: 01902 797110
sales@elefantgratings.com

Web
www.elefantgratings.com

Address
Elefant Gratings
Enterprise Drive
Four Ashes
Wolverhampton WV10 7DF

Additional entries
Plant housing and storage compounds ➤ 400

Elefant Gratings

External flooring: gratings and planks

Elefant Gratings specialises in the design, manufacture and supply of flat bar gratings and perforated planks. Applications range from walkways, balustrade infills, stair treads and landings, to screens, fencing, brise soleil, ventilation, vehicular grilles and balconies.

Composition and manufacture
Gratings are manufactured in carbon steel, stainless steel, Corten A and aluminium.
Planks are manufactured in carbon steel, stainless steel and aluminium.
All products are made according to current British Standards guidelines.

Finish and appearance
Carbon steel products are hot dip galvanised to BS EN 1461:2009 or polyester powder coated in standard RAL colours.
Stainless steel products are chemically cleaned to BS EN 2516:1997 and bead blasted.
Corten A products are self coloured.
Aluminium products are anodised.

Technical support
Elefant Gratings draws on extensive experience and product knowledge to find the best solution for each client's requirements.

Flat bar grating across an external flooring area

Flooring panels

Stair treads

Flat bar grating balustrade and flooring panels

Stair treads

Flat bar grating panels for a walkway and balustrade

Corten A steel grating panels

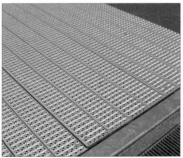

Perforated planks

Contact
Wendy Sykes (sales)
Simon Newby (technical)
t: 01484 606416
f: 01484 608763
enquiries@ctsbridges.co.uk

Web
www.ctsbridges.co.uk

Address
CTS Bridges Ltd
Abbey Road, Shepley
Huddersfield HD8 8BX

Accreditation
ISO 9001:2008; Constructionline; FSC Chain of Custody; CHAS

Affiliations
Register of Qualified Steelwork Contractors
Timber Research & Development Association

Additional entries
Decking and landscape structures ➤ 137

CTS Bridges Ltd

Bridges

CTS is one of the market leaders in the design, construction and installation of footbridges of all types and sizes.

Bridge types include pedestrian only, cycleways, equestrian and light vehicular access, all of which are designed and detailed to reflect their intended use and size, as well as the required aesthetic. The company offers a high-quality, nationwide service with involvement from inception to completion.

Composition and manufacture

Because CTS designs and manufactures in house, designs can be produced in all-timber, all-steel, all-FRP or a combination of materials. Products range from simple short-span bridges to bespoke long-span structures, and accurately match the budgetary restraint of individual schemes, thereby saving on costly separate consultancy fees.

Installation and maintenance

CTS offers an installation service for all of its bridges and structures. The team incorporates fully qualified personnel to ensure safe erection. The installations are planned by professionally qualified engineers and approved appointed persons, and installed with CTS's own qualified slinger banksmen and competent persons.

28x3.7m FSC softwood multi-span bridge   Steel and timber footbridge – Lincolnshire

19.3m Vierendeel cycle bridge – Seatown

Steel beam and parapet bridge – Elgin   Grade II listed Chinese timber bridge – Cambs   Vierendeel cycle bridge – Sefton   FSC-accredited softwood timber kit bridge

45x4m tied arch Vierendeel truss bridge – Bedford   Ornamental garden bridge – Isle of Man   151m cable stay bridge – Ebbw Vale

52m 7-span hardwood bridge – Cruden Bay, Aberdeen

46x3m bow arch cycle bridge – Swansea

Installation of bespoke truss bridge – New Islington, Manchester

Ekki hardwood bridge – Aberfeldy, Tower Hamlets

Bespoke steel bridge – Christchurch College, Oxford

Bespoke bridge, Piccadily Place – Manchester

Steel beam bridge – Dickens Heath

Contact
Chris Brammall
t: 01229 588580
chris@chrisbrammall.com

Web
www.chrisbrammall.com

Address
Chris Brammall Ltd
Low Mill Business Park
Morecambe Road
Ulverston
Cumbria LA12 9EE

Staff/turnover
20 people

Awards
Landscape Institute Awards 2012 – Winner

Additional entries
Bespoke architectural and sculptural metalwork
➤ 415
Sculpture ➤ 425

Chris Brammall Ltd

Bridges

Chris Brammall produces high quality, individual sculptural and architectural metalwork.

Projects
• Barnes Park bridge, Sunderland: 30m curved bridge/walkway with sculptural corten balustrade.
• Skelwith Bridge, Lake District National Park: mild steel and oak footbridge at Skelwith Falls.
• Staveley Footbridge, Lake District National Park: 18m footbridge and disabled ramp.
• White Moss bridge, Cumbria: oak, corten and mild steel bridge built on historic stone piers.

White Moss Bridge, Rydal, Cumbria

Barnes Park, Sunderland

Staveley Footbridge, Lake District National Park

Contact
Graham Howard
t: 01264 811600
info@sarumhardwood.co.uk

Web
www.sarumhardwood.co.uk

Address
Sarum Hardwood Structures Ltd
Unit 1B
Chilbolton Down Farm
Stockbridge SO20 6BU

Accreditation
ISO 9001:2000

Affiliations
Timber Research and Development Association (TRADA)

Operational area
England and Wales

Additional entries
N1 timber highway parapets ➤ 220

Sarum Hardwood Structures Ltd

Bridges

Sarum Hardwood Structures Ltd (SHS) has been constructing bridges and timber structures throughout England and Wales since the early 1980s. SHS also offers boardwalks, jetties, decking, marine timbers and highway parapets.
• **Bridges**
Bridges range from small kits to cable-stay structures up to 100m long. They can be designed for pedestrian, cycle, equestrian or light vehicular use. They can be supplied with grooved, slip-resistant decking in accordance with BD29/04 (Design Criteria for Footbridges). A choice of parapet styles is also available.

Composition and manufacture
SHS is able to offer designs based on a range of different materials to suit specific technical and environmental requirements. Bridges can be constructed from timber – usually hardwood – as well as steel and timber, and lightweight composites.
The natural appearance of timber makes it ideal for use in countryside applications where it blends harmoniously with its surroundings. Timber is procured from managed forests and from FSC certified sustainable sources.

Laminated timber bridge with *Type G* parapet

Hardwood timber truss bridge

Laminated timber footbridge – Chatham

FENCING

Metal panel fencing systems and railings — 160-180

- Panel and grating fencing systems
  Standard and proprietary perimeter fencing and railing systems for boundary demarcation and securing civic, commercial, retail, industrial and recreational facilities. Rigid weld mesh flat and profiled panel systems, steel grating fences and louvred screening systems.
- Zoological fencing systems.
- Decorative and bespoke architectural fences.
- Railings
  For commercial property, prestigious housing developments, schools, playgrounds, parks and private estates. Solid and hollow vertical bar railings; round tubular railings; steel palisade fencing; guardrails; bow top, flat top and architectural railings.

High-security fencing — 181-187

Anti-climb and crash-rated high-security mesh and steel palisade fencing systems to secure embassies, prisons, research establishments, transport termini, utilities and other high risk premises from forced or unauthorised access and exit.

Composite panel fencing — 188

Cement-based boundary wall/fence systems for residential and commercial use.

Recycled plastic fencing — 189-190

Solid tongue and groove and picket fencing for residential property and estates with an expected lifespan of 40+ years.

Timber fencing and slatted screens — 190-192

For residential estates and gardens.
Louvred fencing panels, featherboard fencing, heavy-duty timber screens and slatted garden screens with matching gates.

Acoustic barriers and green screens — 193-198

Sound absorptive and reflective barriers for use along transport networks and to reduce noise pollution from industrial sites.

Willow walls and green screen systems; timber noise barriers; concrete noise barriers; aluminium and steel noise barriers; transparent acrylic barriers; recycled plastic noise attenuation and anti-ballistic systems.

SEE ALSO
Sports fencing 497

EXTERNAL WORKS ONLINE

For detailed information supported by case studies, downloads and tools to help you make faster and better decisions ...
☞ www.externalworks.co.uk

Contact

Sales and Technical Office
t: 0131 441 1255
f: 0131 441 4161
sales@langandfulton.co.uk

Web
www.langandfulton.co.uk

Address
Lang+Fulton
Unit 2b, Newbridge Industrial Estate
Newbridge, Edinburgh EH28 8PJ

Distribution
West Midlands

Accreditation
ISO 9001:2000

Additional entries
External floor gratings and treads ➤ 153
Grating fences ➤ 162
Railings: Modena, Siena and Rimini ➤ 176
Gates ➤ 203
Bin stores, plant housings and compounds ➤ 398

	Visual screening	Standard heights
Italia-100	100%	1596–2929
Italia-80	80%	1608–2937
Delta-100	100%	
Delta-90	90%	
Delta-70	70%	1270–2952
Delta-45	45%	
Panels can be stacked to achieve any height		
Delta information applies to DeltaWing & DeltaBox		

Lang+Fulton

Louvred fences: Italia and Delta

Lang+Fulton are specialists in the supply of louvred fences and custom-designed louvred structures, which offer an attractive and practical screening solution.

A wide range of products is available, providing alternative levels of visual screening and a choice of aesthetic. The mild steel construction is significantly stronger and more economical than aluminium.

• **Italia screening fences**
Italia-80 and *Italia-100* are made from profiled louvres, electrofused on the back to a round transverse bar for a continuous lateral appearance.

• **Delta screening fences**
DeltaWing and *DeltaBox* are pressure-locked louvres with crisp intersections between their horizontal and vertical bars for a sharp, contemporary aesthetic.
The 45° angled flat louvre is supported by flat vertical bars at 22, 33, 44 or 66mm centres for total or partial screening.
DeltaFoil is a particularly robust profiled louvre.

• **Plant housing and bin enclosures**
Bespoke structures can be designed to comply with all screening and ventilation specifications.

• **Posts**
Posts are 120x12mm flat bar; 60x40, 80x40 or 100x50mm RHS.

• **Gates**
Single, double-leaf, pivot or bi-folding gates are available for manual or automatic operation.

Composition and manufacture
Panels are framed for bolting directly to posts; standard centres 1.76m (with 80x40 RHS posts).

Finish and appearance
Products are hot dip galvanised before optional polyester powder coating in any RAL colour.

Technical support
Lang+Fulton offers a complete design service. Products are supplied worldwide with support steelwork as required.

Italia-80V with vertical louvres providing a variable degree of visual screening to school playground area

DeltaWing-90 pressure-locked fencing mounted on a dwarf wall

Italia-80V – Priory School, Croydon, London

Italia-80 fully enclosed, secure bin store – Hackney

Italia-100 sliding gate and 2.3m high closure panels with RHS posts – Four Ashes Estate, Wolverhampton

Italia-80 fence screening car park area – St Mary's Hospital, Merchant Square, Paddington Basin

Italia-80 fencing and gate securing delivery area – Ashford Retail Park, Kent

Italia-100 overlapping louvres deliver 100% visual screening – Lesser Hampden Football Stadium

DeltaWing-90 louvred panels and sliding doors screening service areas – Glasgow Caledonian University

Italia-100 wall-mounted fence panels with 80x8mm flat bar posts – Chelmsford Sports and Athletics Centre

Italia-80 anti-climb balustrade providing shelter around roof-top garden – 661 London Road, Hounslow

Lang+Fulton

Contact
Sales and Technical Office
t: 0131 441 1255
f: 0131 441 4161
sales@langandfulton.co.uk

Web
www.langandfulton.co.uk

Address
Lang+Fulton
Unit 2b, Newbridge Industrial Estate
Newbridge, Edinburgh EH28 8PJ

Distribution
West Midlands

Accreditation
ISO 9001:2000

Additional entries
External floor gratings and treads ➤ 153
Louvred fences: Italia and Delta ➤ 160
Railings: Modena, Siena and Rimini ➤ 176
Gates ➤ 203
Bin stores, plant housings and compounds ➤ 398

	Mesh	Heights
Roma-2, 3, 4	62x132	930–2382
Verona	62x66	930–2382
Genoa	124x132	930–1722
Palermo	43x44	930–2387
Arezzo-25	76x25	1000–3000
Novaro-34	34x100	1000–3000
Novaro-25	25x76	1000–3000
Torino	132x11/22/33	935–2000
Como	33/44/66x132	935-2000
Garda	33/44/55/66sq	935-2000

Grating fences

Lang+Fulton specialises in the supply of both standard and customised fences, and offers a wide choice of aperture and design for all types of general or unique applications. Steel grating fences have a distinctive, contemporary style and a rigid construction for durability.

• **Security fences**
Roma-2, *Roma-3*, *Roma-4* and *Como* are versatile gratings with a rectangular mesh, and alternative sections of flat bar for different levels of security. *Verona*, *Palermo* and *Garda* have a square aperture.
Torino has a distinctive linear aesthetic with horizontal flats spaced at any interval of 11mm.

• **High-security fences**
IPE or RHS posts bolted directly to *Roma-4HS* or *Palermo-HS* panels provide higher security, and can incorporate cranked panel extensions.

• **Anti-climb fences**
Novara-34 and *Novara-25* have closely spaced flat bars that deter climbing, and are particularly appropriate for schools.

• **Green walls**
Genoa provides excellent planting support and boundary demarcation.

• **Barrier fences**
Arezzo-25 grating panels can be designed to BS 6399-1 loadings for security barriers, or as fencing at stadia and crowd control areas.

• **Bespoke fences**
Designs include waved or bowed tops, inserts, decorative rails, finials and radiused panels.

• **Posts**
60x7 and 80x7mm flat bar; 80x40mm RHS; 100x55mm IPE; 50, 76, 89 and 114mm Ø CHS. Panels can be stacked for any fence height.

• **Gates**
Bespoke gates are available to match all fences.

Finish and appearance

Gratings are hot-dip galvanised before optional polyester powder coating in any RAL colour.

Technical support

Lang+Fulton provides a full design service.

Roma-4 robust grating fence with flat bar posts in a galvanised finish – BBC Scotland, Glasgow

Roma-2 custom designed as a structural balustrade with wood and stainless steel handrail – RRS Discovery

Como-66 with bespoke anti-climb top – Manchester

Genoa with an open aperture for green wall planting

Roma4-HS high security fencing – Hampden Park Stadium, Glasgow

Roma-3 with a customised wave top, feature posts and decorative top rail – RNLI Headquarters, Poole

Torino-22 made entirely from flat bars for a distinctive horizontal emphasis – Channelsea House, Stratford

Novaro-25 anti-climb fencing 2.4m high with T-posts and pivot gate – Rokeby School, Newham, London

Roma-3 with RHS posts – Waitrose Distribution Centre, Bracknell

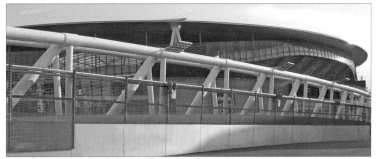

Arezzo-25 crowd control barrier fencing – The Emirates Stadium, North London

Torino-33 custom designed to meet the loadings for a barrier fence – Rochester Station, Kent

ZAUN

Contact
Steve Roberts
t: 01902 796696
f: 01902 796698
sales@zaun.co.uk

Web
www.zaun.co.uk

Address
Zaun Ltd
Steel Drive
Wolverhampton WV10 9ED

Accreditation
ISO 9001:2008
Secured by Design
CHAS

Affiliations
FCA
UVDB
PSSA
Constructionline

Additional entries
Architectural fencing ➤ 173
Railings ➤ 175
Security fencing ➤ 182
DBS acoustic fencing system ➤ 198
Gates and access control ➤ 211
Sports fencing systems ➤ 500

Zaun Ltd

Perimeter fencing

Zaun manufactures high-quality perimeter fencing that is suitable for a wide range of applications. Zaun's range of perimeter fencing is unobtrusive and secure. It is suitable for locations such as schools, parks, housing, sports fields and industrial and commercial premises.

• Mesh perimeter fencing
Axiom perimeter fencing is a lightweight, cost effective profile mesh fencing system that is ideal for perimeter demarcation.
Optima offers a combination of security, aesthetics and value, for projects on tighter budgets. The variable mesh pattern gives an attractive appearance, while closeness of the wires means that the fence is difficult to climb.

• Twin-wire fencing
Duo is a twin-wire fencing panel that provides a strong, rigid but aesthetically pleasing perimeter barrier to secure sites from potential trespassers, vandals and thieves.

• Heavyweight mesh fencing
DualGuard is a heavyweight welded mesh fencing system. Its anti-climb mesh and high strength provides a secure perimeter that is also visually appealing.

• Ring-top mesh fencing
Zariba fencing has an ornate ring-top design and is available with optional finials, which provide decorative aesthetics not commonly found in mesh fencing systems.

Finish and appearance

Zaun offers a choice of colours to polyester powder-coat (PPC) the products, meaning that systems can be completely tailored to suit specific sites.

Technical support

Zaun can undertake site surveys to advise clients on the most appropriate system and specification for their project.

DualGuard heavyweight welded mesh fencing system

Optima mesh fencing provides a combination of security, appearance and value

Fencing is suitable for a wide range of applications

Axiom perimeter fencing

Zariba ring-top decorative mesh fencing

Duo twin-wire fencing panel

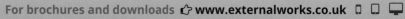

Contact
Adam Savage
t: 01782 319264
f: 01782 599724
sales@barkersfencing.com

Web
www.barkersfencing.com

Address
Barkers Engineering Ltd
Etna Works
Duke Street
Fenton
Stoke-on-Trent ST4 3NS

Accreditation
ISO 9001:2000

Additional entries
Railings ➤ 177
Steel palisade fencing ➤ 181
High-security fencing systems ➤ 185
Sliding gates and swing gates ➤ 200
Sports fencing ➤ 497

Barkers Fencing

Mesh fencing systems

Barkers Fencing manufactures high-performance fencing products to suit a range of applications. The company designs, manufactures, galvanises and powder-coats its products on site.
Both welded mesh and expanded metal mesh fencing is available in various specifications. It is suitable for uses ranging from basic demarcation to maximum security protection.
SecureGuard™ SR1 358 mesh fencing has been rigorously tested by the LPCB to achieve an SR1 rating. It is extensively used to provide a higher level of security than standard 358 mesh.

SecureGuard™ SR1 358 fencing tested by the LPCB

VGUARD mesh fencing

FASTGUARD expanded metal mesh fencing

Secureguard-358 mesh fencing

TWINGUARD rigid mesh fencing

Contact
Chris Bostandji/Kevin O'Grady
t: 01302 364551
heras.sales@herasuk.co.uk

Web
www.herasuk.co.uk

Address
Heras UK Fencing Systems
Herons Way
Carr Hill
Doncaster DN4 8WA

Accreditation
ISO 9001:2008
Constructionline
UVDB Standard
Secured by Design

Additional entries
Self-adjusting railing systems ➤ 180
High-security perimeter protection ➤ 186
Gates and entrance control ➤ 209
Sports fencing and MUGAs ➤ 502

Heras UK Fencing Systems

Perimeter mesh fencing and gates

Heras is one of the UK's leading fencing and gate
manufacturers.
The company specialises in the design and
manufacture of permanent fencing and gate
systems. It operates from a 6-acre custom-built
site in Doncaster and uses laser production
methods and technologies.

• Perimeter fencing
Welded mesh systems are available in several
types and are stylish and unobtrusive.
Pallas flat panel and *Triton* profiled panel systems
both benefit from anti-tamper hexaclip fixings.
Athena fencing has profiled panels on which the
mesh wires are set at variable spacings.
Jupiter and *Apollo Rolled Top* fencing both feature
3m-wide panels, which reduce the number of
posts required.
Horizen fencing has an attractive, strong, close-
mesh pattern and anti-climb profiled panels.

• Swing gates
Single-leaf and double-leaf swing gates can be
supplied to match the range of mesh fencing
systems. Gates are supplied with a standard slip-
latch, lockable drop-bolt and gate posts.

Composition and manufacture
Fencing is manufactured in steel and can have a
galvanised or powder-coated finish.

Apollo Rolled Top fencing features 3m-wide panels

Pallas swing gate

Athena features profiled panels with mesh wires

Triton panels are constructed from 5mm wires

Pallas features strong mesh that gives a stable fence

Jupiter features profiled 3m-wide panels

CLD
Fencing
Systems

Contact
Specification Department
t: 01270 764751
f: 01270 757503
info@cld-fencing.com

Web
www.cld-fencing.com

Address
CLD Fencing Systems
Unit 11, Springvale Business Centre
Millbuck Way
Sandbach CW11 3HY

Accreditation
ISO 9001:2008
LPS 1175
Secured by Design
NBS
BIM

Additional entries
Security fencing systems ➤ 169
UniGril rigid fencing systems ➤ 170
Zoological fencing systems ➤ 171
Bespoke laser-cut fencing ➤ 172
Stone Fence™ walling systems ➤ 172
Gates and access control systems ➤ 201
Perimeter fencing systems for sports pitches and
MUGAs ➤ 498
Sports Rail™ spectator fencing ➤ 499

CLD Fencing Systems

General purpose fencing

CLD manufactures general purpose rigid welded mesh steel wire fencing systems for car parks, business and retail premises, public buildings, schools and open spaces.

Four profiled and rigid panel systems give specifiers design options to suit a range of applications and budgets. Fence posts and panels are galvanised and polyester powder coated, in any RAL colour.

All products are backed by a 15-year guarantee against manufacturing defects.

Dulok-Lite™ 200x50mm double wire panel system

Eclipse™ profiled panel system with 200x50mm mesh

Rotop™ rigid panel system with rolled top

Exempla™ profiled panel system with 200x55mm mesh. CLD's unique hidden fixing system SafeTfix™ makes it easy to step panels up or down a slope.

Contact

Specification Department
t: 01270 764751
f: 01270 757503
info@cld-fencing.com

Web
www.cld-fencing.com

Address
CLD Fencing Systems
Unit 11, Springvale Business Centre
Millbuck Way
Sandbach CW11 3HY

Accreditation
ISO 9001:2008
LPS 1175
Secured by Design
NBS
BIM

Additional entries
General purpose fencing ➤ 168
UniGril rigid fencing systems ➤ 170
Zoological fencing systems ➤ 171
Bespoke laser-cut fencing ➤ 172
Stone Fence™ walling systems ➤ 172
Gates and access control systems ➤ 201
Perimeter fencing systems for sports pitches and
MUGAs ➤ 498
Sports Rail™ spectator fencing ➤ 499

CLD Fencing Systems

Security fencing systems

CLD manufactures rigid welded mesh steel wire security fencing systems for public buildings, car parks, business parks, industrial sites, transport termini, retail premises and schools.
Five profiled and rigid panel systems give specifiers design options to suit a range of security applications with fence heights up to 6090mm. Fence posts and panels are galvanised and polyester powder coated Green RAL 6005 as standard, with the option of any RAL colour.
All products are backed by a 15-year guarantee against manufacturing defects.

Exempla™ profiled panel with 200x55mm mesh

Ultimate Extra SR1™ profiled panel system with 165x25mm mesh; conforms to BS1722-14

Ultimate Extra™ profiled panel system

Securus™ flat panel high security fencing system

Multiplus™ profiled panel system

Dulok Wavetop™ double wire panel system: heights from 830–2430mm in 200mm increments

Exempla™ with SafeTfix™ hidden fixing system

Dulok-25™ double wire panel system, up to 6m

Contact
Specification Department
t: 01270 764751
f: 01270 757503
info@cld-fencing.com

Web
www.cld-fencing.com

Address
CLD Fencing Systems
Unit 11, Springvale Business Centre
Millbuck Way
Sandbach CW11 3HY

Accreditation
ISO 9001:2008
LPS 1175
Secured by Design
NBS
BIM

Additional entries
General purpose fencing ➤ 168
Security fencing systems ➤ 169
Zoological fencing systems ➤ 171
Bespoke laser-cut fencing ➤ 172
Stone Fence™ walling systems ➤ 172
Gates and access control systems ➤ 201
Perimeter fencing systems for sports pitches and MUGAs ➤ 498
Sports Rail™ spectator fencing ➤ 499

CLD Fencing Systems

UniGril rigid fencing systems

For over 40 years, CLD has been creating fencing systems to suit a range of environments.
UniGril fencing systems have been developed to offer architects a more aesthetic alternative to other perimeter fencing systems used in urban environments.
UniGril systems are suitable for applications that include industrial, commercial, residential, education, sports and infrastructure.
Matching gates are available.
The company's high-quality products are backed by a 15-year product guarantee.

Screenogril™ rigid fencing system

C10 Screenogril™ rigid fencing system

Securogril™ rigid fencing system

Safeogril™ rigid fencing system

Fenceogril™ rigid sports fencing system

Vizogril™ rigid fencing system

Contact
Specification Department
t: 01270 764751
f: 01270 757503
info@cld-fencing.com

Web
www.cld-fencing.com

Address
CLD Fencing Systems
Unit 11, Springvale Business Centre
Millbuck Way
Sandbach CW11 3HY

Accreditation
ISO 9001:2008
LPS 1175
Secured by Design
NBS
BIM

Additional entries
General purpose fencing ➤ 168
Security fencing systems ➤ 169
UniGril rigid fencing systems ➤ 170
Bespoke laser-cut fencing ➤ 172
Stone Fence™ walling systems ➤ 172
Gates and access control systems ➤ 201
Perimeter fencing systems for sports pitches and MUGAs ➤ 498
Sports Rail™ spectator fencing ➤ 499

Dulok™ double wire panel system – lion enclosure

CLD Fencing Systems

Zoological fencing systems

CLD's *Dulok™* fencing systems have been used on numerous projects to create enclosures for a variety of animals at zoos throughout the UK, providing security, safety and open viewing. Recent projects include:
• 141 linear metres of *Dulok™* double wire mesh secure fencing with special posts – lion enclosure, London Zoo.
• *Dulok™* security fence, 4m high with a 1m overhang – lion enclosure, Folly Farm Zoo.
• Bespoke fencing system based on *Dulok™* – three monkey enclosures, Isle of Wight Zoo.

Dulok™ double wire panel system – lion enclosure

Dulok™ double wire panel system – lion enclosure, Folly Farm Adventure Park and Zoo

Dulok™ double wire panel system – monkey enclosure, Isle of Wight Zoo

Dulok™ panel system – monkey enclosure

Dulok™ panel system – monkey enclosure

Contact
Specification Department
t: 01270 764751
f: 01270 757503
info@cld-fencing.com

Web
www.cld-fencing.com

Address
CLD Fencing Systems
Unit 11, Springvale Business Centre,
Millbuck Way, Sandbach CW11 3HY

Accreditation
ISO 9001:2008; LPS 1175; Secured by Design;
NBS; BIM

Additional entries
General purpose fencing ➤ 168
UniGril rigid fencing systems ➤ 170
Gates and access control systems ➤ 201
Perimeter fencing systems for sports pitches and
MUGAs ➤ 498

CLD Fencing Systems

Stone Fence™ walling systems

Stone Fence™ is used to create sound-absorbing, vandal-resistant wall dividers and low retainers, typically infilled using locally sourced stone. Welded mesh panels are manufactured from twin 8mm diameter horizontal and 6mm vertical steel wire, galvanised for corrosion protection. Sections are 2506x250mm deep. Heights range from 650 to 2450mm in 200mm increments. *Stone Fence™* can be combined with CLD's standard *Dulok™* system to form barrier fences and walls of varying heights and combinations.

Stone Fence™ – Chester Zoo

Stone Fence™ uses local stone

Options are available to suit specific applications

Stone Fence™ reduces environmental impact

Stone Fence™ can be used to decorative effect

Contact
Specification Department
t: 01270 764751
f: 01270 757503
info@cld-fencing.com

Web
www.cld-fencing.com

Address
CLD Fencing Systems
Unit 11, Springvale Business Centre,
Millbuck Way, Sandbach CW11 3HY

Accreditation
ISO 9001:2008; LPS 1175; Secured by Design;
NBS; BIM

Additional entries
General purpose fencing ➤ 168
UniGril rigid fencing systems ➤ 170
Zoological fencing systems ➤ 171
Gates and access control systems ➤ 201
Sports Rail™ spectator fencing ➤ 499

CLD Fencing Systems

Bespoke laser-cut fencing

CLD is experienced in producing bespoke decorative fence designs to client requirements. Work undertaken ranges from the incorporation of motifs and logos to the manufacture of full bespoke fencing systems.
• Maximum panel size 4x2m.
• Materials worked include corten steel, mild steel and plastic with laser-cutting as required.
• Finishes to client requirements include galvanising and polyester powder coating to any RAL colour, including metallics.

Bespoke laser-cut corten steel fencing around playground

Bespoke laser-cut corten steel panels

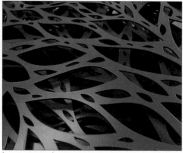
Laser-cut panels

In-house laser cutting

Gemini Convex fencing

ZAUN

Contact
Steve Roberts
t: 01902 796696
f: 01902 796698
sales@zaun.co.uk

Web
www.zaun.co.uk

Address
Zaun Ltd
Steel Drive
Wolverhampton WV10 9ED

Accreditation
ISO 9001:2008
Secured by Design
CHAS

Affiliations
FCA
UVDB
PSSA
Constructionline

Additional entries
Perimeter fencing ➤ 164
Railings ➤ 175
Security fencing ➤ 182
DBS acoustic fencing system ➤ 198
Gates and access control ➤ 211
Sports fencing systems ➤ 500

Zaun Ltd

Architectural fencing

Zaun manufactures architectural fencing and many other types of fencing. Products are suitable for a wide range of applications including commercial, residential and play areas. Zaun's range of architectural fencing features designs such as rings, curves and waves within a secure and functional fencing system. Applications include prestigious frontages, children's playgrounds, zoos and garden centres.

• Curved fencing
Gemini is a decorative fencing system available in four options: *Wave*, *Convex*, *Concave* and *Surf*. Each of these systems has curved styling and can be used to break up rigid fence lines. They are suitable for areas that are aesthetically sensitive or are visible to the public or customers.

• Customised fencing
Zariba Plus is an ornate perimeter fencing system that can be customised with the client's choice of letters, shapes or logos. It is similar to Zaun's standard *Zariba* ring-top fencing, but with the rings replaced by custom design elements.

• Printed fencing
HiSec Print is a printed 358 mesh system that allows branding and customisation for sites such as businesses and schools. It has been developed from Zaun's *HiSec 358* welded mesh security fence system.

Composition and manufacture
Various types of construction are available, including different configurations of horizontal and vertical wire mesh.

Finish and appearance
Fencing can be polyester powder-coated (PPC) in one of a choice of colours, allowing it to be tailored for specific sites.

HiSec Print fencing allows customised branding to be included on the panel

Gemini Wave curved fencing

Zariba Plus ornate fencing system

Contact

Phil Ball (sales)
t: 01623 750214
websales@alpharail.co.uk

Web

www.alpharail.co.uk

Address

Alpha Rail Ltd
Nunn Brook Rise
County Estate
Huthwaite NG17 2PD

Accreditation

ISO 9001:2000; ISO 14001:2004

Affiliations

British Association of Landscape Industries (BALI)
Constructionline
CHAS
CSCS-carded workforce
Association of Fencing Industries (AFI)

Additional entries

Architectural metalwork ➤ 412

Alpha Rail Ltd

Railings

Alpha Rail fabricates and installs galvanised metal railings, gates, pedestrian guardrails, estate fencing and Juliette balconies. A team of specialists manufactures all products in house, supplying bespoke architectural metalwork with logos, motifs or other designs, as well as decorative archways, bollards and barrier gates. The technical team is equipped with the latest CAD systems and offers a full design service. Alpha Rail has worked for over 30 years with public sector clients, architects, engineers, fencing and landscaping contractors and private clients.

Flat-bar infill bar railings

Spear-top railings – the Catalpa Tree, Rochester

Decorative flat-top railings – River Gardens, Derby

Woodhouse Urban Park, London

Decorative wavy flat-top railings – Newark

Ball-top railings – Damstead Park, Alfreton

ZAUN

Contact

Steve Roberts
t: 01902 796696
sales@zaun.co.uk

Web

www.zaun.co.uk

Address

Zaun Ltd
Steel Drive
Wolverhampton WV10 9ED

Accreditation

ISO 9001:2008, Secured by Design, CHAS

Affiliations

FCA, UVDB, PSSA, Constructionline

Additional entries

Perimeter fencing ➤ 164
Architectural fencing ➤ 173
Security fencing ➤ 182
DBS acoustic fencing system ➤ 198
Gates and access control ➤ 211
Sports fencing systems ➤ 500

Bushberry decorative railings

Zaun Ltd

Railings

Zaun manufactures railings and many other types of fencing. The products are suitable for a wide range of applications including commercial, residential and play areas.

• Vertical bar railings

Solid and hollow vertical bar railings are available in a range of sizes and modern styles. They can be complemented with a choice of finials, or with a mitred end finish.

Apex are stylish vertical bar railings that are manufactured using no welded parts. Each panel has hollow vertical bar infill that is fixed into place on a horizontal RHS tube.

Holloway railings use decorative circles, welded between the top two horizontal steels, to give a distinctive, refined look and an overall feel of continuation and longevity.

Barcode railings provide perimeters with a bespoke feel. Each panel can be designed as barcode that can be visually scanned to read a particular word, such as the name of a school.

Bushberry railings are a stylish alternative to vertical bar railings. By adding a mid-rail, the number of vertical bars in the upper section of the panel is reduced, creating an aesthetically pleasing feature.

• Bow-top railings

Traditional bow-top railings are available in varying heights and bar gauges and offer good through visibility. *Bowtop Urban* railings are available on short lead times.

Finish and appearance

Railings are hot dip galvanised to BS 1461. Zaun offers an extensive choice of colours to powder-coat (PPC) their products, ensuring a completely tailored system for specific sites.

Holloway railings with decorative circles

Apex vertical bar railings, made with no welded parts

Bow-top railings for playground application

Bowtop Urban railings

Vertical bar railings

LANG+FULTON
Est 1781 ORSOGRIL

Contact
Sales and Technical Office
t: 0131 441 1255
f: 0131 441 4161
sales@langandfulton.co.uk

Web
www.langandfulton.co.uk

Address
Lang+Fulton
Unit 2b, Newbridge Industrial Estate
Newbridge, Edinburgh EH28 8PJ

Distribution
West Midlands

Accreditation
ISO 9001:2000

Additional entries
External floor gratings and treads ➤ 153
Louvred fences: Italia and Delta ➤ 160
Grating fences ➤ 162
Gates ➤ 203
Bin stores, plant housings and compounds ➤ 398

Lang+Fulton

Railings: Modena, Siena and Rimini

Lang+Fulton offers a choice of high quality traditional and contemporary railing fences.
• **Modena solid bar railings**
Modena is a stylish, solid bar railing with a boltless connection from a leading Italian designer.
Panel heights/width: 1000–2000/2000mm.
Modena-XL is made with tubular pales.
Panel heights/width: 2400–3000/2500mm.
Posts: CHS or SHS.
• **Siena conical railings**
Siena traditional railing fence has a conical top.
Panel heights/width: 1000–1600/2000mm.
Panel heights/width: 1800–2400/2500mm.
Siena Sport is a particularly robust fence with heavier pales, designed for crowd loadings.
Panel heights/width: 2400–3000/2500mm.
Posts: flat bar, CHS or RHS.
• **Rimini flat bar railings**
Rimini is made entirely from equal depth flat bars for a modern, minimalist appearance.
Heights: 550, 750, 950, 1150 and 1450mm.
Post: flat bar.

Finish and appearance
Modena: hot-dip galvanised and polyester powder-coated in textured mica grey.
Siena and *Rimini*: hot-dip galvanised with optional polyester powder-coating in any RAL colour.

Modena solid bar railings mounted on dwarf wall – housing development, Springhead Park, Ebbsfleet Valley

Modena 3m high railings with customised gate in mica grey finish – Caledonian Park, Islington

Siena Sport robust railing fence for crowd control

Rimini custom designed as a balustrade

Rimini contemporary solid flat bar railing fence

Siena Sport – Scottish Rugby Union HQ, Murrayfield

 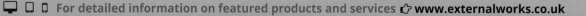

Barkers Fencing

Railings

Barkers Fencing manufactures high-performance railings for applications including schools, play areas, commercial and retail outlets.
The company designs, manufactures, galvanises and powder-coats its products on site.
Barkers maintains a large range of stock, which helps in providing quick delivery.

- **Bespoke railings**
Designer Range railings allow unique designs to be produced, to complement architectural features, or include additional safety features, or help meet local planning requirements.
- **Solid bar railings**
Solid bar railings are characterised by their solid, rigid and durable construction. Co-ordinating forged heads and finials can be supplied.
- **Round tubular railings**
STYLEGUARD-R railings are made from round hollow tube. They can be supplied in heights up to 2.4m, with either a blunt or mitred top.
- **Diamond-to-view tubular railings**
DTV railings are manufactured from square hollow section. They can be supplied in heights up to 3m, with either a blunt or mitred top.
- **Bow top railings**
Bow top and interlaced bow top railings are carried in stock. They can be made to strict playground safety specifications.

Designer Range forged head railings

STYLEGUARD-VB solid vertical bar railings

STYLEGUARD-R round tubular railings

STYLEGUARD-DTV diamond-to-view railings

STYLEGUARD-INT interlaced bow top railings

STYLEGUARD-BT bow top railings

PLAYSAFE bow top railings to BS EN 1176

Jacksons

Guaranteed Quality since 1947

Contact
Central Sales & Advisory Service
t: 0800 096 6360
f: 01233 750403
info@jacksons-fencing.co.uk

Web
www.jacksons-security.co.uk

Address
Jacksons Fencing
Stowting Common, Ashford TN25 6BN

Accreditation
ISO 9001:2000
Jacksons is a Secured by Design licensed company

Operational area
Worldwide

Additional entries
Railings ➤ 179
Timber fencing and gates ➤ 191
Acoustic barriers ➤ 195
Gates, barriers and access control ➤ 210

Jacksons Fencing

Perimeter security

Jacksons Fencing offers an extensive range of high-quality fencing, gates and entry systems. The company's products are designed to provide safe, secure enclosures that offer attractive demarcation and in extreme cases, prevent forced or unauthorised entry or exit.
In addition to standard products, customised solutions are available using Jacksons' in-house technical expertise.

• **Vertical bar fencing**
Unlike riveted palisade fencing, Jacksons vertical bar fencing and gates cannot be easily forced apart. The *Barbican®*, *Sentry®*, *Tri-Guard®* and *Ornamental* ranges all feature welded pale-through-rail construction, which is not only strong but also gives a better finish with no visible joints or unsightly bolts.

• **Safety features**
Jacksons vertical bar fencing and gates conform to UK Building Regulations, which require anti-trap features and 100mm pale-spacing as standard. Jacksons fencing is ideally suited to specification for applications where public safety is a factor. In addition, *Anti-Trap* bow-top fencing, *Playtime®* fencing and self-closing gates are RoSPA approved and conform to BS EN 1176 play fence standards. They are especially suitable for locations where children may be present, such as schools, play areas, parks and leisure facilities.

Composition and manufacture

Jacksons has manufactured in Britain for over 70 years. Products are supplied with a 25-year service-life guarantee covering any defects associated with design, manufacturing, finish or fitness for purpose. Products are galvanised to BS EN 1461 as standard and can be powder coated to BS EN 13438.

Accreditation

Jacksons is an ISO 9001:2000 accredited, LPS 1175 Approved and Secured by Design licensed company.

EuroGuard® Combi fencing system

Barbican® Defender fencing system

Barbican® Extra fencing system

Sentry® fencing system

Jacksons

Guaranteed Quality since 1947

Contact
Central Sales & Advisory Service
t: 0800 096 6360
f: 01233 750403
info@jacksons-fencing.co.uk

Web
www.jacksons-security.co.uk

Address
Jacksons Fencing
Stowting Common, Ashford TN25 6BN

Accreditation
ISO 9001:2000
Jacksons is a Secured by Design licensed company

Operational area
Worldwide

Additional entries
Perimeter security ➤ 178
Timber fencing and gates ➤ 191
Acoustic barriers ➤ 195
Gates, barriers and access control ➤ 210

Jacksons Fencing

Railings

Jacksons offers attractive, aesthetically pleasing security railings that are suitable for a number of applications including public areas, playgrounds and prestigious private dwellings.
In addition to standard products, customised solutions are available, using Jacksons' in-house technical expertise.
All products can be supplied with matching gates (swing or sliding) in either a manual or automated format.

Composition and manufacture
Jacksons has manufactured in Britain for over 70 years. Products are supplied with a 25-year service-life guarantee covering any defects associated with design, manufacturing, finish or fitness for purpose. Products are galvanised to BS EN 1461 as standard and can be powder coated to BS EN 13438.

Accreditation
Jacksons is ISO 9001:2000 accredited and a Secured by Design licensed company.
  • **Environment**
Jacksons is committed to implementing environmentally sound practices which contribute to a more sustainable method of operation.

Bow-top railings

Barbican® Imperial residential railings

Ornamental railings

Contact
Chris Bostandji/Kevin O'Grady
t: 01302 364551
heras.sales@herasuk.co.uk

Web
www.herasuk.co.uk

Address
Heras UK Fencing Systems
Herons Way
Carr Hill
Doncaster DN4 8WA

Accreditation
ISO 9001:2008
Constructionline
UVDB Standard
Secured by Design

Additional entries
Perimeter mesh fencing and gates ➤ 167
High-security perimeter protection ➤ 186
Gates and entrance control ➤ 209
Sports fencing and MUGAs ➤ 502

TR400 Square Bar railing

Heras UK Fencing Systems

Self-adjusting railing systems

Heras is one of the UK's leading fencing and gate manufacturers.

The company offers the *TangoRail* range, which is self-raking, meaning that it accommodates sloping ground on site, removing the need for insecure step fencing panels. The non-welded design allows for quick installation, as the railing adjustments can be made on site.

TangoRail is available in heights ranging from 900 to 2400mm, depending on the style of the fence, and can be supplied in various colour combinations.

• Parks and play areas
TR800 Bow-Top play fencing and *Quantum* self-closing gates comply with RoSPA safety guidelines and offer a safe, secure perimeter system.

• Housing
TR900 Elegance systems provide an attractive, unobtrusive railing for house frontages, and can be used to revitalise an entire project.

• Education
Safe and secure systems are available for perimeter and nursery areas. Six styles have 'Secured by Design' accreditation.
TR800 Play railings comply with RoSPA guidelines.

• Industry and commerce
TR400 railings have square-section infill that give a high level of strength and security. They provide attractive perimeter protection at a low cost.

• Urban regeneration
TangoRail railings can be used for inner city and suburban regeneration to provide imaginative design, colour and height combinations. The galvanised finish ensures a robust and long-lasting system.

• Gates
Single-leaf and double-leaf swing gates can be supplied to match *TangoRail* systems. Gates are supplied with a standard slip-latch, lockable drop-bolt and gate posts.
Quantum Play Safe is a reliable self-closing gate, designed for play areas. It is manufactured to RoSPA guidelines.

TR500 Flat Top self-adjusting railing system

TR900 Elegance bow-top self-adjusting railings

TR800 Play fencing and *Quantum* self-closing gate

TR800 Play bow-top self-adjusting railings

TR300 Ball Finial self-adjusting railing system

TR100 Standard Capped self-adjusting railing system

Barkers Fencing

Contact
Adam Savage
t: 01782 319264
f: 01782 599724
sales@barkersfencing.com

Web
www.barkersfencing.com

Address
Barkers Engineering Ltd
Etna Works
Duke Street
Fenton
Stoke-on-Trent ST4 3NS

Accreditation
ISO 9001:2000

Additional entries
Mesh fencing systems ➤ 166
Railings ➤ 177
High-security fencing systems ➤ 185
Sliding gates and swing gates ➤ 200
Sports fencing ➤ 497

Palisade fencing with security topping

Barkers Fencing

Steel palisade fencing

Barkers Fencing manufactures high-performance steel palisade fencing for medium to high security perimeter protection. Steel palisade fencing is widely used to protect vital assets for electricity, gas and water utilities, and railway infrastructure. It is also used for general purpose applications for commercial premises and industrial depots. Barkers palisade fencing has a strong, durable construction that affords protection against climbing and being cut through.
A large range is kept in stock for quick delivery.

Dimensions
Heights: 1.2, 1.5, 1.8, 2.0, 2.1, 2.4, 3.0 and 3.6m.
• **Paling thickness**
- Commercial specification:
'W' profile 2.0mm.
- General purpose to BS: EN: 1722 Pt 12:
'W' profile 2.5mm; 'D' profile 3.0mm.
- Security purpose to BS: EN: 1722 Pt 12:
'W' profile 3.0mm; 'D' profile 3.5mm; 'D' profile 3.9mm.
• **StronGuard™ palisade fencing**
StronGuard™ security palisade (patent pending) is especially strong and durable. Four versions offer various levels of protection, for securing the most sensitive sites. It is suitable for military, rail, utilities and petrochemical sites.
CPNI BEH (Base, Enhanced and High) certified products are available.
• **StronGuard™ SR2 palisade fencing**
StronGuard™ SR2 palisade fencing has been rigorously tested by the LPCB to achieve an SR2 rating. It is suited to the site conditions that mesh systems struggle to cope with such as military, rail, utilities and petrochemical applications.

Accessories
Standard gates are available or tailor-made to suit requirements. All gates are supplied with rear hung adjustable hinges, pad-lockable drop-bolts, multi-holed to suit site conditions and have anti-climb protection. All palisade gates are to BS: EN: 1722 pt 12.

StronGuard™ palisade fencing at water treatment works

Palisade fencing powder-coated green in-house

Barkers' palisade fencing rakes to suit sloping ground easily

ZAUN

Contact

Steve Roberts
t: 01902 796696
f: 01902 796698
sales@zaun.co.uk

Web

www.zaun.co.uk

Address

Zaun Ltd
Steel Drive
Wolverhampton WV10 9ED

Accreditation

ISO 9001:2008
Secured by Design
CHAS

Affiliations

FCA
UVDB
PSSA
Constructionline

Additional entries

Perimeter fencing ➤ 164
Architectural fencing ➤ 173
Railings ➤ 175
DBS acoustic fencing system ➤ 198
Gates and access control ➤ 211
Sports fencing systems ➤ 500

Zaun Ltd

Security fencing

Zaun manufactures security fencing that is suitable for a wide range of applications. The products are some of the most secure fencing systems available. They use close anti-climb mesh and heavy wires to create a robust barrier.

• Critical security fencing

ArmaWeave is a woven mesh fencing system designed to secure sites of critical national importance. Its tight mesh pattern and high-tensile steel wires can significantly delay attacks from hand and powered non-contact tools, compared to traditional welded mesh systems.

• 358 welded mesh fencing

HiSec welded mesh fencing uses a popular 358 configuration. 358 mesh is difficult to cut and climb, and is suitable for high-security sites. It is used by the Home Office for prison facilities in the UK.

HiSec DualSkin is a double-skin 358 system that has been specifically designed for applications that require a more robust fence than standard 358 mesh. The secondary panel is turned 90 degrees to make a very tight mesh pattern.

HiSec Super is a 358 mesh that is available in 6, 8 or 10mm vertical wires, which provide an increasing level of security for high-profile and sensitive sites.

• PAS 68-rated 358 mesh

HiSec Super PAS68 is an HVM (Hostile Vehicle Mitigation) fencing system, designed to stop a vehicle penetrating the fence line. It has been fully crash tested to PAS 68:2010, and will stop a 2.5 tonne vehicle traveling at 30mph (48km/h).

MultiFence PAS68 is an HVM-rated fencing system used for preventing vehicular attack. It is tested to PAS 68 and to BS EN 1317 Part 2 (vehicle restraint systems). It can be installed as a temporary or permanent system and requires no foundations.

Finish and appearance

Zaun offers an extensive choice of colours to powder-coat (PPC) their products, ensuring a completely tailored system for specific sites.

Accreditation

Zaun offers fencing systems rated to LPCB 1175 Security Ratings 1, 2 or 3 (SR1, SR2 or SR3) and have been approved by Secured by Design.

Technical support

Zaun can undertake site surveys to advise clients on the most appropriate system and specification for their project.

HiSec Super is a 358 welded mesh available with 6, 8 or 10mm vertical wires for additional security

HiSec DualSkin double-skin 358 welded mesh system

MultiFence for HVM applications requires no foundations and can be temporary or permanent

HiSec 358 welded mesh

ArmaWeave is a woven mesh fencing system designed to secure sites of critical national importance

DANGER
PROTECTED BY RAZOR WIRE

ArmaWeave's tight woven mesh pattern

HiSec Super PAS68 is an HVM (Hostile Vehicle Mitigation) fencing system

William Bain Fencing Ltd.
EST. 1859

Contact
Stephen Russell/Gary MacGregor
t: 01236 457333
f: 01236 451166
sales@lochrin-bain.co.uk

Web
www.lochrin-bain.co.uk

Address
William Bain Fencing Ltd
Lochrin Works
7 Limekilns Road
Blairlinn Industrial Estate
Cumbernauld G67 2RN

Accreditation
Secured by Design
Achilles UVDB
ISO 9001:2008
CPNI

Operational area
UK and export markets

William Bain Fencing Ltd

High-security perimeter systems

William Bain Fencing Ltd is a leading manufacturer of security fencing systems. The company's extensive product range includes the patented Home Office approved and CPNI rated *Combi™ Palisade* system, a Police preferred Secured by Design range, and a large stock of general purpose perimeter systems. Security solutions are available for any budget.

• **Lochrin Combi™**
Lochrin Combi™ palisade fencing was developed in conjunction with the Home Office. It utilises the *Classic™* fence's patented V slot and includes a high-security counterbore fixing solution. This design has gained various security accreditations including CPNI and Secured by Design.

• **Lochrin Classic™**
Lochrin Classic™ is a rivetless steel palisade fencing system with a patented V slot design that allows upright pales to pass through the rails rather than bolting to the front face. It can be raked over slopping ground conditions and has an aesthetically pleasing design.

• **Lochrin MeshGUARD™**
Lochrin MeshGUARD™ rigid mesh panel systems are used for demarcation and as boundary fencing. Panels are held in stock and are suitable for use as sports fencing applications and for protecting commercial buildings.

Composition and manufacture

As well as in-house manufacturing capabilities, Lochrin Bain has an extensive fabrication facility for manufacturing pedestrian access and vehicle gates, specialist posts and bespoke security solutions.

Technical support

CAD drawings, data sheets, bill pages and site specific solutions are available from the company's specification team.

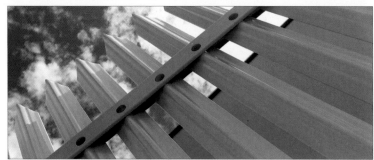
Lochrin Combi™ high-security steel palisade fencing securing a CNI site – available in heights up to 5m

Lochrin Combi™ Secured by Design fencing system – Anfield

Lochrin Classic™ securing UK Network Rail sites

High-security CPNI system

Lochrin FlatGUARD™ twin wire boundary fencing

Lochrin 358™ security mesh – new office build

Lochrin Classic™ rivetless palisade fence shown with barbed wire extensions securing a Porsche dealership

SecureGuard-358 mesh fencing with electrified elements

Barkers Fencing

High-security fencing systems

Barkers Fencing manufactures high-performance fencing products to suit a range of applications. The company designs, manufactures, galvanises and powder-coats its products on site and maintains large stock numbers, all of which helps in providing quick delivery.

• **StronGuard™ palisade fencing**
StronGuard™ security palisade (patent pending) is especially strong and durable.
Four versions offer various levels of protection, for securing the most sensitive sites.
It is suitable for military, rail, utilities and petrochemical sites.

• **StronGuard™ RCS25/RCS75 crash rated palisade fencing**
StronGuard™ RCS systems are the first palisade fences to gain PAS 68 accreditation. They can be supplied new or retrofitted on site.
Systems combine the high security benefits of *StronGuard™* palisade fencing and a PAS 68 vehicle mitigation barrier in a single fenceline.

• **StronGuard™ SR2 palisade fencing**
StronGuard™ SR2 palisade fencing has been rigorously tested by the LPCB to achieve an SR2 rating. It is suited to the site conditions that mesh systems struggle to cope with such as military, rail, utilities and petrochemical applications.
A full range of gates is available.

• **SecureGuard™ SR1 358 mesh fencing**
SecureGuard™ SR1 358 mesh fencing has been rigorously tested by the LPCB to achieve an SR1 rating. It is extensively used to provide a higher level of security than standard 358 mesh.

• **Fastguard expanded metal fencing**
Fastguard expanded metal fencing is made from sheet steel to provide high durability and good see-through visibility. It is supplied with anti-tamper fixings and is suitable for installation on rail tracks, utility sites and water treatment works.

• **Security toppings**
High-security toppings include electric fencing, razor wire coils, razor wire tape, barbed wire, and rotating spikes.

Contact
Adam Savage
t: 01782 319264
f: 01782 599724
sales@barkersfencing.com

Web
www.barkersfencing.com

Address
Barkers Engineering Ltd
Etna Works
Duke Street
Fenton
Stoke-on-Trent ST4 3NS

Accreditation
ISO 9001:2000, PAS 68

Additional entries
Mesh fencing systems ➤ 166
Railings ➤ 177
Steel palisade fencing ➤ 181
Sliding gates and swing gates ➤ 200
Sports fencing ➤ 497

StronGuard™ maximum security palisade fencing

StronGuard™ CPNI enhanced palisade at a WTW

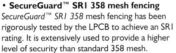

Fastguard expanded metal fencing

SecureGuard-358 mesh fencing for airport perimeter

StronGuard™ RCS is PAS 68 accredited

StronGuard™ palisade fencing at a power station

Contact
Chris Bostandji/Kevin O'Grady
t: 01302 364551
heras.sales@herasuk.co.uk

Web
www.herasuk.co.uk

Address
Heras UK Fencing Systems
Herons Way
Carr Hill
Doncaster DN4 8WA

Accreditation
ISO 9001:2008
Constructionline
CPNI
UVDB Standard
Secured by Design

Additional entries
Perimeter mesh fencing and gates ➤ 167
Self-adjusting railing systems ➤ 180
Gates and entrance control ➤ 209
Sports fencing and MUGAs ➤ 502

Heras UK Fencing Systems

High-security perimeter protection

Heras manufactures industrial, commercial and high security fencing, gates and entrance controls. Several systems have 'Secured by Design' status, the police-preferred specification.

• Security fencing

Pallas Xtra fencing is supplied with flat bar and anti-tamper U-clips that contribute to its Secured by Design accreditation.

Zenith Single Skin fencing has an anti-climb tight mesh configuration that does not provide foot or finger holds.

Zenith Double Skin is an enhanced version of the standard *Zenith* system. Small apertures allow nothing significant to be passed through them, and there are no gaps for use as climbing aids.

Zenith Triple Skin combines a *Zenith* single skin outer layer and a *Zenith* double skin inner layer, providing maximum attack deterrence and perimeter protection.

SensorFence is a perimeter intrusion detection system that combines high-security mesh systems with a concealed detection cable.

TangoRail self-raking railings include a number of styles with Secured by Design approval.

• Security entrance controls

Heras' *Defiant* high-security pedestrian gate has been developed to satisfy highly demanding maximum security criteria. It has been tested to the CPNI 'Enhanced Standard'.

High-security swing gates have been designed to resist attacks to the front cover plate, locking bar, slide bar and gate hangings.

The 972 *Turnstile* entrance control system does not require supervision, and will maintain a secure perimeter through a variety of access control options.

Accreditation

Zenith Single and *Zenith Double Skin* ranges include a product that fully conforms with CPNI requirements and is manufactured strictly in accordance with the specification provided for evaluation.

High-security pedestrian and vehicle access gates

Zenith Triple Skin high-security fencing system

Zenith Double Skin high-security fencing

Zenith SensorFence perimeter intrusion detection

Zenith Double Skin fencing and *Defiant* gate

Zenith Single Skin high-security fencing

Pallas Xtra Secured by Design accredited fencing

High-security turnstile

 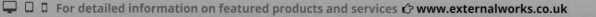

Contact

Samantha Goman, Sales
t: 029 2000 5884
esi@proctercontracts.co.uk

Web
www.proctercontracts.co.uk

Address
North
Procter Fencing Systems
1 Beaconsfield Court
Garforth
Leeds LS25 1QH

South West
Procter Fencing Systems
11 Pantglas Industrial Estate
Bedwas
Caerphilly CF83 8XD

South East
Procter Fencing Systems
Codham Hall
Great Warley
Brentwood CM13 3JT

Accreditation
Alcumus® SafeContractor
BS EN ISO 9001:2008
Building Confidence
CHAS
Construction Skills Certification Scheme (CSCS)
Constructiononline
Secured by Design installer

Operational area
UK

Additional entries
Automatic gates ➤ 202

Procter Fencing Systems

High-security fencing systems

Procter Fencing Systems, a division of Procter Contracts, installs mesh panel and palisade security fencing across the UK.

• **Pro-sure 358 mesh panel fencing**
Pro-sure 358 fencing is offered for medium and high security applications. Posts are made from steel hollow section with a 75x12.5x4mm mesh (commonly termed 358 mesh). These very small apertures do not allow an intruder to get a finger or toe hold for climbing, or insert a cutting tool. It can be installed up to 6m high.

• **Palisade fencing**
Palisade fencing is used for high security locations where vandal resistance is required. It is extremely difficult to climb and its galvanised steel posts are resistant to damage. The posts are 102x44mm RSJ, increasing to 127x76mm for fences above 2.7m high.
D-section palisade is standard, with W-section available for higher levels of security. It can be installed up to 4m high.

• **Security fence extensions**
Security extensions can be added to new or existing fences or walls to prevent climbing and create a visible security deterrent. They include barbed wire, razor wire or razor tape coils; and rotating, spiked *Cacti Toppings* and *Rotospikes*.

• **Electric fencing**
Electric fencing provides a high security solution for sensitive premises. They both detect and deter intruders with a short, sharp, safe pulse. Custom-build security solutions can be tailored to meet requirements, ranging from small commercial applications through to large, enterprise-level high-security sites.

Technical support

Procter Fencing Systems is experienced in the planning process and can advise on whether approval is required before committing to a fencing installation or extension.

358 mesh fencing with barbed wire and razor wire

High security 358 mesh with rotating *Cacti Topping*

6m high acoustic security fence – BBC

Chain link fence fitted with electric fence extension

Palisade fencing, security gate and electric fencing

Pro-sure 358 security mesh fencing with barbed wire extension – Bristol Airport

Palisade security fence – utility site

MODULARWALLS

Contact
t: 0800 915 5429
info@modularwall.co.uk

Web
www.modularwall.co.uk

Address
Modular Wall Systems (UK) Ltd
Unit 2
Rugby Street
Hull HU3 4RB

Accreditation
ISO 9001:2008

Operational area
UK

Country of manufacture
UK

Additional entries
Retaining walls ➤ 36
Acoustic barriers ➤ 197

Modular Wall Systems (UK) Ltd

Boundary fence walls

Modular Walls manufactures four cement-based boundary wall/fence systems that are ideal for residential and commercial applications. The systems can be used to create boundary walls and front feature walls. The wall system is a cost-effective alternative to traditional block walls. Panels are acoustically rated and can retain up to 750mm of soil when used with *TerraFirm™* panels.

Composition

Panels have an EPS core and fibre-cement outer skins. Posts are manufactured from aluminium, steel or universal beam according to the system selected.

Dimensions

Panels are 2400mm long x 50 or 75mm thickness, and produced in three standard heights: 600, 900 or 1200mm.

Finish

The wall system can be finished in textured or acrylic paints of any colour, or clad with stone or other material. Decorative infill panels, post caps and panel joints can also be specified.

Accessories

Options include retaining panels and integrated lighting, intercom and sound systems.

EliteWall™ premium designer fence and feature walls – residential property

BarrierWall™ 3m-high fence system – residential apartments

VogueWall™ 2.4m-high boundary wall – McDonalds

EliteWall™ 2.1m-high perimeter wall – retail outlet

Contact

Michael Janes (Sales)
t: 029 2086 4095
m: 07745 189022
mike@goplastic.co.uk

Sarah Mitchell
(Marketing and general enquiries)
t: 01920 469926
m: 07887 528434
sarah@goplastic.co.uk

Web
www.goplastic.co.uk

Address
GoPlastic Ltd
Waverley
40 St Martins Road
Caerphilly CF83 1EJ

Accreditation
Constructionline

CPD
The economic value of recycled products

Operational area
UK

Additional entries
Recycled plastic profiles for decks, boardwalks, jetties and bridges ➤ 143
Recycled plastic bollards ➤ 234
Recycled plastic seating ➤ 332

GoPlastic Ltd

Recycled plastic fencing

GoPlastic Ltd specialises in recycled plastic products made from *Govaplast®*. It is a high-quality, solid plastic board that is graffiti and vandal resistant, is UV stabilised, requires no maintenance or treatments, and will not crack, rot or shrink. Its expected life span is 40+ years.

• **Govawall® fence**
Govawall® is a complete fence system. Posts and boards are made from *Govaplast®* and fittings are made from recycled aluminium. *Govawall®* withstands high wind loads and has excellent noise abatement properties.

GovaWall® closeboard fence with solid profiles

Recycled plastic picket fencing

Normandie recycled plastic bin bay fence system

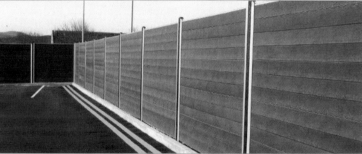

Govawall® recycled plastic solid tongue-and-groove fence system

Govawall® recycled plastic solid tongue-and-groove fence system

Govawall® recycled plastic palisade poles

Contact
t: 0161 850 1965
f: 0161 850 1975
sales@hahnplastics.co.uk

Web
www.hahnplastics.com

Address
Hahn Plastics Ltd
Old Pilkington Tiles Site
Rake Lane
Swinton
Manchester M27 8LJ

Affiliations
BALI

Additional entries
Ecocrib retaining wall system ➤ 41
Recycled plastic palisade profiles ➤ 408

Hahn Plastics Ltd

100% recycled plastic fencing

hanit® fencing makes aesthetically pleasing boundaries with the added benefit of a long-lasting product lifetime. It requires no painting or staining. It is solid, strong, impact- and chemical-resistant which makes it virtually vandal proof. *hanit®* is a cost effective fencing option for commercial contracts in general, and specifically for sectors such as education, local authorities and housing associations.
hanit® fencing has an attractive, brown, timber-effect finish.

Product range
• Picket fencing.
• Post and rail fencing.
• Closeboard panel fencing for privacy screening.
• Round palisade fencing, solid or hollow section.
• Ogee interlocking palisade fencing.

Properties
• Maintenance free.
• Rot proof, durable and long lasting.
• Strong and lightweight.
• Splinter free.
• Easy to handle and install.
• Virtually vandal proof.
• Weather resistant.
• 100% recycled and 100% recyclable.

hanit® picket fencing for housing development

hanit® post and rail fencing

hanit® 200(l)x195cm(h) privacy screening

hanit® palisade fencing

Hoppings Softwood Products

Q-Garden treated pine screening

Hoppings Softwood Products manufactures *Q-Garden* multi-purpose timber screening.

Composition and manufacture
Laths are made from treated Scandinavian pine. They are available in 3.6 and 3.9m lengths.

Finish and appearance
Laths are available pre-finished in *Q-Shades* Pebble Grey or Autumn Brown, a translucent matt stain that retains the character of the pine, highlighting the grain.

Contact
t: 0800 849 6339
f: 01992 561385
decking@hoppings.co.uk

Web
www.timber-cladding.co.uk

Address
Hoppings Softwood Products plc
The Woodyard
Epping Road
Epping CM16 6TT

Accreditation
FSC, PEFC, ISO 9001:2008

Affiliations
Timber Decking & Cladding Association, Wood Preservation Association, Timber Trade Federation

Additional entries
Q-Shades decking ➤ 144
Anti-slip decking ➤ 145

Q-Shades multi-purpose screening – Autumn Brown

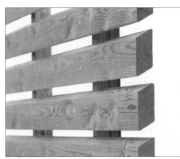
Q-Garden multi-purpose screening

Q-Shades multi-purpose screening – Pebble Grey

Multi-purpose screening

Jacksons
Guaranteed Quality since 1947

Contact
Central Sales & Advisory Service
t: 0800 096 6360
f: 01233 750403
info@jacksons-fencing.co.uk

Web
www.jacksons-fencing.co.uk

Address
Jacksons Fencing
Stowting Common, Ashford TN25 6BN

Accreditation
ISO 9001:2000
FSC and PEFC certification

Operational area
Worldwide

Additional entries
Perimeter security ➤ 178
Railings ➤ 179
Acoustic barriers ➤ 195
Gates, barriers and access control ➤ 210

Jacksons Fencing

Timber fencing and gates

Jacksons has over 70 years experience in high
quality timber fencing, gates and garden products.
• **Timber fencing**
Timber fencing is available to suit garden,
agricultural, equestrian and estate applications,
including post and rail, premium designer panels,
traditional palisade and featherboard designs.
• **Timber gates**
Jacksons' range of timber gates complements the
fencing products and spans entrance, driveway
and field gates that are suitable for manual or
automated operation. Stiles, kissing gates and
other rights of way products are also supplied.
• **Landscape structures**
Jacksons' *Secret Garden Collection* of landscape
structures includes trellis, pergolas, decking,
balustrades, sleepers and timber garden shelters.

Composition and manufacture
Products are made from kiln-dried, vacuum
pressure treated softwood. The *Jakcure®*
pressure treatment and preservative process
guarantees timber for 25 years against rot and
insect attack.

Accreditation
Jacksons is a Secured by Design licensed
company, is ISO 9001:2000 accredited and
supplies FSC and PEFC certified timber.

Canterbury Combi fencing

Louvre fencing

Traditional entrance gates

Contact

t: 0151 495 3111 (Cheshire)
t: 020 8150 8055 (West London)
enquiries@silvatimber.co.uk

Web
www.silvatimber.co.uk

Address
Silva Timber Products Ltd
Unit 4, Albright Road, Widnes WA8 8FY

Unit 7, Skyport Drive
Skyport Trade Park, Harmondsworth UB7 0LB

Accreditation
FSC, PEFC

Affiliations
TRADA, Timber Decking & Cladding Association,
Timber Trade Federation, Cedar Shake & Shingle
Bureau

Additional entries
Timber decking and cladding ➤ 140

Silva Timber Products Ltd

Timber fencing and screens

Silva Timber is one of the UK's leading experts
for specialist timber fencing, slatted screens,
decking, cladding, woodcare and finishing.
A variety of timber species is offered that vary in
texture, grain patterns and colour palettes to suit
individual tastes, including western red cedar,
southern yellow pine, ipé, Siberian larch, iroko
and yellow balau.
Products are sourced from the world's most
reputable primary sawmills, meaning that stock
consistently exceeds grading rules. Silva only uses
suppliers that conform to the strict environmental
standards, sourcing timber harvested legally and
sustainably from independently certified forests.
The vast majority of the product range conforms
to PEFC and FSC® certification.

Technical support

Silva Timber provides landscape professionals
with knowledgeable advice when they specify, so
that clients get the best results from their
projects. Articles and installation guides are also
available on the company's website.

Projects

Traditional and contemporary projects have
included commercial developments, residential
properties, eco-tourism resorts, hotels, marinas
and award-winning gardens.

Slatted garden screen

Slatted screen living wall

Horizontal wide profile slatted screen

Western red cedar fencing

Contact

Harry Frew
t: 01289 386664
f: 01289 386750
sales@etsluk.com

Web
www.etsluk.com

Address
Cheviot Trees Ltd
Newton Brae
Foulden
Berwick upon Tweed TD15 1UL

Accreditation
CE Marked
EN 14388:2005

Operational area
UK, Ireland

Cheviot Trees Ltd

Acoustic barriers: Green Barrier™

The *Green Barrier™* range is available in living or dried woven willow, and is suitable for commercial and residential applications. Products include absorptive acoustic barriers for road, rail and industrial noise-reduction applications, as well as lighter, non-acoustic instant boundary screening and hedging options.

• Acoustic Green Barrier™
The acoustic *Green Barrier™* is aesthetically attractive and offers sustainable acoustic protection provided by a 120mm *Rockdelta* absorptive core.
It can provide noise reduction of up to 22dBA by absorption, and with minimal reflection.
Heights range from 1.5 to 2.5m for living willow barriers, and 1.5 to 4.0m for woven barriers. Additional height can be gained by constructing the barrier on a bund.

• Non-acoustic Green Barrier™
The non-acoustic *Green Barrier™* provides natural privacy, boundary screening and security.
Just a few weeks after installation the living barriers will be densely covered with attractive, strong green shoots. Woven barriers are installed with a variety of climbing plants which grow quickly to cover the barriers.

Acoustic mesh and willow *Green Barrier™*

Galvanised mesh option with extra willow screening

Noise-absorbent core being installed

Woven willow *Green Barrier™* with climbers

Living willow landscape design

Visual screening of busy road

Newly installed living willow barrier

Living willow 3 months after installation

Unsightly metal fence being screened

Fence now concealed by living willow

Acoustic *Green Barrier™* in living willow absorbs noise and provides screening from a major road

Contact
Stephen Whittle
t: 01323 872243
f: 01323 872244
steve@grammbarriers.com

Mark Whittle (Sales office)
t: 0844 225 9002
mark@grammbarriers.com

Web
www.grammbarriers.com

Address
Gramm Barrier Systems Ltd
18 Clinton Place
Seaford BN25 1NP

Staff/turnover
25 people
£7m+ per year

Accreditation
ISO 9001:2008
HA National Highways Sector Scheme 2A, 2B and 2C approved
Link-Up approved by Railtrack
Government Trust Mark

Affiliations
Environmental Noise Barrier Association
European Fencing Industry Association
Fencing Contractors' Association

Operational area
UK

Country of manufacture
UK, Europe

Gramm Barrier Systems Ltd

Acoustic barriers

Gramm Barrier Systems Ltd is a leading supplier and installer of acoustic barriers and high-security fencing systems to the road, construction and railway industries.

• **Timber barriers**
Reflective or absorbing timber barriers are offered in heights from 1 to 6m.
All barriers are approved for use by the Highways Agency and for railways and airports, and conform to BS EN 1793 and BS EN 1794.

• **Aluminium and steel barriers**
High-density mineral wool has good sound deadening properties and can be encased in either high-specification pregalvanised and painted steel, or aluminium panels to produce a lightweight sound-absorbing barrier.

• **Transparent barriers**
A range of systems manufactured from cast acrylic, extruded acrylic and extruded polycarbonate is available. All barriers are weather resistant and highly transparent. They have a light transmittance of up to 92%. All barriers conform to ZTV-law 88 and fire behaviour to BS 476-7, and have sound insulation properties up to 32dB.

• **Concrete barriers**
Reflective or absorptive concrete barriers are constructed from a wood fibre concrete material and are ideal for absorbing road- and railway-generated noise, with absorption exceeding 0.8 over the transport spectrum.

• **Recycled plastic barriers**
Plastic noise barriers are a distinctive recycled product manufactured from mixed plastic waste. They can be made into either reflective or absorptive barriers up to 6m high and up to 5m wide. Acoustic tests show high absorption (9dB) and high airborne sound insulation (29dB).

• **Green barriers**
Green Planta absorptive noise barriers are modular, plantable, environmentally friendly green solutions that provide habitat for micro-organisms.

• **Eco Barrier acoustic barriers**
Eco Barrier noise barriers offer effective protection against noise pollution while also contributing positively to protecting the environment. The barriers comprise a trellis that provides a framework for an extensive green wall. They will blend into the natural environment and become more attractive as the greenery grows. This plant growth also helps to reduce CO_2 in the atmosphere.

• **Photovoltaic noise barriers**
Photovoltaic noise barriers can potentially cover the costs of a noise barrier installation over its 30-year lifespan.

7m high aluminium absorptive barrier – Thames Water

Eco Barrier

Acrylic noise barriers – A2/M2 bridge, Kent

6m cranked timber absorptive barrier – DLR

King post timber noise barrier system

4m high timber reflective barrier – Silwood Sidings

Jacksons
Guaranteed Quality since 1947

Contact
Central Sales & Advisory Service
t: 0800 096 6360
f: 01233 750403
info@jacksons-fencing.co.uk

Web
www.jacksons-fencing.co.uk

Address
Jacksons Fencing
Stowting Common, Ashford TN25 6BN

Accreditation
ISO 9001:2000
FSC and PEFC certification

Operational area
Worldwide

Additional entries
Perimeter security ➤ 178
Railings ➤ 179
Timber fencing and gates ➤ 191
Gates, barriers and access control ➤ 210

Jacksons Fencing

Acoustic barriers

Jacksons' offers timber environmental noise barriers that provide up to 32dB reduction.

• Reflective barriers

Jakoustic® reflective barriers are used in domestic commercial and construction site applications. *Jakoustic®* reflective highway barriers are used for highways, railways and industrial applications. Both are accredited to BS EN 1793-2, category B3, and have a superficial mass density of 25kg/m² to deliver laboratory sound reduction of 28dB. The highway barriers are additionally accredited to BS EN 1794-4:2003 and BS EN 1793-1:1998.

• Absorptive barriers

Both *Jakoustic®* barrier types can be upgraded to *Plus* specification to act as absorptive systems.

• Other products

High-security acoustic barriers, swing and sliding gates, and a flood defence barrier are available.

Composition and manufacture

Jacksons has manufactured in Britain for over 70 years. The company's *Jakcure* pressure treatment and preservative process guarantees timber for 25 years against rot and insect attack.

Accreditation

Jacksons is a Secured by Design licensed company, ISO 9001:2000 accredited and supplies FSC and PEFC certified timber.

Jakoustic® reflective barrier with pedestrian gate

Jakoustic® reflective barrier in domestic application

Jakoustic® reflective barrier for highways application

Jakoustic® Plus absorptive barrier

Contact

Tony Sawyer
t: 0131 440 9804
f: 0131 440 9805
tony.sawyer@livingreendesign.com

Web

www.thegreenscreen.co.uk

Address

Livingreen Design Ltd
Livingreen House
24/6 Dryden Road
Bilston Glen
Loanhead EH20 9HX

Additional entries

Planters for roof gardens ➤ 362
Feature planters ➤ 364

Livingreen Design Ltd

Greenscreen acoustic barriers

Livingreen Design supplies *Greenscreen*, an environmental acoustic barrier and fencing system. It has been widely specified in Europe for environmentally sensitive locations. It is made predominantly from recycled material and waste, and is itself fully recyclable.

Commercial horticultural technology has been used to create the ideal surface to support climbing plants. Once established, the plants give a natural appearance and blend into the landscape.

Installation and maintenance

Greenscreen's lightweight modular construction enables it to be installed quickly on all types of terrain, including sites where soils have low load-bearing capacity that causes problems for heavier systems. *Greenscreen* panels are slim and take up a minimal amount of space on site. With appropriate footings, barriers up to 6m high can be easily achieved by stacking the panels.

Technical data

Greenscreen standard barriers are NEN 1793 Category 1 certified, providing 29dB of sound insulation and up to 20dB of sound absorption. These values are achieved using a combination of the steel noise plate and the coir-wrapped tubing construction.

Greenscreen – front of *Lite* version

Greenscreen – back of *Lite* version

Greenscreen acoustic barrier for railway application

Greenscreen acoustic barrier with Perspex panels

Greenscreen acoustic barrier for a school sports area

Greenscreen – highway application

Greenscreen – just after installation

Greenscreen – plant growth after 12–18 months

Greenscreen installation

Greenscreen *Lite* sloping panels, wood veneer facing

Greenscreen – the same site immediately after installation (left) and with mature plant growth (right)

Contact

Specification Department
t: 01270 764751
f: 01270 757503
info@cld-fencing.com

Web

www.cld-fencing.com

Address

CLD Fencing Systems
Unit 11, Springvale Business Centre
Millbuck Way
Sandbach CW11 3HY

Accreditation

ISO 9001:2008
LPS 1175
Secured by Design
NBS
BIM

Additional entries

General purpose fencing ➤ 168
Security fencing systems ➤ 169
UniGril rigid fencing systems ➤ 170
Zoological fencing systems ➤ 171
Bespoke laser-cut fencing ➤ 172
Stone Fence™ walling systems ➤ 172
Perimeter fencing systems for sports pitches and
MUGAs ➤ 498
Sports Rail™ spectator fencing ➤ 499

CLD Fencing Systems

Gates and access control systems

CLD manufactures gates for industrial and commercial applications. Products range from single and double leaf swing gates to fully automated sliding and cantilevered gates.

- **SlideMaster™ cantilever sliding gates**
SlideMaster™ gates have clear drive through widths of up to 20m. Four systems cater for security requirements ranging from low to the highest level risk for very sensitive sites.
- **LockMaster™ swing gates**
LockMaster™ double and single leaf gates are used to control pedestrian and vehicular access and are compatible with all CLD perimeter fencing systems.
- **SpeedMaster™ bi-folding trackless gates**
SpeedMaster™ speed gates are suitable for high-level security sites where quick opening and closing is essential, or where space is restricted.
- **Automated access control**
Automated solutions range from simple kits for swing gates, to high security packages with code, camera and card access on sliding gates.

Manufacture and composition

Gates are of welded SHS construction. Cladding is rigid welded mesh, secured with the standard CLD clamp bar and through fixings. Hinges are all anti-lift-off and adjustable.

SlideMaster™ fully automated cantilever sliding gate

SlideMaster SR3™ fully automated sliding gate

LockMaster™ gate

LockMaster SR2™ fully automated sliding gate

Sliding security gate

SpeedMaster™ bi-folding trackless speed gate

Contact
Samantha Goman, Sales
t: 029 2000 5884
esi@proctercontracts.co.uk

Web
www.proctercontracts.co.uk

Address
North
Procter Automatic Gates
1 Beaconsfield Court
Garforth
Leeds LS25 1QH

South West
Procter Automatic Gates
11 Pantglas Industrial Estate
Bedwas
Caerphilly CF83 8XD

South East
Procter Automatic Gates
Codham Hall
Great Warley
Brentwood CM13 3JT

Accreditation
Alcumus® SafeContractor
BS EN ISO 9001:2008
Building Confidence
CHAS
Construction Skills Certification Scheme (CSCS)
Constructionline
Secured by Design installer

Operational area
UK

Additional entries
High-security fencing systems ➤ 187

Procter Automatic Gates

Automatic gates

Procter Automatic Gates, a division of Procter Contracts, installs gates, mesh panel and palisade security fencing across the UK.

• Sliding gates
Tracked gates run on a metal rail set into the ground, which allows robust, heavy steel to be specified. They are suitable for very wide openings up to 25m.

Cantilevered sliding gates are suitable where no ground rail is needed, and where the ground surface is uneven or sloping. Less ground work is required than with tracked gates and they can be used on uneven surfaces. They are unaffected by debris, snow and ice and operate more quietly than tracked sliding gates.

Telescopic gates have individual sections that overlap as the gate opens. They take up less space than tracked or cantilevered sliding gates when in the open position.

• Automatic swing gates
Automatic electric swing gates are used at industrial, commercial and utility sites. They are offered in four main styles: welded mesh, palisade, balustrade and ornamental.

• Bi-folding gates
Bi-folding gates, also called speed gates, offer advantages over swing gates and sliding gates, especially where security requirements dictate that an entrance should only remain open for a short period of time. The bi-folding mechanism is also suited to applications where there is limited space for the gate to open into.

Technical support
Procter Automatic Gates can advise on whether approval is required before committing to a fencing installation or extension.

Installation and maintenance
Procter Automatic Gates qualified staff can carry out all electrical installation work to the required regulations.
Maintenance contracts are also provided.

Cantilevered sliding gate with school logo

Automatic bi-folding gate with balustrade infill

Cantilevered sliding gate with customer branding

Bespoke telescopic sliding gate with timber-cladding and powder-coated steel balustrade infill

Bespoke telescopic sliding gate

Cantilevered balustrade gate for new academy

Est 1781

ORSOGRIL

Contact

Sales and Technical Office
t: 0131 441 1255
f: 0131 441 4161
sales@langandfulton.co.uk

Web

www.langandfulton.co.uk

Address

Lang+Fulton
Unit 2b, Newbridge Industrial Estate
Newbridge, Edinburgh EH28 8PJ

Distribution
West Midlands

Additional entries

External floor gratings and treads ➤ 153
Louvred fences: Italia and Delta ➤ 160
Grating fences ➤ 162
Railings: Modena, Siena and Rimini ➤ 176
Bin stores, plant housings and compounds ➤ 398

Lang+Fulton

Gates

Lang+Fulton supplies custom-sized gates with infill panels to match all of the company's fencing systems.

• Grating panel gates

Gates are made with panels from a wide choice of gratings. These can be shaped with bowed or waved tops, or to a unique design.

• Louvre panel gates

The *Italia* and *Delta* ranges of steel louvred gates offer the additional security of 45–100% visual screening and effective anti-climb properties.

• Hinged gates

Single, double-leaf, pivot or bi-folding gates are available for manual or automatic operation. Automation is carried out by specialist engineers. All gates are secured with high-quality euro-profile locks, maglocks or sliding latches.

• Sliding gates

Fixed-rail or cantilevered gates are available up to 2500x6000mm.

Finish and appearance

All mild steel is hot-dip galvanised to BS EN ISO 1461 before optional polyester powder coating to BS 6497 in any RAL colour.

Technical support

Lang+Fulton provides a full design service.

Italia-80 bi-parting sliding gate – Castle Golf Course

Roma-3 swing gate 3x5m – SSE Hydro, Glasgow

Torino-22 sliding gate – Channelsea House, Stratford

Italia-100 secure steel louvred gate – N Kent Police

Contact

Sally Osmond (Brand & Development
Manager)
t: 01293 422801
f: 01293 560650
osmonds@frontierpitts.com

Technical Sales
t: 01293 422800
f: 01293 560650
sales@frontierpitts.com

Technical Support
t: 01293 548301
f: 01293 560650
sales@frontierpitts.com

Web

www.frontierpitts.com

Address

Frontier-Pitts Ltd
Crompton House
Crompton Way
Manor Royal Industrial Estate
Crawley RH10 9QZ

t: 01293 548301
f: 01293 560650

Accreditation

ISO 9001:2008
LPS 1175 (*Terra Diamond* turnstile)
PSSA Verified
Achilles UVDB and Building Confidence
CHAS
Constructionline
SafeContractor
Secured by Design

Operational area

Worldwide

Country of manufacture

UK

Frontier-Pitts Ltd

Gates and barriers

Frontier Pitts is a leading British manufacturer of
security gates, barriers, blockers and bollards. Full
project management combines design and
manufacture with civil and electrical services, site
surveys, maintenance and refurbishment.

• **Gates**

Sliding cantilevered, sliding tracked, swing/hinged,
barricade beams and bi-folding gates are offered.
LoTracker sliding gates: secure widths up to 12m.
Sliding cantilevered gates: widths up to 10m.
Sliding tracked gates: widths up to 35m.
Swing/hinged gates: single leaf widths up to 10m;
double leaf widths up to 20m.
Barricade beams: widths up to 8m.
Bi-folding gates: widths up to 12m.

• **Automatic barriers**

Torque motor barriers and hydraulically driven
barriers are available with a range of accessories:
lower folding skirts, swivel skirts, boom lights,
maglocks, signage, safety loops and photocells
and a range of end-rests.
FBX torque motor barriers: boom up to 6m.
FB torque motor barriers: boom up to 9m.
Hydraulically driven barriers: boom up to 10m.

• **Blockers and bollards**

Hydraulically driven road blockers and rising
kerbs: lift heights of 300, 353, 533 and 800mm.
Rising retractable bollards: lift height of 600mm.

• **Turnstiles and pedestrian gates**

Full height turnstiles are available. Pedestrian
gates are available in hinged or sliding versions.

• **Crash-rated products**

The *Anti Terra* range has been impact tested to
IWA 14 and BSI PAS 68 for stopping various
energies and different vehicles at different speeds.
Terra G8 sliding gate: 7.2t @ 40mph.
Terra sliding cantilevered gate: 7.5t @ 50mph.
Terra V hinged gate: 7.5t @ 50mph.
Terra 180° swing barrier: 7.2t @ 30mph.
Terra swing gate: 7.5t @ 50mph.
Terra swing gate enhanced with security infill:
7.5t @ 50mph.
Terra Compact barrier: 3.5t @ 30mph.
Terra Ultimate barrier: 7.5t @ 50mph.
Terra Surface Mount Blocker: 7.5t @ 50mph.
Terra Shallow Blocker: 7.2t @ 50mph.
Terra Blocker: 7.5tg @ 30mph and 50mph.
Terra automatic rising bollard: 7.5t @ 50mph.
Terra Quantum bollard: 7.5t @ 30mph.
Terra Jupiter static bollard: 7.5t @ 50mph.
Terra Mars static and shallow mount bollards:
7.5t @ 40mph.
Terra Neptune static and standalone shallow
mount bollards: 7.5t @ 40mph.
Terra Venus static and shallow depth bollards:
7.5t @ 30mph.
The *Terra* range also includes the LPCB LPS1175
approved *Terra Diamond* turnstile.

Bi-folding security speed gates

Terra sliding cantilevered gate and *Terra Blocker*

PAS 68 *Terra* cantilevered sliding gate

Security height road blocker

IWA 14 and PAS 68 impact testing

Compact Terra barrier – Queen Elizabeth Olympic Park, London

IWA 14 *Terra* 180° swing barrier

IWA 14 and PAS 68 HVM *Terra* blockers

PAS 68 static stainless steel HVM *Terra* bollards

Terra Diamond turnstile

PAS 68 *Terra Neptune* static bollards

Automatic barrier

Pedestrian turnstile

Contact
t: 01964 535858
f: 01964 532819

Vicky Hughes
Sales Supervisor
vhughes@heald.uk.com

Caroline Robinson
Sales Assistant
crobinson@heald.uk.com

Craig Mason
Business Developer
cmason@heald.uk.com

Wendy Chew
Operations Manager
wchew@heald.uk.com

Gavin Giles
Electrical Electronics Engineer
ggiles@heald.uk.com

Web
www.heald.uk.com

Address
Heald Ltd
Northfield
Atwick Road
Hornsea HU18 1EL

sales@heald.uk.com

Accreditation
ISO 9001:2008
Contractors Health & Safety Assessment Scheme
(CHAS)
SAFEcontractor

Affiliations
British Parking Association (BPA)
British Standards Institution (BSI)
Perimeter Security Suppliers Association (PSSA),
founder member

Awards
Benchmarq for Customer Satisfaction Diamond
Award
Secured by Design (for all PAS 68/K12 crash-tested
roadblockers)
Association of Chief Police Officers (ACPO) awards

Operational area
Worldwide

Country of manufacture
UK

Heald Ltd

Hostile vehicle mitigation and traffic control solutions

For over 30 years, Heald has protected some of the world's most high profile locations from hostile vehicle attacks.

Heald is an award-winning innovator in the field of perimeter technology, and one of the largest designers and manufacturers of security equipment in the UK. The product range includes roadblockers, security bollards, rising arm barriers, speed and height restrictors.

• Roadbockers
Commander is a deep-mount roadblocker tested to the highest standards. It is the only security barrier PAS 68 tested to stop a 30 tonne truck travelling at 80kph (50mph) with zero penetration – the unit remained fully operational after the crash test.

Anti-Vandal Roadblocker provides a highly visible solution in a range of sizes for applications ranging from simple traffic control to security barriers.

• Automatic bollard/roadblocker
Raptor is a shallow-mounted automatic bollard that can be used singly or in an array to form a formidable roadblock. Tested to PAS 68 and ASTM standards, the *Raptor* stopped a 7.5 tonne truck travelling at 80kph (50mph) and operated afterwards. A single unit has a small footprint of 2500x1540mm, requiring a shallow excavation depth of 500mm for installation.

• Surface-mounted sliding bollards
Matador is a surface-mounted automatic sliding bollard. It comprises a baseplate with two fixed bollards on either side of one or two central moving bollards which slide to the side to allow vehicular access. *Matador* is IWA rated to stop a 7.2 tonne truck travelling at 40kph.

• High-security bollards
Mantis is a high-security shallow-mounted static bollard manufactured from sectioned mild steel, with the option of stainless steel covers. *Mantis 64* is PAS 68 rated to stop a 7.5 tonne truck at 64kph; *Mantis 80* is IWA rated to stop a 7.2 tonne truck travelling at 80kph both as a single unit and in an arrayed configuration.

Sparta PAS 68 rated fixed security bollards provide flexible security for a range of sites. Manufactured from sectioned mild steel, they can be supplied with stainless steel covers.

Lift-Assist is a heavy-duty manually operated rising bollard suitable for sites where automated systems are not required.

• Remote monitoring and control
Hydra remote control and monitoring software provides centralised security control for automated barriers through a simple, secure and streamlined interface. The system enables multiple roadblockers, barriers and bollards to be monitored and controlled securely via smartphones, tablets and computers.

Raptor provides the security of a roadblocker with the flexibility of a shallow-mounted bollard

Anti-Vandal Roadblockers provide high visibility security for many locations

Commander is a deep-mount roadblocker tested to the highest standards

Matador 4 IWA rated surface-mounted automatic sliding bollards

Mantis PAS 68 rated shallow-mounted fixed high-security bollard with stainless steel cover

Sparta PAS 68 rated static security bollards provide flexible security for a range of sites

Matador 3 surface-mounted automatic sliding bollard

Lift-Assist manually operated high-security bollards

Sparta static PAS 68 security bollards

Commander is PAS 68 tested to stop a 30 tonne truck travelling at 80kph (50mph) with zero penetration

Contact
Sales
t: 0117 953 5252
f: 0117 953 5373
sales@avon-barrier.co.uk

Web
www.avon-barrier.co.uk

Address
Avon Barrier Corporation Ltd
149 South Liberty Lane
Ashton Vale Trading Estate
Bristol BS3 2TL

Accreditation
ISO 9001:2008
Constructionline
SAFEcontractor

Affiliations
The Perimeter Security Suppliers Associaton (PSSA)

Additional entries
High-security bollards ➤ 232

Avon Barrier Corporation Ltd

Gates, barriers and access control systems

Avon Barrier manufactures, installs and maintains high-security vehicle and pedestrian access control systems throughout the UK and worldwide. The company offers PAS 68 hostile vehicle mitigation barriers that are impact-tested to withstand a 7500kg vehicle travelling at a range of speeds.

• Roadblockers
Avon offers a range of roadblockers, from traditional roadblockers to high-security PAS 68 crash-tested roadblockers that are designed to protect infrastructure from ram raids or terrorist attacks.

• Security gates
The company offers high-security cantilevered and tracked sliding gates, hinged swing gates, speed gates and PAS 68 armoured vehicle gates.

• Turnstiles
Turnstiles are used to prevent pedestrain entrances from unauthorised access. Full-height turnstiles provide additional security.

• Automatic rising barriers
The company offers a range of automatic access control barriers, including PAS 68 barriers. The barriers are suitable for car park, security and traffic control applications, and can be interfaced with a choice of access control systems.

• Manual barriers
Manually-operated barriers are a cost-effective way to secure a parking area or roadway, with arms available in lengths ranging from 3 to 7m.

• Height restrictors
Height restrictors are designed to limit the height of vehicles that are allowed access to specific areas, such as car parks or traffic lanes.

• Security bollards
Scimitar bollards are PAS 68 tested and can be hydraulically-operated or static. The bollards are available with a choice of sleeves or finishes, including stainless steel or bepoke paint. *Scimitar* bollards can be interfaced with access control systems.

RB780 roadblockers and rising barriers

Height restrictor

EB950 drop skirt rising barrier

Full-height turnstiles with security bollards

PAS 68 sliding gate

EB950CR Armstrong barrier

RB780 roadblocker

EB950CR Armstrong barrier

Contact
Chris Bostandji/Kevin O'Grady
t: 01302 364551
heras.sales@herasuk.co.uk

Web
www.herasuk.co.uk

Address
Heras UK Fencing Systems
Herons Way
Carr Hill
Doncaster DN4 8WA

Accreditation
ISO 9001:2008
Constructionline
UVDB Standard
Secured by Design

Additional entries
Perimeter mesh fencing and gates ➤ 167
Self-adjusting railing systems ➤ 180
High-security perimeter protection ➤ 186
Sports fencing and MUGAs ➤ 502

Heras UK Fencing Systems

Gates and entrance control

Heras is one of the UK's leading manufacturers of gates and entrance controls, including the *Broughton* range of products.

• Swing gates
Single-leaf and double-leaf swing gates can be supplied to match Heras mesh fencing and railing systems. Gates are supplied with a standard slip-latch, lockable drop-bolt and gate posts.

• Cantilever sliding gate
The *Safeglide* cantilever gate features the latest technology and has achieved all six EN and BS British Standards for automated gates.

• Rising arm barriers
Broughton rising arm barriers are quick to operate, strong and durable. They are suitable for all applications.

• Roadblockers and bollards
Broughton roadblockers and bollards are available in a range of sizes and can be customised for specific applications.
The *Broughton* range includes units for cost-effective parking control applications through to high-security military sites.

Slidesafe cantilever gate

Swing gate with mesh infill

T1000 pedestrian access control turnstile

Broughton rising arm barrier

Broughton bollards

Jacksons
Guaranteed Quality since 1947

Contact
Central Sales & Advisory Service
t: 0800 096 6360
f: 01233 750403
info@jacksons-fencing.co.uk

Web
www.jacksons-security.co.uk

Address
Jacksons Fencing
Stowting Common, Ashford TN25 6BN

Accreditation
ISO 9001:2000
Jacksons is a Secured by Design licensed company

Operational area
Worldwide

Additional entries
Perimeter security ➤ 178
Railings ➤ 179
Timber fencing and gates ➤ 191
Acoustic barriers ➤ 195

Jacksons Fencing

Gates, barriers and access control

Jacksons offers site security solutions to enhance access control and complement the company's expansive selection of perimeter fencing systems.
• **Swing, sliding and bi-folding speed gates**
Gates are available in manual/automated formats to suit a variety of applications catering for different usage requirements.
• **Barriers and turnstiles**
Static, manual and automated rising arm barriers, blockers and bollards can be configured to meet specific site demands.

Composition and manufacture

Jacksons has manufactured in Britain for over 70 years. Products are supplied with a 25-year service-life guarantee covering any defects associated with design, manufacturing, finish or fitness for purpose. Products are galvanised to BS EN 1461 as standard and can be powder coated to BS EN 13438.

Accreditation

All automated products are compliant with health and safety requirements/CE marked as required by law.
Jacksons is a Secured by Design licensed company and is ISO 9001:2000 accredited.

Sentry® sliding gate, clad with mesh

Road blocker

Bi-folding speed gate

ZAUN

Contact
Steve Roberts
t: 01902 796696
sales@zaun.co.uk

Web
www.zaun.co.uk

Address
Zaun Ltd
Steel Drive
Wolverhampton WV10 9ED

Accreditation
ISO 9001:2008, Secured by Design, CHAS

Affiliations
FCA, UVDB, PSSA, Constructionline

Additional entries
Perimeter fencing ➤ 164
Architectural fencing ➤ 173
Railings ➤ 175
Security fencing ➤ 182
DBS acoustic fencing system ➤ 198
Sports fencing systems ➤ 500

Zaun Ltd

Gates and access control

Zaun manufactures swing gates and sliding gates for factory entrances, airports, and military and public buildings, as well as sites that are short of space and require frequent access.

All gates are manufactured to specific customer specifications, allowing special features or dimensions to be easily accommodated.

They can incorporate various lock options, self-closing systems, spiked or serrated toppings, and electric fencing.

• Swing gates

Swing gates are made from strong rectangular hollow section, and are available with mesh or vertical bar infill to match the fence-line.

Heavy-duty (twin-wire) meshes have every vertical and horizontal wire fully welded inside the frame to add to the structure of the gate leaf.

Swing gates can be specified with internal, external or electric closing systems, and slide locks, mortise locks or combination locks.

Adjustable hinges, slam plates and rugged drop bolts (on double-leaf gates) are supplied.

Swing gates are also fitted with special slide latches to avoid finger trapping injuries.

Swing gates rated to LPCB 1175 SR1 and SR2 security standards are available.

• Sliding gates

Sliding gates can be supplied up to 10m wide as manual or automated systems with infill to match the fence-line. They are cantilevered so require no ground track, avoiding maintenance issues.

Supplied ready to fix, they are easy to install, and smooth and quiet to operate. Gates conform to BS EN 13241.

Diamond automated sliding gates are supplied ready to fix, are easy to install and are smooth and quiet running. These advanced gates conform to BS EN 13241 and come with a flashing warning light, passage lighting and security strip.

• Access control

Products are suitable for motorisation and electronic control. Systems tested to PAS 68 standards can be supplied to meet hostile vehicle mitigation (HVM) risk.

Single-leaf vehicle access gate

Double-leaf swing gate with vertical bar infill

Automated and manual cantilever gates are trackless and smooth running

Single-leaf swing gate at a sports field

Double-leaf swing gate

Access portals, with gate and turnstile entry (hostile vehicle mitigation/PAS 68 options are available)

Contact
t: 01788 550556
f: 01788 550265
info@autopa.co.uk

Web
www.autopa.co.uk

Address
AUTOPA Limited
Cottage Leap
Rugby CV21 3XP

Accreditation
ISO 9001:2008
ISO 14001:2004
OHSAS 18001:2007
Achilles Building Confidence

Affiliations
CHAS
Constructionline

Additional entries
Telescopic posts and automatic bollards ➤ 213
Height restrictors and swing gates ➤ 214
High visibility protection ➤ 217
Traffic flow plates and speed ramps ➤ 221
Bollards ➤ 226
Parking posts ➤ 228
Cycle shelters and compounds ➤ 242
Cycle stands ➤ 244
Illuminated bollards ➤ 268
Street furniture ➤ 283
Shelters, canopies and walkways ➤ 391

AUTOPA Limited

Rising arm barriers

AUTOPA rising arm barriers provide manual and automatic access control solutions for sites ranging from small commercial car parks to large industrial sites.

• **Manual arm barriers**

The AUTOPA *Manual Arm Barrier* is designed for commercial car parks and areas where access needs to be restricted outside of operating hours. Barriers can be locked in the raised and lowered position, the latter giving site owners complete peace of mind when the area is out of use. Manufactured from galvanised mild steel with an aluminium boom, the body is coated blue as standard but can be coated to any BS or RAL colour as required. Pogo sticks, catch posts and signage are available on request.

• **Automatic arm barriers**

AUTOPA *Automatic Arm Barriers* are used to control roadways on commercial and industrial sites and can be adapted to provide tailored access solutions.

Manufactured from high quality aluminium, they are available to suit road widths from 3 to 12m with a single arm.

Cards, fobs, keypads, intercoms and safety loops can be added as required to tailor systems to client requirements.

AUTOPA *Automatic Arm Barrier* access control systems can be customised to suit requirements

AUTOPA *Manual Arm Barrier* with slimline design and boom lengths from 3–7m

AUTOPA *Automatic Arm Barrier* coated green to match customer requirements – Welwyn Garden City

Manual Arm Barrier restricting access to private land

AUTOPA *Automatic Arm Barrier*

AUTOPA *Automatic Arm Barrier* with aluminium cabinet and boom for up to 8m roadways; high quality TRIACS for at least 5,000,000 movements

Contact

t: 01788 550556
f: 01788 550265
info@autopa.co.uk

Web
www.autopa.co.uk

Address
AUTOPA Limited
Cottage Leap
Rugby CV21 3XP

Accreditation
ISO 9001:2008
ISO 14001:2004
OHSAS 18001:2007
Achilles Building Confidence

Affiliations
CHAS
Constructiononline

Additional entries
Rising arm barriers ➤ 212
Height restrictors and swing gates ➤ 214
High visibility protection ➤ 217
Traffic flow plates and speed ramps ➤ 221
Bollards ➤ 226
Parking posts ➤ 228
Cycle shelters and compounds ➤ 242
Cycle stands ➤ 244
Illuminated bollards ➤ 268
Street furniture ➤ 283
Shelters, canopies and walkways ➤ 391

AUTOPA Limited

Telescopic posts and automatic bollards

AUTOPA telescopic posts and automatic bollards are used to control vehicular access to sites.

• RetractaPost

RetractaPost is a range of manually operated retractable and telescopic posts, suitable for commercial and residential use.

Posts are manufactured from galvanised mild steel or stainless steel in a wide range of round or square tube sizes.

Two locking options are available: the original *RetractaPost* is locked using a separate padlock, and the *RetractaPost GL* uses a high security 7 pin integrated lock to secure the posts.

To minimise trip risk, *RetractaPost* is lowered into its integrated socket when not in use.

All *RetractaPosts* are manually operated with lift-assist available on larger bollards to help users safely raise and lower the posts.

• Automatic bollards

The AUTOPA *Automatic Bollard* is designed for commercial and residential projects where aesthetics are important and the objective is to control vehicular access without impeding pedestrians. Powered by an efficient hydraulic system, they can be used intensively at all temperatures and in all weather conditions. Automatic bollards are available in stainless or mild steel in diameters of 127 or 275mm and heights of 600 or 800mm. To ensure that vehicles cannot pass between bollards AUTOPA recommends that they are spaced no more than 1.2m apart.

The bollards can be customised further with the addition of optional features such as LED lights, RAL colour-coating and traffic lights.

AUTOPA *Automatic Bollards* are compatible with a variety of control mechanisms including remote controls, keypads and swipe cards.

RetractaPost GL manually operated telescopic posts in stainless steel with square section – Aston Martin

AUTOPA *Automatic Bollard*, coated black

RetractaPost GL manual posts with square section

AUTOPA *Automatic Bollard* in stainless steel

High visibility *RetractaPosts GLs – Mercedes Benz*

AUTOPA *Automatic Bollard* – residential application

AUTOPA *Automatic Bollard* with card reader access

RetractaPost GL in lowered position

Contact
t: 01788 550556
f: 01788 550265
info@autopa.co.uk

Web
www.autopa.co.uk

Address
AUTOPA Limited
Cottage Leap
Rugby CV21 3XP

Accreditation
ISO 9001:2008
ISO 14001:2004
OHSAS 18001:2007
Achilles Building Confidence

Affiliations
CHAS
Constructionline

Additional entries
Rising arm barriers ➤ 212
Telescopic posts and automatic bollards ➤ 213
High visibility protection ➤ 217
Traffic flow plates and speed ramps ➤ 221
Bollards ➤ 226
Parking posts ➤ 228
Cycle shelters and compounds ➤ 242
Cycle stands ➤ 244
Illuminated bollards ➤ 268
Street furniture ➤ 283
Shelters, canopies and walkways ➤ 391

AUTOPA Limited

Height restrictors and swing gates

AUTOPA manufactures height restrictors and swing gates to help control vehicular access to car parks, commercial and industrial sites.

- **Height restrictors**

AUTOPA *Height Restrictors* are designed for use on industrial, commercial and public realm sites to prevent high-sided vehicles such as HGVs or caravans from accessing areas. They provide a practical and durable method of access control. AUTOPA *Height Restrictors* have a standard height clearance of 2.05m, with other heights available to order. Single spans are available up to 7.0m.

Swing gates can be added to height restrictors to further secure areas outside operating hours.

- **Swing gates**

AUTOPA *Swing Gates* are an easy-to-use, cost effective and durable solution for securing site entrances and car parks outside operating hours. Swing gates are available in a range of widths and are ready to use immediately once installed. Safety features incorporated as standard include a self-latching catch post, short leading edge beam and a low bottom edge. These features reduce the chance of a gate swinging open unexpectedly and decrease the risk of injury should it do so. Gates can be locked in both open and closed positions with a padlock – a second catch post is required to secure the gate in the open position. Swing gates can be supplied separately or with height restrictors.

Manufacture and composition

AUTOPA height restrictors and swing gates are manufactured from mild steel at the company's Rugby works in the UK.

Finish and appearance

Standard finish is galvanised and coated red, with other BS or RAL colours available on request.

AUTOPA *Height Restrictor* and *Swing Gate* used to control access to car park

AUTOPA *Height Restrictors*, coated red as standard

AUTOPA *Height Restrictor*, custom colour coating

AUTOPA *Swing Gate* used on industrial site requiring occasional access – single spans are available up to 7m. Gates can be locked in open or closed positions.

AUTOPA *Swing Gate* with catch post

Contact
Anthony Prosser
t: 01564 773188
entryparkingpost@aol.com

Web
www.entryparkingposts.net

Address
Entry Parking Posts
Norton Reach
Norton Green Lane
Knowle
Solihull B93 8PL

Affiliations
British Parking Association (BPA)

Entry Parking Posts

Access control

Entry Parking Posts manufactures manual barriers and height restrictors for roads and car parks.
• **Height restriction barriers (HRBs)**
Dwyfor HRBs have a bi-parting horizontal beam that can be opened for service vehicles. They are easily operated at ground level. *Dunstable* gauge rails can be suspended under an HRB.
• **Lifting and swing manual barriers**
Counterbalanced with gas struts, *Didcot* and *Dover* lifting barriers are easy to operate. *Swindon* swing barriers allow for a wide opening angle.

Dwyfor barrier/*Dunstable* twin-height gauge rails

8m-long *Dwyfor* height restriction barrier

Dwyfor height restriction barrier

7m-long *Dwyfor* height restriction barrier

Dwyfor height restriction barrier

Swindon manual swing barrier

Didcot manual barrier

Additional entries
Direction and speed restrictors ➤ 224

Contact

Paul Owens (sales)
Scott Chafer (technical)
t: 01484 401414
f: 01484 721398
info@asfco.co.uk

Web
www.asfco.co.uk

Address
Architectural Street Furnishings Ltd
Priory Road
off Armytage Road
Brighouse HD6 1PY

Accreditation
ISO 9001:2008

Additional entries
Bollards ➤ 225
Bespoke street furniture ➤ 277
Seats and benches ➤ 325
Bespoke metalwork ➤ 414

Architectural Street Furnishings

Post and rail systems

Architectural Street Furnishings (ASF) has designed and manufactured high-quality street furniture in the UK for over 25 years.
Fully bespoke products are offered alongside a catalogue of standard designs.
Materials include cast iron, mild steel, stainless steel, aluminium, recycled plastic, timber and granite. Styles range from traditional, to complement classic architecture and urban layouts; to modern, for dynamic spaces or architectural designs.

Bespoke cast iron post and panel – Blackburn

ASF 211 Quayside cast iron post and rail – Southport

Bespoke adaption of ASF 211 Quayside post and rail – Llanelli

ASF 5006 post and bespoke panels with integral step units – Sale

Bespoke hard anodised aluminium post and rail – De Warr Pavilion, Bexhill-on-Sea

Contact
t: 01788 550556
f: 01788 550265
info@autopa.co.uk

Web
www.autopa.co.uk

Address
AUTOPA Limited
Cottage Leap
Rugby CV21 3XP

Accreditation
ISO 9001:2008
ISO 14001:2004
OHSAS 18001:2007
Achilles Building Confidence

Affiliations
CHAS
Constructionline

Additional entries
Rising arm barriers ➤ 212
Telescopic posts and automatic bollards ➤ 213
Height restrictors and swing gates ➤ 214
Traffic flow plates and speed ramps ➤ 221
Bollards ➤ 226
Parking posts ➤ 228
Cycle shelters and compounds ➤ 242
Cycle stands ➤ 244
Illuminated bollards ➤ 268
Street furniture ➤ 283
Shelters, canopies and walkways ➤ 391

AUTOPA Limited

High visibility protection

AUTOPA's high visibility protective furniture is
designed to reduce the risk of accidents and
damage to property at industrial sites,
warehouses and distribution centres.
* **Black & Yellow range**
Black & Yellow is a practical and durable product
range that includes corner protection hoops,
perimeter barriers, bollards and low-level
protection rails.

Composition and manufacture
Products are manufactured from galvanised mild
steel. They are designed to withstand the knocks
and bumps which inevitably occur in busy
warehouse environments.

Finish and appearance
Products are coated black and fitted with yellow
high visibility tape as standard.
Other standard RAL or BS colour coatings are
available on request.
High visibility tape is available in yellow, red,
orange, white, blue and black.
Honeycomb tape, which is suitable for use on
highways, is available on request.

AUTOPA's *High Visibility* range is designed to reduce the risk of accidents on site

AUTOPA *Black & Yellow Perimeter Barrier*

Products can be coated to any BS or RAL colour

AUTOPA *Black & Yellow Bollard 1500*

AUTOPA *Black & Yellow Low Level Protection Rail*

AUTOPA *Black & Yellow Corner Protection Hoop*

Rectangular mild steel high visibility bollard

Furnitubes

Contact
Sales
t: 020 8378 3261
f: 020 8378 3250
esibook@furnitubes.com

Web
www.furnitubes.com

Address
Furnitubes International Ltd
3rd Floor
Meridian House
Royal Hill
Greenwich
London SE10 8RD

Affiliations
Constructionline
Railway Industry Supplier Qualification Scheme
(RISQS)
Builder's Profile

Accreditation
ISO 9001:2008
ISO 14001:2004
OHSAS 18001:2007

Operational area
Worldwide

Country of manufacture
UK

Additional entries
Bollards ➤ 230
Cycle parking ➤ 241
Signage ➤ 260
Co-ordinated street furniture ➤ 308
Seating ➤ 316
Bespoke seating ➤ 331
Litter bins ➤ 356

Furnitubes International Ltd

Railings and guardrails

Furnitubes offers an extensive range of railing systems for protecting pedestrians, buildings and motorists. Products range from simple independent steel railing panels, to systems that can be installed on variable site conditions, and made-to-measure products designed for specific sites.

Furnitubes also supplies gates that can be incorporated into a line of railings, or installed as stand-alone items.

Composition and manufacture

The standard range of railing products includes designs predominantly in mild steel, stainless steel and cast iron. Components can also be supplied in other materials such as aluminium, bronze and timber. A wide range of finishes is available.

Design services

Furnitubes' team of product designers is able to assist in the process of designing site-specific bespoke railings, from concept through to detailed design and installation. Technical and budgetary advice is also available.

Linx400 guardrail with *Kenton* cap

Linx400 guardrail with *Kenton* cap

Linx200 knee rail with *Ashton* cap

PGRM guardrail

OKR guardrail

Hammersmith post and rail

Linx300 guardrail with *Knightsbridge* cap

Bespoke railing based on *Linx100* design

Marshalls

Creating Better Spaces

Contact
t: 0870 444 6217
f: 0870 442 7725
esi.marshalls@web-response.co.uk

Web
www.marshalls.co.uk/commercial

Address
Marshalls Street Furniture
Landscape House, Premier Way,
Lowfields Business Park, Elland HX5 9HT

Additional entries
Bollards ➤ 235
Cycle parking ➤ 249
Signage and wayfinding ➤ 264
Illumination ➤ 272
Co-ordinated street furniture ➤ 278
Protective street furniture ➤ 280
Co-ordinated street furniture ➤ 282
Seats and benches ➤ 320
Litter bins ➤ 357
Planters ➤ 378
Tree protection ➤ 526

Marshalls plc

Protective post and rail

Marshalls has many years of experience in specialist protective post and rail systems. Modern materials such as steel, stainless steel and *Ferrocast* are used to create restraint systems that increase the safety of pedestrians and other non-vehicle highway users, while integrating with their architectural surroundings.

Design services

Robust and elegant bespoke products can be created by Marshalls' experienced, specialist in-house design team.

Sineu Graff Series 9600 post, rail and tension wire

Geo bespoke handrail – The Sage, Newcastle

Ferrocast Harbour post and rail with DDA handrail

Ferrocast Waterside II post and rail system – Rhyl

Geo illuminated handrail

Bespoke handrail system – The Sage, Gateshead Quays, Newcastle

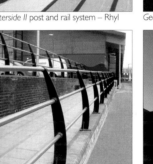
Ollerton Festival post and rail system – Tipton

Illuminated handrail – Glasgow

Illuminated bespoke handrail – Coventry

Contact
Graham Howard
t: 01264 811600
info@sarumhardwood.co.uk

Web
www.sarumhardwood.co.uk

Address
Sarum Hardwood Structures Ltd
Unit 1B, Chilbolton Down Farm
Stockbridge SO20 6BU

Accreditation
ISO 9001:2000

Affiliations
Timber Research and Development Association
(TRADA)

Operational area
England and Wales

Additional entries
Bridges ➤ 158

Sarum Hardwood Structures Ltd

N1 timber highway parapets

Sarum Hardwood Structures Ltd (SHS) has been
constructing hardwood structures throughout
England and Wales since the early 1980s.
• **Hardwood vehicle parapets**
SHS specialises in the provision of hardwood
timber vehicle parapets that are designed and
tested to the latest N1 highway standards.
The parapets are aesthetically more sympathetic
than aluminium or concrete systems when used
in rural locations.

SHS N1 highway parapets

Bridge with SHS highway parapets

Contact

t: 01788 550556
f: 01788 550265
info@autopa.co.uk

Web
www.autopa.co.uk

Address
AUTOPA Limited
Cottage Leap
Rugby CV21 3XP

Accreditation
ISO 9001:2008
ISO 14001:2004
OHSAS 18001:2007
Achilles Building Confidence

Affiliations
CHAS
Constructionline

Additional entries
Rising arm barriers ➤ 212
Telescopic posts and automatic bollards ➤ 213
Height restrictors and swing gates ➤ 214
High visibility protection ➤ 217
Bollards ➤ 226
Parking posts ➤ 228
Cycle shelters and compounds ➤ 242
Cycle stands ➤ 244
Illuminated bollards ➤ 268
Street furniture ➤ 283
Shelters, canopies and walkways ➤ 391

AUTOPA Limited

Traffic flow plates and speed ramps

AUTOPA access control solutions include rising arm barriers, telescopic bollards and sliding gates, as well as products to control the directional flow and speed of traffic.

• One way flow plates

AUTOPA's *One Way Flow Plate* controls the direction and flow of traffic. Units are available either cast into the ground or surface-mounted. Manufactured from galvanised mild steel, the top plate is coated yellow as standard to ensure high visibility in all conditions. They are best used in a group to ensure vehicles cannot circumvent the desired direction of flow.

• Speed ramps

AUTOPA *Speed Ramps* are suitable for a wide range of vehicle types, including heavy goods vehicles with pneumatic tyres up to 44 tonnes. They are fully modular allowing any length of speed ramp to be created.

Manufactured from heavy-duty recycled plastic, the speed ramps have integrated reflectors to ensure visibility in all conditions.

Speed Ramp 50 is designed to reduce traffic speed to 10mph and is 50mm high.

Speed Ramp 75 is designed to reduce traffic speed to 5mph and is 75mm high.

AUTOPA *One Way Flow Plate* controls the direction of traffic flow

336mm wide; 115mm aboveground height

AUTOPA *One Way Flow Plate* cast in ground

Speed Ramp 50 (10mph max) is a fully modular system, allowing any length of speed ramp to be created

Speed Ramp 50 (10mph max) is highly visible

AUTOPA speed ramps improve road safety

![Marshalls logo]

Marshalls

Creating Better Spaces

Contact
t: 0870 444 6217
f: 0870 442 7725
esi.marshalls@web-response.co.uk

Web
www.marshalls.co.uk/commercial/traffic-calming

Address
Marshalls plc
Landscape House
Premier Way
Lowfields Business Park
Elland HX5 9HT

Additional entries
Priora permeable block paving ➤ 76
Linear drainage systems ➤ 80
Combined kerb & drainage systems ➤ 84
Kerb systems ➤ 86
Concrete paving systems ➤ 104
Concrete block paving and setts ➤ 112
Natural stone ➤ 124

Marshalls plc

Traffic calming systems

Marshalls traffic calming products are manufactured in accurate preformed shapes and profiles, to quality controlled manufacturing processes, ensuring their compliance to Standards and specifications.

- **Ramp systems**

Kerb-to-kerb ramp systems are made to measure. Ramp heights can be adjusted to help meet the target oncoming traffic speed decrease. *Sinusoidal Ramp System* and *S Ramp* are precast reinforced concrete ramp systems.
Speedcheck is a concrete starter block ramp system that acts as a restraint allowing ramps to be constructed using block paving.

- **Speed cushions**

Reinforced Concrete Speed Cushions are designed to reduce traffic speeds. Four sizes are produced in plateau and domed top designs.
Rubber Speed Cushions are modular segmental units that can be used for instant traffic calming.

- **Traffic islands**

Cycle Segregation Unit creates a protective barrier between cyclists and vehicles. Preformed reinforced *Concrete Traffic Islands* are produced in Satellite or Refuge configurations.

- **Traffic blocks**

Interlocking Concrete Traffic Blocks are used to create temporary junctions on busy roads.

S Ramp reinforced concrete ramp system

Sinusoidal reinforced concrete ramp system

Speedcheck concrete starter block ramp system

S Ramp reinforced concrete ramp system

Cycle Segregation Unit

Concrete *Refuge Island* for wide roads

Temporary interlocking *Traffic Blocks*

Reinforced concrete speed cushion, plateau top

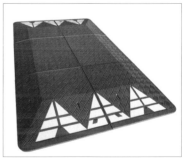

Rubber speed cushions

Rubber speed bump

Contact
Anthony Prosser
t: 01564 773188
entryparkingpost@aol.com

Web
www.entryparkingposts.net

Address
Entry Parking Posts
Norton Reach
Norton Green Lane
Knowle
Solihull B93 8PL

Affiliations
British Parking Association (BPA)

Additional entries
Access control ➤ 215

Entry Parking Posts

Direction and speed restrictors

Entry Parking Posts manufactures traffic direction restrictors (TDRs) and speed restrictors for cars, buses and HGVs.

Alligator Teeth® TDRs enforce vehicle direction in a one-way traffic system at entrances or exits.

Alligator Jaws TDR units, rated at 10mph, lie flush when lowered.

Alligator Ramp TDSR-5 units are surface-fixed speed ramps with *Alligator Teeth*®. They provide one-way speed restrictors for high-volume traffic, and are suitable for all vehicles except tracked.

Alligator Teeth traffic direction restrictor

Alligator Ramp TDSR-5 speed ramp

Alligator Ramp

Alligator Jaws traffic direction restrictor in a trough

Alligator Teeth® with security spikes

Alligator Jaws traffic direction restrictor

Alligator Teeth traffic direction enforcers

Alligator Teeth with signage

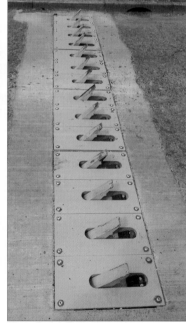
Alligator Teeth traffic direction restrictor

Alligator Jaws traffic direction restrictor

Alligator Ramp in a car park

Contact
Paul Owens (sales)
Scott Chafer (technical)
t: 01484 401414
f: 01484 721398
info@asfco.co.uk

Web
www.asfco.co.uk

Address
Architectural Street Furnishings Ltd
Priory Road
off Armytage Road
Brighouse HD6 1PY

Accreditation
ISO 9001:2008

Additional entries
Post and rail systems ➤ 216
Bespoke street furniture ➤ 277
Seats and benches ➤ 325
Bespoke metalwork ➤ 414

Architectural Street Furnishings

Bollards

Architectural Street Furnishings (ASF) has designed and manufactured high-quality street furniture in the UK for over 15 years.
Bollards are produced in cast iron, stainless steel, steel and composite, granite and recycled plastic. Illuminated bollards are also available.
Standard styles range from traditional to modern. Bespoke designs can feature coats of arms, insignias, lettering or signage.

ASF Cubist granite bollards – Blackburn

ASF 129 recycled cast iron spherical bollards

ASF 134 Whitwood cast iron bollards – nr Wakefield

ASF 5009 stainless steel bollards with visibility band

ASF 5001 stainless steel bollards with polished bands – Blackburn

Contact
t: 01788 550556
f: 01788 550265
info@autopa.co.uk

Web
www.autopa.co.uk

Address
AUTOPA Limited
Cottage Leap
Rugby CV21 3XP

Accreditation
ISO 9001:2008
ISO 14001:2004
OHSAS 18001:2007
Achilles Building Confidence

Affiliations
CHAS
Constructionline

Additional entries
Rising arm barriers ➤ 212
Telescopic posts and automatic bollards ➤ 213
Height restrictors and swing gates ➤ 214
High visibility protection ➤ 217
Traffic flow plates and speed ramps ➤ 221
Parking posts ➤ 228
Cycle shelters and compounds ➤ 242
Cycle stands ➤ 244
Illuminated bollards ➤ 268
Street furniture ➤ 283
Shelters, canopies and walkways ➤ 391

AUTOPA Limited

Bollards

AUTOPA manufactures an extensive range of bollards and posts in stainless steel and galvanised mild steel at its Rugby works. AUTOPA bollards are used around pedestrian precincts, pavements, play and parking areas, as part of traffic calming measures and as a deterrent to ram-raiders. Most designs are available flanged, ragged or removable to suit ground conditions on site.

• **Galvanised mild steel posts and bollards**
AUTOPA mild steel bollards are suitable for a wide range of applications. All are galvanised as standard to ensure longevity and can be coated to any standard RAL or BS colour.
Outside diameters range from 48 to 406mm, with the most popular diameters held in stock for short lead times.

• **Stainless steel posts and bollards**
AUTOPA stainless steel bollards are suitable for contemporary, high-quality applications. They are manufactured in grade 304 and grade 316 stainless steel. Outside diameters range from 60 to 204mm.

• **Ornamental bollards**
Attractive, robust and long-lasting, AUTOPA's *GFC* ornamental bollards combine the strength of steel with the design benefits of cast iron.
They are made from mild steel tube with decorative cast iron rings and caps.
Ornamental bollards are galvanised or galvanised and coated to any standard BS or RAL colour. Other options include the addition of eyelets, hooks and chains.

• **Reinforced bollards**
AUTOPA reinforced bollards are designed to protect perimeters on busy commercial and retail sites. All have a strong galvanised mild steel core over which an external sleeve is fitted. The addition of the core strengthens the bollard, increasing its resistance to ram-raiders, a quality that is amplified when the core is filled with concrete. Sleeves are available in galvanised mild steel, stainless steel and hardwearing MDPE. Available ragged only for ground fixing.

AUTOPA plain square stainless steel bollards – Aston Martin, Newcastle

AUTOPA plain round stainless steel bollards with yellow reflective banding

AUTOPA stainless steel bollards with eyelets and chains

AUTOPA plain round stainless steel bollards for retail park; grade 304 and 316 options available

AUTOPA plain round stainless steel bollards identifying pedestrian areas

AUTOPA mild steel mitre-top bollards in black

AUTOPA stainless steel mitre-top bollards

AUTOPA GFC 5000 ornamental bollards with chain. Mild steel tube with high grade, impact-resistant, malleable cast iron caps and rings.

GFC7000 ornamental bollard; cast iron cap and ring

AUTOPA

Contact
t: 01788 550556
f: 01788 550265
info@autopa.co.uk

Web
www.autopa.co.uk

Address
AUTOPA Limited
Cottage Leap
Rugby CV21 3XP

Accreditation
ISO 9001:2008
ISO 14001:2004
OHSAS 18001:2007
Achilles Building Confidence

Affiliations
CHAS
Constructionline

Additional entries
Rising arm barriers ➤ 212
Telescopic posts and automatic bollards ➤ 213
Height restrictors and swing gates ➤ 214
High visibility protection ➤ 217
Traffic flow plates and speed ramps ➤ 221
Bollards ➤ 226
Cycle shelters and compounds ➤ 242
Cycle stands ➤ 244
Illuminated bollards ➤ 268
Street furniture ➤ 283
Shelters, canopies and walkways ➤ 391

AUTOPA Limited

Parking posts

AUTOPA patented the first parking post in 1959 and has been manufacturing them in the UK ever since. AUTOPA parking posts provide a simple and cost-effective way to secure individual parking spaces from unauthorised users.

All parking post are lockable in the up and down positions. There are three locking options for the *Hinged Parking Post* and the *Stealth Parking Post*:
1. Randomly keyed – posts have different locks.
2. Identically keyed – posts are keyed to the same key number.
3. Master Suited – posts are randomly keyed, but can be unlocked using a master key.

• **AUTOPA Hinged Parking Post**
The AUTOPA *Hinged Parking Post* was patented in 1959, and over 50 years on, is one of the preferred choices for protecting individual parking spaces throughout Britain.
The reliable design guarantees parking spaces will be available when required; the reflective, high-visibility band ensures parking posts are seen.
It is available in a galvanised, galvanised and coated, or stainless steel finish.

• **AUTOPA Stealth Parking Post**
The *Stealth Parking Post* has all the benefits of the original *Hinged Parking Post* but with the further advantage of a fully flush to ground level socket.
When lowered, the post disappears into its integrated socket and is covered by the integral lid. It is available in a galvanised, galvanised and coated or stainless steel finish.

• **AUTOPA TOPLOK Parking Post**
TOPLOK is the padlockable variant of the original *Hinged Parking Post*. Round and square designs are available. *TOPLOK* parking posts can be supplied in a galvanised, galvanised and coated, or stainless steel (round only) finish.

• **Sprung Boundary Post**
The *Sprung Boundary Post* is designed to mark the edges of car parking spaces. The base has a spring that enables it to absorb low speed impacts, deflect up to 30 degrees from vertical and return to its original position. It is available in a galvanised or galvanised and coated finish.

AUTOPA *Hinged Parking Post* colour-coated yellow

AUTOPA *TOPLOK Parking Post* in mild steel

AUTOPA *Hinged Parking Post* in stainless steel

AUTOPA *Square TOPLOK Parking Posts*

AUTOPA *Hinged Parking Post* in lowered position

AUTOPA *Hinged Parking Post* in stainless steel

AUTOPA *Stealth Parking Post* in mild steel

AUTOPA *Stealth Parking Post* in lowered position

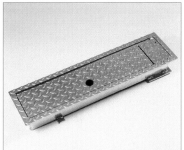

Fully flush to ground level socket

AUTOPA *Stealth Parking Post* in upright position

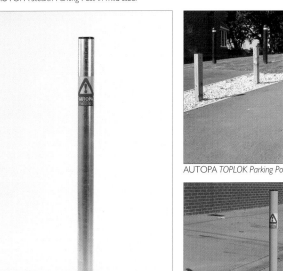

AUTOPA *Sprung Boundary Post* in stainless steel

AUTOPA *TOPLOK Parking Post*, locked in place

AUTOPA *Sprung Boundary Post* coated yellow

AUTOPA *Stealth Parking Post* provides a discreet way to secure parking spaces

Furnitubes

Contact
Sales
t: 020 8378 3261
f: 020 8378 3250
esibook@furnitubes.com

Web
www.furnitubes.com

Address
Furnitubes International Ltd
3rd Floor
Meridian House
Royal Hill
Greenwich
London SE10 8RD

Affiliations
Constructionline
Railway Industry Supplier Qualification Scheme
(RISQS)
Builder's Profile

Accreditation
ISO 9001:2008
ISO 14001:2004
OHSAS 18001:2007

Operational area
Worldwide

Country of manufacture
UK

Additional entries
Railings and guardrails ➤ 218
Cycle parking ➤ 241
Signage ➤ 260
Co-ordinated street furniture ➤ 308
Seating ➤ 316
Bespoke seating ➤ 331
Litter bins ➤ 356

Furnitubes International Ltd

Bollards

Furnitubes manufactures and supplies one of the largest selections of bollards available in the UK. Over 80 ranges are available in materials including cast iron, aluminium, steel and timber. The company exclusively manufactures and supplies the *Bell* bollard.

Design services

Furnitubes' design team is able to offer advice and assistance in the design of bespoke products, from concept through to detailed design and installation. Technical and budgetary advice is also available.

Installation

All bollards can be supplied as root-fixed versions, with many also available as surface-mounted or removable with a ground socket.

Bell 100 cast iron bollards

City cast iron bollards

Doric cast iron bollards

Cannon cast iron bollard

Capital cast aluminium removable bollards

Corporation cast iron bollards

Global cast iron bollards

Epping timber bollards

Zenith stainless steel bollards

Manchester round base cast iron bollards

Linx400 steel bollard with stainless Kenton cap

Transport stainless steel bollards

Kenton double-neck steel bollards

Zenith Sloped stainless steel bollards

Stirling steel bollards

Harrow double-ring steel bollards

Telescopic stainless steel bollards

Avon Barrier Corporation Ltd

High-security bollards

Avon Barrier manufactures, installs and maintains high-security vehicle and pedestrian access control systems throughout the UK and worldwide.

The company offers high-security PAS 68 crash tested bollards, including *Scimitar* bollards, which can be static or hydraulically operated. The bollards are available with a choice of sleeves or finishes, including stainless steel or bespoke paint. *Scimitar* bollards can be interfaced with access control systems.

Contact
Sales
t: 0117 953 5252
f: 0117 953 5373
sales@avon-barrier.co.uk

Web
www.avon-barrier.co.uk

Address
Avon Barrier Corporation Ltd
149 South Liberty Lane
Ashton Vale Trading Estate
Bristol BS3 2TL

Accreditation
ISO 9001:2008
Constructionline
SAFEcontractor

Affiliations
The Perimeter Security Suppliers Associaton (PSSA)

Additional entries
Gates, barriers and access control systems ➤ 208

Stainless steel *Scimitar* bollards

Stainless steel *Scimitar* bollards

PAS 68 high-security bollards

Stainless steel bollards

PAS 68 high-security bollards

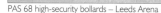

PAS 68 high-security bollards – Leeds Arena

Bollards – Scottish Parliament

PAS 68 high-security bollards

Static bollards

Contact

Lottie Bagust (Sales)
Dylan Bagust (Technical)
t: 01285 740488
bollards@bandbinnovations.co.uk

Web

www.bandbbollards.co.uk
www.bandbinnovations.co.uk

Address

BandB Innovations Ltd
Unit 2, Dovecot Workshops
Barnsley Park Estate
Barnsley
Cirencester GL7 5EG

Country of manufacture

UK

Additional entries

Litter bins ➤ 353

BandB Innovations Ltd

Removable and static bollards

BandB Innovations produces a range of traditional bollards with contemporary designs. They can be used in a rural environment or as part of a modern development.

Bollards are available as static or removable units. Two locking socket systems are offered: stainless steel heavy-duty and galvanised steel mid-duty. Both systems can be used for traffic control and, once removed, leave no trip hazard. An unobtrusive plate sits flush with the road or path and is completely safe to walk or drive over. Removable lockable bollards are available with a lifting hole and steel bar, allowing a simple twist and lift action to remove them.

Composition and manufacture

Each bollard is created from a single piece of hand-turned timber to form a unique unit. *Combination* and *Classic* bollards are available in durable oak or western red cedar.

Dimensions

Heavy-duty removable bollard with 6mm thick stainless steel foot and baseplate: above-ground height – 980mm; diameter – 170mm.
Light-duty removable bollard with 3mm thick galvanised mild steel foot and baseplate: above-ground height – 980mm; diameter – 140mm.

Classic removable western red cedar bollard – Center Parcs Woburn Forest

Unobtrusive plate sits flush with the road

Classic removable western red cedar bollard

Combination heavy-duty removable oak bollard

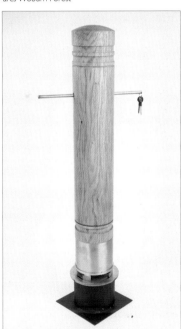

Classic heavy-duty removable oak bollard

QUALITY RECYCLED PRODUCTS

Contact
Michael Janes (Sales)
t: 029 2086 4095
m: 07745 189022
mike@goplastic.co.uk

Sarah Mitchell
(Marketing and general enquiries)
t: 01920 469926
m: 07887 528434
sarah@goplastic.co.uk

Web
www.goplastic.co.uk

Address
GoPlastic Ltd
Waverley
40 St Martins Road
Caerphilly CF83 1EJ

Accreditation
Constructionline

CPD
The economic value of recycled products

Operational area
UK

Additional entries
Recycled plastic profiles for decks, boardwalks,
jetties and bridges ➤ 143
Recycled plastic fencing ➤ 189
Recycled plastic seating ➤ 332

GoPlastic Ltd

Recycled plastic bollards

GoPlastic Ltd specialises in recycled plastic products made from *Govaplast*®, a high-quality, solid plastic material that is graffiti and vandal resistant. It requires no maintenance or treatments, and will not crack, rot or shrink. It contains a UV stabiliser and has an expected life span of 40+ years.
The company offers bollards made from 100% recycled *Govaplast*®.

Govaplast® recycled plastic dome-top bollards

Govaplast® recycled plastic square bollard

Govaplast® recycled plastic dome-top bollards

Govaplast® recycled plastic square bollards

Govaplast® recycled plastic square bollards

Protective post and rail ➤ 219
Cycle parking ➤ 249
Signage and wayfinding ➤ 264
Illumination ➤ 272
Co-ordinated street furniture ➤ 278
Protective street furniture ➤ 280
Co-ordinated street furniture ➤ 282
Seats and benches ➤ 320
Litter bins ➤ 357
Planters ➤ 378
Tree protection ➤ 526

Marshalls plc

Bollards

Marshalls offers an extensive choice of bollards in a variety of materials and styles.

The range includes static and telescopic bollards, as well as hoop barriers, which can be tailored to suit any project, meaning that a product can be provided to suit every application.

Anti-ram and anti-terrorism bollards, tested to PAS 68 specification, are available upon request.

Rhino RS001 stainless steel lift out bollard

Loci steel bollards can be colour customised

Ferrocast Waterside II bollard

Bespoke *Ferrocast* bollards – Hemel Hempstead

Manchester Ferrocast bollards are extremely strong and will not rust. Anti-ram specification available.

Rhino RS004 stainless steel bollard – Mayflower

Geo lift-out bollard – Camden

Rhino RT SS5 stainless steel telescopic bollards – BMW garage, Borehamwood

Carya conical bollards, designed by Alfredo Farné

Street Furnishings Ltd

Bollards

Street Furnishings provides a complete range of products for highway and traffic management, parking control and pedestrian safety.
A wide range of bollards is available including fixed, flexible, removeable, lockable, fold-down, telescopic, baseplated, decorative, reflective, illuminated and anti-ram bollards.
A choice of materials can also be selected including cast polymer, cast iron, hardwood, softwood, mild and stainless steel, rubber, plastic, concrete and recycled materials.

Contact
Tony Barnes (sales)
t: 0118 940 4717
f: 0118 940 3216
mail@streetfurnishings.co.uk

Web
www.streetfurnishings.co.uk

Address
Street Furnishings Ltd
Festival House
Mumbery Hill
Wargrave
Reading RG10 8EE

Accreditation
ISO 9001:2008

Additional entries
Solar sign lighting systems and reflective bollards
➤ 276

Heritage range

Sentinel range

Manchester removable bollard

Bollards for highway and traffic management, parking control and pedestrian safety

Timber bollard

Contact
Richard Williams
t: 07890 585768
uk@urbastyle.com

Web
www.urbastyle.com

Address
URBASTYLE®
Severn House
Hazell Drive
Newport NP10 8FY

Additional entries

Silkstone Fasonado paving ➤ 109
Architectural concrete street furniture ➤ 312
Architectural concrete benches and seats ➤ 340
Architectural concrete planters ➤ 381

URBASTYLE®

Architectural concrete bollards

URBASTYLE® offers landscape bollards in architectural concrete. They range from simple and functional products, through to contemporary designs that have evolved in collaboration with creative product designers from throughout Europe.

Products such as barrier and parking posts, spheres and eclectic designs can enhance the aesthetics of a landscape without compromising on security or traffic management.

An extensive choice of shapes and sizes is available from the standard range, while cost-effective custom-made options are often produced to clients' requirements.

Finish and appearance

Bollards are produced in four finishes: fair faced, micro etched, polished and velvet.

The four standard colours are white, silver grey, dark grey and buff. Other colour/aggregate combinations can be produced to order. All products have factory-applied waterproofing and anti-graffiti protection.

Dimensions

Standard bollards are available from 15 to 115cm high and in various diameters and cross sections.

Paperboat bollards

Cubo bollards

Porta bollards

Hanso bollards

Chunk bollards

Fino bollards

Round bollards

Semi bollards

Stabilo bollards

MACS
AUTOMATED BOLLARD SYSTEMS

Contact
Damian Corcoran, Projects Manager
t: 0161 320 6462
f: 0161 320 6463
damian@macs-bollards.com

Web
www.macs-bollards.com

Address
Macs Automated Bollard Systems Ltd
Unit 8.1b
Tameside Business Park
Windmill Lane
Denton
Manchester M34 3QS

Accreditation
TR2207A Highways Agency Approval
CHAS
SafeContractor
Constructionline
Eurosafe UK

Macs Automated Bollard Systems Ltd

Automatic rising bollards

Macs offers perimeter security products and services for any project. Services include installation of automatic bollards to Highways Agency standard for public realm, hostile vehicle mitigation (HVM) bollards for high security areas, and installation and supply of automatic and manual retractable bollards for commercial sites. Retractable power distribution towers, static hoops and barriers, access control systems, and maintenance services are also available.

Retractable energy and services distribution tower

Manual retractable bollards – BMW car dealership

Public realm traffic management

Highways approved automatic bollard

Pedestrianisation scheme

Hostile Vehicle Mitigation (HVM) system

Hoop barriers – Mini car dealership

Bollard maintenance service

Kent Stainless (Wexford) Ltd

In-ground units

Kent Stainless is a specialist stainless steel fabricator that offers a range of in-ground units. Applications include stadia, town squares, retail parks, markets and marinas.

Three main categories of in-ground units are available.

- **Electrical in-ground unit**

The electrical in-ground unit is used to supply power to public areas while reducing cable clutter. Three different sizes are available.

Type 1 (KIGU400/450) has a 450x400mm recessed cover.

Type 2 (KIGU450/600) has a 450x600mm recessed cover.

Type 3 (KIGU600/600) has a 600x600mm recessed cover.

Power capacities increase in line with the size of the units.

- **Wastewater in-ground unit**

The *Kent In-Ground Grey Water Unit (KIGGWU400/45)0* is used to dispose of any produce/grey water left over from public vendors.

- **Water supply unit**

The *Kent Potable Water Unit (KIGPWU400/450)* is used to supply clean water to vendors in public squares. It can also be used for soft landscape irrigation and as a power hose connection point.

Contact

UK freefone: 0800 376 8377
t: +353 (0) 53 914 3216
f: +353 (0) 53 914 1802
info@kentstainless.com

Web
www.kentstainless.com

Address
Kent Stainless (Wexford) Ltd
Ardcavan
Wexford
Republic of Ireland

Accreditation
ISO 9001:2008
ISO 14001:2004
OHSAS 18001:2007

Country of manufacture
Republic of Ireland

Additional entries
Lift-assist manholes ➤ 131
Heelproof ventilation access grilles ➤ 132
Wayfinding signage ➤ 262
Planters ➤ 383

Type 1 in-ground power unit (KIGU400/450)

EP008 electrical enclosure with DP004 data outlets

Type 4 in-ground unit – potable water

Type 5 in-ground unit – grey water

Type 2 in-ground power unit (KIGU600/450)

Contact

George Parker
t: 020 8277 0208
gparker@popuppower.co.uk

Web

www.popuppower.co.uk

Address

Pop UP Power® Ltd
PO Box 1447
Ilford IG2 6GT

Operational area

UK, Ireland

Pop UP Power® Ltd
Retractable power units

Pop UP Power® retractable service units provide electricity, water and air supply to public spaces. The company works closely with architects, specifiers, contractors and industry professionals to design the most effective outdoor power solution for specific projects.

• **Pop up units**

Pop up units provide a secure and silent outdoor power source for events such as markets, heritage sites, town centres, urban areas, universities, recreational areas and stadiums. Units are manufactured in AISI 304 stainless steel and tested to BS EN 124 B125 load classification. Recessed lids accept paving or other infill.

• **In-ground/flip lid units**

In-ground and flip lid units feature an improved design with a new hydraulic system to open the lid, a sturdier case, and a more practical arrangement for the power sockets and cables within the unit. Units provide a safe and secure power source with the lid locked down, and only the power cable protruding.

• **Power bollards**

Power bollards can be used as street furniture while also providing a power supply for outdoor areas. Standard configurations are supplied with additional equipment also available.

Square pop up service unit

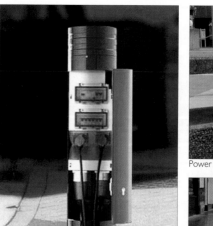

Power bollard

Power bollard

Square pop up service unit partially raised

Square service unit fully raised

I.G.U. (In Ground Units) at an outdoor market site

Flip lid service units

Furnitubes

Contact
Sales
t: 020 8378 3261
f: 020 8378 3250
esibook@furnitubes.com

Web
www.furnitubes.com

Address
Furnitubes International Ltd
3rd Floor
Meridian House
Royal Hill
Greenwich
London SE10 8RD

Affiliations
Constructionline
Railway Industry Supplier Qualification Scheme
(RISQS)
Builder's Profile

Accreditation
ISO 9001:2008
ISO 14001:2004
OHSAS 18001:2007

Operational area
Worldwide

Country of manufacture
UK

Additional entries
Railings and guardrails ➤ 218
Bollards ➤ 230
Signage ➤ 260
Co-ordinated street furniture ➤ 308
Seating ➤ 316
Bespoke seating ➤ 331
Litter bins ➤ 356

Furnitubes International Ltd

Cycle parking

Furnitubes offers a wide range of cycle parking products, from simple economic hoop-style stands for individual cycles, to longer racks for multiple cycle parking. Overhead shelters and secure enclosures are also available.

Composition and manufacture

Most cycle stands are manufactured from steel and stainless steel, which provide high strength and long-term durability.
Steel is generally galvanised as standard, with the option of various tough supplementary coating systems, if a coloured finish is required.
Stainless steel is offered in either a brushed or bright polished finish.

Delivery

Selected products from the standard range of steel and stainless steel cycle stands are available from stock for next day delivery.

Fin cycle stands

College cycle stands

Academy cycle shelter with *Fin* cycle stands

Transport cycle stands

Bespoke DLR cycle stands

AUTOPA

Contact
t: 01788 550556
f: 01788 550265
info@autopa.co.uk

Web
www.autopa.co.uk

Address
AUTOPA Limited
Cottage Leap
Rugby CV21 3XP

Accreditation
ISO 9001:2008
ISO 14001:2004
OHSAS 18001:2007
Achilles Building Confidence

Affiliations
CHAS
Constructionline

Additional entries
Rising arm barriers ➤ 212
Telescopic posts and automatic bollards ➤ 213
Height restrictors and swing gates ➤ 214
High visibility protection ➤ 217
Traffic flow plates and speed ramps ➤ 221
Bollards ➤ 226
Parking posts ➤ 228
Cycle stands ➤ 244
Illuminated bollards ➤ 268
Street furniture ➤ 283
Shelters, canopies and walkways ➤ 391

AUTOPA Limited

Cycle shelters and compounds

VELOPA cycle shelters and compounds are manufactured from mild steel, galvanised as standard for longevity, at the company's Rugby works. BREEAM compliant, the cycle shelter range has evolved over the past 60 years to meet the changing needs of cyclists.

• **Single-sided cycle shelters**
Three distinct cycle shelter ranges cater for a wide variety of budgets and architectural styles. *The Heritage Range*, based on a design first established in the 1950s, offers cost effective solutions where storage is the main requirement. *The Classic Range*, which includes the popular *Cambridge* and *Canterbury* designs, offers robust storage solutions for demanding applications. *The Contemporary Range* incorporates sleek roofing styles and materials to complement modern architecture.

• **Double-width cycle shelters**
VELOPA *Ashton* and *Bowerham* cycle shelters hold two rows of bikes and are compatible with double-sided, double stack racks.

• **Cycle compounds**
VELOPA secure cycle compounds are based on two popular cycle shelters designs, the *Boston* and the *Stratford*. When placed face to face with a mesh gate at one end and a fixed panel at the other end, the shelters combine to form a secure compound. Both can be specified with an infill central roof panel and colour-coated finish. Access control options include a choice of locking options, including padlocks and card readers. Other options are available upon request.

Composition and manufacture

VELOPA cycle shelters and compounds are manufactured from mild steel, galvanised as standard for longevity. *Classic* and *Contemporary* frame finishes can be colour-coated to order. Roofing is manufactured from PETG UV stabilised clear sheet as standard, with other options also available.

VELOPA *Bowerham Cycle Shelter*

VELOPA *Stratford Cycle Shelter*

VELOPA *Stratford Cycle Compound*

VELOPA *Boston Cycle Shelter* with mesh doors

The VELOPA *Stratford Cycle Shelter* requires minimal maintenance throughout its lifetime

VELOPA *Cambridge Cycle Shelter* with painted frame and polycarbonate roof

VELOPA *Cambridge Cycle Shelter* – Ealing College

VELOPA *Harbledown Cycle Shelter*

VELOPA *Cambourne Cycle Shelter* with *Sheffield* stands provide parking for 130 bicycles – NPS Humber

VELOPA *Boston Cycle Compound*

Canterbury Cycle Shelter – St Albans Railway Station

The VELOPA *Banbury Cycle Shelter* is compatible with all standard height VELOPA cycle stands and racks

Contact
t: 01788 550556
f: 01788 550265
info@autopa.co.uk

Web
www.autopa.co.uk

Address
AUTOPA Limited
Cottage Leap
Rugby CV21 3XP

Accreditation
ISO 9001:2008
ISO 14001:2004
OHSAS 18001:2007
Achilles Building Confidence

Affiliations
CHAS
Constructionline

Additional entries
Rising arm barriers ➤ 212
Telescopic posts and automatic bollards ➤ 213
Height restrictors and swing gates ➤ 214
High visibility protection ➤ 217
Traffic flow plates and speed ramps ➤ 221
Bollards ➤ 226
Parking posts ➤ 228
Cycle shelters and compounds ➤ 242
Illuminated bollards ➤ 268
Street furniture ➤ 283
Shelters, canopies and walkways ➤ 391

AUTOPA Limited

Cycle stands

VELOPA cycle stands, holders and racks are designed to last for many years. They are manufactured at AUTOPA's Rugby works from galvanised mild steel or stainless steel.

• Cycle holders
Heritage cycle stands and holders include some of VELOPA's longest running designs. Based on the original cycle holder (launched in the 1950s), *Models R, F, SR-V* and *SU-V Cycle Holders* all provide secure, cost-effective, cycle parking.

• Cycle stands
VELOPA's cycle stand range includes the best-selling *Sheffield Cycle Stand* which allows the wheel and the frame to be locked to the stand simultaneously. Other VELOPA cycle stands incorporate this feature, with a design available to suit most architectural styles.

• Transport cycle stands
VELOPA *Transport Cycle Stands* are designed for city life. Hardwearing and robust, they comply with cycle parking regulations for all major UK cities. DDA compliant, they feature tapping rails and high visibility banding as standard.

• Cycle racks
VELOPA cycle racks give site owners a flexible high density cycle storage option for sites where space is at a premium.

• Double height cycle racks
The VELOPA *Double Stack Cycle Rack* doubles the number of bicycles that can be stored in a space. It is designed for intensive use.
Manually operated, the top level slides easily between upper and lower positions. Large handles are positioned either side of the upper trough to facilitate racking. The *Double Stack Cycle Rack* is compatible with the *Ashton* and *Bowerham* cycle shelters.

• VELOPA Kids
Two products are specifically designed for children – the *Junior Sheffield Cycle Stand* and the *Scooter Rack*. Both can be colour-coated in any standard BS or RAL colour, making them ideal for use in schools and nurseries.

VELOPA *Sheffield 'Toastrack' Cycle Rack*

VELOPA *Sheffield Cycle Stand*

VELOPA *Transport Cycle Stand*

VELOPA *Dallington Cycle Stand*

VELOPA *Model R 90° cycle holders*

The VELOPA *Double Stack Cycle Rack* doubles the number of bicycles that can be stored in a space and is designed for intensive use

VELOPA *Duston Cycle Stand*

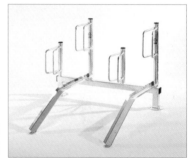

VELOPA *Type B Cycle Rack*

VELOPA *Hillmorton Cycle Stand*

VELOPA *Scooter Rack*

VELOPA *Kirby Cycle Stands*

VELOPA *Circular Cycle Rack* (bespoke)

Contact

Jason Hamlyn
t: 01752 202116
info@bikeaway.com

Web

www.bikeaway.com

Address

BikeAway Ltd
Head Office
Bell Close
Newnham Industrial Estate
Plympton
Plymouth PL7 4JH

Richard Strahan (Ireland agent)
BikeAway Ltd
t: 00 353 1 283 2823
m: 00 353 87 242 3634
info@rss.ie
www.rss.ie

Lockers powder-coated Oxford blue

Lockers can be installed on site by BikeAway's fitters

BikeAway Ltd

Cycle stands and lockers

BikeAway manufactures space-saving vertical cycle storage systems.

• Stands

Cycle stands are suitable for factories and locations where space is at a premium, such as domestic garages, lobbies and communal entrance halls.

The patented hoop design around which the storage system is built allows the bike to be held in a secure upright position whilst the ramp lifts the mudguard off the ground, avoiding damage.

• Lockers

BikeAway vertical cycle lockers have been installed throughout the UK for local authorities, schools, hospitals, leisure centres and railway stations, amongst other applications.

BikeAway Warrior gained Sold Secure Bicycle Gold accreditation for its strength and security. This accreditation is widely recognised within the insurance industry and recognised by Secured by Design. The locker is supplied as a fully assembled individual unit and provides secure, space-saving vertical cycle parking.

BikeAway Standard lockers provide secure, dry storage for cycles, preventing the vandalism and theft to which traditional racks can be vulnerable. *BikeAway Heavy Duty* lockers are used in areas where security can be a particular problem. 12 lockers will fit into the footprint of one parking space. Levelling feet on *Standard* and *Heavy Duty* lockers adjust for sloping or uneven ground. A locker management service is offered to complement locker sales.

Composition and manufacture

BikeAway lockers are manufactured in galvanised steel, with a polyester powder-coated finish in a choice of colours, designs and specifications.

Sitework

Standard and *Heavy Duty* lockers are built and installed on site in clusters by BikeAway's fitters. *Warrior* lockers are delivered fully assembled, ready to be fixed to the ground. An installation service is available on request.

BikeAway lockers are manufactured from galvanised steel, with a choice of door thickness and locks

Double *BikeAway* stand

Single *BikeAway* stand

Lockers powder-coated green

BikeAway lockers in custom RAL colour

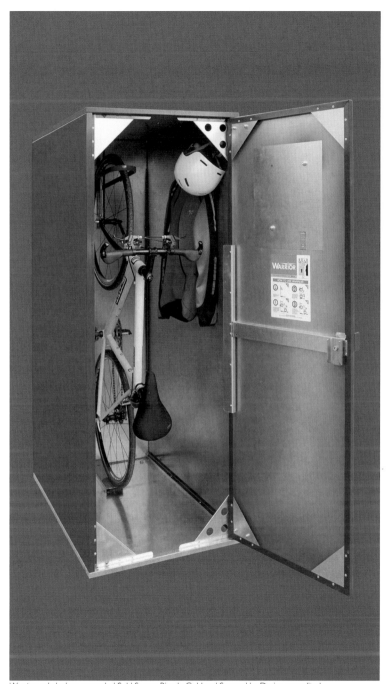
Warrior cycle locker – awarded Sold Secure Bicycle Gold and Secured by Design accredited

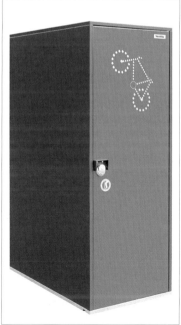
BikeAway Warrior locker is competetively priced

BikeAway Wall Hoop and chain

LANGLEY DESIGN
EXTERNAL FURNITURE SOLUTIONS

Contact
t: 01793 759461
f: 01793 759462
info@langleydesign.co.uk

Web
www.langleydesign.co.uk

Address
Langley Design
Unit L (Gate 1)
Chelworth Industrial Estate
Cricklade
Swindon SN6 6HE

Accreditation
Achilles BuildingConfidence
ISO 9001:2008

Affiliations
CHAS, Constructionline, Construction Skills
Certification Scheme (CSCS), TRADA

Additional entries
Co-ordinated street furniture ➤ 296
Outdoor seats and benches ➤ 333

Langley Design

Cycle parking

Langley Design is experienced in designing and providing cycle parking facilities. The company can work to budgets, available space (BREEAM compliant if required) or planning requirements. Cycle parking facilities with sedum roofs are a speciality.

Product range

Products include single bay, double row, modular units, secure enclosures, simple racks or all-in-one enclosures.

There are also environmental options for eco-friendly projects, with green roofed shelters available that blend into the landscape and offset emissions.

All designs can be adapted to suit specific site requirements.

Composition and manufacture

Materials options include:
• Steel-framed cycle shelters with galvanised, powder-coated or stainless steel finishes.
• Timber-framed shelters built using sustainably sourced timber. They can be open sided or full-clad for greater protection from the elements. Products are manufactured in the UK.

Sitework

A full installation service is available, if required.

Cycle shelter and bin store combination unit (SCS311) – University of Hertfordshire

Secure sedum roof cycle shelter (SCS314) – Queens Park Place, South Kilburn

Green roof cycle shelter (SCS304) – Newfield and Talbot Schools, Sheffield

Fully enclosed, secure cycle shelter (SCS309) – Leeds East Academy

Semi-enclosed cycle shelter (SCS310) – DTTCP Training Facility, Lyneham

Marshalls plc

Cycle parking

Promoting cycling as an integrated part of everyday sustainable transport brings about benefits such as saving money on fuel, tackling health issues, reducing traffic congestion and greenhouse gas emissions, and creating a better environment for all.

Marshalls has established a reputation for providing sustainable transport infrastructure. Marshalls' cycle stands and shelters are available in many materials and finishes. As well as standard products, the companys' in-house design team can create bespoke solutions upon request.

Pluto shelter

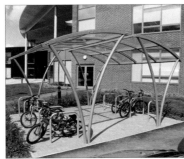
Ollerton Saturn cycle shelter

Ferrocast Red Route cycle stands

Sheffield cycle stands

Geo Pennant cycle stands

Hoop cycle stands

QUEENSBURY SHELTERS

Contact
t: 023 9221 0052
f: 023 9221 0059
sales@queensburyshelters.co.uk

Web
www.queensburyshelters.co.uk

Address
Queensbury Shelters Ltd
Fitzherbert Road, Farlington
Portsmouth PO6 1SE

Accreditation
ISO 9001:2008
ISO 14001:2004
ISO 18001:2007
OHSAS 18001:2007
ISO 22301

Affiliations
NICEIC, CHAS, RISQS, Constructionline

Additional entries
Passenger shelters ➤ 384
Walkways and canopies ➤ 385

Queensbury Shelters Ltd

Cycle storage solutions

Queensbury manufactures high-quality, secure, low maintenance cycle storage solutions to suit any environment and budget.

• **Cycle shelters and canopies**
The *Queensbury Cycle Shelter* is a robust design that can be supplied in a wide range of sizes to suit any location.
The *Queensbury Cycle Canopy* provides a contemporary storage solution for 10 cycles. Both designs are modular to allow adaptation to larger sites. They are manufactured from a zinc protected steel framework with UV protected polycarbonate glazing, secured in Queensbury's aluminium glazing clamp. Stainless steel fixings are used throughout.

• **Bespoke solutions**
Queensbury provides a bespoke design and build service for cycle storage solutions to meet specific requirements, including material finishes, storage capacity and security features.

• **Cycle stands**
Cycle stands are available in individual and 'toast rack' configurations.

Sitework

Queensbury installs shelters across the UK using in-house personnel where possible. All products can be bolted down or embedded into the floor.

Queensbury Cycle Shelter with *Sheffield* cycle rack. The shelter can be supplied in a range of sizes.

Bespoke cycle storage design and build solution to meet project specific requirements

Sheffield cycle rack

Bespoke cycle storage

Queensbury Cycle Canopy with *Sheffield* stands. The canopy can accommodate up to 10 cycles.

Contact
David Ruffell
Business Development Manager
t: 0117 370 7710
david@rocklyn.co.uk

Web
www.rocklyn.co.uk

Address
Rocklyn Engineering Ltd
Dirac Crescent
Bristol & Bath Science Park
Emersons Green
Bristol BS16 7FR

Accreditation
ISO 9001:2008, OHSAS 18001:2010,
SafeContractor, Constructionline, CE Marking

Additional entries
Shelters, canopies and covered walkways ➤ 393
Sports shelters ➤ 504

Rocklyn Engineering Ltd

Cycle parking

Rocklyn Engineering Ltd is a leading manufacturer of shelters and street furniture, with extensive experience of providing engineering solutions for commercial and domestic applications.

• Dargle cycle shelters
Rocklyn's most popular cycle storage products are *Dargle* shelters, with models for 10, 20 and 30 cycles. Their modular design allows them to be customised as lockable compounds if required. They are made from galvanised heavy-duty steel with polycarbonate panels, making them weather resistant, maintenance free and vandal resistant. Options include internal mains or solar lighting and polyester powder coating to RAL colours.

Composition and manufacture
The company has two fully equipped workshops for fabrication in mild steel and stainless steel/aluminium as well as timber and composites.

Technical support
Rocklyn has 3D design capability, and can discuss preliminary designs to help clients to develop ideas and make the best use of space.

Projects
Clients include building contractors, shopping centres, supermarkets, libraries, schools, universities, airports, and railway and bus authorities throughout the UK and Ireland.

Dargle 30 cycle shelter with *Silver* cycle racks

Dargle 20 cycle shelter with two *Tar 10* cycle racks

Xeron shelter and stainless steel *Sheffield* stands

Angle cycle stands

Eske cycle rack

Lockable compound comprising 2 *Dargle 20* shelters

Yeti cycle shelter with *Tar 10* cycle rack

Cycle-Works Ltd

Secure cycle parking

Cycle-Works designs, manufactures, distributes and installs high-quality, secure cycle parking products from the UK, Germany and the USA.

• Cycle lockers

Cycle lockers include the space saving, wedge-shaped *Velo-Safe* locker, which can be installed in many different layouts.

Velo-Safe and *Velo-Box* lockers are SOLD Secure Silver approved and Secure by Design certified. Other lockers include *Bikeaway*, *Cycle-Safe* and *Bykebin*, as well as *VeloStore* multi-bike units.

• High-capacity cycle racks

Cycle-Works is the sole UK supplier of *Josta* 2-tier cycle racks. They are a secure and easy to use high-capacity system with a patented wheel-gripping mechanism. Other 2-tier and high-capacity options are also available.

• Cycle racks and stands

Sheffield cycle racks and stands include Cycle-Works' *Rounded-A* and *Lock2Me* designs. Products come in a choice of materials and colours and can be customised with logos. Vertical and semi-vertical systems are also available.

• Cycle shelters

Cycle shelters and lockable cycle compounds are available in a wide choice of styles and sizes, and can be customised with access control systems.

cycle-works

Contact
Sales
t: 023 9281 5555
f: 023 9281 5544
info@cycle-works.com

Web
www.cycle-works.com

Address
Cycle-Works Ltd
8–9 Rodney Road
Portsmouth PO4 8BF

Operational area
UK, Europe, Worldwide

Country of manufacture
UK, Germany, USA

Velo-Safe SOLD Secure cycle lockers

VeloStore multi-bike locker – Totnes railway station

Josta 2-tier cycle racks and *Higher Kennet* shelter

Lock2Me cycle stand

Fitzpatrick Woolmer

Creative sign solutions

Fitzpatrick Woolmer is one of the UK's leading providers of public space signage.

Products include interpretation and orientation displays, welcome signs, notice boards and waymarking systems. They are extremely robust and can be manufactured in a range of materials, including metal, timber and recycled plastic.

In addition to standard sign displays Fitzpatrick Woolmer also manufactures to bespoke specifications as required.

Contact
Sales
t: 01634 711771
f: 01634 711761
info@fwdp.co.uk

Web
www.fwdp.co.uk

Address
Head Office
Fitzpatrick Woolmer Design & Publishing Ltd
Unit 7, Lakeside Park
Neptune Close
Rochester ME2 4LT

Welsh Office
221 The Innovation Centre
Festival Drive
Victoria Business Park
Ebbw Vale NP23 8XA

t: 01495 357924

Wayfinding monolith

Interpretation display

Interpretive badging sign

Fingerpost wayfinding

Directional ladder sign

Sense of place wayfinding

Orientation monolith

Interpretive bench

Welcome information display

Greenbarnes Ltd.

Contact
Andy Brewer
t: 01280 701093
f: 01280 702843
sales@greenbarnes.co.uk

Web
www.greenbarnes.co.uk

Address
Greenbarnes Ltd
Unit 7, Barrington Court
Ward Road
Buckingham Road Industrial Estate
Brackley NN13 7LE

Operational area
UK

Greenbarnes Ltd

Signing systems

Greenbarnes Ltd manufactures noticeboards and information sign panels.

• **Noticeboards**
Noticeboards can be supplied glazed or unglazed, with single or multiple display windows. They can incorporate customised header panels, and can be post- or wall-mounted. They are available in hardwood, *Man-made Timber* and aluminium.
Man-made Timber is made from recycled plastics but has a grained timber appearance. It does not warp, rot, split or fade and is maintenance-free.
Man-made Timber noticeboards feature vandal-resistant glazing, an integral weatherstrip and ventilation, and self-healing rubber pinboards. They have a 5-year guarantee.
A-Max aluminium boards are heavy-duty units for demanding applications. They are available as single- or double-sided units.
Solar receptors can be housed in a small range of aluminium noticeboards to enable illumination.

• **Information sign panels**
Information sign panels are available in a variety of formats, ranging from simple flat plate aluminium signage to bespoke items. Signs are constructed in a wide variety of materials including hardwood, aluminium, plastics and composites. Graphics can be applied in computer-cut vinyl or using digital print, and may include anti-graffiti laminate.

Two-bay, post-mounted noticeboard in dark oak

Small oak poster case

A3 poster case in *Man-made Timber*

Two-bay, post-mounted noticeboard in dark oak

Oak noticeboard with opaque woodstain finish

V-Case poster cases

Bespoke *V-Case* for displaying posters

Three-bay oak noticeboard with central sign panel

Oak noticeboard with graphic panel

 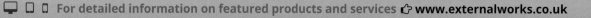

Three-bay glazed noticeboard in *Man-Made Timber*

A-Max aluminium noticeboard

Unglazed *Man-made Timber* noticeboard

Two-bay glazed noticeboard in *Man-Made Timber*

Two-bay *AF30* aluminium noticeboard

Contemporary multi-bay aluminium noticeboard

Man-made Timber noticeboard with sign panel

Lectern in maintenance-free *Man-made Timber*

Solar-illuminated aluminium noticeboard

A-Max aluminium noticeboard with decorative posts

SIGN 2000

Contact
Sales
t: 01732 772000
info@sign2000.co.uk

Web
www.sign2000.co.uk
www.municipalsigns.co.uk
www.signmaintenance.co.uk

Address
Sign 2000 Ltd
Units 3 & 4
Deacon Trading Estate
209–211 Vale Road
Tonbridge TN9 1SU

Accreditation
ISO 9001:2000
ISO 14001: 2004
OHSAS 18001
Investors in People
SAFEcontractor

Affiliations
British Safety Council
British Sign and Graphics Association
International Sign Association

Additional entries
Corporate branding signs ➤ 266

Sign 2000 Ltd

Architectural signs

Sign 2000, established in 1988, is a leading manufacturer of exterior and interior signs. The company provides both architectural and urban signage to municipal clients.
Services include initial concepts, project management, manufacture and installation.
Sign 2000 provides standard systems as well as bespoke products that are individually tailored to the clients brand requirements. The service can include recommendation of energy-saving measures and manufacturing techniques that use sustainable materials.

Projects
• Hounslow Borough Council.
• Speke Regeneration Scheme.
• London Aquarium (County Hall).
• O2 Arena.
• Borough of Newham.
• Guy's Hospital (London).
• Merthyr Tydfil (Urban Scheme).
• Greenwich Borough Council.
• Milton Keynes (central wayfinding).
• Lee Valley Park.
• Tapi Carpets.
• Hopyard.
• Embassy Gardens.
• Netley Campus.

Signage for school building

Interior signage

Solar-powered, freestanding architectural signage

Guy's Hospital – stainless steel lettering on panel

O2 Arena – freestanding monolith banner and sign

Door entry signage

Interior architectural signage

Glass-clad main ID totem

Municipal borough signage

Signage for bar

Apartment block signage

Main ID building text

Architectural feature branding

Signage for commercial development

Signscape AND Signconex Ltd

Wayfinding signs and information displays

Signscape is a leading manufacturer of wayfinding signs, information displays and external noticeboard products.

Primarily using its own proprietary systems, the company produces a wide range of solutions for architectural, corporate and public sector projects, often without the need for fully bespoke designs.

With over 40 years' manufacturing experience, Signscape specialises in tailoring and adapting its products to suit different applications and environments, or combining them to create co-ordinated sign and display schemes.

Product range
- Post and panel signs.
- Fingerpost signs.
- Monolith signs and map boards.
- Noticeboards and poster cases.
- Solar powered product illumination.

Services
Signscape works directly with architects, designers, specifiers, contractors and general sign companies. Services range from initial design and surveys to project completion, including specifications for tender documentation.

Contact
Sales
t: 01934 852888
f: 01934 852816
sales@signscape.co.uk

Web
www.signscape.co.uk
www.signconex.co.uk

Address
Signscape AND Signconex Ltd
Pear Tree Industrial Estate
Bath Road
Bristol BS40 5DJ

Operational area
UK, Ireland, Europe

Country of manufacture
UK

Bespoke wayfinding entrance sign with stainless steel column

Modern style park noticeboard

Eco-Vision solar-powered illuminated noticeboard

Eco-Vision solar-powered illuminated monolith

Infocurve map monolith

Bespoke wayfinding signage

Post and panel wayfinding sign

Traditional fingerpost with collars and ring finial

Contemporary fingerpost

Lectern map sign

Fingerpost arms with wall/post brackets

Furnitubes International Ltd

Signage

Furnitubes specialises in two areas of signage – directional fingerposts and complementary display cases. Both ranges are offered in traditional and utility/contemporary styles. Signage can be used in parks or street schemes, providing residents and visitors with directional guidance, local interpretation and up-to-date event information.

Design services

Standard signage components, such as columns and cases, always come complete with scheme-specific graphical information.

The company can work from basic written information to develop designs and produce a representation of how they will appear when recreated in three dimensions.

The company's designers are also able to offer advice on the various manufacturing options for recreating flat artwork in a signage application.

Delivery

Although various components are held in stock, all signage contracts are made to order.

Contact
Sales
t: 020 8378 3261
f: 020 8378 3250
esibook@furnitubes.com

Web
www.furnitubes.com

Address
Furnitubes International Ltd
3rd Floor
Meridian House
Royal Hill
Greenwich
London SE10 8RD

Affiliations
Constructionline
Railway Industry Supplier Qualification Scheme
(RISQS)
Builder's Profile

Accreditation
ISO 9001:2008
ISO 14001:2004
OHSAS 18001:2007

Operational area
Worldwide

Country of manufacture
UK

Additional entries
Railings and guardrails ➤ 218
Bollards ➤ 230
Cycle parking ➤ 241
Co-ordinated street furniture ➤ 308
Seating ➤ 316
Bespoke seating ➤ 331
Litter bins ➤ 356

Kingston column fingerpost assembly

Guildford column fingerpost assembly

Zenith fingerpost signage

Traditional display case with *Guildford* columns

Kingston column fingerpost assembly

Zenith column fingerpost assembly

fw.d sign solutions

Contact

Roger Crabtree
t: 020 7928 0412
enquire@fwdsignsolutions.com

Web

www.fwdesign.com
www.fwdsignsolutions.com

Address

fwdesign Ltd
The Design Hub
41 Brookley Road
Brockenhurst SO42 7RB

Country of manufacture

UK

fwdesign Ltd

Signage and wayfinding systems

fwdesign specialises in the design of brand implementation, place making and wayfinding systems and has developed its own range of high-quality, cost-effective signage products.
Value engineered, modular products are available in numerous configurations and material specifications. They are designed to quickly and easily accommodate information and brand requirements to capital budgets.
Installations include St Katharine Docks in London, Burgess Park, City of Lincoln and Bath.

frank fingerpost

frank architectural signage

jack contemporary signage

kara pedestrian and vehicular signage

mark cycle and walk route marker

daisy signage for parks and green spaces

lily signage in a cemetery

Contact
UK freefone: 0800 376 8377
t: +353 (0) 53 914 3216
f: +353 (0) 53 914 1802
info@kentstainless.com

Web
www.kentstainless.com

Address
Kent Stainless (Wexford) Ltd
Ardcavan
Wexford
Republic of Ireland

Accreditation
ISO 9001:2008
ISO 14001:2004
OHSAS 18001:2007

Country of manufacture
Republic of Ireland

Additional entries
Lift-assist manholes ➤ 131
Heelproof ventilation access grilles ➤ 132
In-ground units ➤ 239
Planters ➤ 383

Kent Stainless (Wexford) Ltd
Wayfinding signage

Kent Stainless is a specialist stainless steel fabricator that produces a range of street furniture products for public realm projects. A key area of Kent Stainless' products is stainless steel wayfinding signage. Bespoke wayfinding products range from fingerposts to monoliths.

Projects
• Fingerposts and monoliths – Tallaght, Dublin. The *Kent Dubline Wayfinding Monolith* was developed for the Dubline project in Dublin city. Kent Stainless created a co-ordinated range of monoliths that are situated in various historical sites across the city. A range of *Tallaght Monoliths* were also supplied with fingerposts to direct pedestrians.
• Fingerposts and monoliths – Wild Atlantic Way, west of Ireland tourist trail.
• Fingerposts and monoliths – Wexford Viking Trail, Ireland.
• Wayfinding kiosk – Grangegorman Campus, Dublin Institute of Technology. The *Kent Interactive Wayfinding Kiosk* offers students a help point to navigate around the campus.
• *Kent Galway Fingerpost* – Galway. Fingerposts were manufactured with bespoke powder coating that was developed to suit the client's request for a site in Galway.

Kent Tallaght Monolith with fingerposts

Kent Galway Fingerpost

Kent Dubline Wayfinding Monolith

Kent Interactive Wayfinding Kiosk

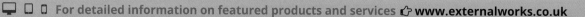

Contact

Sales
t: 0808 129 3773
f: 0808 129 3774
enquiries@madebylandmark.com

Web
www.madebylandmark.com

Address
Landmark
32 Henry Road
Barnet EN4 8BD

Operational area
UK

Landmark

Visitor signage

Landmark specialises in visitor experience signage for public spaces. The company can provide a full service from survey and design through to manufacture and installation.

Projects include country parks, heritage trails, historic properties and museums.

• Product range

Products include wayfinding signage, site interpretation signage and furniture, all of which are designed to give visitors a rewarding experience.

Composition and manufacture

Materials used include metal, FSC timber and recycled plastic, which are selected for durability and aesthetic appeal.

Accreditation

The company is FSC certified, ISO 9001 and ISO 14001 accredited, and a member of Constructionline.

Lectern with interpretation board

Shelter with interpretation board and notice case

FSC English oak ladder sign

Solid oak A-frame sign with printed insert

Natural and painted FSC oak and *Tricoya®* sign

Fingerpost with engraved legend and ACM inserts

V-format ladder sign with interpretation boards

Powder-coated aluminium entrance sign

3D digital modelling service available

Marshalls

Creating Better Spaces

Contact
t: 0870 444 6217
f: 0870 442 7725
esi.marshalls@web-response.co.uk

Web
www.marshalls.co.uk/commercial

Address
Marshalls plc
Landscape House, Premier Way,
Lowfields Business Park, Elland HX5 9HT

Additional entries
Protective post and rail ➤ 219
Bollards ➤ 235
Cycle parking ➤ 249
Illumination ➤ 272
Co-ordinated street furniture ➤ 278
Protective street furniture ➤ 280
Co-ordinated street furniture ➤ 282
Seats and benches ➤ 320
Litter bins ➤ 357
Planters ➤ 378
Tree protection ➤ 526

Marshalls plc

Signage and wayfinding

Marshalls offers signage, noticeboards and wayfinding in steel, stainless steel, polyurethane, aluminium and traditional cast iron. They are available in a number of sizes and finishes, in both landscape and portrait orientations.

The products are extremely versatile – they can co-ordinate with corresponding furniture and lighting ranges or can be specified as independent units. They can also be used to help to create iconic landscapes and a true sense of space.

Monolith illuminated map – Oxford Road, London

Geo monolith signage

Geo stainless steel fingerpost

Loci monolith

Geo monolith bespoke signage

Imperial A0 double-sided cast iron noticeboard

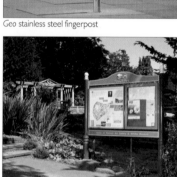
Ferrocast double-sided noticeboard

Geo monolith stainless steel signage

Ollerton stainless steel bespoke noticeboard and fingerpost – Blackpool

Contact

Robert Shelley
t: 01743 460996
sales@shelleysigns.co.uk

Web

www.shelleysigns.co.uk

Address

Shelley Signs Ltd
54 Cartmel Drive
Harlescott
Shrewsbury SY1 3TB

Operational area

UK

Country of manufacture

UK

Shelley Signs Ltd

Signs and panels

Shelley Signs specialises in the design and production of signs for parks, nature reserves and open spaces.

The wide range of processes include full-colour printing, routing and sandblasting for tactile graphics.

Signs can be finished in GRP, polycarbonate, vinyl or various timbers, while frames are frequently in softwood, oak, steel or recycled plastic.

Oak lectern frame and printed GRP sign

Robust GRP sign with aluminium lectern frame

Interpretation panel in vertical oak frame

Entrance sign with raised lettering

Routed oak plaque and post

Park sign with integral noticeboard

Oak directional fingerpost

SIGN 2000

Contact
Sales
t: 01732 772000
info@sign2000.co.uk

Web
www.sign2000.co.uk
www.municipalsigns.co.uk
www.signmaintenance.co.uk

Address
Sign 2000 Ltd
Units 3 & 4, Deacon Trading Estate
209–211 Vale Road, Tonbridge TN9 1SU

Accreditation
ISO 9001:2000; ISO 14001: 2004; OHSAS 18001;
Investors in People; SAFEcontractor

Affiliations
British Safety Council; British Sign and Graphics
Association; International Sign Association

Additional entries
Architectural signs ➤ 256

Sign 2000 Ltd

Corporate branding signs

In addition to working with Local Authorities,
Sign 2000 provides retail and corporate signage to
a number of blue chip retailers. Products include
external and interior signage, window and wall
manifestation, and DDA works.
• **Signing systems**
The scope of the company's work includes fascia
signage and projecting signs, building identification
signs, free-standing structures, various forms of
specialist lighting, architectural steelwork, as well
as complementary interior signage.

Projects
• Tesco.
• Tapi Carpets.
• Hilton.
• Vision Express.
• Premier Inn.
• Superdrug.
• M & S.
• Beefeater.
• O2.
• Post Office.
• 3 Mobile.
• Booker.
• Nike.
• Virgin Media.
• British Steel.

Corporate branding

Feature entrance sign

Corporate branding

Edge of town branding

Supermarket signage

Corporate branding ID totem

trueform

Contact
Amanda O'Connor (Sales)
t: 020 8561 4959
f: 020 8848 1397
amanda.oconnor@trueform.co.uk

Web
www.trueform.co.uk

Address
Trueform
Pasadena Trading Estate
Pasadena Close
Hayes UB3 3NQ

Accreditation
ISO 9001:2008
ISO 14001:2004
OHSAS 18001

Operational area
UK, USA, Europe, Middle East

Additional entries
Shelters, canopies and walkways ➤ 388

Trueform

Signs, wayfinding and digital displays

Trueform is a leading designer, manufacturer and installer of external and internal signage systems. Products include wayfinding monoliths, fingerposts, bespoke displays, electronic and interactive signage. Signage can be Illuminated, solar powered and display real time information. With over 37 years in the industry the company provides resources and expertise in design, graphic reproduction, manufacture and installation of signage, with a high level of detail and quality.

Wayfinding totem – Portsmouth

Digital monolith – Heathrow Airport

Legible London Interlith totem

Station entrance sign

Illuminated way out sign – London Underground

Legible London totem

Digital totem – Ealing Broadway bus interchange

Bus stop totem – BCCI

TSG digital totem – Vauxhall bus station

Wayfinding totem – New York

SBS wayfinding totem – New York

AUTOPA Limited

Illuminated bollards

AUTOPA open spaces illuminated bollards and cycle stands form part of an extensive range of street furniture designed for public and commercial applications.

• Illuminated bollards

AUTOPA *GFC 9000i* illuminated bollards are manufactured from galvanised steel and stainless steel. Both variants are fitted with a low-energy LED corn lamp which provides site owners with a clear, bright light.

Both are designed for use in high-traffic areas such as city squares, public parks and university campuses and are IP57 rated.

The galvanised mild steel *GFC 9000i* illuminated bollard is supplied coated black as standard, but can be coated in any standard RAL or BS colour.

• Illuminated cycle stands

The first of its kind in the UK marketplace, the VELOPA *Illuminated Sheffield Cycle Stand* provides an innovative lighting solution for external cycle parking areas. The inconspicuous 1.2W LED encased in the underside of the cycle stand provides illumination for cyclists and secure storage for up to two bicycles.

Illuminated bollard

Contact
t: 01788 550556
f: 01788 550265
info@autopa.co.uk

Web
www.autopa.co.uk

Address
AUTOPA Limited
Cottage Leap
Rugby CV21 3XP

Accreditation
ISO 9001:2008
ISO 14001:2004
OHSAS 18001:2007
Achilles Building Confidence

Affiliations
CHAS
Constructionline

Additional entries
Rising arm barriers ➤ 212
Telescopic posts and automatic bollards ➤ 213
Height restrictors and swing gates ➤ 214
High visibility protection ➤ 217
Traffic flow plates and speed ramps ➤ 221
Bollards ➤ 226
Parking posts ➤ 228
Cycle shelters and compounds ➤ 242
Cycle stands ➤ 244
Street furniture ➤ 283
Shelters, canopies and walkways ➤ 391

Illuminated Sheffield Cycle Stand

GFC 9000i mild steel bollards, coated black

Stainless steel illuminated bollards

GFC 9000i mild steel bollards, coated black

Candela Light Ltd

Illuminated bollards and bulkheads

Candela Light designs and manufactures standard and bespoke illuminated bollards in contemporary and traditional styles, as well as wall-mounted bulkheads and pathway lights.

• **Illuminated bollards**
Illuminated bollards come in two styles: *Heritage* classic cannon-style cast bollards, such as the *Vanguard,* the *Resolute* and the *Warrior*; or more contemporary, fabricated bollards such as the *Meriden*, the *Centurion* and the stainless *Centurion*. All bollards have the option of a louvre system that eliminates glare.

• **Bulkheads and walkway lighting**
Arbor lanterns are primarily used for pathway lighting. They are usually mounted as wall lights, but can also be fitted on columns or posts with the use of an adaptor.

Composition and manufacture

Resolute and *Vanguard* bollards are produced from either cast iron, SG ductile iron or cast aluminium. *Centurion*, *Tyburn* and *Meriden* bollards are offered in galvanised steel.
Arbor lanterns have a die-cast aluminium body with anti-vandal polycarbonate glazing, rated to IP66.

Vanguard

Warrior

Meriden

Centurion in stainless steel

Centurion flat top bollard

Somerset

Lumena Lights

Illuminated bollards

Lumena Lights Ltd specialises in high quality, durable outdoor lighting, including illuminated bollards and garden lighting.

Illuminated bollards are manufactured from 316 stainless steel, aluminium, brass or pressure-sealed wood such as teak or pine.

Large stocks are held for next day delivery.

• Product range

Over 300 variations are available.

LEDifice and *Stelled* bollards can be used to illuminate larger areas. They are specially designed to accommodate high output 20W LED *Corn* bulbs. *Pro-Bollards* can be surface-mounted or professionally root-mounted, with photocell and PIR options. The company offers some of the only bollards with integrated sensors in the UK.

Composition and manufacture

Commercial bollards feature a highly robust construction. Materials include 2.5mm die-cast aluminium and 3mm thick marine grade 316 stainless steel. High IP ratings and security features such as pin hex screws make them ideal for use in commercial and public areas.

Smaller bollards/path lights and garden lighting is made from solid brass, natural copper, marine grade stainless steel and anodised aluminium. They are designed to withstand harsh weather.

Contact
Sales
t: 01327 871161
f: 0800 066 4410
sales@lumenalights.com

Web
www.lumenalights.com

Address
Lumena Lights Ltd
Centre 33 Long March
Long March Industrial Estate
Daventry NN11 4NR

Operational area
UK

Stelled – 3mm-thick marine grade stainless steel

Ledifice LED bollard for illuminating larger areas

Charleston brass brick light with frosted lens

Radiata pine sleeper bollard with brass LED light

Tristar slimline 500 or 800mm LED path light

Cubic die-cast aluminium wood-effect bollard

Beacon traditional polished brass 560mm path lights

AMENITIES

Road, street and amenity lighting — 272-276

Lighting for public realm, commercial and residential settings including roads, car parks, streets, precincts, architectural features, parks and gardens.

Solar lighting systems and reflective traffic bollards.

Co-ordinated street furniture — 277-313

Products designed in co-ordinating materials and styles for town centres, green spaces and other public areas. Seats, benches, litter bins, bollards, cycle parking, signage, planters, railings, tree guards and grilles.

Protective street furniture to promote safety in shared public places.

Seats and benches — 313-345

Standard and bespoke seating in contemporary and traditional styles.

Seats, benches and picnic tables in metals, timber, natural stone, concrete and plastics for public areas, commercial landscapes, gardens and restful spaces.

Litter bins and recycling units — 346-359

Standard and customised bins and recycling units for pedestrian zones, retail centres, transport termini, parks, playgrounds and areas near public buildings.

Bins for litter, dog waste, cigarettes and chewing gum.

Recycling units, including high-volume compaction and underground systems.

Planters and planting systems — 360-383

Planters to demarcate outdoor areas and bring greenery to urban streetscapes, commercial and retail spaces, roof gardens, raised terraces, public parks, residential areas and gardens.

Modular planters, tree planters, barrier planters, pots and troughs.

Tiered planters, pole-mounted planters, barrier baskets and hanging baskets.

Shelters, canopies and walkways — 384-395

Shelters, canopies, walkways and covered areas to provide shade and protection against the weather for transport termini, schools, hospitals, business premises, visitor attractions, playgrounds and recreational areas.

Plant housing and storage compounds — 395-400

Bespoke prefabricated structures for plant housings, equipment cabinets, storage compounds and bin stores. Gatehouses and kiosks.
Products in timber, GRP, steel louvre or steel grating.

Amenity and leisure buildings — 401-403

Modular, bespoke and kit-form amenity and leisure buildings for applications ranging from visitor toilets and changing facilities through to large pavilions, clubhouses, garages, home offices and garden buildings.

EXTERNAL WORKS ONLINE

For detailed information supported by case studies, downloads and tools to help you make faster and better decisions ...
☞ www.externalworks.co.uk

Marshalls

Creating Better Spaces

Contact
t: 0870 444 6217
f: 0870 442 7725
esi.marshalls@web-response.co.uk

Web
www.marshalls.co.uk/commercial

Address
Marshalls plc
Landscape House, Premier Way,
Lowfields Business Park, Elland HX5 9HT

Additional entries
Protective post and rail ➤ 219
Bollards ➤ 235
Cycle parking ➤ 249
Signage and wayfinding ➤ 264
Co-ordinated street furniture ➤ 278
Protective street furniture ➤ 280
Co-ordinated street furniture ➤ 282
Seats and benches ➤ 320
Litter bins ➤ 357
Planters ➤ 378
Tree protection ➤ 526

Marshalls plc

Illumination

Marshalls works as a lighting partner for designers and architects with challenging projects and ambitious creative vision. The company's in-house lighting expertise, technological knowledge and design experience help to create distinctive, attractive places while also addressing the requirements for functional street lighting. High design, technical precision and photometric performance are fundamental to Marshalls lighting philosophy. The correct illumination of a public space can deter crime and enhance the economic potential of an area.

Geo Disc

CODA luminaire (part of CODA co-ordinated range)

Geo lightstacks – Wembley Stadium, London

Aubrilam Elea column – Westfield Shopping Centre

Bespoke lightstacks – Ferrari World, Abu Dhabi

Bespoke lighting columns – Canary Wharf

Bespoke lighting columns – Exhibition Road, London

Aubrilam Dome column

Bespoke lightstacks – Dublin

Aubrilam Sumu columns

Bespoke LED masts – Southend-on-Sea

Aloa luminaire

Hydra luminaires

Illuminated handrail

All Urban Ltd

Contact
t: 0114 282 1283
f: 0114 282 3463
info@allurban.co.uk

Web
www.allurban.co.uk

Address
All Urban Ltd
Aizlewoods Mill Nursery Street
Sheffield S3 8GG

Additional entries
Contemporary seating ➤ 324
Youth shelters ➤ 390

All Urban Ltd

Santa & Cole lighting

All Urban supplies Santa & Cole lighting and street furniture. The simple designs and high quality construction of the products can enhance urban environments.

• **Contemporary lighting ranges**
All lighting elements are assessed against sustainability criteria at the development stage. They are energy saving, prevent light pollution, use recycled and recyclable materials and are designed to minimise on-going maintenance. Products are designed to perform not only at night, when only the light affects the landscape, but also during the day, when the fittings need to blend well into the area.

Design services

All Urban's lighting team offers a consultative approach for lighting designers, landscape architects and architects to help create award-winning lighting schemes. The company's experienced Projects Department provides specialist lighting knowledge to devise creative, bespoke solutions. The inter-relationships of the space are carefully considered, as well as how the lighting will work with all users of the space, and with the landscaping, furniture, traffic, buildings and vegetation.

Via Lactea – highly adaptable modular pergola

Sara street light – compatible with *Arne* LED

Latina – for illuminating large areas

Candela – high-level city lighting

Skyline wall-mounted lighting

Skyline Beacon

Rama – with various asymmetric light distributions

Arne – simplistic and compact

Candela Light Ltd
Road, street and amenity lighting

Candela Light is a UK company that designs and manufactures exterior lighting products. Applications include highways, streets, estate roads, car parks, amenity areas, town centre regeneration schemes and railways. Special bespoke products can also be produced.

• Luminaires
All luminaires are specifically designed to meet local authority requirements and all relevant British Standards. A wide range of reflectors, optics and light sources is offered. LED lanterns incorporate a minimum of an IP65 optic area.

• Columns, brackets and embellishments
Lighting columns and brackets are designed and manufactured in a variety of materials and finishes. Embellishment kits are available to suit a variety of column sizes to enhance the appearance of standard columns.

Projects
• Bespoke LED lighting – Eberle St, Liverpool.
• Exterior LED lighting – £50 million Park Regis Development, Birmingham.
• Portmarine lantern designed and manufactured for Bristol Council – Portishead, Bristol.
• Bespoke design for Glasgow City Council – Glasgow Green.
• Woodbury Down, Dickens Heath Village, Solihull town centre and Bath city centre.

Contact
Sales
t: 0121 678 6700
f: 0121 678 6701
sales@candela.co.uk

Web
www.candela.co.uk

Address
Candela Light Ltd
319 Long Acre
Waterlinks Nechells
Birmingham B7 5JT

Accreditation
ISO 9001–2000/AS 9100
ISO 9002:2003

Additional entries
Illuminated bollards and bulkheads ➤ 269

Fleet luminaire – Ocean Terminal, Leith, Edinburgh

Aston LED

Linea LED

Vale LED

Borough LED

Rothesey LED

Street Furnishings Ltd

Solar sign lighting systems and reflective bollards

The *Street Solar Signlight* from Street Furnishings is constructed from LM6 aluminium die-casting and features vandal resistant fixings and polycarbonate glazing. It is offered with a grey, silver or black finish. A double-headed version is available for back-to-back signs.

Night Owl reflective bollards require no light source and are mainly used as Keep Left signs on traffic islands. The bollards will self-right if hit. An LED baselight version is also available.

Contact
Tony Barnes (sales)
t: 0118 940 4717
f: 0118 940 3216
mail@streetfurnishings.co.uk

Web
www.streetfurnishings.co.uk

Address
Street Furnishings Ltd
Festival House
Mumbery Hill
Wargrave
Reading RG10 8EE

Accreditation
ISO 9001:2008
BS 8442; BS EN 12767; TSRGD 2015 (Night Owl)

Additional entries
Bollards ➤ 236

Street Solar Signlight

Street Solar Signlight

Street Solar Signlight

Dalek emergency lighting replacement bollard

Night Owl bollard

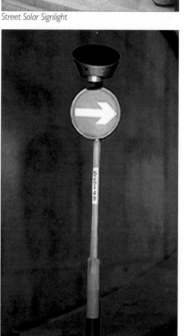
Night Owl is highly visible during the day

Street Solar Signlight

Street Solar Signlight

Contact
Paul Owens (sales)
Scott Chafer (technical)
t: 01484 401414
f: 01484 721398
info@asfco.co.uk

Web
www.asfco.co.uk

Address
Architectural Street Furnishings Ltd
Priory Road
off Armytage Road
Brighouse HD6 1PY

Accreditation
ISO 9001:2008

Additional entries
Post and rail systems ➤ 216
Bollards ➤ 225
Seats and benches ➤ 325
Bespoke metalwork ➤ 414

Architectural Street Furnishings

Bespoke street furniture

ASF designs and manufactures bespoke street furniture in the UK. The company's manufacturing capability allows it to work closely with its clients to create stylish co-ordinated street furniture schemes. ASF produces modern, intuitive and creative schemes, as well as undertaking retrofit and renovation projects.

• **Materials**
ASF works with a wide variety of high-quality materials, including marine-grade stainless steel, mild steel, cast iron from its own foundry, natural stone and FSC-accredited iroko timber.

• **Expertise and skill base**
The creative team includes designers, draughtsmen, pattern makers, casting engineers and fabricators, meaning both traditional crafts and modern skills can be drawn upon to develop street furniture products.

• **Recycling**
ASF operates an on-site recycling plant that ensures products are as environmentally sustainable as possible. All castings are 100% recycled as well as being 100% recyclable, with an estimated lifespan of in excess of 100 years.

Stainless steel bollards

Stainless steel post and rail system

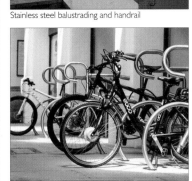
Stainless steel balustrading and handrail

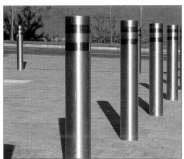
Bespoke stainless steel cycle stands – Halfords

ASF 6012 stainless steel and timber seat and stainless steel post and rail

Glass balustrading with stainless steel fittings

ASF 5001 stainless steel bollards with polished bands

Marshalls

Creating Better Spaces

Contact
t: 0870 444 6217
f: 0870 442 7725
esi.marshalls@web-response.co.uk

Web
www.marshalls.co.uk/commercial

Address
Marshalls plc
Landscape House, Premier Way,
Lowfields Business Park, Elland HX5 9HT

Additional entries
Protective post and rail ➤ 219
Bollards ➤ 235
Cycle parking ➤ 249
Signage and wayfinding ➤ 264
Illumination ➤ 272
Protective street furniture ➤ 280
Co-ordinated street furniture ➤ 282
Seats and benches ➤ 320
Litter bins ➤ 357
Planters ➤ 378
Tree protection ➤ 526

Marshalls plc

Co-ordinated street furniture

Marshalls co-ordinated street furniture ranges are designed to meet the demands of modern urban landscapes, regardless of complexity or budget. A solution is available whether the project is a town centre refurbishment, a retail park, a waterfront, or a leisure area for local communities, universities or schools.

• Flexible furniture ranges
Marshalls' ranges provide flexible seating arrangements that enable bespoke configurations and can add value to any scheme.
Products include seats and benches in standard and bespoke lengths, innovative planters and litter bins, contemporary signage, modern cycle stands and bollards.
A wide palette of materials is offered to cater for aesthetic and budgetary requirements, including concrete, cast stone, stainless steel and mild steel. Timber elements are iroko hardwood with other FSC-certified timbers available to order.

Technical support

Marshalls offers support and advice from design to installation. A bespoke product solutions service is offered by the experienced team of Technical Sales Consultants and Design Engineers who have completed many successful projects.

Waterside range – benches, bollards, litter bins and protective guardrails in polyurethane and FSC timber

Geo range – seats, benches, litter bins, bollards, cycle parking and signage in 316 stainless steel and iroko

Ollerton M3 range – benches, seats, litter bins and fingerposts in 316 grade stainless steel

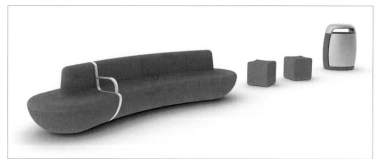

Igneo range – modular benches, seats and litter bins in concrete

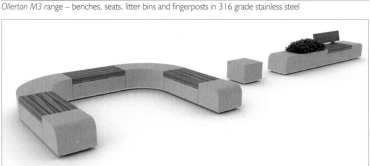

Metrolinia range – modular seating and bench planters in concrete and timber

Loci range – benches, seats, bollards, cycle stands, monoliths and litter bins in steel, timber and aluminium

CODA range – cycle stands, benches, seats, litter bins, bollards, fingerposts and monoliths in concrete, aluminium, steel and timber

Escofet range – benches, seats, picnic tables, planters, bollards, litter bins and tree protection in slimline concrete

Eos PAS 68 seat

Marshalls plc

Protective street furniture

Marshalls protective street furniture promotes safety in shared public spaces. PAS 68 rated products include bollards, planters, seating and litter bins manufactured from a variety of materials, with increased structural support to help protect against disruption and attacks.

• Protective bollards

Rhinoguard™ protective bollards are the first port of call for many security minded projects – many of the products in the range have been rigorously tested to withstand vehicle attacks. *Rhinoguard™* protective bollards are available in standard or shallow-mount versions.

• Protective planters

The *Bellitalia Large Giove Protective Planter* is cast from a mix of concrete and fine Italian marble, and has a smooth, polished finish. PAS 68 security rated timber designs are also available.

• Protective seating

Designs include the *Igneo* seat, manufactured from fibre reinforced concrete with Ferrocast polyurethane armrests, and the *Eos* seat in Ferrocast and timber.

Technical support

Marshalls provides advice on furnishing urban areas for public safety and aesthetic appeal using standard products or bespoke solutions.

RhinoGuard™ PAS 68 bollards

![Marshalls – Creating Better Spaces]

Contact
t: 0870 444 6217
f: 0870 442 7725
esi.marshalls@web-response.co.uk

Web
www.marshalls.co.uk/commercial

Address
Marshalls plc
Landscape House, Premier Way,
Lowfields Business Park, Elland HX5 9HT

Additional entries
Protective post and rail ➤ 219
Bollards ➤ 235
Cycle parking ➤ 249
Signage and wayfinding ➤ 264
Illumination ➤ 272
Co-ordinated street furniture ➤ 278
Co-ordinated street furniture ➤ 282
Seats and benches ➤ 320
Litter bins ➤ 357
Planters ➤ 378
Tree protection ➤ 526

Geo PAS 68 bollards

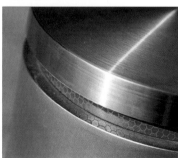
Geo PAS 68 litter bin

Geo PAS 68 bollard

RhinoGuard™ PAS 68 shallow-mount bollards

RhinoGuard™ PAS 68 bollard crash test

Igneo PAS 68 seating

Igneo PAS 68 seat

Giove PAS 68 planter frame crash test

Igneo PAS 68 seat crash test

MIRA
Post Test K0019

Giove PAS 68 planters

Marshalls plc

Co-ordinated street furniture

Marshalls co-ordinated street furniture ranges are designed to meet the demands of modern urban landscapes, regardless of complexity or budget. A solution is available whether the project is a town centre refurbishment, a retail park, a waterfront, or a leisure area for local communities, universities or schools.

• **Flexible furniture ranges**

Marshalls' ranges provide flexible seating arrangements that enable bespoke configurations and can add value to any scheme.

Products include seats and benches in standard and bespoke lengths, innovative planters and litter bins, contemporary signage, modern cycle stands and bollards.

A wide palette of materials is offered to cater for aesthetic and budgetary requirements, including concrete, cast stone, stainless steel and mild steel. Timber elements are iroko hardwood with other FSC-certified timbers available to order.

Technical support

Marshalls offers support and advice from design to installation. A bespoke product solutions service is offered by the experienced team of Technical Sales Consultants and Design Engineers who have completed many successful projects.

Mac range – seat, bench, chair, stool, litter bin and cycle stand with industrial styling in steel and iroko

Spring range – stool, seat, bench, table, litter bin and tree grille in strong, sleek *Ultratense®* concrete

Igneo range – modular bench, seat, cube and litter bin in cast concrete

Charm range – seat, bench planter, bollard, bin and cycle stand with decorative patterning in steel and timber

Carya range – bench, bollard, litter bin and shelter in modular cast iron, iroko, steel and stainless steel

Demetra range – modular seating, curved bench and bench planter in white granite or precious stone

Contact
t: 01788 550556
f: 01788 550265
info@autopa.co.uk

Web
www.autopa.co.uk

Address
AUTOPA Limited
Cottage Leap
Rugby CV21 3XP

Accreditation
ISO 9001:2008
ISO 14001:2004
OHSAS 18001:2007
Achilles Building Confidence

Affiliations
CHAS
Constructionline

Additional entries
Rising arm barriers ➤ 212
Telescopic posts and automatic bollards ➤ 213
Height restrictors and swing gates ➤ 214
High visibility protection ➤ 217
Traffic flow plates and speed ramps ➤ 221
Bollards ➤ 226
Parking posts ➤ 228
Cycle shelters and compounds ➤ 242
Cycle stands ➤ 244
Illuminated bollards ➤ 268
Shelters, canopies and walkways ➤ 391

AUTOPA Limited

Street furniture

AUTOPA open spaces street furniture is manufactured to stand the rigours of daily intensive use in public places ranging from streetscapes, to retail centres, schools and parks. Products include benches, picnic tables, litter bins and bollards, in a variety of materials and styles.

• Stainless steel and mild steel benches
Rockingham seats, benches and picnic tables are manufactured in grade 304 stainless steel or mild steel.
Drayton seats and benches are manufactured in 304 stainless steel or mild steel.
Mild steel benches are galvanised as standard and can be colour coated to any BS or RAL colour.

• Stainless steel and iroko benches
Rochester seats and *Chatham* benches are designed to withstand tough conditions and to retain their aesthetics for years with minimal maintenance. They combine high quality, durable grade 304 stainless steel and iroko hardwood.

• Litter bins
AUTOPA open spaces litter bins are available in stainless steel, galvanised mild steel and MDPE. The *Flared Top Bin* is manufactured from galvanised mild steel as standard. Colour-coated finishes and stainless steel options are available on request.

AUTOPA open spaces Rockingham Seat in 304 stainless steel; mild steel also available

AUTOPA open spaces Drayton Seat is available in galvanised mild steel or grade 304 stainless steel

Stainless steel illuminated bollards

AUTOPA open spaces Drayton Bench

AUTOPA open spaces Rockingham Bench

Traditional MDPE litter bin

Chatham Bench in 304 stainless steel and iroko

Rochester Seat in 304 stainless steel and iroko

AUTOPA open spaces Flared Top Bin

artform
urban furniture

Contact
Sales and technical
t: 0800 542 8118 / 01625 877544
enquiries@artformurban.co.uk

Web
www.artformurban.co.uk

Address
Artform Urban Furniture Ltd
Adlington Business Park
London Road
Adlington SK10 4NL

Additional entries
Seats and benches ➤ 326

Artform Urban Furniture Ltd

Co-ordinated street furniture

Artform Urban Furniture supplies design-led street furniture solutions and is at the leading edge of integrated landscape design. The company provides inspiring, forward-thinking public realm furniture to help landscape architects and specifiers bring their visions to life.

• **Global product ranges**
Artform has the exclusive UK distribution rights for co-ordinated ranges designed by some of the world's leading studios including: BMW Design Group, Frog Design, Yves Behar/Fuse Project and Jangir Maddadi.

• **Landscape Forms (USA)**
Artform is the UK distributor and manufacturing partner for Landscape Forms, which is an industry leader for integrated collections of high-concept street furniture and advanced LED lighting.

• **Metalco (Italy)**
As the exclusive UK distributor for Metalco, Artform is able to provide some of the most stylish public realm furniture in Europe, including the popular corten steel ranges.

• **Jangir Maddadi Design Bureau (Sweden)**
Artform is the UK supplier for Janghir Maddadi, offering forward-thinking street furniture with innovative designs for public and private spaces.

MultipliCITY range by Landscape Forms

Chiave cycle stand by Metalco – corten steel option

Spencer litter bin by Metalco – corten steel option

Chill seat by Landscape Forms

Hesperia corten steel bollard by Metalco

Dahlia planter by Metalco – corten steel option

Guide illuminated bollards by Landscape Forms

Stay seat by Landscape Forms

Custom planter by Metalco

FGP bike rack by Landscape Forms

FGP litter bin by Landscape Forms

FGP seat by Landscape Forms

FGP path lighting by Landscape Forms

Air picnic table by Metalco

Lorenz modular granite/marble seating with integral timber seat by Metalco

STRATA bench by Landscape Forms

Botte litter bin by Metalco

Stone bench by Metalco

Bailey streetscene

Let's talk. The answer is yes.

Contact
Sales and technical
t: 01625 855900
sales@baileystreetscene.co.uk

Web
www.baileystreetscene.co.uk

Address
Bailey Streetscene
Adlington Business Park
London Road
Adlington SK10 4NL

Additional entries
Shelters and canopies ➤ 392

Bailey Streetscene

Co-ordinated street furniture

Bailey Streetscene designs, manufactures and installs street furniture. With over 30 years' experience, the company partners with the UK construction industry across a wide range of sectors, from education, local authority, commercial and retail to new build and regeneration projects.

Composition and manufacture

Based in Cheshire, and with a 20,000 square foot production facility in Staffordshire, Bailey creates premium site-specific, design-led street furniture, from seats and benches to walkways and canopies.

Technical support

The company's strength lies in its ability to work with architects, specifiers and contractors, and in its 'know-how, can do' approach.
The company has the resources, flexibility and know-how to deliver more performance than a client's budget specifies, or the same performance at a lower cost.
Even if part of the client's brief is undefined, Baileys is able to help achieve the vision.

Bradford seat – City Park, Bradford town centre

Deacon bench – Wade Deacon High School

Bespoke *Westminster* bench – Nottingham One

Woking double-sided seat – Surrey high street

Westminster bench – Leicester University

Stoke litter bin – Hanley city centre

Hazard banded bollards – Slatyford Business Park

Toscana seat – Old Moat School

Imperial seating – Bam headquarters

Tree seat – Llanelli Bus Station

Timber planter – Leicester University

Record groove bollards – Giltbrook Retail Park

Holgate bench – Kingswell High School

Stoke seat – North Staffordshire Hospital

Orion seat – Llanelli Bus Station

Concrete cubes – Leicester University

Linares seat

Cado Corpus seat

Stainless steel *Sheffield* cycle stands – Victoria Park

Benchmark

STREET FURNITURE

Contact
Anthony Cox
t: 01243 545926
f: 01243 545453
info@benchmark-ltd.co.uk

Mark Wolfenden
t: 01243 545926
f: 01243 545453
wolfy@btinternet.com

Web
www.benchmark-ltd.co.uk

Address
Benchmark Design Ltd
Cheriton House
Barnham Lane
Walberton
Arundel BN18 0AZ

Awards
Civic Trust Partnership Award 1998 – Supplier of
Furniture (Chapel Wharf)

Operational area
UK, Europe

Country of manufacture
UK

Additional entries
Contemporary shaped seating ➤ 314
Picnic tables ➤ 344
Contemporary litter bins ➤ 354
Planters ➤ 374

Benchmark Design Ltd

Co-ordinated street furniture

Benchmark designs and manufactures
contemporary street furniture.
Co-ordinated suites of products include seating,
litter bins, bollards, tree guards and grilles,
planters, cycle stands and screens.
They are specified for projects including major
town centre refurbishments, parks, schools,
universities, offices and housing developments.
A design-and-build service allows urban designers
to specify individual items.

• **Centerline street furniture**
Centerline street furniture is widely specified for
public and private projects where a robust yet
stylish solution is called for. Available in grade 316
stainless steel, powder-coated galvanised steel or
a combination of the two, *Centerline* provides
landscape designers with versatile products that
can be shaped to suit specific locations.

• **Baseline street furniture**
Baseline street furniture offers a cost-effective
solution for the provision of smart, functional and
durable seating.
Products are manufactured in either grade 316
stainless steel or powder-coated galvanised steel.

• **Shoreline street furniture**
Shoreline street furniture follows the same
ergonomic shape as the popular *Centerline* range,
but has attractive natural timber slats.
A stainless steel framework provides protection
to the timber edges and a distinctive style.

Composition and manufacture

Products are made to precise standards.
Tubular mild steel is shot-blasted and chemically
cleaned before getting anti-corrosive treatment.
Grade 316 stainless steel gives integral corrosion
resistance suitable for marine environments.
Products can be finished in any RAL colour.
Timber slats are available in either FSC-approved
hardwood or Douglas fir.

Sitework

Furniture is installed using one of three methods:
embedding, fixing below ground with a base-
plate, or fixing above ground with a base-plate.

Centerline CL050 litter bin and *CL003* seat

Centerline CL10 curved seat – King's Cross, London

Centerline CL007 curved bench, tables and stools

Centerline CL011 tree seat

Centerline CL005 bench and *CL046* litter bin

Centerline CL011 seat

Centerline planters and curved benches

Centerline CL001 seats and *CL054* litter bins

Shoreline SL052 litter bin and *Centerline* seat

Shoreline planter

Shoreline SL003bb seat, planter and *SL054* litter bin

Shoreline SL008 curved bench and screening

Baseline litter bin and *BL005* bench

Baseline BL005 bench

Campus aluminium planter, timber bench and table

Campus picnic set and planter

Contact
Paul Strong, Sales Manager
t: 07423 431510
Paul.Strong@rud.co.uk

Web
www.erlauuk.co.uk

Address
Erlau AG
Units 10–14
John Wilson Business Park
Thanet Way
Whitstable CT5 3QT

Accreditation
ISO 9001:2008

Operational area
Worldwide

Country of manufacture
Germany

Erlau AG

Co-ordinated street furniture

Erlau AG was founded in 1828 in Aalen in Germany, and is a leading manufacturer of outdoor furniture. The company provides street, park and open space furniture, made to withstand the toughest environmental conditions. Products have been specified for projects in the Norwegian mountains, in Europe's rainiest city, and in Rhiad, where temperatures reach 45°C in the shade. In addition to standard products, customised designs meet the needs of senior citizens, children and disabled people.

Composition and manufacture

Products are made in Germany and are ISO 9001 certified. Those made using *Pagwood* composite material offer especially good protection against the elements. The resin-soaked laminate comprises very thin, cross-bonded veneers of European beech. It is fracture proof, does not splinter, and is water and chemical resistant.

Finish and appearance

Product are also powder coated with 350μm of *Rilsan*, a polyamide treatment made from renewable resources, which guarantees durability and insulation. Erlau seating, for example, will not get hotter than 42°C, unlike benches made of wood, stone or untreated metal. Exclusive anti-graffiti coatings also help safeguard products.

Modular outdoor bench with advertising insert

Bella Via street furniture suite

Strada outdoor bench

Charisma pagwood and steel bench

Stella outdoor bench

Parador steel table and multi-seat unit

Vasura litter bin

Strada wire mesh bench

Olympia Nova outdoor seating

Multi seating system

Intersit outdoor bench

Pedalo cycle stand

Siesta outdoor bench

Bambino children's picnic suite

Factory Furniture Ltd

Contemporary street furniture

Factory Furniture is a British designer-maker specialising in contemporary street furniture. The company places particular emphasis on attention to detail, both in design and specification, as well as on the sustainability of its business and products.

• Product range
Products include street benches, tree seats, litter bins, planters and wayfinding signage.
The company's designs are used in town and city centres, gardens, play areas, hospitals, universities, and corporate break-out areas.

Composition and manufacture
Products are mainly manufactured in house at the company's Oxfordshire workshops to ensure high build quality.
Drawing on 28 years of experience allows Factory Furniture to offer custom design services for bespoke street furniture projects.

Design services
Factory Furniture works in close collaboration with clients through each stage of the design and manufacturing process to enable full realisation of the brief. Attention to detail provides a unique identity to each project.

Contact
Sales
t: 01367 242731
sales@factoryfurniture.co.uk

Web
www.factoryfurniture.co.uk

Address
Factory Furniture Ltd
5 Pioneer Road
Faringdon SN7 7BU

Accreditation
Forest Stewardship Council (FSC)

Operational area
Worldwide

Additional entries
Seats and benches ➤ 329
Litter bins ➤ 355
Tree planters ➤ 375

Ribbon slatted bench

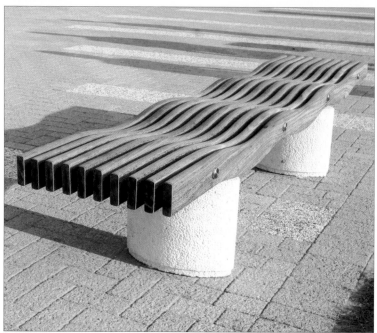
Serpentine slatted bench

Bespoke curved seating – courtyard garden, Guy's & St Thomas' Hospital, London

Osso bench

Bespoke *Flo* granite bench – High Street, Bromley

Heavy duty curved seating – Canal Walk, Swindon

Bespoke concrete seat and furniture – Hornchurch

Chronos seating – Brighton & Hove College

Bespoke seat in patinated cast bronze and FSC® hardwood, developed from concept designs – Bath

Bespoke 60 metre picnic table, comprising various sections curved at different radii – Tournai, Belgium

Sinu hardwood and stainless steel bench

Bespoke tree seat – Twickenham High Street

Goose Foot Street Furniture

Standard and bespoke furniture

Goose Foot Street Furniture brings together the design skills of Ollerton Engineering Services, and the manufacturing expertise of the WEC Group. The company's street furniture is designed to perform in public areas, is made with inherently recyclable materials, and is priced to compete with the biggest names on the market.

Composition and manufacture

Products are made in satin finish stainless steel, in various grades, and in mild steel. They can be painted/powder coated in 25 standard colours.

Contact
Sales
t: 01254 700213
enquiries@goosefootuk.com

Web
www.goosefootuk.com

Address
Goose Foot Street Furniture Ltd
Britannia House
Junction Street
Darwen BB3 2RB

Magellan stainless steel seat with arms

Tula stainless steel seat

Magellan timber slatted seat

Lander timber slatted seat

Tula picnic sets

Tula curved seat

Bollards are available in powder coated steel or stainless steel to co-ordinate with seating and litter bins

Stainless steel *Sheffield* cycle stand

Tula stainless steel seat and *Magpie* steel litter bin

Tula powder coated steel seat

Tula curved seat

Bespoke seating – waterfront regeneration, Colwyn Bay

Bespoke seating – Fishergate Central Gateway, Preston

Bespoke corten-look seating to co-ordinate with tree grilles and cycle stands – Goose Green, Altrincham

Bespoke seating – ITV HQ, Media City, Salford

Seating to match arch by sister company m-tec

Bespoke seating – WW1 War Memorial, Folkestone

Bespoke tree grille and cycle stands – Altrincham

Bespoke tree grille – Goose Green, Altrincham

Bespoke cycle stand – Goose Green, Altrincham

LANGLEYDESIGN
EXTERNAL FURNITURE SOLUTIONS

Contact
t: 01793 759461
f: 01793 759462
info@langleydesign.co.uk

Web
www.langleydesign.co.uk

Address
Langley Design
Unit L (Gate 1)
Chelworth Industrial Estate
Cricklade
Swindon SN6 6HE

Accreditation
Achilles BuildingConfidence, ISO 9001:2008

Affiliations
CHAS, Constructionline, Construction Skills
Certification Scheme (CSCS), TRADA

Additional entries
Cycle parking ➤ 248
Outdoor seats and benches ➤ 333

Langley Design

Co-ordinated street furniture

Langley Design manufactures a wide range of street furniture using steel, stainless steel, granite, concrete, recycled plastic, and a variety of hardwood and softwood timbers.

Product range

The company can produce complete suites of street furniture. Products include bollards and bins, benches and seating, cycle racks, large cycle shelters and canopies.
Products are manufactured to order and can be made to suit specific sites.

Services provided

Langley Design offers a comprehensive service, ranging from initial discussions on design style and material selection through to installation.
As part of the process, the eco-sustainability of materials is taken into account and strong visual material is provided for presentation to clients.
Once designs are approved, products are made and delivered to meet project schedules.

External dining canopy with coloured polycarbonate roofing (SPG326)

Modular curved plinth-mounted bench (SBN321) – Athena Studios, Birmingham

External dining area, table and bench set (LPT105/LBN114) – DTTCP Training Facility, Lyneham

Cycle shelter with combination smoking shelter add on (SCS310) – Stoneleigh Park, Warwickshire

Plinth-mounted timber benches (SBN304)

Dome-top litter bin (SLC302)

Free-standing timber planters (*SPL305*) – Barnoldswick Primary School

Fixed stainless steel bollards (*MBD203*)

Recycling station – Cheltenham Racecourse

Combination cycle shelter and bin store unit (*SCS311*) – University of Hertfordshire

Secure sedum roof cycle shelter (*SCS314*) – Queens Park Palace, South Kilburn

Courtyard garden pergola (*SPG329*) – Queens Park Place, South Kilburn

Plinth-mounted seat (*SST302*)

All-timber picnic tables (*SPT306*)

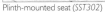

CHRIS NANGLE
FURNITURE

Contact
Chris Nangle
t: 01691 611864
info@chrisnanglefurniture.co.uk

Web
www.chrisnanglefurniture.co.uk

Address
Chris Nangle Furniture
Unit 8
Site A, Rednal Industrial Estate
West Felton SY11 4HS

Operational area
UK

Country of manufacture
UK

Additional entries
Bespoke seating ➤ 335

Chris Nangle Furniture

Co-ordinated street furniture

Chris Nangle Furniture specialises in the design and manufacture of bespoke, ecologically responsible hardwood street furniture. All of the products are extremely durable, vandal resistant and maintenance free. They have subtle lines, and are suitable for use in urban, rural, traditional or contemporary environments.

• Public seating
The standard product range includes contemporary public seating, traditional park benches, curved seating, wall- or gabion-mounted benches, and very large, charred oak seats hand-sculpted from a single length of timber.

• Planters
Hardwood planters are available to complement a variety of environments. Bespoke planters can be made in any size and shape, and in various timbers and finishes, including natural or charred oak, FSC hardwoods, larch or Accoya® wood.

• Other street furniture
Products such as tree seats, litter bins, bollards, gates and pergolas can also be produced.

Design services

Chris Nangle Furniture offers a complete design and build service, working closely with architects and designers to create site-specific street furniture for a range of projects.

Wave bench in natural green oak

Wrap bench

Green oak bench with back and arms

Four-seater *Ripple* bench in charred FSC green oak

Type 6 curved hardwood planter

Wrap bench with arms

Removable bespoke oak bollard with bronze cap

Rocker bench

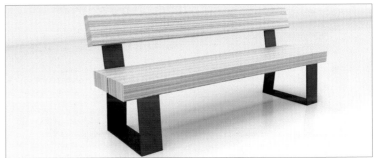

Fold Back bench

Slab Side Back bench

Poet bench

Green oak picnic set

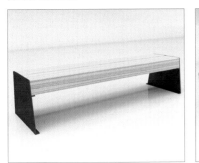

Slab Side bench

Type 5 hardwood planter

Skate contemporary bench

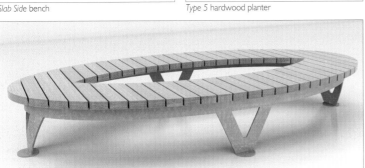

Skate tree seat

Port bench

street furniture works

Contact
Richard Woolerton
t: 0117 403 3604
sales@streetfurnitureworks.info

Web
www.streetfurnitureworks.info

Address
Street Furniture Works Ltd
3rd Floor
7 Nova Scotia Place
Spike Island
Bristol BS1 6XJ

Operational area
UK

Country of manufacture
UK

Street Furniture Works Ltd

Street furniture

Street Furniture Works designs and supplies contemporary and robust street furniture using high-quality materials.

The range includes outdoor seating, benches, tables, cycle stands, litter bins, recycling bins and fixed and removable bollards.

All products are designed in house. The range appeals to specifiers looking for well-designed objects that improve the quality of their environment, whether in an urban or historical setting. Products have clean lines and simple forms giving them a sculptural quality that makes them attractive features in their own right.

Composition and manufacture

Products are made from sustainable and recyclable materials, mainly in stainless steel and FSC certified timber.

Items are fabricated by specialist local companies, which helps keep the carbon footprint low.

Many components are CNC machine-cut then assembled, finished and quality-checked by hand.

Bs10 Bertie benches – long 4-bay version

Cs20 Cleef cycle stands

Cs30 Cirque cycle stands

Lb10t Ellipse timber litter bin

Bs11 Bertie seat with backrest and extra armrests

Bs10 Bentlie seats

Bs10 Bertie bench with extra armrests

Lb10 Ellipse litter bin – surface-mounted version

Tb20 Broadmead bollard

Streetlife

Co-ordinated street furniture

Streetlife offers an innovative, contemporary collection of products for public space. These include benches, the *Isles* range of flexible seating/planter units, picnic tables, mobile tree planters, corten steel tree grilles and bicycle and pedestrian bridges.

The diverse range of products have sustainability and local production as key aspects of the design. Many of Streetlife's products can be combined with each other.

• **Rough&Ready street furniture range**
The *Rough&Ready* range, originally created over 10 years ago, is sturdy and features carefully designed detailing and contemporary aesthetics. The range is characterised by 7x15cm beams that can be placed lengthwise or crosswise. New products are added to the *Rough&Ready* range every 2 years.

• **Solid Series street furniture**
The *Solid Series* is related to the *Rough&Ready* range but is based on 7x7cm beams. This smaller beam spacing gives it an individual appearance but with a softer look, while maintaining sturdiness.

Composition and manufacture

Products are available in FSC® hardwood, recycled plastic, stainless steel, corten steel and aluminium. FSC® license number: FSC-C105477.

Rough&Ready Oval Tree Isles in corten steel with integrated seating

Solid Surf and *Podium Isles*

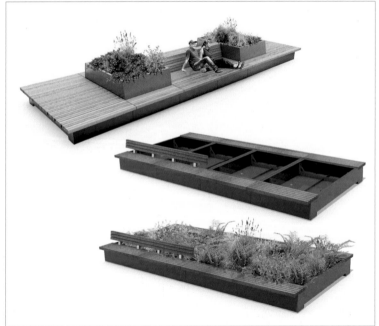

Mobile Green Isles modules

Rough&Ready Hug a Tub with single sided, double sided, L-shaped, U-shaped or surrounding seats

Rough&Ready Curved Bench in timber

Solid X-Table

Rough&Ready plastic cycle stand, seating, bollards and tree planter

Contact

The Sales Team
t: 01254 685185
f: 01254 671237
sales@woodscape.co.uk

Web

www.woodscape.co.uk

Address

Woodscape Ltd
1 Sett End Road West
Shadsworth Business Park
Blackburn BB1 2QJ

Accreditation

ISO 9001:2008
FSC, PEFC and FPCC certification
Approved supplier to Tesco

Additional entries

Hardwood decking, raised decks and boardwalks
➤ 149
Hardwood seating ➤ 342
Landscape structures ➤ 407

Woodscape Ltd

Co-ordinated street furniture

Woodscape designs and manufactures high quality street furniture, fully harnessing the design potential of hardwood and allowing its natural character to shine through.

The company works with leading architects, landscape designers, and public and private sector clients to develop bespoke solutions for individual and large-scale schemes.

- **Seating**

Seating includes straight, curved, L-shaped and multiple-width designs. They are wall, below-ground or surface mounted, and are supplied with or without armrests and backrests. Bespoke designs have also included S-shaped, perch-style, loafer, bale and in-line seats.

- **Litter bins**

Round or square litter bins have fixed tops and lockable front openings, with or without stainless steel flaps. Multiple bin housings and wheelie bin enclosures are also available.

- **Bollards**

Round or square bollards are available with a choice of top profiles, and in illuminated, removable, hinge-down or cycle parking versions. Reflective bands, rails or chains, and eye-bolt fittings can be attached.

- **Other street furniture elements**

Other co-ordinating hardwood street furniture products include picnic sets, tree seats, planters, pergolas, retaining walls, panel planter systems, gates, signage, structures, bridges and decking.

Composition and manufacture

Woodscape's standard street furniture is made from naturally very durable hardwood, which co-ordinates to create beautiful, distinctive, outdoor landscapes. Products are available with FSC Chain of Custody certification.

Design services

The company offers a complete design service for clients looking for innovative solutions. In-house designers draw on years of experience of working with the world's most durable timbers to produce striking street furniture components.

Lancaster seat with galvanised and powder-coated legs – Queens Park, Bolton

Clifton bench

Square banded bollards

LBS 112 litter bin

Hardwood timber retaining wall system

Custom hardwood timber planter in oak

 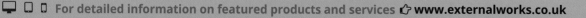

Type 2 seat – Southbank Tower, London

Bale seat – Ancoats, Manchester

Hornsea bin housing

Bespoke Westbrook seat – Daniel Owen Square, Flintshire

Loafer seat – Scarborough harbourside

Custom hardwood signage – Hilton Vacations Club, Scotland

Custom signage – Queen Elizabeth Triangle

Burlington picnic set

Benkert Street Furniture Ltd

Contemporary street furniture

Benkert is one of Europe's most influential designers and manufacturers of street furniture, with a product range built around sustainability and longevity. Its furniture is characterised by simplicity of design, functionality and freedom from cluttered design features.

Ranges encompass seating, waste bins, bike racks and bollards. Product suites like the *Comfony* range provide new design concepts for public areas. The complete range is used by many city councils and architects because of its robust nature, lack of maintenance and durability.

Composition and manufacture

All Benkert furniture is manufactured in stainless steel, augmented by carefully selected materials. Complete stainless steel products will withstand whatever conditions they are placed in. *PAGwood* products are based on an FSC approved timber product, which keeps its colour throughout its life and requires little maintenance. This year the company has introduced a new version of its products using aluminium and PET sleeves for seating slats as an alternative to the stainless steel or *PAGwood* already offered.

Finish and appearance

Furniture can be finished in most RAL colours and in textured and metallic finishes.

Comfony 10 benches with armrests

Comfony 50 stool bench without armrests

Comfony 100 double bench without armrests

Comfony 10 bench with armrests

Comfony 400 bench with armrests

Comfony 10 chair with armrests

Siardo L40R bench with armrests

230 litter bins

C100 bike stand

Contact

International Sales Office
t: 0845 606 6095
sales@worldofesf.com

Web
www.worldofesf.com

Address
Environmental Street Furniture
Valley Business Centre
67 Church Road
Newtownabbey
Belfast BT36 7LS

Accreditation
Constructionline
Made in Britain

Affiliations
Institution of Lighting Professionals (ILP)
Northern Ireland Chamber of Commerce & Industry

Awards
Chamber Awards 2014 – Highly Commended
Regional Winner
Newtownabbey Business Awards 2014 – Winner
Aer Lingus Viscount Awards 2016 – Innovator of the
Year
Northern Ireland Electrical Awards 2015 –
Innovative Sustainable Green Product of the Year
Ulster Bank Business Achievers Awards 2015 – Best
Start-Up Business
UTV Business Eye Small Business Awards 2016 –
Exporter of the Year

Operational area
Worldwide

Country of manufacture
UK, Ireland, Czech Republic, China, Philippines

Additional entries
External seats and benches ➤ 313
Litter bins ➤ 351

Environmental Street Furniture

Co-ordinated street furniture

Environmental Street Furniture has been
supplying exterior products for over 25 years.

• **Signature Collection**
The *Signature Collection* features innovative
mmcité products, characterised by their
distinctive contemporary forms. Products include
bollards, seating, litter bins, tree protection and
shelters. All offer resilience to bad weather and
vandalism, without compromising visual appeal.

• **Sustainable Collection**
The *Sustainable Collection* is made from 100%
recycled plastic which reduces the carbon
footprint of projects. The range includes seating,
litter bins, picnic units, bollards, planters and
raised beds. Products are maintenance-free, rot
and algae proof, and crack and chip resistant.

• **Simplicity Collection**
The *Simplicity Collection* of innovative, affordable
products are simple yet stylish. They are available
from stock in a choice of materials and colours.

• **Street Charge mobile charging station**
Street Charge is a solar powered mobile
phone/tablet charging station that charges up to
six devices simultaneously.

• **Senergy Smart Bench charging station**
The *Senergy Smart Bench* is a solar powered
bench for charging mobile devices. It also offers
free emergency calls and local information.

Signature Collection: Regio cycle shelter – University of Warwick

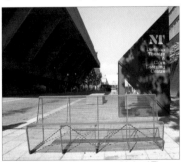
Signature Collection: Limpido seat – National Theatre

Simplicity Collection: picnic table – SERC Bangor

Simplicity Collection: stainless steel bollards

Senergy Smart Bench: solar charging station

Street Charge: solar charging station – Irish Open

Contact
Sales
t: 020 8378 3261
f: 020 8378 3250
esibook@furnitubes.com

Web
www.furnitubes.com

Address
Furnitubes International Ltd
3rd Floor
Meridian House
Royal Hill
Greenwich
London SE10 8RD

Affiliations
Constructionline
Railway Industry Supplier Qualification Scheme
(RISQS)
Builder's Profile

Accreditation
ISO 9001:2008
ISO 14001:2004
OHSAS 18001:2007

Operational area
Worldwide

Country of manufacture
UK

Additional entries
Railings and guardrails ➤ 218
Bollards ➤ 230
Cycle parking ➤ 241
Signage ➤ 260
Seating ➤ 316
Bespoke seating ➤ 331
Litter bins ➤ 356

Furnitubes International Ltd

Co-ordinated street furniture

Furnitubes offers co-ordinated, complementary street furniture products that can be used to create a cohesive overall appearance in street schemes.

Product range
• *Zenith* bollards, cycle stands, seating, litter bins and signage.
• *Elements* seating and *Arca* litter bins.
• *RailRoad* seating and planters.
• *Blyth* concrete seating and planters.
• *Linx* railings and bollards.
• *District* seating, bollards and traffic signage.
• *Wave* seating and litter bins.
• *Lambeth* seating and litter bins.

Design services
Furnitubes' in-house design team can develop bespoke products, if a particular co-ordinating item cannot be found. The team has decades of experience in managing the process of design development, approval of proposals, and manufacture, to enable a full realisation of the brief.

RailRoad seating and planters, and *Hollo* tables

Linx bespoke guardrail and *Zenith* litter bin

Blyth bench

Zenith picnic tables and benches

Neptune Street Furniture

Co-ordinated street furniture

Neptune is a UK manufacturer of high-quality, heavy-duty street furniture ranges with matching bins, benches, seats, planters and bollards. Neptune works to strict ISO 9001 guidelines and procedures to design and manufacture quality outdoor furniture that will last for many years with minimal maintenance.

Composition and manufacture
• **Wooden furniture**
Wooden furniture is produced using hardwood and softwood timber that has been selected from sustainable sources.
• **Concrete furniture**
Concrete furniture is manufactured to BS 8110 standards and can have smooth or exposed aggregate finishes.
• **Metal furniture**
Metal furniture can be made in stainless steel, corten steel and copper with natural, polished, painted or patinated finishes.

Design services
Designs can include council crests, company logos, full colour vinyl wrap advertising, integrated planters, seating and clock features.

Timor seats and benches

Hudson litter bins and seats

Avenue wooden tree bench and seats

omos

Contact

Alastair Wallace (sales, head office)
t: 0870 471 3557
t: 00 353 4589 9802
f: 00 353 4589 9803
alastair@omos.ie

Web

www.omos.ie

Address

Head office
Omos Ltd
Unit 1–3 Military Road Industrial Park
Naas, County Kildare
Ireland

Additional entries

Seating ➤ 337
Litter bins ➤ 359
Planters ➤ 380

Omos Ltd

Street furniture

Omos has been designing and manufacturing street furniture since 1996.

The company and its products have received a number of awards, including the Glen Dimplex Grand Prix, the ICAD Silver Bell and most recently the 2014 IPA Designer of the Year. Omos' clients include local authorities, architects, landscape architects, construction companies and property managers.

• Co-ordinated street furniture

Design is central to every Omos product. Many years of experience have led to a comprehensive range of products where design and engineering go hand in hand. Omos' products offer solutions for a wide spectrum of requirements and budgets. The clean, uncluttered aesthetic that prevails throughout the range enables specifiers to create co-ordinated environments that combine function with striking visual impact.

• Bespoke products

In addition to the existing product range, Omos offers a bespoke design and manufacture service, based upon many years' experience in bringing ideas from conception to production.

Many of the products within the current range are the result of responding to customers' specific needs.

s83 bespoke seating, s16 litter bins, and illuminated glazed display cabinets in powder-coated aluminium

s39 tree planters and s11.3 litter bin with chamfer aperture

s26 galvanised steel bollards with stainless steel cap

s97 modular benches and seats

Street Design Ltd

Co-ordinated street furniture

Established in 1986, Street Design specialises in the design and manufacture of a range of matching planters and seating in a variety of materials and finishes.

Composition and manufacture
Co-ordinated planters and seating can be manufactured from timber, galvanised mild steel, stainless steel and powder coated aluminium.

Design services
The company can assist clients with design and technical details for individual projects.

Contact
Sales
t: 01509 815335
f: 01509 815332
sdl@street-design.com

Web
www.street-design.com

Address
Street Design Ltd
Unit 47, Hayhill Industrial Estate
Barrow upon Soar LE12 8LD

Accreditation
ISO 9001:2008, ISO 14001:2004, ISO18001:2007, PAS 99:2006, FSC Cert. No. TT-COC-002561

Affiliations
Timber Research and Development Association (TRADA); BALI Affiliate member

Additional entries
Seating ➤ 339
Planters ➤ 370

Versatile tiered planter

Versatile large shaped planters with bench

Versatile elliptical tree planters

Versatile long barrier planter

Versatile curved planter bench with armrests

Versatile long barrier planter

Contact

Richard Williams
t: 07890 585768
uk@urbastyle.com

Web
www.urbastyle.com

Address
URBASTYLE®
Severn House
Hazell Drive
Newport NP10 8FY

Additional entries
Silkstone Fasonado paving ➤ 109
Architectural concrete bollards ➤ 237
Architectural concrete benches and seats ➤ 340
Architectural concrete planters ➤ 381

URBASTYLE®

Architectural concrete street furniture

URBASTYLE® offers the a diverse choice of co-ordinated landscape furniture in architectural concrete. Benches, seats, planters, bollards, retaining walls, copings and steps can all be incorporated into a landscape design.

The company's extensive standard offering is supplemented by an active and efficient facility that custom manufactures products to client requirements.

In addition, the range can be complemented with the *Fasonado* and *Klostermann* paving solutions.

Finish and appearance
• Colour: standard white, silver grey, dark grey and buff. Other colour/aggregate combinations produced to order.
• Surface: standard fair faced, micro-etched, polished and velvet. Exposed aggregate and form-lined surface textures available to order.
• Incorporation of graphics, copy, metal inserts, photo engraving and hardwood seating is readily accommodated.
• All units can be supplied with factory-applied waterproofing and anti-graffiti protection.

Bespoke benches – Green Alley, Rotterdam

Co-ordinated project – Oostende, Belgium

Bespoke benches – Versailles, France

Bespoke benches – Warande, Aalter, Belgium

Co-ordinated project – Schaarbeek, Belgium

Co-ordinated project – Le Touquet, France

Co-ordinated project – KØS Museum, Køge, Denmark

Green Alley benches – Molenbeek-Brussels, Belgium

Co-ordinated project – KDG School, Antwerp

PUCZYŃSKI

Contact
Neil Richardson (sales)
t: 07966 754529
neil@kfsent.com

Andre Mikulicz (technical)
t: 07576 581 872
andre@kfsent.com

Web
www.kfsstreetfurniture.co.uk
www.puczynski.pl

Address
KFS Enterprises Ltd
1 Possil House
23 Copse Hill
London SW20 0NB

Operational area
UK, Ireland

Country of manufacture
Poland

KFS Enterprises Ltd

Co-ordinated street furniture

KFS Enterprises Ltd is the sole distributor in the UK and Ireland for Puczynski Street Furniture. Puczynski specialises in the production of high-quality, in-house designed, bespoke co-ordinated street furniture in a variety of materials.
The extensive range includes seating, benches, litter bins, bollards, planters, cycle stands and tree protection products. All furniture is robust and durable, and offers a high standard of comfort and aesthetic appeal. Products can be designed to exact client requirements.

Puczynski bespoke concrete and hardwood seating

Puczynski 19-04-78 seat

Puczynski 07-11-16 cycle stand

Puczynski bespoke seating and planter

Puczynski 10-15-16 litter bin

Contact
International Sales Office
t: 0845 606 6095
sales@worldofesf.com

Web
www.worldofesf.com

Address
Environmental Street Furniture
Valley Business Centre
67 Church Road
Newtownabbey
Belfast BT36 7LS

Affiliations
Institution of Lighting Professionals (ILP)
Northern Ireland Chamber of Commerce & Industry

Additional entries
Co-ordinated street furniture ➤ 307
Litter bins ➤ 351

Environmental Street Furniture

External seats and benches

Environmental Street Furniture Ltd (ESF) supplies seating in distinctive designs and profiles, from simple seats and park benches to solid granite and illuminated stainless steel seating. Bespoke units, geometric combinations and curved shapes add new dimension to public spaces.
• **Cast iron seating**
Cast iron seating is available in traditional and contemporary designs. Products have iroko slats and cast iron frames made to BS EN 1561:1997.
• **Stainless steel seating**
Stainless steel seating is contemporary in design and requires little maintenance. Satin, brushed or electropolished versions are available.
• **Recycled plastic seating**
100% recycled plastic park seating is robust and maintenance-free.
• **Timber seating**
Oak and iroko seating comes in traditional park bench and rustic styles with matching picnic units.
• **Granite seating**
Granite seating uses modular components to create unique seating arrangements.
• **Mild steel seating**
Mild steel seating is available in simple yet stylish modern designs. Products are hot dip galvanised and powder coated in any RAL or BS colour.

Limpido seating – The Innovation Factory, Belfast

Woody seating – Glasgow Fort Shopping Centre

Portiqoa seating – Burgess Park, London

Miela seating – Canary Wharf, London

Benchmark
STREET FURNITURE

Contact
Anthony Cox
t: 01243 545926
f: 01243 545453
info@benchmark-ltd.co.uk

Mark Wolfenden
t: 01243 545926
f: 01243 545453
wolfy@btinternet.com

Web
www.benchmark-ltd.co.uk

Address
Benchmark Design Ltd
Cheriton House
Barnham Lane
Walberton
Arundel BN18 0AZ

Awards
Civic Trust Partnership Award 1998 – Supplier of
Furniture (Chapel Wharf)

Operational area
UK, Europe

Country of manufacture
UK

Additional entries
Co-ordinated street furniture ➤ 288
Picnic tables ➤ 344
Contemporary litter bins ➤ 354
Planters ➤ 374

Benchmark Design Ltd

Contemporary shaped seating

Benchmark designs and manufactures
contemporary seats and benches. Curved or
circular arrangements are often used by
architects in imaginative ways within schemes.
Benchmark's curved seating can be made to any
radius and any length, or formed into specific
configurations to suit each individual project.
Armrests can be positioned at any point to meet
specific requirements. Accessible designs, back-
to-back and design-to-build are also available.

• **Centerline seating**
Centerline seating is widely specified for public
and private projects where a robust yet stylish
solution is called for. Available in grade 316
stainless steel, powder-coated galvanised steel or
a combination of the two, seats and benches give
landscape designers versatile products that can be
shaped to suit specific locations.

• **Baseline seating**
Baseline seating offers a cost-effective solution for
the provision of smart, functional and seating.
Products are made in grade 316 stainless steel or
powder-coated galvanised steel.

• **Shoreline seating**
Shoreline seating follows the same ergonomic
shape as the popular *Centerline* range, but has
attractive natural timber slats.
A stainless steel framework provides protection
for the timber edges and give a distinctive style.

Composition and manufacture

Products are made to precise standards.
Tubular mild steel is shot-blasted and chemically
cleaned before getting an anti-corrosive
treatment.
Grade 316 stainless steel gives integral corrosion
resistance suitable for marine environments.
Products can be finished in any RAL colour.
Timber slats are available in either FSC-approved
hardwood or Douglas fir.

Sitework

Furniture is installed using one of three methods:
embedding, fixing below ground with a base-
plate, or fixing above ground with a base-plate.

Centerline CL010 curved seat and CL048 litter bin

Centerline CL005 bench

Centerline CL007 curved bench

Centerline CL001 seating

Centerline CL011 tree seat and CL007 curved bench

Baseline BL100 bench

Baseline BL003 seat

Centerline CL003 seating, CL054 litter bin and planter

Shoreline SL006 benches

Shoreline SL007 curved benches

Shoreline SL003 seat

Shoreline one-off seating

Exeter EX005 bench

Exeter EX003 seat

Campus street furniture range

Campus co-ordinated benches, tables and planters

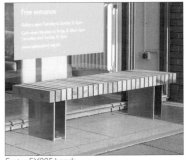

Exeter EX005 bench

Furnitubes International Ltd

Seating

Furnitubes offers seating in a wide range of styles and materials to meet project budget and design requirements.

Composition and manufacture

Products are available in traditional materials such as cast iron and timber. More contemporary materials include concrete, steel and wood plastic composite.

Design services

Many of Furnitubes' seating ranges can be adapted to suit specific requirements. For example, seating can be designed in non-standard lengths, and with armrests and backrests in different positions.

The company's team of product designers is able to assist in the process of designing new site-specific seating solutions, from concept through to detailed design and installation. Technical and budgetary advice is also available.

RailRoad Delta curved bench and straight seat with integrated planter

Contact
Sales
t: 020 8378 3261
f: 020 8378 3250
esibook@furnitubes.com

Web
www.furnitubes.com

Address
Furnitubes International Ltd
3rd Floor
Meridian House
Royal Hill
Greenwich
London SE10 8RD

Affiliations
Constructionline
Railway Industry Supplier Qualification Scheme
(RISQS)
Builder's Profile

Accreditation
ISO 9001:2008
ISO 14001:2004
OHSAS 18001:2007

Operational area
Worldwide

Country of manufacture
UK

Additional entries
Railings and guardrails ➤ 218
Bollards ➤ 230
Cycle parking ➤ 241
Signage ➤ 260
Co-ordinated street furniture ➤ 308
Bespoke seating ➤ 331
Litter bins ➤ 356

RailRoad Edge bench with chaise longue backrest

RailRoad tablet surface

RailRoad Loop wave bench

RailRoad Delta circular bench

Elements gabion bench

RailRoad seat and bench

Elements seat with granite ends

Blyth bench with LED lighting

Alta wall-top seat

Fordham seat

Zenith bench

Lapa gabion-top seat

Podium bench with anti-skate devices

Zenith Horizon seat

Logic Street & Park Furniture Ltd

External benches and seating

Logic Street & Park Furniture, recognised for its sustainable British craftsmanship, manufactures a wide range of benches and seating.
Products include straight and curved benches and seats, cubes, tree seats, and combined seating and planter units.
Materials are combined to achieve the best results, both aesthetically and for comfort. These include stainless steel and hardwood timber, timber, corten steel and mild steel.

Contact
t: 01642 373400
enquiries@logic-sf.co.uk

Web
www.logic-sf.co.uk

Address
Logic Street & Park Furniture Ltd
Royce House
Royce Avenue
Billingham TS23 4BX

Operational area
UK, Ireland, Europe

Country of manufacture
UK

Additional entries
Ullswater timber seating ➤ 334
Planters ➤ 377

Ambleside cube

Ambleside seat

Ambleside straight bench

Ambleside curved bench

Trinity seat

Fruit Boxes

Bamburgh seat

HCC bench and *HCC* cubes – Kingston upon Hull

Marshalls plc

Seats and benches

Marshalls offers seating in a choice of materials, styles and colourways to fit any budget and any space, both internally and externally.

Products are available in traditional materials such as concrete, steel and natural stone and more contemporary materials such as ferrocast plastic, stainless steel and precious stone.

Marshalls can create bespoke commissions and provides full technical advice and design services to take creative concepts through to production. PAS 68 anti-terrorism versions of many products are also available.

Contact

t: 0870 444 6217
f: 0870 442 7725
esi.marshalls@web-response.co.uk

Web

www.marshalls.co.uk/commercial

Address

Marshalls plc
Landscape House, Premier Way,
Lowfields Business Park, Elland HX5 9HT

Additional entries

Protective post and rail ➤ 219
Bollards ➤ 235
Cycle parking ➤ 249
Signage and wayfinding ➤ 264
Illumination ➤ 272
Co-ordinated street furniture ➤ 278
Protective street furniture ➤ 280
Co-ordinated street furniture ➤ 282
Litter bins ➤ 357
Planters ➤ 378
Tree protection ➤ 526

Carya seats

Metrolinia seating – Marshalls Design Space

Geo stainless steel and timber bench – London

Igneo seating – Bradford

Bespoke seating – Elefant & Castle

Spring bench

Wing benches with timber slats

Escofet Rio seating

M3 seat

Tramet table and bench

Organic chairs and tables

Rendezvous picnic tables and benches

walesᴐ⅃ɒw

MADE IN ENGLAND BY

BENCHMARK

Contact
t: 01488 658184
sales@benchmarkfurniture.com

Web
www.benchmarkfurniture.com

Address
Benchmark Furniture
Bath Road
Kintbury
Hungerford RG17 9SA

Accreditation
FSC certification

Awards
The Queen's Awards for Enterprise – 2007

Wales & Wales

Street and park furniture

Made in England in FSC timbers by leading furniture maker Benchmark, the Wales & Wales collection of seating is designed for landscape, corporate and leisure clients.
Contemporary designs in wood and metal include full benches, backless benches and chairs.
Products are available in various sizes and configurations which enhance urban or provincial schemes as well as the most sensitive architectural settings.

Chico bench

Meko curved bench

Norfolk bench

DB bench

Meko straight bench

Chico curved backless bench – Kennington Park

Chico bench – Hereford Cathedral

Norfolk benches – Fulham Reach

All Urban Ltd

Contemporary seating

All Urban supplies Santa & Cole, Concrete Urban Design and Handspring Design street furniture and lighting. The simple designs and high quality construction of the products can enhance urban environments.

As well as being practical, products are designed to decorate public spaces and help create community focal points that are suitable for everyone. Their clean lines and discreet designs suit urban settings. The methods of manufacture have minimum impact on the environment. Other products include cycle racks and planters.

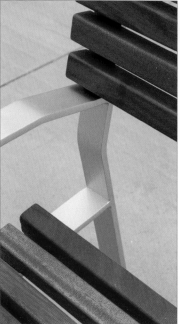

Detail of *Harpo* bench

Osa seat

Stone seating

Trapecio seat

Comunitario wooden seat and bench

Nu seat

Moon seating – Tower Bridge, London

Liviano aluminium seating

Arpa concrete and wood seats

Contact
Paul Owens (sales)
Scott Chafer (technical)
t: 01484 401414
f: 01484 721398
info@asfco.co.uk

Web
www.asfco.co.uk

Address
Architectural Street Furnishings Ltd
Priory Road
off Armytage Road
Brighouse HD6 1PY

Accreditation
ISO 9001:2008

Additional entries
Post and rail systems ➤ 216
Bollards ➤ 225
Bespoke street furniture ➤ 277
Bespoke metalwork ➤ 414

Architectural Street Furnishings

Seats and benches

Architectural Street Furnishings designs and manufactures an extensive range seating for the public realm.
Materials include cast iron, steel, stainless steel, timber, aluminium, granite and other natural stones.
As well as the company's standard range, bespoke seating can be produced in styles ranging from traditional to contemporary and post-modern.

ASF Leeds West End stainless steel benches

ASF 6012 stainless steel and timber seat and stainless steel post and rail

ASF Blackburn granite and timber seat

Circular wooden seating

ASF Modernist granite bench

ASF Leeds West End stainless steel bench

artform
urban furniture

Contact
Sales and technical
t: 0800 542 8118 / 01625 877544
enquiries@artformurban.co.uk

Web
www.artformurban.co.uk

Address
Artform Urban Furniture Ltd
Adlington Business Park
London Road
Adlington SK10 4NL

Additional entries
Co-ordinated street furniture ➤ 284

Artform Urban Furniture Ltd

Seats and benches

Artform Urban Furniture supplies design-led urban realm benches and public seating solutions and is at the leading edge of integrated landscape design. The company provides inspiring, forward-thinking ranges to help landscape architects and specifiers bring their visions to life. Many seating products have won international design awards.
• **Global product ranges**
Artform has the exclusive UK distribution rights for co-ordinated seating ranges designed by some of the world's leading studios including: BMW Design Group, Frog Design, Yves Behar/Fuse Project and Jangir Maddadi.
• **Landscape Forms (USA)**
Artform is the UK distributor and manufacturing partner for Landscape Forms, which is an industry leader for integrated collections of high-concept street furniture and advanced LED lighting.
• **Metalco (Italy)**
As the exclusive UK distributor for Metalco, Artform is able to provide some of the most stylish public realm furniture in Europe, including the popular corten steel ranges.
• **Jangir Maddadi Design Bureau (Sweden)**
Artform is the UK supplier for Janghir Maddadi, offering forward-thinking street furniture with innovative designs for public and private spaces.

Harris Isola bench by Metalco

Union concrete bench Jangir Maddadi

Rest seat by Landscape Forms

Panonto bench and *Panontino* seat by Metalco

Twin bench by Metalco

Tree Line bench by Metalco

Parallel 42 bench by Landscape Forms

Barlow Tyrie Ltd

Outdoor seating

Barlow Tyrie, founded in 1920, manufactures teak leisure furniture. Collections include outdoor furniture in stainless steel, powder-coated aluminium, and hand-woven synthetic fibre. Barlow Tyrie combines form and function with manufacturing expertise and experience to create pleasing designs with good ergonomic performance. These elements make a piece 'correct' to the eye and body.

The company has an international reputation for stylish yet practical designs, traditional craftsmanship, and excellent customer service.

Contact
James Tyrie, Sales Director
t: 01376 557600
f: 0870 460 1100
info@teak.com

Web
www.teak.com

Address
Barlow Tyrie Ltd
Springwood Drive
Braintree CM7 2RN

Accreditation
Investors in People

Awards
Consumers Digest 2015 – In Recognition of Excellence Award – Avon outdoor dining set and Equinox chaise lounger
Design Excellence Award 2009 – International Casual Furniture and Accessories Market (Tubular Materials category) – Quattro sun lounger (with Infinity backrest adjuster)

Adirondack armchair, footstool and side table

Aura extending dining table and armchairs

Glenham teak bench with inscription

Glenham teak tree seat

London teak armchairs and bench

Branson Leisure Ltd

Seats and benches

Branson Leisure manufactures and supplies a wide range of high quality, robust outdoor furniture. Clients include some of the UK's highest profile local authorities and parks, as well as schools, museums and landscaping companies. Seats and benches are available in a wide range of designs, and in a choice of materials including certified hardwood, softwood and steel. Commemorative or memorial inscriptions, and lacquered brass or stainless steel plaques can also be supplied.

Design services

For projects that require something different from the standard product range, the company can manufacture bespoke furniture to suit.
A selection of the company's bespoke work can be seen online, along with product information. A restoration service is also available.

Sitework

The company offers an installation service for all furniture items.

Contact
Kris Laskowski
t: 01279 432151
sales@bransonleisure.co.uk

Web
www.bransonleisure.co.uk

Address
Branson Leisure Ltd
Fosters Croft
Foster Street
Harlow CM17 9HS

Operational area
UK

Country of manufacture
UK

Additional entries
Picnic suites ➤ 345

Arbour seat

Tree seat

Bespoke seating

Langford 1.8m bench

Westminster 1.95m benches

Cranham seat

![Factory Furniture logo](Factory Furniture)

Contact
Sales
t: 01367 242731
sales@factoryfurniture.co.uk

Web
www.factoryfurniture.co.uk

Address
Factory Furniture Ltd
5 Pioneer Road
Faringdon SN7 7BU

Accreditation
Forest Stewardship Council (FSC)

Operational area
Worldwide

Additional entries
Contemporary street furniture ➤ 292
Litter bins ➤ 355
Tree planters ➤ 375

Factory Furniture Ltd

Seats and benches

Factory Furniture is a British designer-maker specialising in contemporary street furniture. Factory Furniture designs and manufactures products that realise their clients' brief, while placing particular emphasis on attention to detail both in design and specification.

Factory Furniture's designs are used in town and city centres, gardens, play areas, hospitals, universities, and corporate break-out areas. Products are mainly manufactured in house at the company's Oxfordshire workshops to ensure high build quality.

Murton seat

Chronos seating – Brighton & Hove College

Scroll seat – Marine Walk, Roker, Sunderland

Wood BLOC benches – RBS, London

Soca benches

Osso 3 seat

Flo granite bench – High Street, Bromley

Serpentine slatted bench

Contact
t: 0333 123 7373
info@formalandscapes.com

Web
www.formalandscapes.com

Address
Forma Landscapes
The Mill House
Walsham le Willows
Bury St Edmunds IP31 3BD

Operational area
UK

Country of manufacture
Denmark

Forma Landscapes

Scandinavian outdoor seating

Forma Landscapes works with Danish design house Out-sider to provide outdoor polyethylene seating in a wide range of colours. Applications include public spaces, educational settings, sports facilities, hotels and restaurants. The *Loop* range includes a circular seat, *Loop Light* illuminated seating, *Loop Line* straight benches, and *Loop Arc* for creating curved seating areas. *HopOp* stools can be used to sit on, for children to jump on, or as a decorative landscape element. Seats are UV-, wind- and weather-resistant, and are easily cleaned with a high-pressure washer.

Loop bench

Loop Line bench

HopOp 500 stools are available in a range of colours

Loop benches

Loop Arc benches can be configured around trees

HopOp stools can be used to play on

Loop Light illuminated bench (image: Geert Wolters)

HopOp 500 stools

Plateau HPL and steel picnic tables and benches

Furnitubes®

Contact

Sales
t: 020 8378 3261
f: 020 8378 3250
esibook@furnitubes.com

Web
www.furnitubes.com

Address
Furnitubes International Ltd
3rd Floor
Meridian House
Royal Hill
Greenwich
London SE10 8RD

Affiliations
Constructionline
Railway Industry Supplier Qualification Scheme (RISQS)
Builder's Profile

Accreditation
ISO 9001:2008
ISO 14001:2004
OHSAS 18001:2007

Operational area
Worldwide

Country of manufacture
UK

Additional entries
Railings and guardrails ➤ 218
Bollards ➤ 230
Cycle parking ➤ 241
Signage ➤ 260
Co-ordinated street furniture ➤ 308
Seating ➤ 316
Litter bins ➤ 356

Furnitubes International Ltd

Bespoke seating

Furnitubes offers bespoke seating for high profile developments where seating is a key central feature.

The company's team of product designers is able to assist in the concept and detailed design of bespoke seating solutions. Small batch production items can be designed and manufactured to specific requirements.

Advice is also offered on costings and production programming at all stages in the development of bespoke seating to ensure that products are delivered on time and within budget.

Custom-designed seating platforms – Thomas More Square, London

Custom-designed seating platforms – London

Pavilion seating – Gainsborough Square, Bristol

Illuminated seating – Peterborough Long Causeway

Circular seating – Peterborough Long Causeway

Circular seating – Peterborough Long Causeway

QUALITY
RECYCLED PRODUCTS

Contact

Michael Janes (Sales)
t: 029 2086 4095
m: 07745 189022
mike@goplastic.co.uk

Sarah Mitchell
(Marketing and general enquiries)
t: 01920 469926
m: 07887 528434
sarah@goplastic.co.uk

Web

www.goplastic.co.uk

Address

GoPlastic Ltd
Waverley
40 St Martins Road
Caerphilly CF83 1EJ

Accreditation

Constructionline

CPD

The economic value of recycled products

Operational area

UK

Additional entries

Recycled plastic profiles for decks, boardwalks,
jetties and bridges ➤ 143
Recycled plastic fencing ➤ 189
Recycled plastic bollards ➤ 234

GoPlastic Ltd

Recycled plastic seating

GoPlastic Ltd specialises in recycled plastic
products made from *Govaplast®*, a high-quality,
solid plastic board that is graffiti and vandal
resistant, requires no maintenance or treatments,
and will not splinter, rot or crack. It contains a
UV stabiliser and has an expected life span of
40+ years.

• **Govaplast® seating**
The company's award-winning seating designs are
suitable for cityscape and landscape locations.
They are available in a choice of 7 colours.

Govaplast® recycled plastic bench – Matrix

Govaplast® recycled plastic picnic table and bench set – Matrix

Govaplast® recycled plastic bench – Level X

Govaplast® Canvas recycled plastic table and benches

Govaplast® recycled plastic bench – Agora

Govaplast® recycled plastic bench – Avenue

Govaplast® recycled plastic picnic table – Roma

Govaplast® recycled plastic benches – Canvas 30

Govaplast® recycled plastic bench – Canvas 30

Langley Design

Outdoor seats and benches

Langley Design manufactures a wide range of outdoor seating that can be tailored to match design and practical needs.

- **Designs**

Designs include straight, curved and modular seats and benches. The standard range of benches can be customised to almost any length, curve or amount of seating required.

- **Materials**

Materials used include hardwood, redwood, recycled plastic, stainless steel and concrete.

- **Plinth-mounted seats and benches**

Plinth-mounting is a process that Langley Design originated. Plinth-mounted seats and benches are quick and easy to install as they require no groundwork and, in turn, lower the cost of installation. This means that all groundworks and complex paving patterns can be complete before the benches are installed. Benches can then be placed directly onto finished grade. They are useful in renovation or non-specialist projects.

Installation

Various fixing options are available including root-fixed, free-standing, wall-mounted and plinth-mounted.

Steel-framed, hardwood slat benches (SBN332) | Recycled plastic plinth-mounted benches (SBN310)

Hardwood timber seats on granite plinth mounts (SST302) – Chilton Trinity, Bridgewater

Contact
t: 01793 759461
f: 01793 759462
info@langleydesign.co.uk

Web
www.langleydesign.co.uk

Address
Langley Design
Unit L (Gate 1)
Chelworth Industrial Estate
Cricklade
Swindon SN6 6HE

Accreditation
Achilles BuildingConfidence
ISO 9001:2008

Affiliations
CHAS, Constructionline, Construction Skills
Certification Scheme (CSCS), TRADA

Additional entries
Cycle parking ➤ 248
Co-ordinated street furniture ➤ 296

Concrete bench modules (PBN411)

Single plinth-mount timber bench pods (LBN112)

Timber bench with steel legs (LBN118)

Wall- and plinth-mount seating (SBN330/SBN338)

Sturdy all-timber bench (SBN329)

Curve cut bench with plinth mounts (SBN330)

Hardwood timber seat with steel frame (LST101)

Contact

t: 01642 373400
enquiries@logic-sf.co.uk

Web
www.logic-sf.co.uk

Address
Logic Street & Park Furniture Ltd
Royce House
Royce Avenue
Billingham TS23 4BX

Operational area
UK, Ireland, Europe

Country of manufacture
UK

Additional entries
External benches and seating ➤ 318
Planters ➤ 377

Logic Street & Park Furniture Ltd

Ullswater timber seating

Logic, recognised for its sustainable British craftsmanship, manufactures the *Ullswater* range of FSC-certified hardwood timber seating. Products include the *Ullswater* cube, curved bench, curved seat, straight bench, straight seat and octagonal tree seat.

Seats and benches have hidden fixings and can be surface- or root-fixed.

An NHS-friendly design makes them particularly suitable for mental health schemes.

Ullswater tree seat – Woodlands Hospital

Ullswater straight seats – Monklands Hospital, Airdrie

Ullswater curved seats – Garden of Tranquillity, Blyth

Ullswater straight benches – Exhibition Park

Ullswater picnic set and cubes – Ayrshire Hospital

Ullswater curved bench and picnic sets – Bentley Park, Doncaster

Oak gabion seating

Chris Nangle Furniture

Bespoke seating

Chris Nangle Furniture designs and manufactures bespoke contemporary seating in any size, configuration or curvature. The products are aesthetically pleasing, durable and highly practical. Products are produced in a wide variety of materials and finishes. Standard designs can be altered to suit customers' requirements.

The company offers a full drawing to delivery service, working closely with architects and designers to create site-specific street furniture for a range of projects.

Contact
Chris Nangle
t: 01691 611864
info@chrisnanglefurniture.co.uk

Web
www.chrisnanglefurniture.co.uk

Address
Chris Nangle Furniture
Unit 8
Site A, Rednal Industrial Estate
West Felton SY11 4HS

Operational area
UK

Country of manufacture
UK

Additional entries
Co-ordinated street furniture ➤ 298

Sweep bench

Curved bench in charred green oak

Beam bench

Carved *Flute* bench

Bespoke bench

Bespoke oak benches – Northwich Quay

NEPTUNE
CONTEMPORARY AND TRADITIONAL STREET FURNITURE

Contact
Sales
t: 01962 777799
f: 01962 777723
enquiries@neptunestreetfurniture.co.uk

Web
www.neptunestreetfurniture.co.uk

Address
Neptune Street Furniture
Time House, 19 Hillsons Road
Botley SO30 2DY

Accreditation
ISO 9001

Country of manufacture
UK

Additional entries
Co-ordinated street furniture ➤ 309
Litter bins ➤ 358
Planters ➤ 379
Exterior clocks ➤ 441

Neptune Street Furniture

Seats and benches
Neptune is a UK manufacturer of high-quality, heavy-duty seats, benches and picnic tables. Products form part of the company's larger street furniture range with matching planters, litter bins and bollards.
Neptune works to strict ISO 9001 guidelines and procedures to design and manufacture high-quality outdoor furniture that will last for many years with minimal maintenance.

Composition and manufacture
• **Wooden seats and benches**
Wooden seating is produced using hardwood and softwood timber that has been selected from sustainable sources.
• **Metal seats and benches**
Metal seating can be made in cast iron, cast aluminium, stainless steel, corten steel and copper with natural, polished, painted or patinated finishes.
• **GRP seats and benches**
GRP seating is durable, versatile and low maintenance. GRP can be formed into shapes and designs unachievable in other materials.

Design services
Designs can include commemorative plaques, council crests, company logos, integrated planters and clock features.

Beaufort tree seat

Friendship seat in recycled plastic

Lincoln seats and curved bench planters

Cerro seat

Southampton seat

omos

Contact

Alastair Wallace (sales, head office)
t: 0870 471 3557
t: 00 353 4589 9802
f: 00 353 4589 9803
alastair@omos.ie

Web

www.omos.ie

Address

Head office
Omos Ltd
Unit 1–3 Military Road Industrial Park
Naas, County Kildare
Ireland

Additional entries

Street furniture ➤ 310
Litter bins ➤ 359
Planters ➤ 380

Omos Ltd

Seating

Omos has been designing and manufacturing street furniture since 1996. The company has received a number of awards, including the Glen Dimplex Grand Prix, the ICAD Silver Bell and most recently the 2014 IPA Designer of the Year. Omos' clients include local authorities, architects, landscape architects, construction companies and property managers.

Produced in materials such as wood, stainless steel and galvanised steel, Omos' range includes seating, litter bins, cigarette bins, bollards, cycle stands, planters and tree grilles.

- **Seats and benches**

Omos offers seating with clean, uncluttered lines. A comprehensive choice of designs is offered to cater for a wide range of environments and budgets. Omos offers advice on the best seating products to specify for residential, retail, city, village, vandal-prone or corrosive environments. Many designs are available with optional anti-skate blocks.

- **Bespoke products**

In addition to the existing product range, Omos offers a bespoke design and manufacture service, based upon many years' experience in bringing ideas from conception to production. Many of the products within the current range are the result of responding to customers' specific needs.

t3 seat in powder-coated aluminium with grade 316 stainless steel backrest

s83 bench in granite, stainless steel and treated iroko

s96w asymmetric bench, galvanised steel and iroko

s31 seat in 316 grade stainless steel and iroko timber, finished with micro porous stain

t3 trapezoidal benches in powder-coated aluminium

s97 curved bench in galvanised steel with treated iroko timber

Public Spaces

Contact
UK Sales Office
t: 0808 101 1590
(UK freephone number)
t: 00 353 1 286 4995
sales@publicspaces.eu

Web
www.publicspaces.eu

Address
UK Sales Office
Public Spaces
Unit 1A, Southern Cross Business Park
Bray
Co. Wicklow
Ireland

Country of manufacture
Spain

Public Spaces

External furniture/urban elements

Public Spaces offers practical, designer urban elements for the UK and Irish market. The company also specialises in bespoke designs. Public Spaces exclusively represents DAE/Escofet, MAGO Urban, Cyria and Larus Design, as well as many more specialist companies. The *Montseny* bench has been adopted by many cities around the country as a standard, accepted design that can be used within their area on any street furniture project.

Composition and manufacture

Products are offered in mild steel, stainless steel, corten steel, or in cast aluminium or cast iron. Most products use only FSC approved timber. Concrete products are also offered.

Finish and appearance

Almost all normal finishes for timber, steel or concrete products are available. This includes metallic and matte paint finishes in RAL and special shades.

Design services

Public Spaces can develop designs, using materials such as corten steel, to take ideas through to a finished product. This can help achieve the design aspirations of the many different types of locations a specifier may work on.

Montseny seats

Zen concrete seating

Loop bench

Damero concrete bench

Plus 1 bench

Crossed corten steel bench

Trave Round 74 bench

Contact

Sales
t: 01509 815335
f: 01509 815332
sdl@street-design.com

Web

www.street-design.com

Address
Street Design Ltd
Unit 47, Hayhill Industrial Estate
Barrow upon Soar LE12 8LD

Accreditation
ISO 9001:2008, ISO 14001:2004, ISO18001:2007,
PAS 99:2006, FSC Cert. No. TT-COC-002561

Affiliations
Timber Research and Development Association
(TRADA); BALI Affiliate member

Additional entries
Co-ordinated street furniture ➤ 311
Planters ➤ 370

Street Design Ltd

Seating

Established in 1986, Street Design specialises in
the design and manufacture of a range of seating
in a variety of materials and finishes.

Composition and manufacture

Seating can be manufactured from timber,
galvanised mild steel and powder coated
aluminium. Full details of all products can be
found on the company's website.

Design services

The company can assist clients with design and
technical details for individual projects.

Spalding large curved bench

Spalding curved seats with optional armrests

Rochford long and curved benches

Sheldon benches and tables

URBASTYLE®

Contact
Richard Williams
t: 07890 585768
uk@urbastyle.com

Web
www.urbastyle.com

Address
URBASTYLE®
Severn House
Hazell Drive
Newport NP10 8FY

Additional entries
Silkstone Fasonado paving ➤ 109
Architectural concrete bollards ➤ 237
Architectural concrete street furniture ➤ 312
Architectural concrete planters ➤ 381

URBASTYLE®

Architectural concrete benches and seats

URBASTYLE® produces benches and seats in four architectural concrete finishes – fair faced, micro-etched, polished and velvet – and in a wide range of natural colours. Standard ranges include traditional, contemporary and innovative design styles. Planters, seats, bollards and steps are available in matching finishes.

Composition and manufacture

URBASTYLE's products are made in a modern production facility and the company draws on in-house expertise in traditional and contemporary concrete forming and finishing techniques. Because of that, custom-made units are easily accommodated. Incorporating LED lighting, artistic inserts and graphic designs are all within the factory's capabilities.
All items benefit from a factory-applied, dirt-, stain- and graffiti-resistant protective coating.

Technical support

URBASTYLE's production facilities have sufficient capacity for individual units up to 20 tonnes. A stable, skilled workforce and flexible production methods can handle any size of project, from modest to very large.
Full technical support and planning form part of the service provided.

LED Line 3 illuminated benches – St-Omer, France

In & Out bench – London, UK

LED Line 1 bench – Izegem, Belgium

Centenaire bench – Dubai, United Arab Emirates

Galet benches – Charleroi, Belgium

Circular bench – Antwerp, Belgium

Soft seat – Miranda de Ebro, Spain

Ouvertura bench – Portsmouth, UK

Woodberry of Leamington Spa

Seats and benches

Woodberry is a long-established family-run joinery business specialising in outdoor furniture. The company offers products designed and built to ISO 9001:2008 certification to withstand heavy, regular use in the commercial and public environment.

• **Gabion furniture**

Gabion benches, tables and bench sets can be supplied with Cotswold stone or Atlantic cobbles in the base, or can be filled with material to match their surroundings.

• **Street furniture**

The *Street Furniture* range includes benches made to withstand the requirements of public spaces. It includes products in backed, backless, straight, curved, chunky, slatted and traditional designs.

Composition and manufacture

Most products are available in a choice of hardwood or softwood, and in FSC® certified timber (FSC-C115839).
Metal is available in galvanised or stainless steel. Recycled plastics are also available.

Design services

Woodberry offers in-house design services and can manufacture products to bespoke requirements through its dedicated production facility.

Contact
Chris Barr
t: 01926 889922
f: 01926 430044
chris@woodberryofleamingtonspa.com

Web
www.woodberryofleamingtonspa.com

Address
Woodberry of Leamington Spa
Bericote Woodyard
Bericote Road
Blackdown
Leamington Spa CV32 6QP

Accreditation
ISO 9001:2008

Operational area
UK

Gabion picnic table and benches

Dorchester recycled plastic benches

Dorchester hardwood bench

Bericote teak bench

Greendine A-frame picnic table and benches

Estate litter bin

Contact
The Sales Team
t: 01254 685185
f: 01254 671237
sales@woodscape.co.uk

Web
www.woodscape.co.uk

Address
Woodscape Ltd
1 Sett End Road West
Shadsworth Business Park
Blackburn BB1 2QJ

Accreditation
ISO 9001:2008
FSC, PEFC and FPCC certification
Approved supplier to Tesco

Additional entries
Hardwood decking, raised decks and boardwalks
➤ 149
Co-ordinated street furniture ➤ 304
Landscape structures ➤ 407

Woodscape Ltd

Hardwood seating

Woodscape designs and manufactures high quality street furniture, fully harnessing the design potential of hardwood and allowing its natural character to shine through.

The company works with leading architects, landscape designers, and public and private sector clients to develop bespoke solutions for individual and large-scale schemes.

The hardwood seating range includes curved, L-shaped and multiple-width designs, and seats supplied with or without backrests.

Composition and manufacture

Woodscape hardwood seating is available with FSC Chain of Custody certification, and combines a simple, natural appearance with a robust construction and resistance to vandalism.

Design services

Seats can be made to order, with an in-house team offering a design and build service for clients looking for innovative solutions. Designers draw on years of experience of working with the world's most durable timbers to make striking timber engineered components.

Sitework

Seats are supplied assembled, with a choice of wall, surface or below-ground fixings.

Lime Grove seats – University of Manchester

Evo Seat 1 – First Street North, Manchester

Pavilion Satellite seat – New Road, Brighton

Loafer seat – Scarborough harbourside

Type 8 seat

Trefoil seat – Southampton

Type 2 waved seat

Woodberry wall seat

Chaise longue – Queen Elizabeth Olympic Park, London

Handspring Design Ltd

Bespoke timber seats and benches

Handspring Design has been creating bespoke timber seating for over ten years. They are specified for schools, parks, healthcare environments and urban areas as well as for private clients. Handspring works to commission, in response to project briefs, and has a product range that can be individually tailored. The company can provide bespoke oak seating for free-standing and wall-top installation to any radius and length. Many alternative individual solutions can also be developed.

Bespoke oak curved seat, which can be made to any radius and length

Contact
Graeme Ritchie
Scot Fletcher
t: 0114 221 7785
graeme@handspringdesign.co.uk
scot@handspringdesign.co.uk

Web
handspringdesign.co.uk

Address
Handspring Design Ltd
Ecclesall Woods Sawmill
Abbey Lane, Sheffield S7 2QZ

Operational area
UK

Country of manufacture
UK

Additional entries
Bespoke timber shelters ➤ 395
Timber engineering ➤ 406

Main entrance seating commission for NHS building – Aintree, Liverpool

Mini *Apple* and *Onion* seating/shelters

Pomery Natural Stone Ltd

Natural stone seating

Pomery Natural Stone Ltd was formed in 1996 to provide high-quality materials and support to the building industry. Stones available include granite, Yorkstone, porphyry, limestone, slate, quartzite, travertine and Canadian hard limestone.
Bespoke seating is made to order in various finishes for town squares, parks, memorials, pedestrian areas and landscape design.
Seating can incorporate a mix of finishes, including textured and polished surfaces to show off the beauty of the stone.

Black Zimbabwe stone – Crossrail, Canary Wharf

Curved granite seat

Contact
Julian Pomery
t: 01489 789444
sales@pomery.co.uk

Web
www.pomery.co.uk

Address
Pomery Natural Stone Ltd
Little Heathers
Outlands Lane
Curdridge SO30 2HD

Operational area
UK, Ireland

Additional entries
Natural stone kerbs ➤ 87
Tactile paving, natural stone ➤ 87
Natural stone specialists ➤ 127

Architectural stone – Belfast

Polished bench with associated paving and setts

Curved, polished stone seat – pedestrian area

Benchmark

STREET FURNITURE

Contact
Anthony Cox
t: 01243 545926
f: 01243 545453
info@benchmark-ltd.co.uk

Web
www.benchmark-ltd.co.uk

Address
Benchmark Design Ltd
Cheriton House
Barnham Lane
Walberton
Arundel BN18 0AZ

Awards
Civic Trust Partnership Award 1998 – Supplier of
Furniture (Chapel Wharf)

Additional entries
Co-ordinated street furniture ➤ 288
Contemporary shaped seating ➤ 314
Contemporary litter bins ➤ 354
Planters ➤ 374

Benchmark Design Ltd

Picnic tables

Benchmark designs and manufactures
contemporary picnic tables and benches that are
designed to cope with harsh environments.
Manufactured in the UK, products are made to
order enabling any size and shape to be created.
They can be configured with other Benchmark
products for a co-ordinated approach.

• Centerline picnic tables
Centerline tables can be made to any diameter
and can be used with any *Centerline* bench.
The *CL025* picnic table is 1800mm long, with
matching benches.

• Campus picnic tables
The *Campus* table is part of a co-ordinated
system. It has an aluminium framework and either
FSC approved timber or treated softwood slats.
The standard table is 1200x1200x750mm high,
but can be produced to any dimensions.

Composition and manufacture

Picnic tables are produced in 316 stainless steel,
powder coated galvanised steel, or aluminium
and can be finished in hardwood timber. Options
include perforated stainless steel, disabled access
and engraving.

Installation

Picnic sets can be surface-mounted or fixed
below ground.

Campus picnic tables, benches and planters

Shoreline plinth-mounted picnic table

Baseline picnic tables and *BL007* benches

Centerline picnic table, stools and *CL007* bench

Centerline CL025 picnic sets

Branson Leisure Ltd

Picnic suites

Branson Leisure manufactures and supplies a wide range of high quality, robust outdoor furniture. Clients include some of the UK's highest profile local authorities and parks, as well as schools, museums and landscaping companies. Picnic suites are available in a wide range of designs, and in a choice of materials including certified hardwood, softwood and steel. Bespoke picnic suites can be produced upon request.

Pelham steel picnic suite

Cranham green oak picnic suite

Contact
Kris Laskowski
t: 01279 432151
sales@bransonleisure.co.uk

Web
www.bransonleisure.co.uk

Address
Branson Leisure Ltd
Fosters Croft
Foster Street
Harlow CM17 9HS

Operational area
UK

Country of manufacture
UK

Additional entries
Seats and benches ➤ 328

Round iroko picnic suite

4m *A-frame* picnic suite – seats up to 16 people

Deluxe iroko picnic suite

Contact

Patience Atkinson-Gregory
t: 01773 830930
f: 01773 834191
sales@amberol.co.uk

Web
www.amberol.co.uk

Address
Amberol Ltd
The Plantation
King Street
Alfreton DE55 7TT

Country of manufacture
UK

Additional entries
Recycling bins ➤ 347
Self-watering planting baskets ➤ 372
Self-watering planting systems ➤ 373

Amberol Ltd

Litter, dog waste and grit bins

Amberol offers a range of stylish litter bins and recycling bins. The company can advise on the most effective places to install bins, so as to encourage people to deposit litter responsibly, rather than dropping it.
• **Litter bins**
Amberol's waste deposit bins have been developed to combine capacity with a space-efficient footprint. They are suitable for use on pavements, in parks and gardens, in and around stadiums and in other public spaces. They are clearly labelled and colour-coded for ease of use.
• **Educational talking bins**
Novelty talking bins, in the shape of animals and birds, are suitable for schools, nurseries and play areas. The bins 'speak' every time litter is placed into them, affirming positive behaviour.
• **Dog waste bins**
Dog waste bins are available in two standard sizes and are supplied with a moulded dog graphic.
• **Gum and cigarette bins**
The *Gum & Ciggy Bin* is a discreet, clearly labelled, wall- or post-mounted bin. It has an integral cigarette stubber and internal fire-retardant liner.
• **Grit bins**
Grit bins and boxes are available in three shapes and sizes and provide a road-side source of grit.

Talking litter bins for learning and play areas

Ambere litter bin

Gum & Ciggy Bin

Custom bin for McDonald's

Enviro-Bin

Post-mounted *Screwball* bin

Grit bin

Tapered hood bin

Westminster bin

Contact

Patience Atkinson-Gregory
t: 01773 830930
f: 01773 834191
sales@amberol.co.uk

Web
www.amberol.co.uk

Address
Amberol Ltd
The Plantation
King Street
Alfreton DE55 7TT

Country of manufacture
UK

Additional entries
Litter, dog waste and grit bins ➤ 346
Self-watering planting baskets ➤ 372
Self-watering planting systems ➤ 373

Amberol Ltd

Recycling bins

Amberol offers a range of recycling bins, featuring stylish designs. The company is experienced in the most effective places to install recycling bins, so as to encourage separation of waste at source. Amberol's bins feature clear, WRAP-approved signage and colour coding to ensure people recycle and dispose of waste responsibly.

• Individual recycling bins
The *Olympic Dual Bin* and *Chatsworth Recycling* bins have a large capacity of 180 litres, within a small footprint.
The *Olympic Dual Bin* was specifically developed to support 'recycling on-the-go' initiatives in urban areas and can bring noticeable improvements to street cleanliness.

• Banks of recycling bins
The *Eco-Bin* and the *Slim Bin Recycle* are available in capacities of 140 and 240 litres. They are best used in banks of four or five.

Composition and manufacture

Amberol bins are manufactured to be robust and vandal resistant, with most products being double-walled. Integral pull-out liners are quick and easy to empty.

Eco-Bin recycling bins

Eco-Bin 240L

Chatsworth recycling bin 180L

Slim Bin

Attractive, practical bins encourage disposal of litter

Olympic Dual Bin, Westminster 180L

Olympic Dual Bin with WRAP-approved signage

Olympic Dual Bin 180L

Iles Waste Systems

Litter bins

Established in 1973, Iles Waste Systems supplies the waste and recycling industry with metal and plastic litter bins. Products are designed to be aesthetically pleasing, durable and practical.

All bins are polyester powder-coated and are fully recyclable at the end of their usage.

The *Knight Warrant* bin is hot dipped galvanised and carries a 10-year corrosion guarantee.

A bespoke service is available to meet individual requirements. Options include post- and wall-mounted versions, graphics, ashtrays and stubbing plates.

Contact
Graham Iles
t: 01274 728837
f: 01274 734351
wastesystems@trevoriles.co.uk

Web
www.ileswastesystems.co.uk

Address
Iles Waste Systems
Valley Mills
Valley Road
Bradford BD1 4RU

Accreditation
ISO 9001:2008

Affiliations
Chartered Institute of Waste Management

Additional entries
Recycling bins ➤ 349

Godiva litter bin

Knight free-standing litter bin

Glade litter bin

Citadel litter bin

Valley 100 and *Valley 200* litter bins

Grenadier litter bin

Contact
Graham Iles
t: 01274 728837
f: 01274 734351
wastesystems@trevoriles.co.uk

Web
www.ileswastesystems.co.uk

Address
Iles Waste Systems
Valley Mills
Valley Road
Bradford BD1 4RU

Accreditation
ISO 9001:2008

Affiliations
Chartered Institute of Waste Management

Additional entries
Litter bins ➤ 348

Iles Waste Systems

Recycling bins

Established in 1973, Iles Waste Systems supplies the waste and recycling industry with metal and plastic recycling bins. Products are designed to be aesthetically pleasing, durable and practical. Recycling bins can be produced for any outdoor or indoor waste stream, including paper, cans, bottles and plastics.

All bins are polyester powder-coated and are fully recyclable at the end of their usage.

A bespoke service is available to meet individual requirements. Options include WRAP colours and graphics to suit specific colour schemes.

Valley recycling bins

Terrace recycling bin with multiple apertures

Valley 80 recycling bin

Glade bin for paper recycling

Recycling bin with split liner

Contact
t: 01530 277900
f: 01530 277911
sales@eseworld.co.uk

Web
www.eseworld.co.uk

Address
ESE World Ltd
Beacon House
Reg's Way
Bardon Hill
Coalville LE67 1GH

Accreditation
ISO 9001:2008
ISO 14001:2004
ISO 50001

Operational area
UK

Additional entries
Underground waste systems ➤ 351

ESE World Ltd

Solar energy compaction bins

ESE World has been producing and marketing waste disposal systems for more than 80 years.

• **Clean Cube solar compaction bin**
The *Clean Cube* is a solar-powered compaction bin for streets, densely populated and busy areas. It is available in two sizes, to house 120 or 240 litre wheelie bins. *Clean Cube* bins compress waste with 500kg of compacting power, which allows them to hold 6–8 times more waste than traditional waste containers.
A smart communication system sends fill-level, battery capacity and monitoring data to a central operation point. Solar photovoltaic (PV) panels generate electricity using energy from the sun.

Finish and appearance

Various colour options, including a stainless steel body version are available. Units can feature optional advertisement panels embedded on either side. *Clean Cube's* LED-backlit advertising panels are clearly visible even at night.

Technical support

ESE World can work with customers, including councils, leisure parks, shopping centres, airports and other transport hubs, to streamline waste management processes and achieve sustainability goals. The company offers project management services, planning and data acquisition.

Clean Cube solar energy compaction bins can hold 6–8 times more waste than traditional containers

Clean Cube solar energy compaction bin

Clean Cube bins can feature optional advertising side panels, that are LED-backlit and clearly visible at night

ESE World Ltd

Underground waste systems

ESE World Ltd offers *Underground Waste Systems* (UWS) and *Semi-Underground Waste Systems* (SUWS). In addition to UWS and SUWS systems, the company also produces mobile containers, litter bins, hazardous waste containers and collection boxes.

• Underground/semi-underground systems

The *Ingenio* UWS has a capacity of 3–5 m³, with bespoke apertures available.

The *Bagio* SUWS features an HDPE outer container and woven inner bag.

The *Semio* SUWS is a reinforced concrete system, with a long-life plastic or steel collection liner.

Bagio and *Semio* systems can both be specified with a range of claddings.

Accreditation

Ingenio, *Bagio* and *Semio* systems fulfil all current European and UK standards, and are certified in accordance with EN 13071.

Technical support

ESE World can help customers to streamline waste management processes and achieve sustainability goals, offering project management services, planning and data acquisition.

Contact
t: 01530 277900
f: 01530 277911
sales@eseworld.co.uk

Web
www.eseworld.co.uk

Address
ESE World Ltd
Beacon House
Reg's Way
Bardon Hill
Coalville LE67 1GH

Accreditation
ISO 9001:2008
ISO 14001:2004
ISO 50001

Operational area
UK

Additional entries
Solar energy compaction bins ➤ 350

Ingenio underground waste systems

Environmental Street Furniture

Litter bins

Environmental Street Furniture Ltd (ESF) has been supplying litter bins for prestigious projects for over 25 years.

ESF works closely with designers and clients to create a wide range of litter bins that can be supplied in steel, cast iron, aluminium, timber and plastic.

The company is the exclusive representative of *mmcité* in the UK and Ireland.

Contact
International Sales Office
t: 0845 606 6095
sales@worldofesf.com

Web
www.worldofesf.com

Address
Environmental Street Furniture
Valley Business Centre
67 Church Road
Newtownabbey
Belfast BT36 7LS

Affiliations
Institution of Lighting Professionals (ILP)
Northern Ireland Chamber of Commerce & Industry

Additional entries
Co-ordinated street furniture ➤ 307
External seats and benches ➤ 313

Radium litter bin – Basingstoke

Diagonal litter bin – Princes Gate, Catterick

Crystal litter bin – Whitley Shopping Centre

Prax litter bin – 399 Edgeware Road, London

Street Tidy solar-powered display litter bin

Glasdon®
Quality By Design

Contact
Sales
t: 01253 600410
sales@glasdon-uk.co.uk

Web
www.glasdon.com

Address
Glasdon UK Ltd
Preston New Road
Blackpool FY4 4UL

Accreditation
ISO 9001
ISO14001
CHAS
Constructionline

Glasdon UK Ltd

Litter and recycling bins

Glasdon designs and manufactures litter and recycling bins, as well as road safety products, modular building systems, shelters and seating.

• Litter bins
Robust, functional litter bins are made using materials that have been selected to resist wear and tear in the urban landscape. The range includes designs that can complement traditional or contemporary surroundings.

Bins can be personalised by adding a company logo, image or other custom elements such as a town council identity.

Glasdon also supplies children's novelty litter bins, cigarette bins and dog waste bins.

• Recycling bins
Recycling bins are available in a choice of capacities, materials and styles to suit a variety of uses and environments. They feature colour-coded apertures and clear graphics to help encourage the efficient collection and segregation of recyclable waste. Units are designed to be hard-wearing, long-lasting and low maintenance.

Composition and manufacture

Bins are available in metals including coated aluminium, coated steel, 316 stainless steel; and in *Durapol®*, a hard-wearing polymer.

Electra litter bin

Invicta litter bin

Nexus City 140 recycling bin

Nexus 200 recycling bin

Topsy 2000 litter bin

Glasdon *Jubilee* litter bin

Sherwood litter bin

Topsy Royale litter bin

Contact

Lottie Bagust (Sales)
Dylan Bagust (Technical)
t: 01285 740488
bins@bandbinnovations.co.uk

Web
www.bandbbins.co.uk
www.bandbinnovations.co.uk

Address
BandB Innovations Ltd
Unit 2, Dovecot Workshops
Barnsley Park Estate
Barnsley
Cirencester GL7 5EG

Country of manufacture
UK

Additional entries
Removable and static bollards ➤ 233

BandB Innovations Ltd

Litter bins

BandB Innovations produces high-quality, extremely robust litter bins in 316 stainless steel. Clients can choose the finishes, inserts and colours required to match the surroundings. A bin surround insert feature allows timber, steel, and other materials to be used to decorate the exterior. Clear inserts can be filled with various materials to create a unique appearance. Branded vinyl graphics can be added to powder-coated bins, or branding can be etched into stainless steel models.

- **Pivot and Open litter bins**

Pivot and *Open* are available in 316 stainless steel and can finished as either polished stainless steel or powder-coated to any RAL colour. A lockable lift lid houses a stainless steel 90-litre capacity liner and features a 200mm open hole or pivot opening for rubbish disposal.

- **Arbour litter bin**

Arbour is available in 316 stainless steel, powder-coated to any RAL colour. It has a soft-close lid, a fixing bracket for fence-, post- or wall-mounting and a 90-litre capacity stainless steel liner.

- **Urban litter bin**

Urban is made from 316 stainless steel and has a lockable round lift lid with straight edge hinge and a lift point. The lid stands open for easy bag change. 90-litre capacity stainless steel liner.

Arbour bin with *Forest* softwood inserts

Bins can incorporate branding

Open stainless steel bin with profiled oak inserts

Urban bin with sapele inserts

Open bin powder-coated red, filled with jelly beans

BandB Innovations produces bins that blend with the environment

Benchmark
STREET FURNITURE

Contact
Anthony Cox
t: 01243 545926
f: 01243 545453
info@benchmark-ltd.co.uk

Web
www.benchmark-ltd.co.uk

Address
Benchmark Design Ltd
Cheriton House
Barnham Lane
Walberton
Arundel BN18 0AZ

Awards
Civic Trust Partnership Award 1998 – Supplier of
Furniture (Chapel Wharf)

Additional entries
Co-ordinated street furniture ➤ 288
Contemporary shaped seating ➤ 314
Picnic tables ➤ 344
Planters ➤ 374

Benchmark Design Ltd

Contemporary litter bins

Benchmark designs and makes contemporary
litter bins in open top, dome top or flat top
formats. Enclosed bins have side-opening access
with sturdy locking mechanisms. Units can be
supplied alongside co-ordinating seating, bollards,
tree guards, planters, cycle stands and screens.
Recycling options and ashtray units are also
available. A design-and-build service allows urban
designers to specify individual items.
• **Centerline litter bins**
Centerline litter bins are widely specified for
public and private projects where a robust yet
stylish solution is called for. They are available in
grade 316 stainless steel, powder-coated
galvanised steel or a combination of the two.
• **Baseline litter bins**
Baseline litter bins offer a cost-effective and
durable solution. Products are manufactured in
either grade 316 stainless steel or powder-coated
galvanised steel.
• **Shoreline litter bins**
Shoreline litter bins have the same ergonomic
shape as the *Centerline* range, but with natural
timber slats. A stainless steel frame protects the
timber edges and gives a distinctive style.

Centerline CL050 litter bin and co-ordinated seating

Centerline CL048 litter bin and *CL001* seats

Centerline CL052 litter bin

Baseline BL048 litter bin

Baseline BL052 litter bin

Baseline co-ordinating planters

Shoreline SL052 litter bin

Shoreline SL054 litter bin

Shoreline SL048 litter bin

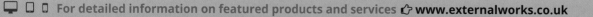

Factory Furniture Ltd

Litter bins

Factory Furniture is a British designer-maker specialising in contemporary street furniture. The company designs and manufactures products that realise their clients' brief, while placing particular emphasis on attention to detail both in design and specification.

Factory Furniture's designs are used in town and city centres, gardens, play areas, hospitals, universities, and corporate break-out areas. Products are mainly manufactured in house at the company's Oxfordshire workshops to ensure high build quality.

Contact
Sales
t: 01367 242731
sales@factoryfurniture.co.uk

Web
www.factoryfurniture.co.uk

Address
Factory Furniture Ltd
5 Pioneer Road
Faringdon SN7 7BU

Accreditation
Forest Stewardship Council (FSC)

Operational area
Worldwide

Additional entries
Contemporary street furniture ➤ 292
Seats and benches ➤ 329
Tree planters ➤ 375

Skop bin

Osso bin

Wall-mounted ashtray

Wood Bloc bin

Boort litter bin

Round litter bin

Murton bin

Furnitubes

Contact
Sales
t: 020 8378 3261
f: 020 8378 3250
esibook@furnitubes.com

Web
www.furnitubes.com

Address
Furnitubes International Ltd
3rd Floor
Meridian House
Royal Hill
Greenwich
London SE10 8RD

Affiliations
Constructionline
Railway Industry Supplier Qualification Scheme
(RISQS)
Builder's Profile

Accreditation
ISO 9001:2008
ISO 14001:2004
OHSAS 18001:2007

Operational area
Worldwide

Country of manufacture
UK

Additional entries
Railings and guardrails ➤ 218
Bollards ➤ 230
Cycle parking ➤ 241
Signage ➤ 260
Co-ordinated street furniture ➤ 308
Seating ➤ 316
Bespoke seating ➤ 331

Furnitubes International Ltd

Litter bins

Furnitubes' extensive range of litter bins are suitable for a variety of uses and environments. A wide range of designs allows the bins to be used in many different applications, including public realm, educational, healthcare, sport and leisure, retail and residential.

Product range

Products range from simple plastic utility bins to ornate cast iron designs.
Many litter bins can feature recycling and/or ash waste facilities.
Optional add-ons include rodent bait bases and bird-proof flaps.
Laser-cut words or graphics and vinyl logos are also available.

Composition and manufacture

Materials used include cast iron, steel and stainless steel, timber and plastic. Many bins can be manufactured to any RAL colour.

Installation

Bins are available as either root-fixed or bolt-down, with some available for wall- or post-mounting.

Zenith litter and recycling bins

Arca square litter bins

Lucky dog waste bin

Zenith 200 cigarette bin

Arca circular litter bin

Covent Garden circular litter bin

Marshalls

Creating Better Spaces

Contact
t: 0870 444 6217
f: 0870 442 7725
esi.marshalls@web-response.co.uk

Web
www.marshalls.co.uk/commercial

Address
Marshalls plc
Landscape House, Premier Way,
Lowfields Business Park, Elland HX5 9HT

Additional entries
Protective post and rail ➤ 219
Bollards ➤ 235
Cycle parking ➤ 249
Signage and wayfinding ➤ 264
Illumination ➤ 272
Co-ordinated street furniture ➤ 278
Protective street furniture ➤ 280
Co-ordinated street furniture ➤ 282
Seats and benches ➤ 320
Planters ➤ 378
Tree protection ➤ 526

Marshalls plc

Litter bins

Marshalls' litter bins range from simple, functional units to design-led statement pieces.

Designs are available in a variety of textures, materials and styles to fit any project and budget. Bins can include rainshields, ashtrays and bespoke engraving. Many other accessories can also be specified, along with co-ordinating ranges of street furniture.

Material options are diverse, ranging from concrete, steel and natural stone to modern materials such as ferrocast plastic, stainless steel and precious stone.

Spring litter bin

Carya litter bins

GEO stainless steel litter bin with bespoke engraving

Loci litter bins

Igneo litter bins

Rendezvous litter bin

Ollerton Albion 120 litre standard bin, with ashtray

NEPTUNE
CONTEMPORARY AND TRADITIONAL STREET FURNITURE

Contact
Sales
t: 01962 777799
f: 01962 777723
enquiries@neptunestreetfurniture.co.uk

Web
www.neptunestreetfurniture.co.uk

Address
Neptune Street Furniture
Time House, 19 Hillsons Road
Botley SO30 2DY

Accreditation
ISO 9001

Country of manufacture
UK

Additional entries
Co-ordinated street furniture ➤ 309
Seats and benches ➤ 336
Planters ➤ 379
Exterior clocks ➤ 441

Neptune Street Furniture

Litter bins

Neptune is a UK manufacturer of high-quality, heavy-duty litter bins and dog waste bins. Products form part of the company's larger street furniture range with matching benches, seats, planters and bollards available.
Neptune works to strict ISO 9001 guidelines and procedures to design and manufacture quality outdoor furniture that will last for many years with minimal maintenance.

Composition and manufacture
• **Wooden bins**
Wooden bins are produced using hardwood and softwood timber that has been selected from sustainable sources.
• **Concrete bins**
Concrete bins are manufactured to BS 8110 standards and can have smooth or exposed aggregate finishes.
• **Metal bins**
Metal bins can be made in stainless steel, corten steel and copper with natural, polished, painted or patinated finishes.

Design services
Designs can include council crests, company logos, full colour vinyl wrap advertising, integrated planters, seating and clock features.

Heathland litter bin

Barrent litter bin

Neptune recycled plastic litter bin

Hudson litter bin

Butt and gum bin

omos

Contact

Alastair Wallace (sales, head office)
t: 0870 471 3557
t: 00 353 4589 9802
f: 00 353 4589 9803
alastair@omos.ie

Web

www.omos.ie

Address

Head office
Omos Ltd
Unit 1–3 Military Road Industrial Park
Naas, County Kildare
Ireland

Additional entries

Street furniture ➤ 310
Seating ➤ 337
Planters ➤ 380

Omos Ltd

Litter bins

Omos has been designing and manufacturing street furniture since 1996. Encompassing litter bins, seating, planters, cycle parking, bollards and tree grilles, the company's co-ordinated products have received a number of awards.

• Litter bins and cigarette bins
Omos offers a range of litter bins designed to meet the functional and aesthetic demands of a wide range of locations. Produced from stainless or galvanised steel, hardwood or aluminium, the bins have clean, uncluttered lines with a variety of practical features to suit many applications.

s72 bin in galvanised and stainless steel, with iroko

s11.3 litter bin with chamfer aperture

s53 dog litter bin, galvanised steel, powder-coated

s45 TA bin, galvanised throughout, powder-coated

s16.2 litter bin, S355 galvanised mild steel

s16.2 recycling and general waste litter bins with customer-specific finish and decals

Contact
Mark Chessell
t: 01934 522617
info@iotagarden.com

Web
www.iotagarden.com

Address
IOTA Garden and Home Ltd
Wick Road
Wick St Lawrence
Weston-super-Mare BS22 7YQ

Affiliations
British Association of Landscape Industries (BALI)

Operational area
Worldwide

Country of manufacture
UK
Switzerland
China

IOTA Garden and Home Ltd

Planters

IOTA is a leading specialist supplier of high-specification planters suitable for commercial, residential and public sector projects of all sizes. Within the UK, IOTA's services include, design, manufacture, supply, delivery and installation.

• **Materials and product range**
IOTA supplies planters in steel and other metals such as aluminium, lead, and copper/bronze. They can also be supplied in natural stone and composite materials.
The company's product range also extends to outdoor furniture, street furniture and sculpture in the same materials as planters.

• **Strategic product alliances**
IOTA is the exclusive UK distributor of the internationally renowned e-form range of FRC planters, manufactured by Swiss company Swisspearl.

Design services

IOTA offers a bespoke design and manufacture service in all product areas and materials.
Many IOTA designs are also available from stock.

Projects

Products are supplied worldwide, and international projects in 2015/16 included commercial developments in Qatar and the Kingdom of Bahrain.

Bespoke steel planters polyester powder-coated to RAL 7012 (Basalt grey) – Leamington Spa

Bespoke grade 316 stainless steel planters, 1200 (l) x 1200 (w) x 1200mm (h) – Clackmannanshire Council

Bespoke granite-clad steel planters – Northamptonshire Highways

KYOTO 120 FRC planters, 1200 (dia) x 900mm (h)

Bespoke grade 304 stainless steel planters – Ealing

SOUTH QUAY PLAZA
LONDON'S YOUNGEST LANDMARK

Bespoke polyester powder-coated steel planters – Warner Bros. head office, London

Bespoke powder-coated steel planters – Berkeley Homes' South Quay Plaza development

Bespoke steel planters polyester powder-coated to RAL 2003 (Pastel Orange) – University of Manchester

Bespoke stainless steel tree planters – UCLH

Contact
Tony Sawyer
t: 0131 440 9804
f: 0131 440 9805
tony.sawyer@livingreendesign.com

Web
www.livingreendesign.com

Address
Livingreen Design Ltd
Livingreen House
24/6 Dryden Road
Bilston Glen
Loanhead EH20 9HX

Country of manufacture
UK

Operational area
Planters are exported worldwide, with daily
deliveries to mainland Europe.

Additional entries
Greenscreen acoustic barriers ➤ 196
Feature planters ➤ 364

Livingreen Design Ltd

Planters for roof gardens

Livingreen Design manufactures planters for roof
gardens and raised terraces, with complimentary
tables, seating and cabinets available as required.

• Advanced composite planters
All products are designed and manufactured in
the UK using advanced composite technology to
create a modern fibreglass composite, similar to
that used in aircraft and race cars. The material is
highly suitable for planter manufacture and ideal
for roof gardens. Lightweight, very strong and
UV-resistant, it can be finished to resemble
natural stone, metal, terracotta or ceramics.
An extensive standard range is available including
tree planters up to 2m in diameter.

• Bespoke projects
Livingreen Design's specialist project fulfilment
division offers a bespoke CAD design and build
service to specifiers, regularly undertaking
development work 2–3 years ahead.
The company also manufactures in metals and
wood, or any combination of materials.

Finish and appearance

Roof garden planters are available in a variety of
polished, matt and natural look finishes.
Options include LED lighting, castor bases,
moulded dates/words, pallet bases, logos and full
fire retardant construction.

Standard range planters for roof terrace

Cube planters in corten finish

Colourful planters and deck pond

Contemporary planters for restaurant balcony

Bespoke composite planter with Livingreen Design's unique corten steel finish for residential balcony

Bespoke lightweight roof garden planters engineered to fit steelwork – London

Bespoke rooftop barriers and tree planters

Large-scale bespoke modular curved beds, lightweight for suspended floor – shopping centre, Scotland

Bespoke planters, cabinets and tables in corten steel finish for large roof garden – BBC White City, London

Client-concept *Surf* planters – rooftop, London

Bespoke *Knot Garden* planters for large roof deck

Lightweight terracotta finish planters

Bespoke modular beds and integrated seating for suspended terrace – University of Nottingham

Contact
Tony Sawyer
t: 0131 440 9804
f: 0131 440 9805
tony.sawyer@livingreendesign.com

Web
www.livingreendesign.com

Address
Livingreen Design Ltd
Livingreen House
24/6 Dryden Road
Bilston Glen
Loanhead EH20 9HX

Country of manufacture
UK

Additional entries
Greenscreen acoustic barriers ➤ 196
Planters for roof gardens ➤ 362

Livingreen Design Ltd

Feature planters

Livingreen Design manufactures planters and complementary associated furniture for public and private sector use.

All products are designed and manufactured in the UK using advanced composite technology (a modern form of GRP) which is lightweight, very strong, UV-resistant and capable of being finished to resemble stone, metal, terracotta and ceramics.

Bespoke planters are a speciality with full CAD design facilities and professional product designers ready to take a project from concept to fully engineered production drawings.
Manufacturing is possible in composites, wood and metals, or any combination of materials.

Finish and appearance

Around 200 standard ranges from 20cm–2m are available for both exterior and interior use in a variety of polished, matt and natural look finishes. Options include LED lighting, castor bases, moulded dates/words, pallet bases, logos and full fire retardant construction.

Delivery

Planters are exported worldwide, with daily deliveries to mainland Europe. The company has a specialist project fulfilment division and regularly undertakes development work 2–3 years ahead.

Tree 3 planters with integral pallet base – St Austell

Tree 8 planter – Silverburn Shopping Centre

Blob tree planters – interior office (also suitable for exterior use)

Cube tree planter

Bespoke curved planter beds and water feature

Bespoke composite planters in corten steel (rust) finish – Saudi Arabia

Bronze finish *Cirkik* planters, from 20cm–1m diameter

Sphere planter balls in stepped sizes

Bespoke GRP planter beds, corten steel finish

Dhow planter range, 8 standard sizes

Bespoke barrier planters in aged lead finish

Strong, close ribbing gives *Julius* planters a contemporary look; available in over 20 standard sizes

Brunel planters in aged lead finish

Bill flowerpot style tree planter

Snapback seat planters – RHS's own stand, Chelsea. Relocated to various Royal Palace gardens.

Contact
James Booth
t: 01903 716960
info@outdoordesign.co.uk

Web
www.outdoordesign.co.uk

Address
Outdoor Design
Unit 1, Block A
Ford Airfield Industrial Estate
Ford
Arundel BN18 0HY

Operational area
Worldwide

Country of manufacture
UK

Additional entries
Bespoke metal fabrication for landscape and garden
designers ➤ 417

Outdoor Design

Bespoke planters

Outdoor Design combines design skills and
precision engineering capabilities to make its
clients' visions a reality. Using the latest 3D
modelling software, complete CGI models
of the project are produced before planters
are manufactured in steel or bronze.
Outdoor Design has particular expertise in
solving complex fabrication and installation
challenges, including unusual shapes, profiles
and finishes, locations with restricted access,
and combining metal with other materials.

Steel trough planters – London roof garden

Curved steel planters surrounding stone amphitheatre with cast iron wall – London

Steel indoor planter recessed into raised floor

Complex curved planter scheme in galvanised steel with bronze-effect finish, plus interface for hardwood seating and tables

Galvanised, powder-coated steel trough planters

Bronze planter set in stone bench

2.3m high steel planter – Canary Wharf

Large steel street planter (2.5x2.5m) – Central London

Contact
t: 01892 890353
sales@thepotco.com

Web
www.thepotco.com

Address
The Pot Company
Maynards Farm
Lamberhurst Quarter
Tunbridge Wells TN3 8AL

Operational area
Europe

The Pot Company

Planters

The Pot Company has over 30 years of experience in supplying planters to industry professionals.

Over 30 ranges of planters are available, including contemporary, rustic and traditional styles, ranging from value lines to high end items.

A bespoke service is available on certain ranges.

Over 150,000 pots are at held in stock at the company's warehouse in Kent.

An established delivery network enables The Pot Company to quickly fulfil both UK and international orders.

Tuscan style planters from the *Terracino* range

Valencia hardwood low cube planter

Corten steel fire bowl

Florida high cube aluminium planters

Palm pots hand carved from palm tree trunks

 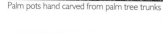

Bodil polymer concrete circular seat planters

Chelsea fibrestone box planters

Polystone planters

Contact

Sales
t: 01509 815335
f: 01509 815332
sdl@street-design.com

Web

www.street-design.com

Address

Street Design Ltd
Unit 47, Hayhill Industrial Estate
Barrow upon Soar LE12 8LD

Accreditation

ISO 9001:2008, ISO 14001:2004, ISO18001:2007,
PAS 99:2006, FSC Cert. No. TT-COC-002561

Affiliations

Timber Research and Development Association
(TRADA); BALI Affiliate member

Additional entries

Co-ordinated street furniture ➤ 311
Seating ➤ 339

Street Design Ltd

Planters

Established in 1986, Street Design specialises in
the design and manufacture of a range of planters
in a variety of materials.

Composition and manufacture

Planters can be manufactured from timber, mild
steel, stainless steel, and aluminium. Full details
can be found on the company's website.

Design services

The company can assist with design and technical
details for individual projects, working with clients
to create bespoke products to suit each scheme.

Grenadier tree planters

Castleton elliptical planters

Grenadier large planters with benches

Castleton curved planters

Grenadier roof garden planters with *Henley* planter benches

Stratum aluminium roof garden planter

Mews large tree planters

Stockport elliptical planter

Diplomat long barrier planter

Kensington tree planters

Grenadier movable planters

Amberol Ltd

Self-watering planting baskets

Amberol is a market leader in the provision of self-watering planting systems for individually designed floral displays, to introduce colour into dull urban landscapes.

• **Hanging baskets**

Hanging baskets provide a lift to public environments, regardless of the season. Unlike traditional hanging baskets, Amberol self-watering baskets do not leak, minimise evaporation and need to be watered on average once a week.

• **Up-the-pole hanging baskets**

Up-the-Pole hanging baskets can be safely secured to almost any type of pole, post or bollard using easy-to-mount brackets.

• **Barrier baskets and window boxes**

Barrier baskets and window boxes are a practical way to create a vibrant display. They fit on top of, in front of or onto railings, ledges, building frontages and flat rooftops.

• **Aquafeed™ self-watering system**

Amberol's products incorporate the *Aquafeed™* self-watering system. It reduces the number of journeys required to water plants from daily to once a week, saving costs and reducing carbon footprint. The planters' integral reservoirs also reduce the amount of water required. This means that flower displays in Amberol planters require less maintenance than traditional systems.

Contact

Patience Atkinson-Gregory
t: 01773 830930
f: 01773 834191
sales@amberol.co.uk

Web

www.amberol.co.uk
www.selfwateringplanters.co.uk

Address

Amberol Ltd
The Plantation
King Street
Alfreton DE55 7TT

Country of manufacture

UK

Additional entries

Litter, dog waste and grit bins ➤ 346
Recycling bins ➤ 347
Self-watering planting systems ➤ 373

Self-watering hanging basket

Self-watering barrier planting basket

Imperial self-watering hanging basket

Up-the-Pole self-watering basket

Self-watering hanging baskets

Wicker self-watering hanging basket

Up-the-Pole self-watering basket

Contact

Patience Atkinson-Gregory
t: 01773 830930
f: 01773 834191
sales@amberol.co.uk

Web

www.amberol.co.uk
www.selfwateringplanters.co.uk

Address

Amberol Ltd
The Plantation
King Street
Alfreton DE55 7TT

Country of manufacture

UK

Additional entries

Litter, dog waste and grit bins ➤ 346
Recycling bins ➤ 347
Self-watering planting baskets ➤ 372

Amberol Ltd

Self-watering planting systems

Amberol is a market leader in the provision of self-watering planters. All products incorporate the *Aquafeed*™ self-watering system that reduces watering and maintenance requirements.

- **Large floor-standing planters**

Large floor planters create eye-catching floral displays for shopping precincts, pedestrian walkways, outdoor cafes and other open spaces.

- **Tiered planter systems**

Tiered planter systems create striking displays and can be specified with a choice of base and tier sections, crests, plaques and inset panels.

Self-watering *Metre Square* planters

Self-watering *Giant Precinct* planters

Self-watering barrel planter

Self-watering *Cup & Saucer* planters

Self-watering *Quarto* planter

Self-watering *Promenade* planter

Beehive tiered self-watering planting systems

Self-watering tiered *Petal* planting system

Self-watering stone trough

Benchmark
STREET FURNITURE

Contact

Anthony Cox
t: 01243 545926
f: 01243 545453
info@benchmark-ltd.co.uk

Web

www.benchmark-ltd.co.uk

Address

Benchmark Design Ltd
Cheriton House
Barnham Lane
Walberton
Arundel BN18 0AZ

Awards

Civic Trust Partnership Award 1998 – Supplier of
Furniture (Chapel Wharf)

Additional entries

Co-ordinated street furniture ➤ 288
Contemporary shaped seating ➤ 314
Picnic tables ➤ 344
Contemporary litter bins ➤ 354

Benchmark Design Ltd

Planters

Benchmark designs and manufactures planters to complement other elements of its street furniture ranges, allowing a co-ordinated approach to be taken to landscape projects.

Each planter is fitted with a galvanised steel liner. Frameworks are designed to allow the planters to be easily moved by a forklift or trolley jack.

• Centerline planters

Centerline planters are made from grade 316 stainless steel, powder-coated galvanised steel or a combination of the two. The robust framework can be fitted with adjustable feet for uneven surfaces. Square, rectangular, round and oval versions are available.

• Shoreline planters

Shoreline planters have a grade 316 stainless steel framework clad with either iroko or Douglas fir slats. Square, rectangular, round and oval versions are available.

• Baseline planters

Baseline planters are produced in grade 316 stainless steel. Square or rectangular versions are available.

Design services

The planters have been designed so that the size and shape can be tailored to meet clients' specific planting requirements.

The *Campus* range includes a planter, bench and table

Centreline CLPL planter with seating

Shoreline SLPL planter and *Shoreline SL008* plinth-mounted bench

Centreline CLPL planter

Baseline BLPL planters

Contact
Sales
t: 01367 242731
sales@factoryfurniture.co.uk

Web
www.factoryfurniture.co.uk

Address
Factory Furniture Ltd
5 Pioneer Road
Faringdon SN7 7BU

Accreditation
Forest Stewardship Council (FSC)

Operational area
Worldwide

Additional entries
Contemporary street furniture ➤ 292
Seats and benches ➤ 329
Litter bins ➤ 355

Factory Furniture Ltd

Tree planters

Factory Furniture is a British designer-maker
specialising in contemporary street furniture.
The company places particular emphasis on
attention to detail, both in design and
specification, as well as on the sustainability of its
business and products.

• Product range
Tree planters are available in timber-clad and
mild steel galvanised designs.
Timber-clad tree planters feature a box-section
sub-frame and 2mm galvanised steel liner,
allowing them to be lifted when full. They have
FSC® hardwood timber slat panels and are
available in 500 litre small, 1300 litre medium and
2400 litre large capacities.
Galvanised planters are constructed in all-welded
mild steel and are 585 litres in capacity.

Composition and manufacture
Products are mainly manufactured in house at the
company's Oxfordshire workshops to ensure
high build quality.

Design services
Factory Furniture offers custom design services
for bespoke street furniture projects. The
company works closely with clients through each
stage of the design and manufacturing process to
enable full realisation of the brief.

Tree planters' slatted timber cladding allows airflow

Bespoke curved planters – Birmingham

Tree planters can be lifted when full

Bespoke tree planter with granite cladding, that can be moved via forklift when full – Cambourne

Bespoke curved tree planters, manufactured in sections – 'pocket park', Colmore Square, Birmingham

Contact
David Poole/Ryan Markham
t: 01233 720097
f: 01233 720098
sales@hy-tex.co.uk

Web
www.hy-tex.co.uk

Address
Hy-Tex (UK) Ltd
Aldington Mill, Mill Lane
Aldington
Ashford TN25 7AJ

Accreditation
ISO 9001

Affiliations
BALI

Additional entries
Silt and run-off pollution control ➤ 10
Biodegradables ➤ 26
Root barriers ➤ 520

Hy-Tex (UK) Ltd

Vertical green wall planters

Pixel-Garden can be used to create modular vegetation walls in public spaces and private gardens. The system can be used to enhance feelings of well-being, improve air quality, increase bio-diversity and absorb noise.

• Modular design
Pixel-Garden is modular system that is simple to use and versatile. It can be used to face walls and fences, creating interesting and colourful plant displays and floral patterns. Pots can be easily re-arranged and replanted. The technical components of the system are unobtrusive.

• Cascading irrigation system
A key component of this system is the angle of inclination of the pots, which facilitates hydration and feeding. The cascade irrigation system is designed so that water only needs to be supplied to the highest rows – the height of the water storage level is set in each module and excess water percolates to lower interconnected levels.

Properties
Pixel-Garden modules are manufactured from grey recycled PP, PE and HDPE.
Model *PG09*: 123x199x60mm, 40 units per sqm, 90mm diameter pots.
Model *PG14*: 186x300x90mm, 18 units per sqm, 140mm diameter pots.

Pixel-Garden used to create colourful flower display

Pixel-Garden PG09 starter plants – domestic project

Pixel-Garden – exhibition wall display

Pixel-Garden vertical green wall planter system

Pixel Garden PG09 and *PG14* planter modules

Pixel-Garden PG14 pot holder and water reservoir

Contact

t: 01642 373400
enquiries@logic-sf.co.uk

Web
www.logic-sf.co.uk

Address
Logic Street & Park Furniture Ltd
Royce House
Royce Avenue
Billingham TS23 4BX

Operational area
UK, Ireland, Europe

Country of manufacture
UK

Additional entries
External benches and seating ➤ 318
Ullswater timber seating ➤ 334

Logic Street & Park Furniture Ltd

Planters

Logic Street & Park Furniture manufactures a wide range of standard and traditional planters for open spaces, and is recognised for its sustainable British craftsmanship.

Planters can be manufactured in stainless steel and hardwood timber, mild steel and hardwood timber, hardwood timber only, corten steel, and mild steel.

Combined planter and seating units are also available.

Thirlmere Platform Bench with Tree Grille 1 – Teesside University

Honister planter – Hallsville Quarter, London

Branthwaite planters – Hartlepool

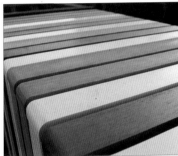

Rosthwaite planter – Chancery Lane, London

Thirlmere Platform Bench with Tree Grille 1

Ambleside planters – University of Bristol

Marshalls

Creating Better Spaces

Contact
t: 0870 444 6217
f: 0870 442 7725
esi.marshalls@web-response.co.uk

Web
www.marshalls.co.uk/commercial

Address
Marshalls plc
Landscape House, Premier Way,
Lowfields Business Park, Elland HX5 9HT

Additional entries
Protective post and rail ➤ 219
Bollards ➤ 235
Cycle parking ➤ 249
Signage and wayfinding ➤ 264
Illumination ➤ 272
Co-ordinated street furniture ➤ 278
Protective street furniture ➤ 280
Co-ordinated street furniture ➤ 282
Seats and benches ➤ 320
Litter bins ➤ 357
Tree protection ➤ 526

Marshalls plc

Planters

Marshalls offers elegant, innovative planters for introducing green landscaping into spaces that cannot feature planting using conventional methods. They can be used either as a part of a wider range of street furniture or to complement Marshalls paving products. The variety of materials and styles available can enhance any landscape and suit any budget. Materials include concrete, steel, natural stone, ferrocast plastic, stainless steel and precious stone.
Anti-ram and anti-terrorism PAS 68 alternatives are also available.

Bilbao planters

Escofet Dama planter – Birmingham

Demetra planters

Mplas Newforest plastic planter, dark wood finish

Mplas Heritage square planter

Demetra seat and planter unit

Bellitalia Large Giove PAS 68-rated protective planter in Precious Stone

NEPTUNE
CONTEMPORARY AND TRADITIONAL STREET FURNITURE

Contact
Sales
t: 01962 777799
f: 01962 777723
enquiries@neptunestreetfurniture.co.uk

Web
www.neptunestreetfurniture.co.uk

Address
Neptune Street Furniture
Time House, 19 Hillsons Road
Botley SO30 2DY

Accreditation
ISO 9001

Country of manufacture
UK

Additional entries
Co-ordinated street furniture ➤ 309
Seats and benches ➤ 336
Litter bins ➤ 358
Exterior clocks ➤ 441

Neptune Street Furniture

Planters

Neptune is a UK manufacturer of high-quality, heavy-duty freestanding planters, including planters with integrated seating.

Products form part of the company's larger street furniture range with matching benches, seats, litter bins and bollards.

Neptune works to strict ISO 9001 guidelines and procedures to design and manufacture high-quality outdoor furniture that will last for many years with minimal maintenance.

Composition and manufacture
• Wooden planters
Wooden planters are produced using hardwood and softwood timber that has been selected from sustainable sources.
• Concrete planters
Concrete planters are manufactured to BS 8110 standards and can have smooth or exposed aggregate finishes.
• Metal planters
Metal planters can be made in stainless steel, corten steel and copper with natural, polished, painted or patinated finishes.
• GRP planters
GRP planters are durable, versatile and low maintenance. GRP can be formed into shapes and designs unachievable in other materials.

Woodland planters

Heathland planter

Beaufort hexagonal planter with *Beaufort* bench surround

omos

Contact

Alastair Wallace (sales, head office)
t: 0870 471 3557
t: 00 353 4589 9802
f: 00 353 4589 9803
alastair@omos.ie

Web

www.omos.ie

Address

Head office
Omos Ltd
Unit 1–3 Military Road Industrial Park
Naas, County Kildare
Ireland

Additional entries

Street furniture ➤ 310
Seating ➤ 337
Litter bins ➤ 359

Omos Ltd

Planters

Omos has been designing and manufacturing street furniture since 1996.

The company and its products have received a number of awards, including the Glen Dimplex Grand Prix, the ICAD Silver Bell and most recently the 2014 IPA Designer of the Year. Omos' clients include local authorities, architects, landscape architects, construction companies and property managers.

• Planters

Tree planters provide an attractive and versatile approach to landscaping. From town and city streets to apartment and business complexes, Omos tree planters provide striking visual impact. Produced in a range of materials such as iroko timber, aluminium, stainless or galvanised steel, most planters are available in standard or custom sizes. Options include integrated seating and a choice of colours and finishes.

Tree grilles and tree guards are also offered.

• Bespoke products

In addition to the existing product range, Omos offers a bespoke design and manufacture service, based upon many years' experience in bringing ideas from conception to production.

Many of the products within the current range are the result of responding to customers' specific needs.

s39 tree planter, 1.5x1.5x1m, with treated iroko cladding, galvanised steel interior and stainless steel top rim

s57 tree planter in stainless steel with iroko benches

t2 tree planter in aluminium, powder-coated finish

s21 modular planter in black with powder-coated finish, constructed on site by bolting panels together

s21 modular planter in grey finish with integrated lighting

s95.2 planters in powder-coated aluminium with rim in brushed stainless steel

URBASTYLE®

Architectural concrete planters

URBASTYLE® produces planters in four architectural concrete finishes – fair faced, micro-etched, polished and velvet – and in a wide range of natural colours. Standard ranges include traditional, contemporary and innovative design styles. Benches, seats, bollards and steps are available in matching finishes.

Composition and manufacture

URBASTYLE's products are made in a modern production facility and the company draws on in-house expertise in traditional and contemporary concrete forming and finishing techniques. Because of that, custom-made units are easily accommodated. Incorporating LED lighting, artistic inserts and graphic designs are all within the factory's capabilities.

All items benefit from a factory-applied, dirt-, stain- and graffiti-resistant protective coating.

Technical support

URBASTYLE's production facilities have sufficient capacity for individual units of up to 20 tonnes. A stable, skilled workforce and flexible production methods can handle any size of project, from modest to very large.

Full technical support and planning form part of the service provided.

Contact
Richard Williams
t: 07890 585768
uk@urbastyle.com

Web
www.urbastyle.com

Address
URBASTYLE®
Severn House
Hazell Drive
Newport NP10 8FY

Additional entries
Silkstone Fasonado paving ➤ 109
Architectural concrete bollards ➤ 237
Architectural concrete street furniture ➤ 312
Architectural concrete benches and seats ➤ 340

Concrete planters – Dronten, The Netherlands

Concrete planters – Bruges, Belgium

Concrete planters – Mechelen, Belgium

Concrete planters – Antwerp, Belgium

Concrete planters – St Jans Molenbeek, Belgium

Concrete planters – De Klinge, Belgium

WoodBlocX

Modular timber planters

WoodBlocX manufactures a modular timber system that allows any size and shape of planter to be built. *WoodBlocX* are lighter and easier to handle on site than traditional timbers or railway sleepers, and is inherently stronger when built up. WoodBlocX structures have a 15 year guarantee.

Composition and manufacture

WoodBlocX are made from sustainably-sourced, FSC-accredited, treated Scots pine and are fitted together using recycled plastic dowels. WoodBlocX harvests and manufactures all of its own softwood, which allows full quality control throughout the production process.

Design services

A supply-only package includes free design and CAD production for any size of project.
A supply and project manage service includes the supervision of the client's labour and overseeing the construction process.
Full design and installation services include management of the project, which is built by one of WoodBlocX's own CHAS-registered teams.

Projects
- Planting structures, Westfield Stratford London.
- Roof terrace, Unite Stratford One apartments.
- Planters for podium deck – Unite Angel Lane.

Contact

Henry Blake
t: 0800 389 1420
f: 01349 864508
admin@woodblocx-landscaping.co.uk

Web
www.woodblocx-landscaping.co.uk

Address
WoodBlocX Landscaping Ltd
Munro Sawmills
Old Evanton Road
Dingwall IV15 9UN

Accreditation
CHAS, TRADA, BALI, FSC

CPD
Urban regeneration and inner-city greening

Country of manufacture
UK

Additional entries
Modular timber retaining walls ➤ 40

Planters designed to step down the main staircase – Westfield Stratford London shopping centre

Unite Stratford One student apartments

Outdoor learning area for primary school

Curved planters incorporating seating

Large planters for rooftop podiums – Unite Angel Lane student apartments

Planters for pedestrian areas – Westfield Stratford London shopping centre

Contact
UK freefone: 0800 376 8377
t: +353 (0) 53 914 3216
f: +353 (0) 53 914 1802
info@kentstainless.com

Web
www.kentstainless.com

Address
Kent Stainless (Wexford) Ltd
Ardcavan
Wexford
Republic of Ireland

Accreditation
ISO 9001:2008, ISO 14001:2004,
OHSAS 18001:2007

Additional entries
Lift-assist manholes ➤ 131
Heelproof ventilation access grilles ➤ 132
In-ground units ➤ 239
Wayfinding signage ➤ 262

Kent Stainless (Wexford) Ltd

Planters

Kent Stainless manufactures bespoke modern planters for individual public realm projects.
The *Kent St George Planter* has an antique copper finish and a bright satin logo.
The *Kent Bromley Self-Watering Planter* has a powder-coated finish as standard.
The *Cork Library Planter* is a large-scale, heavy-duty planter that can be used to create planting areas on large and open public realm areas.
The *Kent PAS68 Planter* will stop and render immobile a 7.5 tonne vehicle at 48 km/hr.

Kent St George Planter

Kent Bromley Self-Watering Planter

Kent PAS68 Planter

Kent Cork Library Planter

Kent One Tower Bridge Planter

Contact
t: 01580 830688
sales@kinley.co.uk

Web
www.kinley.co.uk

Address
Kinley Systems Ltd
Northpoint
Compass Park
Staplecross TN32 5BS

Operational area
UK, Europe

Additional entries
Landscape edging: ExcelEdge® ➤ 91
Decking and paving ➤ 147

Kinley Systems Ltd

Perimeta planter systems

Kinley Systems manufactures the *Perimeta* range of modular planter systems that are suitable for trees and plants. *Perimeta* planters are available in a wide range of metals, including corten steel. Various finishes are also offered. Products require minimal maintenance.
Planters are available from stock or can be custom-built for specific projects.
Applications include ground-level areas, urban roof gardens, balconies and roof terraces.

Perimeta planters – Oldham Leisure Centre

Perimeta planters require minimal maintenance

Perimeta corten planters – Trafalgar Place, London

QUEENSBURY
SHELTERS

Contact
t: 023 9221 0052
f: 023 9221 0059
sales@queensburyshelters.co.uk

Web
www.queensburyshelters.co.uk

Address
Queensbury Shelters Ltd
Fitzherbert Road, Farlington
Portsmouth PO6 1SE

Accreditation
ISO 9001:2008
ISO 14001:2004
ISO 18001:2007
OHSAS 18001:2007
ISO 22301

Affiliations
NICEIC, CHAS, RISQS, Constructionline

Additional entries
Cycle storage solutions ➤ 250
Walkways and canopies ➤ 385

Queensbury Shelters

Passenger shelters

Queensbury designs, manufactures, installs and
maintains bus shelters and bespoke canopies.
Nine standard passenger shelters are available.
• **Product options**
Shelter styles range from traditional wooden
shelters through to contemporary point glazed
structures, providing options to suit any
environment or location. Advertising and non-
advertising shelters are available.
Shelters are all available in a standard range of
sizes. All designs can be adapted to suit specific
design requirements or site conditions.
• **Design service**
Queensbury's design department works closely
with clients to finalise exact specifications and
finishes required.

Accessories
Shelter options include:
• Integrated seating.
• Mains or solar powered lighting.
• CCTV.
• Timetable or poster cases.
• Real time passenger information (RTPI)
brackets.
• Flag brackets.
• Graphic treatment.
• Bus stop poles.

G2 shelter

Meridian flat roof shelter

Meridian shelter

Ely advertising shelter

Arun shelter

Chester shelter

Promenade shelter

QUEENSBURY SHELTERS

Contact
t: 023 9221 0052
f: 023 9221 0059
sales@queensburyshelters.co.uk

Web
www.queensburyshelters.co.uk

Address
Queensbury Shelters Ltd
Fitzherbert Road, Farlington
Portsmouth PO6 1SE

Accreditation
ISO 9001:2008
ISO 14001:2004
ISO 18001:2007
OHSAS 18001:2007
ISO 22301

Affiliations
NICEIC, CHAS, RISQS, Constructionline

Additional entries
Cycle storage solutions ➤ 250
Passenger shelters ➤ 384

Queensbury Shelters

Walkways and canopies

Queensbury manufactures standard and bespoke
walkways and canopies.

• Standard designs
The majority of Queensbury's standard bus
shelter ranges have an 'extended' option
whereby they can be designed and built to create
enclosed and semi-enclosed walkway structures.
The three products commonly transformed into
walkways are the *Arun*, *Meridian* and *G2*.
As the walkways are based on a standard shelter
structure, all shelter accessories and options are
available: seating, mains or solar powered lighting,
CCTV, timetable or poster cases, real time
passenger information (RTPI) brackets, flag
brackets, graphic treatment, bus stop poles and
wayfinding signage. Automatic door systems and
speaker systems can be included and integrated
into the shelter design.
The design department works with clients to
finalise specifications and finishes required.

• Bespoke solutions
From premium single point glazed designs to
more cost conscious options, Queensbury's
in-house design team works closely with
architects and contractors to design and produce
steel structured canopies to requirements.
Structural calculations, project management and
installation are all part of the bespoke service.

G2 walkway

Bespoke walkway

Arun walkway

Meridian walkway

Bespoke walkway

Bespoke entrance canopy

Setter Shelters

Shelters and canopies

A family-run business based in Bedfordshire, Setter Shelters, part of Setter Play Equipment, designs and installs bespoke timber shelters. Applications include entranceways, covered teaching areas, and public spaces such as country parks and visitor attractions.

Integrated roller shutters can be used to provide extended and secure teaching spaces.

Entrance canopies have been installed at many locations, including canopies with a spectrum of coloured roofs at a number of schools across Bedfordshire.

Contact
Jonathan Bhowmick
t: 01462 817538
jonathan@setterplay.co.uk

Web
www.settershelters.co.uk

Address
Setter Play Equipment
Unit 6A
Shefford Mill
Stanford Road
Shefford SG17 5NR

Accreditation
ISO 9001:2008
CHAS

Affiliations
Association of Play Industries (API)

Additional entries
Play equipment ➤ 471

Bespoke wrap-around canopy for pre-school

Entrance canopies are made in a rainbow of colours with softwood, cedar and oak post cladding options

Integrated roller shutters create additional secure teaching space

Quadrant cycle shelter

Classroom link walkway creating an additional 120m² of valuable all-weather space

Curved canopy/covered walkway

Contemporary bus shelter in laminated timber

Forest Shelter is a large amenity shelter that is suitable for countryside locations

Distinctive cycle shelter

Bespoke curved glulam canopy with downpipe

Conservation shelter – Milton Ernest Lower School

Shelters provide outside space for children to play

Straight beam shelter/canopy

Playground feature shelter

Contact
Amanda O'Connor (Sales)
t: 020 8561 4959
f: 020 8848 1397
amanda.oconnor@trueform.co.uk

Web
www.trueform.co.uk

Address
Trueform
Pasadena Trading Estate
Pasadena Close
Hayes UB3 3NQ

Accreditation
ISO 9001:2008
ISO 14001:2004
OHSAS 18001

Operational area
UK, USA, Europe, Middle East

Additional entries
Signs, wayfinding and digital displays ➤ 267

Trueform

Shelters, canopies and walkways

Trueform is a leading designer, manufacturer and installer of hardware for the public transportation, construction, architectural and airport industries.

Trueform's in-house design, manufacturing and installation facilities enable the creation of high-quality, contemporary shelters, canopies, and walkways, as well as associated hardware such as signage systems, seating, timetable displays, glazing systems, electronic and interactive displays, solar-powered systems, wayfinding signage and mapping systems. Products are used across a range of markets, including bus, rail, underground, tram and airport shelters, as well as building and construction applications.

Composition and manufacture
All products are manufactured in-house using specialist architectural materials such as stainless steel, aluminium alloys, specialist glazing, vitreous enamel, composites and natural stone, with a range of contemporary, hard-wearing architectural finishes and surfaces.

Design services
In addition to the company's large range of off-the-shelf products, Trueform's in-house designers and engineers work in collaboration with clients, architects and designers to produce custom-designed products to suit individual customer requirements.

Installation and maintenance
Trueform provides a nationwide on-site installation and construction service, which includes site survey, civils, foundation work, erection and reinstatement to the highest quality, and heath and safety standards.
The company's in-house teams are fully trained and NRSWA, CSCS and CHASS certified. From Trueform's wide network of operating sectors, the company is able to provide routine maintenance, cleaning and emergency response maintenance services.

Discovery shelter – Dundee

Landmark shelter – Moorgate, London

Centro gullwing shelter – BCCI

Discovery shelter – Dundee

Integra shelter – Manchester Metrolink, Deansgate

Prestige rail waiting shelter

Sinewave shelter – Las Vegas

Fishergate gullwing shelter – Preston

Aviator anti-terrorist shelter – Heathrow

Sinewave BRT shelter

Platform gullwing shelter – TfGM, Manchester

Metro shelter – Windsor and Maidenhead

Taxi canopy – King's Cross Station

Canopy – Bond Street Station

NET2 gullwing tram shelter – Nottingham

All Urban Ltd

Youth shelters

All Urban supplies timber youth shelters designed and manufactured by Handspring Design at their workshop in Sheffield. They are typically specified for schools, parks and urban areas.

Robust and long-lasting youth shelters are made to commission, in response to project briefs, and can be individually tailored from a standard product range.

Shelters can be open, clad with sheet steel or fabric, or have a green roof.

All timber is FSC accredited and European sourced.

Contact
t: 0114 282 1283
f: 0114 282 3463
info@allurban.co.uk

Web
www.allurban.co.uk

Address
All Urban Ltd
Aizlewoods Mill Nursery Street
Sheffield S3 8GG

Additional entries
Santa & Cole lighting ➤ 274
Contemporary seating ➤ 324

Spider shelter

Hoop youth shelter

Spider youth shelter in milled oak – Fordham Park, London

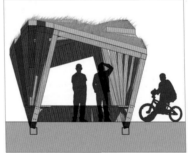
Twisting Frame youth shelter with green roof

Hoop youth shelter

Bird's Nest youth shelter

Crow's Nest youth shelter – Heeley Millenium Park

Contact

t: 01788 550556
f: 01788 550265
info@autopa.co.uk

Web

www.autopa.co.uk

Address

AUTOPA Limited
Cottage Leap
Rugby CV21 3XP

Accreditation

ISO 9001:2008
ISO 14001:2004
OHSAS 18001:2007
Achilles Building Confidence

Affiliations

CHAS
Constructionline

Additional entries

Rising arm barriers ➤ 212
Telescopic posts and automatic bollards ➤ 213
Height restrictors and swing gates ➤ 214
High visibility protection ➤ 217
Traffic flow plates and speed ramps ➤ 221
Bollards ➤ 226
Parking posts ➤ 228
Cycle shelters and compounds ➤ 242
Cycle stands ➤ 244
Illuminated bollards ➤ 268
Street furniture ➤ 283

AUTOPA Limited

Shelters, canopies and walkways

AUTOPA open spaces canopies and shelters are used to transform outdoor spaces, providing shelter from the elements for entranceways, walkways, outdoor play and recreational areas. Products can be manufactured to site specific requirements at AUTOPA's Rugby works.

• Walkways and door canopies

AUTOPA open spaces walkways and door canopies offer site owners stylish and functional coverings which can be tailored to site requirements. Hardwearing and robust, they can be used to provide cover to protect entranceways or to create covered link-ways between buildings. Manufactured in the UK from galvanised mild steel, all door canopies can be coated in any BS or RAL colour.

• Smoking shelters

The *AUTOPA open spaces Smoking Shelter* gives smokers protection from the elements.
They are manufactured in a range of standard sizes or to special order using high quality aluminium and UV stable PETG sheeting.
Only the top half of the shelter is clad to comply with UK and Irish regulations.
Coated grey as standard, any standard BS or RAL colour is available to order.
The shelter has adjustable feet to make installation easier on uneven surfaces.

• Trolley shelters

The *AUTOPA Trolley Shelter* is suitable for retail sites and will keep shopping trolleys dry and organised at all times. The standard shelter is designed to fit inside a car parking space and can store up to 36 standard sized trolleys. Manufactured from galvanised mild steel and UV stabilised PETG, *AUTOPA Trolley Shelters* are fully modular and can be extended to provide additional storage as required.

• Bespoke structures

As an experienced UK manufacturer with extensive fabrication facilities at its Rugby works, AUTOPA can create canopies, shelters and walkways in cantilevered, lean-to or freestanding designs to suit any architectural style.

Bespoke entranceway with frame for automatic sliding doors – Sydenhams Builders Merchants

Bespoke school playground canopy with PET roof

AUTOPA open spaces Smoking Shelter

Single-legged bespoke cantilever canopy reduces trip hazard – Little Ripley Day Nursery

AUTOPA Trolley Shelter

Bespoke lean-to canopy in corporate colours

Contact
Sales and technical
t: 01625 855900
sales@baileystreetscene.co.uk

Web
www.baileystreetscene.co.uk

Address
Bailey Streetscene
Adlington Business Park
London Road
Adlington SK10 4NL

Additional entries
Co-ordinated street furniture ➤ 286

Bailey Streetscene

Shelters and canopies

Bailey Streetscene creates covered structures that improve and enhance communities.
From smoking shelters and cycle shelters to large-scale canopies and walkways, the company manufactures all products in its 20,000 square foot facility in Staffordshire. These impressive facilities, combined with Bailey's 'know-how, can do' approach, allow the company to accommodate any site-specific requirement.

Composition and manufacture

All shelters are hot dip galvanised and can be powder coated in any RAL or BS colour to suit clients' requirements.
All shelters can be clad in a variety of materials including: up to 8mm thick UV-stable shatter reistant PET in either clear, opal or tinted colours; Plastisol steel sheet; or toughened glass.

Technical support

Bailey's cycle parking products range from standard fittings to complex installations.
A bespoke service includes made-to-measure production of shelters and compounds, integral cycle racks and stand-alone parking. Even if part of a client's brief is undefined, Bailey is able to help achieve the vision.

8m *Mayfair* cycle shelter

Columbus canopy

Oxford shelter

Barrell canopy

Deacon shelter

Birley canopy

Bexley canopy

4m *Mayfair* cycle shelter

4m *Bromley* cycle shelter

Arbor canopy

Brandon canopy

Benfield shelter

rocklyn
engineering ltd

Contact
David Ruffell
Business Development Manager
t: 0117 370 7710
david@rocklyn.co.uk

Web
www.rocklyn.co.uk

Address
Rocklyn Engineering Ltd
Dirac Crescent
Bristol & Bath Science Park
Emersons Green, Bristol BS16 7FR

Accreditation
ISO 9001:2008
OHSAS 18001:2010
SafeContractor
Constructionline
CE Marking

Additional entries
Cycle parking ➤ 251
Sports shelters ➤ 504

Rocklyn Engineering Ltd

Shelters, canopies and covered walkways

Rocklyn Engineering Ltd is a leading designer and manufacturer of shelters, canopies, covered walkways and street furniture. The products can be used as passenger waiting areas; entrance canopies; sports dug-outs; and trolley, smoking, bus or cycle/motorcycle shelters.

They are made from galvanised heavy-duty steel with polycarbonate panels, making them weather resistant, maintenance free and vandal resistant. A modular design allows them to be extended. Options include internal mains or solar lighting, powder coating to RAL colours, manufacture in grade 316 stainless steel and toughened glazing.

Composition and manufacture

Rocklyn has two fully equipped workshops and works regularly in mild steel, stainless steel, aluminium, timber and composites.

Technical support

Rocklyn has 3D design capability, and can discuss preliminary designs to help clients to develop ideas and make the best use of space.

Projects

Clients include building contractors, shopping centres, supermarkets, airports, and railway and bus authorities throughout the UK and Ireland.

Shelter – Father Collins Park, Dublin

Bus shelter – Belfast City Airport

Tempo bus shelter

Covered walkway – London City Airport

Bus shelter – Belfast High School

Timber trolley shelter

Trolley shelter

Entrance canopy

ZENITH™
Canopy Structures Limited

Contact
t: 0118 978 9072
info@zenithcsl.com

Web
www.zenithcsl.com

Address
Zenith Canopy Structures Ltd
Units 1 & 2
Stokes Farm
Binfield Road
Wokingham RG40 5PR

Affiliations
CHAS
Constructionline

Operational area
UK

Zenith Canopy Structures Ltd

Modular canopy shelters

Zenith Canopy Structures designs and manufactures modular tensile canopy structures in a variety of standard sizes. Canopies can also be made to special order.

The structures have either steel frames, which are galvanised and powder-coated in a choice of colours, or aluminium, which can also be powder-coated. The canopies are available with soft PVC, polycarbonate or photovoltaic panels. Products are CE marked.

Clients include schools, councils, building contractors, architects and the leisure industry.

Cicogna shelter

Airone Max canopy shelter over outdoor seating area – Reigate School

Polycarbonate canopy shelter

Multi-purpose play area

Photovoltaic panels

Airone Tipo canopy shelter over play area

Albatross canopy shelter – Titchfield Primary School

Airone Tipo canopy shelter over outdoor dining area

Contact
Graeme Ritchie
Scot Fletcher
t: 0114 221 7785
graeme@handspringdesign.co.uk
scot@handspringdesign.co.uk

Web
handspringdesign.co.uk

Address
Handspring Design Ltd
Ecclesall Woods Sawmill
Abbey Lane, Sheffield S7 2QZ

Operational area
UK

Country of manufacture
UK

Additional entries
Bespoke timber seats and benches ➤ 343
Timber engineering ➤ 406

Handspring Design Ltd

Bespoke timber shelters

Handspring Design has been creating bespoke timber shelters for over ten years. They are specified for schools, parks, healthcare environments, urban areas and private clients. Handspring works to commission, in response to project briefs, and can individually tailor its product range. The flagship *Apple* and *Onion* shelters are made in curved, steam-bent glue-laminated oak. They can be unroofed or clad with sheet steel or fabric, or have a green roof. When installed, they can become a popular centrepiece of any scheme or project.

Onion arbour with Siberian larch internal cladding

Oak *Apple* shelter with metal roof and oak stage – Special School, Rotherham

---

Contact
William Deacon
t: 08450 750 760
enquiries@metrostor.eu

Web
www.metrostor.eu

Address
metroSTOR®
Streetspace Group
Wootton Lane
Wootton
Canterbury CT4 6RP

metroSTOR®

Outdoor storage systems

metroSTOR® is a tough, modular system for storing waste and recycling containers, mobility scooters and cycles.
Frequently specified to provide safe, secure storage outside dwellings, *metroSTOR®* units reduce fire risk and waste disposal costs while enhancing their environment and residents' quality of life.
Specifiers can select from a standard range of module sizes, façades, roofs, doors and locks to configure a unit for almost any purpose.

COSMO™ CBH waste stream enclosure

CBH enclosure: steel, iroko cladding and green roof

COSMO™ CBE waste stream enclosure

PBM wasteSTOR™ for 660–1280L wheeled bins

PSM scooterSTOR™ mobility scooter charging station

Fibaform
Design • Manufacture • Installation

Contact
Mark Buchanan
t: 01524 60182
f: 01524 389829
sales@fibaform.co.uk

Web
www.fibaform.co.uk

Address
Fibaform Products Ltd
Unit 22
Lansil Industrial Estate
Caton Road
Lancaster LA1 3PQ

Accreditation
ISO 9001:2000
UKAS
Network Rail Approved

Operational area
UK and Europe

Fibaform Products Ltd

Bespoke prefabricated cabinets, kiosks and buildings

Fibaform Products manufactures modular glass fibre buildings, kiosks and protection enclosures. The *Guardian* and *Guardmaster* ranges are suitable for applications such as car park kiosks, gatehouses, CCTV control rooms, and ticket and vending booths.
A full range of sizes and colours can be supplied, from one-man kiosks up to office suites.
Plant and machinery protection enclosures can be supplied to match customers' specification and size requirements. The enclosures can incorporate a choice of doors, as well as electrical fittings and ventilation installations.

Design services
Fibaform works with customers at an early stage to ensure that buildings are designed to meet exact criteria. All elements of construction, such as dimensions, doors, windows and electrics, can be designed to suit specific requirements.

Sitework
Most buildings can be delivered ready-built and a full installation service is available. Where size prohibits transport by road, buildings can be delivered in part form and assembled on site by Fibaform engineers.

Delivery
Fibaform will always try to match customers' required delivery dates, and can often fast-track an order where a shorter lead-time is required. Smaller cabinets and kiosks are usually held in stock for immediate delivery.

Projects
Recent customers include: McLaren Construction, Asda, Apcoa Parking, Network Rail, Readie Construction, Simons Group, Manx Electricity Authority, Birse Civils, Volker Fitzpatrick, Imperial War Museum, NHS Logistics, and J Sainsbury.

6.4x3m gatehouse

Network Rail specification enclosure

1.4x2.35m enclosure with vents and access flap

2.5x2.5m enclosure

8x3m gatehouse

Bioethanol plant room

Kiosk with raised plinth

Small refuse bin store

Lang+Fulton

Bin stores, plant housings and compounds

Bin stores, compounds and plant housings provide security and visual screening. Robust steel panels combine ventilation and natural daylight with a high level of security and anti-climb properties. The choice of louvred panels provides total or partial screening (45–100%).

- **Bin stores**

The bin stores range includes customised installations or the *Europa* modular system, specifically designed for 1100 litre wheelie bins. All designs can be made with or without a roof.

- **Plant housings and compounds**

Ground-level or roof-top housings are individually designed for the protection of mechanical plant.

- **Bike stores**

Freestanding enclosures or partition screens within an undercroft are tailor-made for secure bicycle or general storage.

Finish and appearance

All mild steel is hot dip galvanised before optional polyester powder coating in any RAL colour.

Technical support

Lang+Fulton offers a full design service. Products are supplied worldwide fully finished, with detailed drawings for on-site fixing.

Contact
Sales and Technical Office
t: 0131 441 1255
f: 0131 441 4161
sales@langandfulton.co.uk

Web
www.langandfulton.co.uk

Address
Lang+Fulton
Unit 2b, Newbridge Industrial Estate
Newbridge, Edinburgh EH28 8PJ

Distribution
West Midlands

Accreditation
ISO 9001:2000

Additional entries
External floor gratings and treads ➤ 153
Louvred fences: Italia and Delta ➤ 160
Grating fences ➤ 162
Railings: Modena, Siena and Rimini ➤ 176
Gates ➤ 203

Europa-4 bin store designed from modular panels of *Italia-80* to accommodate four 1100 litre wheeled bins

Italia-80 – Ashford Retail Park, Kent

Piazza-44 community bin store enclosure

Italia-80 with decorative laser-cut doors and *Piazza-44* plant trellis

Italia-100 providing ventilation and 100% screening to a roof-top air-conditioning plant

Italia-80 custom-sized doors to fit recycling area and bin stores – Tranent Primary School, East Lothian

DeltaWing-90 – The Fort Retail Park, Glasgow

Plastisol steel roofing

Sliding latch with cover plate

DeltaWing-90 contemporary pressure-locked louvre

Italia-100 bike storage

Piazza-44 bike store – St Matthews Estate, Brixton

Italia-80 provides 80% visual screening with a robust steel construction – Newham Mental Health Centre

Stereo-4 galvanised grating with a 62x132mm aperture creating a secure cycle shelter – Edinburgh University

Contact
Peter Webster (UK sales and technical)
t: 01902 797110
sales@elefantgratings.com

Web
www.elefantgratings.com

Address
Elefant Gratings
Enterprise Drive
Four Ashes
Wolverhampton WV10 7DF

Additional entries
External flooring: gratings and planks ➤ 154

Elefant Gratings

Plant housings and storage compounds

Elefant Gratings specialises in the design, manufacture and supply of flat bar gratings and perforated planks. Applications range from walkways, plant housings and storage compounds, to screens, fencing, brise soleil, ventilation, vehicular grilles and balconies.

Composition and manufacture
Gratings are manufactured in carbon steel, stainless steel, Corten A and aluminium. Planks are manufactured in carbon steel, stainless steel and aluminium.
All products are made according to current British Standards guidelines.

Finish and appearance
Carbon steel products are hot dip galvanised to BS EN 1461:2009 or polyester powder coated in standard RAL colours.
Stainless steel products are chemically cleaned to BS EN 2516:1997 and bead blasted.
Corten A products are self coloured.
Aluminium products are anodised.

Technical support
Elefant Gratings draws on extensive experience and product knowledge to find the best solution for each client's requirements.

Storage compound

Walkway and balustrade

Fencing

Cladding

Fencing

ROUND WOOD
of Mayfield

Contact
t: 01435 867072
f: 01435 864708
sales@roundwood.com

Web
www.roundwood.com

Address
Round Wood of Mayfield Ltd
Round Wood
Newick Lane
Mayfield
East Sussex TN20 6RG

Operational area
Europe

Additional entries
Hardwood timber decking ➤ 148

Round Wood of Mayfield Ltd

Oak-framed buildings

Over the last twenty years Round Wood of Mayfield has planned, erected and finished thousands of oak-framed buildings.

• Bespoke buildings
Bespoke oak-framed buildings have ranged from garden gazebos and single-bay garages, up to large office complexes and houses. Regardless of size, every project is approached with the same close attention to detail.

• Kit buildings
Whilst the majority of buildings are tailored to bespoke requirements, kit garages are available through the company's *Chippy* range. A total of 47 standard designs are offered with gable, hip or barn-end roofs. These can include half-bays, aisles and log-stores.

Composition and manufacture

All frames are traditionally crafted to a very high specification using oak-pegged mortice-and-tenon joints. Green oak is always used, as this tightens the structure when drying out.

Sitework

To ensure fit, oak frames are pre-assembled before leaving the workshop. They can then be erected by Round Wood's own nationwide team, or other carpenters/fitters who may already be on site.

Oak-framed cricket pavilion with dormer windows

4-bay garage with first floor and clock tower

Pool house with oak windows and doors

Garage complex with first floor

4-bay garage with forward-facing gable and doors

Oak-framed extension with glazed gable and vaulted internal roof

Cleveland SITESAFE

Contact
Sales
t: 01642 244663
f: 01642 244664
sales@cleveland-sitesafe.ltd.uk

Web
www.cleveland-sitesafe.ltd.uk

Address
Cleveland Sitesafe Ltd
Riverside Works
Dockside Road
Middlesbrough TS3 8AT

Staff/turnover
25 people
£3m per year

Operational area
UK
Europe

Cleveland Sitesafe Ltd

Modular leisure buildings

Cleveland Sitesafe Ltd designs and manufactures steel structures and buildings.
Buildings can be used for changing rooms, pavilions, kiosks, public toilets, visitor centres and clubhouses, as well as many other applications.

Composition and manufacture

Able to withstand constant wear and vandalism, the buildings are prefabricated as single-piece or modular steel structures. They can be finished in a range of different cladding materials.

Ticket office

Sports pavilion

Groundsman's shed

Maintenance store

Bird hide – interior

Bowls pavilion

Visitor centre

Shop

Modular bowls pavilion

Bird hide – entrance

Sports equipment store

Grounds depot

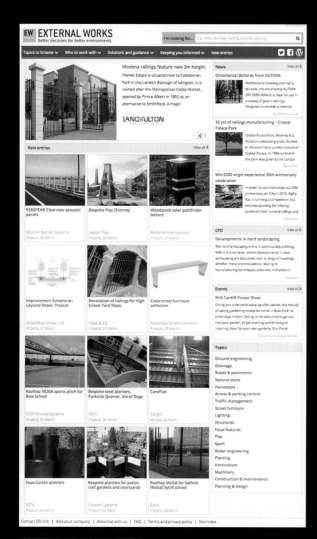

There's a lot **MORE INFORMATION** on all the products and companies featured in this edition on the **EXTERNAL WORKS** website

Search online to access a wealth of additional information ...

- Detailed factual descriptions
- Key data and fast facts
- More illustrations
- Downloads and videos
- Related products and case studies

... and use workflow tools designed to save you time and effort ...

- Compare similar
- Review alternatives
- Copy specifications
- Save for later
- Email enquiries

EW INDEX **EXTERNAL WORKS**
better decisions for better environments
👉 **www.externalworks.co.uk**

FEATURES

Bespoke timberwork	406-407

Timber landscape structures, shelters, bridges and sculptures.

Recycled plastic palisade profiles	408

Round and square palisade profiles for building planters, retaining walls, play areas and delineating edges in public and private settings.

Architectural cast stone	409

Balustrades and parapet screening; traditional steps; copings and finials; columns, pergolas, temples and pavilions.

Bespoke metalwork	410-423

Architectural metalworkers and artist blacksmiths specialising in bespoke commissions for outdoor areas, including: railings, gates, balustrades and guardrails; planters, trellising and plant support systems; bandstands, canopies and viewing platforms; sculpture and public memorials.

Replacement and restoration services for historic metalwork including bandstands, statues and memorials.

Public art, sculpture, letter carving, mosaics and murals	424-440

Sculpture and artworks for public and private spaces.

Letter and stone carvers.

Mosaics in glass, ceramics, stone, marble and mixed media.
Murals from domestic trompe l'oeil to historical panoramas for public sites.

Outdoor clocks	441

Pillar, square, drum, floral and tower clocks for public and private spaces.

Landscape ornament	442-443

Jardinieres, urns, sundials, armillary spheres, statues, fountains and garden furniture in cast stone, bronze, brass and stainless steel.

Fountains and water displays	444-449

Fountains and water features for public, commercial and garden water displays.

Swimming pools and spas	450

Bespoke outdoor swimming pools and spas.

EXTERNAL WORKS ONLINE

For detailed information supported by case studies, downloads and tools to help you make faster and better decisions ...
⚐ www.externalworks.co.uk

Contact
Graeme Ritchie
Scot Fletcher
t: 0114 221 7785
graeme@handspringdesign.co.uk
scot@handspringdesign.co.uk

Web
handspringdesign.co.uk

Address
Handspring Design Ltd
Ecclesall Woods Sawmill
Abbey Lane
Sheffield S7 2QZ

Operational area
UK

Country of manufacture
UK

Additional entries
Bespoke timber seats and benches ➤ 343
Bespoke timber shelters ➤ 395

Handspring Design Ltd

Timber engineering

Handspring Design has been creating bespoke timber structures, shelters and sculptures across the UK and into Europe for over ten years. They are specified for schools, healthcare environments, parks and urban areas as well as for private clients. Handspring works to commission, in response to project briefs, and can individually tailor its product range. The company has a strong environmental ethos and aims to make structures that engage and delight end users while being robust and long-lasting. All timber is FSC accredited and European sourced.

Baseplate detail for school entrance canopy

Outdoor classroom – Dore Primary School, Sheffield

Oak pergola – Leicester

Arched entrance – Swanswell Park, Coventry

Twisting Frame and swing seat in Douglas fir – Newton-le-Willows

Curved entrance canopy – NHS Rotherham

Contact
The Sales Team
t: 01254 685185
f: 01254 671237
sales@woodscape.co.uk

Web
www.woodscape.co.uk

Address
Woodscape Ltd
1 Sett End Road West
Shadsworth Business Park
Blackburn BB1 2QJ

Accreditation
ISO 9001:2008
FSC, PEFC and FPCC certification
Approved supplier to Tesco

Additional entries
Hardwood decking, raised decks and boardwalks
➤ 149
Co-ordinated street furniture ➤ 304
Hardwood seating ➤ 342

Woodscape Ltd
Landscape structures
Woodscape designs and manufactures timber landscape structures for small private and large-scale commercial projects.
Foot, cycle and light vehicular bridges can be produced with single spans up to 16m. Longer bridges feature multiple spans and supports. Decking, boardwalks and ramps are available in marine-grade, naturally very durable hardwoods. Other products include pergolas, shelters, seating, planters, sculptures, gates and signage.

Composition and manufacture
Woodscape's structures and bespoke designs can be supplied with FSC, PEFC or FPCC Chain of Custody certification.
150mm cross-sections have a life expectancy of more than 100 years in ground contact.

Design services
An in-house team offers a design and build service. They draw on years of experience of working with the world's most durable timbers to make striking timber engineered components.

Sitework
Most structures are supplied in kit form for on-site assembly.

Bus shelter – Scarborough harbourside

Hardwood pergola – Florence Shipley Community Care Centre, Heanor, Derbyshire

Trolley shelter – Tesco stores (nationwide)

Lincoln shelter

Hardwood timber balcony – Fleet, Hampshire

Hardwood timber balcony – Fleet, Hampshire

Hardwood parapet – Harewood House, Leeds

Hardwood timber bridge

HAHN
P L A S T I C S

Contact
t: 0161 850 1965
f: 0161 850 1975
sales@hahnplastics.co.uk

Web
www.hahnplastics.com

Address
Hahn Plastics Ltd
Old Pilkington Tiles Site
Rake Lane
Swinton
Manchester M27 8LJ

Affiliations
BALI

Additional entries
Ecocrib retaining wall system ➤ 41
100% recycled plastic fencing ➤ 190

Hahn Plastics Ltd

Recycled plastic palisade profiles

hanit® recycled plastic palisade profiles are used to create structures and delineate edges in a wide range of public and private environments. Palisades are manufactured in round and square profiles, with options of solid or hollow sections. Being lightweight, they can be installed without the use of heavy equipment, which is especially useful in hard to access terrain.

Applications
• Raised planters and flowerbeds.
• Retaining walls.
• Pond construction.
• Garden screening.
• Playing field edging.
• Sandbox and playground edging.
• Pathway delineation.
• Perimeter fencing.

Properties
• Maintenance free.
• Rot proof, durable and long lasting.
• Strong and lightweight.
• Splinter free.
• Easy to handle and install.
• Virtually vandal proof.
• Weather resistant.
• 100% recycled and 100% recyclable.

Planters and wall created using recycled plastic palisade profiles

Recycled plastic palisade profiles around play area

Recycled plastic palisade profiles

Recycled plastic palisade fencing around play area

Recycled plastic palisade profiles

Recycled plastic palisade wall

Steps and low wall created with recycled plastic palisade profiles

Haddonstone Ltd

Contact
Sales
t: 01604 770711
f: 01604 770027
info@haddonstone.co.uk

Web
www.haddonstone.com

Address
Haddonstone Ltd
The Forge House
East Haddon
Northampton NN6 8DB

CPD
The history of cast stone; latest manufacturing methods; and traditional and innovative applications

Country of manufacture
UK, USA

Additional entries
Garden ornament ➤ 443

Haddonstone Ltd

Architectural cast stone

Haddonstone Ltd manufactures ornamental and architectural stone pieces to any shape or size. The company is a founder member of the United Kingdom Cast Stone Association (UKCSA) and distributes worldwide.
Standard designs include balustrades, columns, copings, door and window surrounds, pier caps, finials and landscape ornaments. Custom designs to individual requirements are a speciality.
Materials include dry cast *Haddonstone®*, wet cast *TecStone®* and *GRC TecLite®*.

Haddonstone offers numerous balustrade designs

Gibbs Porch developed by Adam Architecture

Eagles used to frame an entrance

Classical facade showcasing a colonnaded portico and balustraded parapet – Surrey

Small Classical Temple with statue and sundial

Classical Tuscan Column Pavilion

Traditional steps with copings to the retaining garden wall, including the *Ball* and *Base* finial designs

Parapet Screening is an alternative to balustrading

m-tec

Contact
Tom Elliott
t: 01254 773718
m: 07974 783287
f: 01254 783287
info@m-tec.uk.com

Web
www.m-tec.uk.com

Address
m-tec
Britannia House
Junction Street
Darwen BB3 2RB

Accreditation
ISO 9001:2000
Link Up

Operational area
UK, Europe

m-tec

Specialist metal fabricator

m-tec is the architectural metalwork division of specialist metal fabricators WEC Group Ltd, and specialises in stainless steel fabrication.
m-tec works with public artists, architects and regeneration specialists.
Services include fabrication expertise, design, consultation and installation.
Projects include sculptures, public art, bridges, canopies, staircases, lighting and seating, all in stainless steel.
m-tec also specialises in bespoke architectural fabrication, form work and concrete moulds.

Lowry Man and his Dog – Knott End-On-Sea

Revolving Wind Shelter – Blackpool

Spires – Abertillery Gateway, South Wales

The Wave Project – Blackpool

The Seed sculpture – Manchester

Stainless Steel Canopy – Napp Pharmaceutical, Cambridge

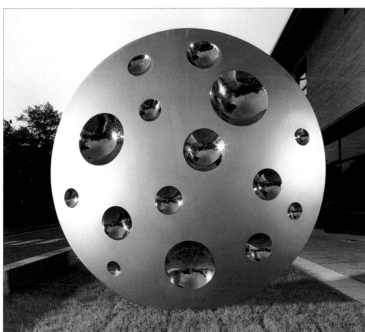

Sun-Moon sculpture – Gartnavel Royal Hospital, Glasgow

Two Hearts sculpture – Gartnavel Royal Hospital, Glasgow

Braid – Blackburn

Skyramp – Birmingham

Minaret – Brick Lane, London

Trinity Mirror – Irvine

Airburst sculptures – BAE Systems

Meads Reach Bridge – Temple Quay, Bristol

Contact
Phil Ball (sales)
t: 01623 750214
websales@alpharail.co.uk

Web
www.alpharail.co.uk

Address
Alpha Rail Ltd
Nunn Brook Rise
County Estate
Huthwaite NG17 2PD

Accreditation
ISO 9001:2000; ISO 14001:2004

Affiliations
British Association of Landscape Industries (BALI)
Constructionline
CHAS
CSCS-carded workforce
Association of Fencing Industries (AFI)

Additional entries
Railings ➤ 174

Alpha Rail Ltd
Architectural metalwork

Alpha Rail fabricates and installs galvanised metal railings, gates, pedestrian guardrails, estate fencing and Juliette balconies. A team of specialists manufactures all products in house, supplying bespoke architectural metalwork with logos, motifs or other designs, as well as decorative archways, bollards and barrier gates. The technical team is equipped with the latest CAD systems and offers a full design service. Alpha Rail has worked for over 30 years with public sector clients, architects, engineers, fencing and landscaping contractors and private clients.

Sliding gate with donkey formed from perforated plate – Pets Corner, Harlow Town Park

Bow-top railings with poppy detail – Harlow

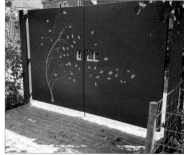

Gate with laser profile plate – Tunbridge Wells

Decorative arch – Persian Sephardi Synagogue

Decorative railings and archway – Solihull

Antique Bronze Ltd
Conservation - Restoration - Patination

Contact
t: 020 8340 0931
f: 020 8340 0743
info@antiquebronze.co.uk

Web
www.antiquebronze.co.uk

Address
Antique Bronze Ltd
44 Hillway
Holly Lodge Estate
London N6 6EP

Accreditation
Altius
CHAS
Constructionline
ICON

Affiliations
Institute of Conservation

Operational area
UK

Antique Bronze Ltd

Conservation and restoration

Antique Bronze Ltd, established in 1955, is one of the UK's leading conservation and restoration companies specialising in historic and contemporary sculpture, monuments and architectural features.

Services
• Statue, war memorial and monument cleaning, conservation and restoration.
• Architectural bronze cleaning and restoration.
• Art services including gilding, carving and faux-finishing.
• Consultancy, training and CPD.

Projects
Antique Bronze has worked on many of the UK's most high-profile projects including Nelson's Column, Eros, The Albert Memorial, County Hall in London, historic royal palaces, and Cambridge University.
Typical projects include the restoration of bronze architectural features in public spaces, complex restoration of bronze public monuments, cleaning and removal of graffiti from war memorials, and conservation of contemporary sculutpre collections.

Restoration of lion sculpture and plaque – Nelson's Column, Trafalgar Square, London

Full restoration of Michael Faraday statue – London

Bronze war memorial plaques

Fountain statuary – Trafalgar Square

Field of Vision – Glaxo Smith Kline HQ

Bronze doors – County Hall Apartments, London

Shaftesbury Memorial Fountain and Eros statue

Contact

Paul Owens (sales)
Scott Chafer (technical)
t: 01484 401414
f: 01484 721398
info@asfco.co.uk

Web
www.asfco.co.uk

Address
Architectural Street Furnishings Ltd
Priory Road
off Armytage Road
Brighouse HD6 1PY

Accreditation
ISO 9001:2008

Additional entries
Post and rail systems ➤ 216
Bollards ➤ 225
Bespoke street furniture ➤ 277
Seats and benches ➤ 325

Architectural Street Furnishings

Bespoke metalwork

Building on over 150 years' experience of casting, ASF manufactures high-quality architectural metalwork in cast iron, ductile iron, steel, stainless steel, aluminium and bronze.
Typical commissions include railings and street furniture. Decorative items such as finials, urns, brackets, sculptures and figureheads can also be produced.
The company has in-house casting and fabrication facilities. Design support is also available.

Bespoke stainless steel railings – Blackburn

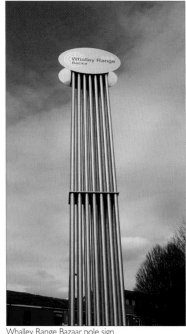

Whalley Range Bazaar pole sign

Bespoke steel/stainless steel post and panel system

Cleggford Bridge refurbishment – Dewsbury

Laser-cut tree guard – Ruthin Art Trail

Bespoke bronze tree grille

 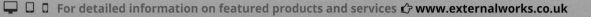

Contact
Chris Brammall
t: 01229 588580
chris@chrisbrammall.com

Web
www.chrisbrammall.com

Address
Chris Brammall Ltd
Low Mill Business Park
Morecambe Road
Ulverston
Cumbria LA12 9EE

Staff/turnover
20 people

Awards
Landscape Institute Awards 2012 – Winner

Additional entries
Bridges ➤ 158
Sculpture ➤ 425

Chris Brammall Ltd

Bespoke architectural and sculptural metalwork

Chris Brammall produces high quality, individual sculptural and architectural metalwork. Designs are tailored to each project and carried out with strict attention to detail, being carefully thought, planned and delivered from design and manufacture through to installation.

Work undertaken and media used
Working with a variety of media including corten and mild steel, Chris designs and creates one-off commissioned pieces of art.

Projects
• Project Genesis, Consett: corten and mild steel sculptural interpretation panels.
• Churchill War Rooms, Westminster, London: new entrance canopy and signage.
• Brockhole jetty project, Lake District National Park: landside works including structural sub-frame, deck, seating, canopy, railings and kiosk.
• Claife Viewing Station, Windermere, Cumbria: restoration of historic National Trust property on the shores of England's longest lake.
• Chester Roman Gardens: bespoke corten steel tunnel and gate.
• Falls of Falloch, Loch Lomond National Park: national scenic route sculptural viewpoint.

Bandstand – The Glebe, Bowness on Windermere

Corten tunnel and gate – Chester Roman Gardens

Museum canopy – Churchill War Rooms, London

Jetty landside works – Brockhole Visitor Centre

Claife Viewing Station, Windermere

dp structures

Contact
Dave Palmer
t: 01282 697563
m: 07766 242059
enquiries@dpstructures.co.uk

Web
www.dpstructures.co.uk

Address
DP Structures Ltd
Unit 12, Dale Mill
Hallam Road
Nelson BB9 8AN

Operational area
UK

Additional entries
Bespoke metalwork ➤ 420

DP Structures Ltd

Bespoke architectural metalwork

DP Structures specialises in the design, fabrication and installation of bespoke architectural steel structures. Clients include local authorities, education authorities, and commercial and private clients, including retail, leisure and garden centres.

Work undertaken and media used
A full service is provided, from concept design through to fabrication and construction on site, providing the client with a complete solution. Materials worked include corten steel, mild steel, stainless steel, timber, stone, glass and perspex.

Projects
• Bespoke canopies.
• Trellis arches.
• Tensile structures.
• Entrance canopies.
• Bus shelters.
• Kiosks and pavilions.
• Portal framed buildings.
• Bespoke planters.
• Paving set trays and tree guards.
• Gates, fencing, railings and balustrades.

WW1 replica footbridge – Lostock Hall, South Ribble

Bus shelter – Pendle

Gate – St Catherine's Hospice, Leyland

Street market – Northern Quarter, Manchester

Corten steel walkway – Jewellery Quarter

Temporary street food cafe pavilion – Manchester

outdoor design
BESPOKE METAL FABRICATION

Contact
James Booth
t: 01903 716960
info@outdoordesign.co.uk

Web
www.outdoordesign.co.uk

Address
Outdoor Design
Unit 1, Block A
Ford Airfield Industrial Estate
Ford
Arundel BN18 0HY

Operational area
Worldwide

Country of manufacture
UK

Additional entries
Bespoke planters ➤ 366

Outdoor Design

Bespoke metal fabrication for landscape and garden designers

Outdoor Design is a precision engineering company with decades of experience in designing and manufacturing bespoke metal structures. Outdoor Design works closely with landscape architects, specifiers and professional garden designers on projects for residential developments, commercial buildings and private homes worldwide.

Always eager to take on a new challenge, the company produces highly accomplished work in all materials and at all scales, from the small and delicate to the massive and monolithic.

• **Skills and capabilities**

Whatever the project, however complex the design, the process starts with the creation of a 3D computer model.

This approach allows any engineering and fabrication issues to be addressed early, and modifications or enhancements to be suggested to the original concept.

Outdoor Design's full range of skills and capabilities are then applied to produce a finished article that is precisely engineered, aesthetically pleasing and completely fit for purpose.

Decorative porthole grille in laser-cut stainless steel – Hampton Court Palace

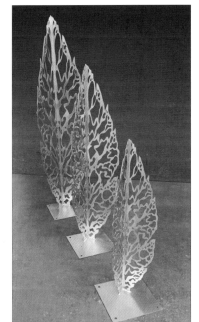

Laser-cut copper garden features

Garden arch, 1.8m high, in corten steel

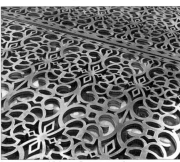

Laser-cut steel light-well cover panels

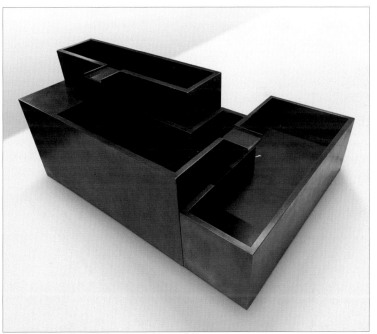

Large bronze water feature patinated to an old penny finish

HARRY GRAY

Contact
Harry Gray
m: 07880 813526
hg@harrygray.co.uk

Web
www.harrygray.co.uk

Address
Harry Gray
The Carving Workshop
53A St Phillips Road
Cambridge CB1 3DA

Awards
Commended for Bill Tutte Monument
National Placemaking Awards 2014

Additional entries
Artworks for public spaces ➤ 430

Harry Gray

Architectural metalwork

The Rose and Poppy Gates were designed and made by Harry Gray to form the West entrance to Twickenham Ruby Stadium.
There are 15 roses on each gate, modelled on those worn by the Grand Slam-winning England team of 1914. The poppies at the top of each gate are formed from German shell-casings fired in anger during the 1914–18 conflict.
The hand-modelled bronze roses, which gradually transform into poppies, represent the transformation of rugby players into soldiers.

Harry Gray adding detail to the gates

Rose and Poppy Gates – Twickenham Rugby Stadium

Detailing of the *Rose and Poppy Gates*

TOPP & Co.

Architectural metalwork

Founded in 1980, TOPP & Co creates high-quality architectural metalwork for some of the most prestigious properties in the world. A leading authority in the craft of blacksmithing, the company is innovative and thrives on demanding creative and technical challenges. Long-established skills and techniques are developed and applied to both traditional and contemporary environments.

The Real Wrought Iron Company specialist division is the only supplier of genuine wrought iron in the world.

Entrance gates for stately home

Mild steel railings

Wrought iron railings

Mild steel railings

Contact
Jeremy Bowman
t: 01347 833173
enquiry@toppandco.com

Web
www.toppandco.com

Address
TOPP & Co.
Unit 5
The Airfield Industrial Estate
Tholthorpe
York YO61 1ST

Awards
Diploma of Excellence – the Worshipful Company of Blacksmiths
Copper in Architecture Award – John Smith Award for Craftsmanship

Operational area
Worldwide

Wrought iron railings – South Hill Park

Bandstand restoration – Exhibition Park, Newcastle

Wrought iron gate

Wrought iron entrance detail

dpstudio

Contact
Dave Palmer
t: 01282 697563
m: 07766 242059
enquiries@dpstructures.co.uk

Web
www.dpstudio.co.uk

Address
DP Studio
Unit 12, Dale Mill
Hallam Road
Nelson BB9 8AN

Operational area
Worldwide

Additional entries
Bespoke architectural metalwork ➤ 416

DP Studio

Bespoke metalwork

DP Studio, the structural metalwork division of DP Structures, designs, fabricates and installs bespoke sculptures, memorials and focal features for the public realm.
Services range from concept design, illustrations and 3D CAD modelling of preferred concepts, through to technical design, manufacture and assembly of the finished product. The company can also work to artist's concepts.

Work undertaken and media used
Design and fabrication teams work collaboratively on bespoke creations to clients' requirements. Materials worked are primarily corten steel, mild steel and stainless steel, with other materials including timber, stone and glass incorporated to create unique features.

Projects
• Design, manufacture and installation of WWI memorial in corten steel, commissioned by South Ribble Council – Lostock, Lancashire.
• *The Shuttle* monument in corten steel to celebrate the town's historic role in textile manufacturing – Nelson, Lancashire.
• Gateway *Burnley 'b'* sculpture fabricated in corten steel – Burnley, Lancashire.

The Shuttle 12m high corten steel monument – Nelson

Burnley 'b' sculpture

Corten steel sculpture, design by Broadbent Studio

WWI 9m high corten steel war memorial – Peace Garden, Lostock Hall, South Ribble

Alice Nutter (Pendle Witch) sculpture

Jenny Pickford

Artist blacksmith

Contact
Jenny Pickford
m: 07985 246056
info@jennypickford.co.uk

Web
www.jennypickford.co.uk

Address
Jenny Pickford
12c Shucknall Court
Weston Beggard HR1 4BH

Jenny Pickford designs and creates sculptures, water features and architectural ironwork for corporate, public and private clients worldwide. Jenny challenges the heritage of blacksmithing and glass blowing, giving it a feminine and sensual perspective inspired by the spirit of nature.
A bespoke service is provided from initial concept to final installation.
Public art commissions can be carried out with community involvement.

Hibiscus floral sculpture – Chengdu, China

Bluebell sculpture – Royal Derby Hospital

Forged steel automated gates

Agapanthus sculpture – Eden Gardens, Australia

Galvanised forged steel and blown glass school gates – Bromsgrove

Contact
Stan Jankowski
m: 07929 566342
stan@panjankowski.com

Web
www.panjankowski.com

Address
Jankowski Weathervanes
Unit 6
Cain Valley Trading Estate
Llanffyllin SY22 5DD

Operational area
Worldwide

Jankowski Weathervanes

Weathervanes and garden art

Jankowski Weathervanes specialises in bespoke garden art made from copper and brass. Unique fountains, sculptures, kinetic art, wind sculptures, house signs and plaques are all hand crafted in the studio in Llanffyllin using traditional techniques.

Wind sculpture with rotating wheels

Scottish lion weathervane

Bespoke police box kinetic sculpture

Wind sculpture spinning on five axes

Brun copper dragon fountain sculpture

Contact
Melissa Cole
m: 07711 325209
melissa@melissacole.co.uk

Web
www.melissacole.co.uk

Address
Melissa Cole
Moonraker Farm
Bottlesford
Pewsey SN9 6LU

Melissa Cole

Ironwork and sculpture

Melissa Cole is an established artist-blacksmith and works with forged and fabricated metal to create bespoke, contemporary designs. Collaborations can be undertaken with other artists, schools and community groups to realise designs, create sculpture exhibitions and fulfill client briefs.
Site-specific, one-off pieces range from gates and railings, to sculpture and wall installations.
Materials used include steel, stainless steel, bronze and copper.

Brain Neuron Pathways – Oxford

River Route wall installation – Oxford

Bridge railings – Chippenham

Gates – Rabley Barn

LANDSCAPE No II, NH5690 sculpture

James Price Blacksmith Ltd

Bespoke metalwork

James Price Blacksmith Ltd produces original contemporary metalwork for public art, architectural and sculptural metalwork commissions.

Materials used range from forged iron and bronze to stainless steel, and ancient hot forging techniques are combined with modern design. Keen attention to detail and craftsmanship are brought to every project, from concept through to final installation.

Contact
James Price
t: 01273 890398
info@blacksmithdesigner.com

Web
www.blacksmithdesigner.com

Address
James Price Blacksmith Ltd
The Workshop
Highbridge Lane
East Chiltington
Lewes BN7 3QY

Saplings sculptural light installation

Fernabank anvil

Withywindle Salt Rakes walkway panels

Fishermans Quay gates

Jon Mills Ltd

Bespoke metalwork

Jon Mills fabricates site-specific decorative ironwork and public sculpture.

Each piece can be inspired by a variety of influences, from local history to the environment and adjacent architectural details. These influences bring wit and a human element to the different projects.

Work undertaken and media used

All work is fabricated in Jon's workshop, and supplied shot-blasted, hot-zinc sprayed and powder-coated to agreed RAL colours prior to delivery to site.

Installation

An installation service is available, if required.

Projects

Commissions include gate and railing projects for schools and community groups, with children's design input and participation; school trips to the workshop can be arranged to see work in progress.

Contact
Jon Mills
t: 01273 235810
m: 07793 321039
jon@metaljon.com

Web
www.metaljon.com

Address
Jon Mills Ltd
Robertson Yard
42A Robertson Road
Brighton BN1 5NJ

Deco Dancers steel cut-outs – Sussex

Gates – Ebenezer Baptist Church, Brighton

Ghost Train full-size replica of 1847 steam engine

ArtParkS International Ltd
Sculpture commissions

ArtParkS International holds a searchable databank of over 7500 sculptures from a selection of artists worldwide. Sculptures range from realistic to abstract, very large-scale to small, and traditional to contemporary.
Materials used include bronze, stone, stainless steel, wood and resin.
Site-specific bespoke commission statuary are made by shortlisted or client-selected sculptors after prices and completion dates are agreed.
Sculptures are suitable for town squares, schools, gardens and hospitals.

Contact
Peter de Sausmarez
t: 01481 235571
f: 01481 235572
peter@artparks.co.uk

Web
www.artparks.co.uk

Address
ArtParkS International Ltd
Sausmarez Manor
St Martin
Guernsey GY4 6SG

Affiliations
Institute of Patentees and Inventors

Operational area
Worldwide

Ingravity by Nando Alvarez

Searching Souls by Eppe de Haan

Infinity Curve No.3 by Wenqin Chen

Hard Bop by John Atkin

Intestinal Fortitude by Mike Hansel

Hala by Peter Moorhouse

Serenity Portal by Teo San Jose

Contact
Chris Brammall
t: 01229 588580
chris@chrisbrammall.com

Web
www.chrisbrammall.com

Address
Chris Brammall Ltd
Low Mill Business Park
Morecambe Road
Ulverston
Cumbria LA12 9EE

Staff/turnover
20 people

Awards
Landscape Institute Awards 2012 – Winner

Additional entries
Bridges ➤ 158
Bespoke architectural and sculptural metalwork
➤ 415

Chris Brammall Ltd

Sculpture

Chris Brammall creates artistic sculptures that are manufactured to the highest possible standard. From complex large-scale pieces through to more simplistic designs, each sculpture is carefully conceived to create a true 'sense of place'. Sculptures are built for low maintenance and longevity.

Projects
• *Mary's Shell*, Cleveleys: 9m long, 15t stainless steel shell installed on the beach as part of the Mythic Coast Artwork Trail for Wyre Council.
• *Chesterfield Flower (Growth)*, Hornsbridge: 8.5m corten and stainless steel sculpture.
• *Flight & Navigation*, Andover: flight and navigation inspired sculpture which pays homage to the history of its location on the site of the former RAF Andover.
• *Derby Innovation Centre*: 18.5m two-blade sculpture inspired by the industries in Derby.
• *Books to Birds*, Cumbria: corten, stainless steel and iroko timber sculpture for a school.
• *The Semple Trail*, Renfrewshire: seven bespoke sculptures around Castle Semple Loch, Lochwinnoch.

Flight & Navigation – Andover

Derby Innovation Centre – credit Jakt Photography

Books to Birds – Cumbria

The Semple Trail – Renfrewshire

Mary's Shell, Thornton Cleveleys – Lancashire

Andrea Geile MRBS

Contact
Andrea Geile
t: 0131 556 0251
m: 07789 247182
info@andreageile.co.uk

Web
www.andreageile.co.uk

Address
Andrea Geile
17 Clarence Street
Edinburgh EH3 5AE

Recent public art commissions
Energised Landscape with Deveron Projects, funded by Forrestry Commission Scotland
The Chlorophylls with Comar, funded by Heritage Lottery Fund and Forestry Commission Scotland
Tree Tags in Pilrig Park with Citizen Curator, funded by Grow Wild UK
Leaf Cloud for Macmillan Palliative Care Unit, Royal Infirmary Perth

Andrea Geile

Sculpture

Andrea Geile designs, fabricates and installs environmental sculptures. Collaborations are undertaken with architects, landscape companies, art organisations, galleries and public bodies. Public engagement programmes can be delivered with public art commissions.

Work undertaken and media used
Using oxidised corten steel shaped by hand, Andrea explores the relationship between landscape, buildings and living plants.

Tree Tag project – Edinburgh

The Chlorophylls sculpture – Isle of Mull

Tumbling hand-cut corten steel sculpture – Bute

Leaf arbour – private garden

Level the Field corten steel sculpture

CoralieTurpin
ARTIST

Contact
m: 07946 424602
turpinthomson@gmail.com

Web
www.coralieturpin.co.uk

Address
Coralie Turpin
Yorkshire Artspace
Persistence Works
21 Brown Street
Sheffield S1 2BS

Coralie Turpin

Large-scale public art

Coralie Turpin creates one-off site-specific sculptures and mosaics for public and private clients from sites ranging from city centres and public parks, to schools and private gardens. Coralie's sculptures are designed to complement and enhance the experience of visiting the landscape in which the work is placed.

Projects
• Seven 4x3.5m stainless steel screens with detailed cast bronze and aluminium inserts, collaboratively designed with silversmith Owen Waterhouse, Sheffield's Retail Quarter.
• Creation of 27 themed park entrance archways to six parks in Darlington, Heritage Lottery and Groundwork Darlington.
• Design and creation of play area and garden at Sheffield Children's Hospital.
• Installation and design of 2x6m wide animal themed gates at Firs Hill School, Sheffield.
• Two large metal artworks including a creative fence and wall artwork for a Chelmsford school.
• Gateway artwork and mosaic for a refurbished estate, Great Places Housing Association.
• Mosaics for Irwell Valley Housing Association.
• Installation of artworks across entrances and in quiet spaces of new-build schools in Sheffield.

Detail of handmade porcelain mosaic elements

Mosaic flooring – Horsleygate hall, Derbyshire

Mosaic mussel sculpture

Stainless steel sculpture with detailed castings

Creative Spiral

Public sculpture

Creative Spiral has over 20 years' experience in producing distinctive, site-specific sculptural metalwork for public spaces.
The company works closely with the client from the initial concept through to final installation.
A design service is offered, or Creative Spiral can work to clients' specifications.

Contact
Gideon Petersen
t: 01437 563308
m: 07813 382724
gideon@creativespiral.co.uk

Web
www.creativespiral.co.uk

Address
Creative Spiral
Pontprenddu
Llandissilio
Clunderwen SA66 7TT

Copper sheet mountain bike trailhead marker

Stamp for Wales – relief sculpture

Cardiff Metropolitan University Crest

Giant Daisies – Tower Hamlets

David A Annand

Public art

David Annand works on large public art projects in the UK and Ireland.
His works are designed to create a sense of place for people to engage with, especially when combined with street furniture such as seating. Bronze and stainless steel are used for the sculptures, which often feature digitally bead-blasted poetry.
Commissioned poems are often a key feature in David's work – they help engage the public, encouraging them to take time with the piece.

Contact
David Annand
t: 01382 330714
david@davidannand.com

Web
www.davidannand.com

Address
David A Annand
Pigscrave Cottage
The Wynd
Kilmany
Cupar KY15 4PT

Affiliations
Royal British Society of Sculptors

The Prop steel and bronze sculpture – Lochgelly

The Value of Perspective bronze tubular sculpture

Poetry commissioned for *Still*

Still – Marie Curie Hospice, Belfast

DAVID BACKHOUSE
SCULPTURES

Contact
David Backhouse
t: 01934 863049
jennieweston@yahoo.co.uk

Web
www.backhousesculptures.com

Address
David Backhouse
Yew Trees
Langford Place
Lower Langford
Bristol BS40 5BT

Affiliations
Fellow of the Royal Society of British Sculptors
Royal West of England Academian
Fellow of the Royal Society of Arts
Founder Member of the Society of Equestrian Arts
Member of the Society of Portrait Sculptors

David Backhouse

Sculpture

David Backhouse creates large-scale bronze site- and subject-specific public memorials and statues. David's work meditates on the human and animal condition in the modern world, reflecting loss and tragedy, hope and delight, and above all, tenacity of spirit.

As well as bespoke products, some pieces may be available from stock.

Services include enlargement and installation, if required.

Animals in War Memorial – London

Animals in War Memorial – London

Aspiration – Royal West of England Academy

DAVID WATKINSON SCULPTURE

Contact
David Watkinson Sculpture
t: 0113 265 7984
m: 07817 968216
david@davidwatkinsonsculpture.co.uk

Web
www.davidwatkinsonsculpture.co.uk

Address
David Watkinson Sculpture
Stockheld Crossing
Stockheld Lane
Scholes
Leeds LS15 4NG

Awards
Chelsea Flower Show 2015, 2016 – 4 Star Award
Hampton Court Flower Show 2014, 2015 – 4 Star Award
Chelsea Flower Show 2013, 2014 – 3 Star Award
Hampton Court Flower Show 2013 – 3 Star Award
BALI Awards 2010 – Tree of Life Sculpture, Edwards Trust Memorial Garden

David Watkinson

Kinetic sculpture

David Watkinson produces unique kinetic and static sculptures for both private and public commissions.

David's works explore form and movement, whether actual movement through space, or implied. Works may be delicately balanced on precision bearings, where small air currents cause large forms to tip and move through space before returning to a balanced position.

David regularly works on site-specific pieces as well as bespoke versions of his existing collection.

Wall Orchid steel, bronze and gold leaf sculpture

Sycamore Seed steel and bronze sculpture

Cube Cloud Trilogy steel sculpture

Ekkehard Altenburger

Ekkehard Altenburger

Contact
Ekkehard Altenburger
m: 07788 458902
e@altenburger.co.uk

Web
www.altenburger.co.uk

Address
Ekkehard Altenburger
APT Studios Deptford
6 Creek Side
Deptford
London SE8 4SA

Affiliations
Royal British Society of Sculptors

Ekkehard Altenburger

Sculpture

Ekkehard Altenburger produces large-scale sculptures and water features in stone and steel for both public and private clients.
Ekkehard has close ties within the stone industry and regularly works with quarries and factories in Portugal, Norway and Italy.

Projects
• Norwegian Larvekitte granite sculpture – Volkswagen Financial Services, Milton Keynes.
• Italian Carrara marble sculpture – Nottingham University.

Thoughts in a Banked Curve – Milton Keynes

House for a Gordian Knot – Nottingham University

Angola granite and bronze water feature – Kent

Saima Kivi powder-coated steel sculpture

Cochlea – Royal Borough of Greenwich, London

Emma Stothard

Emma Stothard
SCULPTURE

Contact
Emma Stothard
t: 01947 605706
sculpture@emmastothard.com

Web
www.emmastothard.com

Address
Emma Stothard
Unit 5a
Enterprise Way
Whitby YO22 4NH

Emma Stothard

Sculpture

Emma Stothard's work takes inspiration from the wildlife and landscape around her in Yorkshire.

Work undertaken and media used
Sculptures are formed from a fabricated steel frame which is then handwoven either in willow or wire. Mild steel wire sculptures are hot-dipped galvanised and can be powder-coated. Drawn phosphor bronze wire sculptures offer another permanent solution for public commissions.

Hambletonian – Wynyard Hall

Dancing Hares – private collection

Ebbsfleet Straight Tusked Elephants

Coronation Lobster – Staithes, North Yorkshire

GMJ WOODCARVING

GMJ Woodcarving

Wooden sculptures

GMJ Woodcarving has over 30 years' experience designing and producing public and private commissions in wood. Sculptures can be created for gardens, parks, schools and woodlands. Types of work undertaken include portraits, tree carvings, abstract forms, chainsaw carvings, figures, animals, lettering and signs.

Contact
Graham Jones
m: 07963 193944
info@gmjwoodcarving.co.uk

Web
www.gmjwoodcarving.co.uk

Address
GMJ Woodcarving
Flat 1, 114 Salisbury Road
Moseley
Birmingham B13 8JZ

Gateway to school garden – Birmingham

Apple Core play sculpture – Bewdley

Wooden badger carving

Play and climbing sculpture made from a cedar tree

HARRY GRAY

Harry Gray

Artworks for public spaces

Harry Gray has an established art practice and has worked on numerous public projects both as lead artist and as a team collaborator.
Harry specialises in permanent artworks where concept, craftsmanship and the relationship of the work to the site are of equal importance. All projects evolve from a close working relationship with the client and other design professionals.

Contact
Harry Gray
m: 07880 813526
hg@harrygray.co.uk

Web
www.harrygray.co.uk

Address
Harry Gray
The Carving Workshop
53A St Phillips Road
Cambridge CB1 3DA

Awards
Commended for Bill Tutte Monument
National Placemaking Awards 2014

Additional entries
Architectural metalwork ➤ 418

Monument to Bill Tutte, WWII codebreaker

The Rose and Poppy Gates – Twickenham Stadium

Stone Lion – The Magic Garden, Hampton Court

Movable bronze bookstacks – Cambridge University

IAN MARLOW
SCULPTOR

Contact
Ian Marlow
t: 01373 471711
m: 07967 642513
ian@marlowsculpture.co.uk

Web
www.marlowsculpture.co.uk

Address
Ian Marlow
Ebenezer Chapel
Buckland Dinham
nr Frome BA11 2QT

Affiliations
Royal British Society of Sculptors

Ian Marlow

Sculpture

Ian Marlow produces individual sculptures from stainless steel. Other materials and finishes such as corten steel, glass and powder-coating can also be used for texture and accents.

Ian's works are inspired by natural forms. They have a freshness and fluidity and are suited to contemporary urban settings (both exterior and interior), as well as public landscaping and private gardens.

Chameleon Leaves powder-coated steel sculpture

Aspire – St Catherine's, Guildford

Steel *Hare* sculpture

Lily steel garden feature

Ivan Black - Kinetic Sculpture

Contact
Ivan Black
t: 01834 870087
info@ivanblack.co.uk

Web
www.ivanblack.com

Address
Ivan Black
Whitewell in the Ruins
Penally
Tenby SA70 7RY

Ivan Black

Kinetic sculpture

Ivan Black designs and fabricates kinetic sculptures that are set in motion by wind, motor or interaction. Sculptures are suitable for external and interior spaces.

These engineered designs are inspired by natural forms and are a synergy between science, art and technology.

Sculptures are available from stock or by commission.

Blue Squares – private collection

Stealth – Jimo City, China

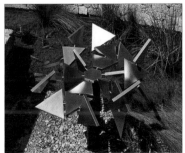
Hex – Mosman Park, Western Australia

Golden Section – Cottesloe, Western Australia

JOSEPH INGLEBY
SCULPTOR

Contact
Joseph Ingleby
t: 0141 337 2184
m: 07815 832313
joe@josephingleby.com

Web
www.josephingleby.com

Address
Joseph Ingleby
Glasgow Sculpture Studios
The Whisky Bond
2 Dawson Road
Glasgow G4 9SS

Awards
Gottlieb Foundation – 2013
Pollock-Krasner Foundation – 1997

Joseph Ingleby

Public sculpture

Joseph Ingleby specialises in site-specific sculptures in metal for public and private spaces. These sculptures explore the organic process of metamorphosis – they are evolved forms that are inspired by nature but also retain memories of functional artefacts.

Projects

• *Time Vessel* – Alloa, Scotland: 2.9m long copper, steel and glass sculpture for Clackmannanshire Council.
• *Slipstream* – River Clyde, Glasgow: 11.3m long steel and copper sculpture for South Lanarkshire Council.
• *Waterland* – Bulwell Riverside, Nottingham: 7.3m long steel and copper sculpture for Nottingham City Council.

Waterland microscopic river particles sculpture

Slipstream galvanised steel and copper sculpture

Waterland sculpture detail

Time Vessel copper plate sculpture

KEITH-McCARTER

Contact
Keith McCarter
t: 01896 751112
keith@keith-mccarter.com

Web
www.keith-mccarter.com

Address
Keith McCarter
10 Coopersknowe Crescent
Galashiels TD1 2DS

Affiliations
Royal British Society of Sculptors

Awards
Sir Otto Beit medal – Royal British Society of Sculptors

Keith McCarter

Sculpture

Keith McCarter works primarily in bronze and stainless steel and has created over 30 major public sculptures in the UK and abroad. Keith can work with architects and landscape architects. Two-dimensional works have also been created in concrete, ranging from murals to complete cladding of buildings.

Cycloidal Form stainless steel sculpture – London

Helios stainless steel sculpture – Norwich

Encounter bronze – Guy's Hospital, London

Covenant bronze sculpture – Rye Brook, New York

MALLON
THE ANCESTRAL FOUNDRY

Contact
Charlie Mallon
m: 07899 913537
Charlie@mallonfoundry.com

Web
www.mallonfoundry.com

Address
Mallon Foundry
22 High Street
Moneymore
Magherafelt BT45 7PD

Mallon Foundry

Sculpture

Charlie Mallon of Mallon Foundry is an artistic metalworker. He has been working in iron and steel for over 25 years and can cast his own sculptures in bronze.

Projects include a small number of large-scale Celtic-inspired bronzes, the first of which is being exhibited at Kew Gardens in 2017.

Mallon Foundry works on all types of commissions, particularly in collaboration with architects and garden designers.

Fiacc the Raven bronze sculpture

Boar of Ben Gulbain bronze sculpture

Giant storybook – The Giant's Lair, Slieve Gullion

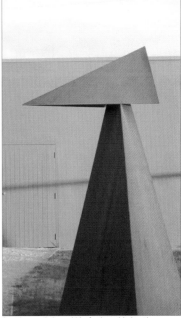
Druid commission – Wexford seaside location

MARION SMITH SCULPTOR

Contact
Marion Smith
m: 07870 957971
info@marionsmithsculptor.co.uk

Web
www.marionsmithsculptor.co.uk

Address
Marion Smith
Auchendownie
Leven KY8 5QH

Marion Smith

Sculpture

Marion Smith creates site-specific commissions for the public realm that embody an understanding of their context.

Projects
• *Panmure Passage* in Norden granite – Dundee.
• *The Plough and the Reaper* in phosphor bronze and whinstone – Anstruther, Fife.
• *Lancastria Memorial* in phosphor bronze and granite – Clydebank.

Panmure Passage (615x180x240cm) – Dundee

Panmure Passage in Norden granite – Dundee

The Plough and the Reaper – Anstruther, Fife

Lancastria Memorial in bronze and granite

MICHAEL COOPER SCULPTOR

Contact
Michael Cooper
t: 01494 482226
michael@michaelcoopersculptor.co.uk

Web
www.michaelcoopersculptor.co.uk

Address
Michael Cooper
Grange Farm
Radnage
High Wycombe HP14 4ED

Affiliations
Royal British Society of Sculptors

Michael Cooper

Sculpture and carvings

Michael Cooper uses marble, stone and bronze to create sculptures and carvings of a variety of animals, birds and the human figure.
There is a strong emphasis on the tactile nature of the pieces and the different media are worked to create smooth, flowing surfaces.

Projects

Large-scale commissions include:
• Reclining figure in Travertine marble – Covent Garden.
• Three bears in Belgian Fossil marble – Bicester.

Gorilla in Kilkenny limestone

Snail in Kilkenny limestone

Apples in Kilkenny limestone and bronze

Baboon in Kilkenny limestone

NOEL BLAKEMAN

Contact
Noel Blakeman
t: 01327 843995
m: 07976 851110
studio@noelblakeman.com

Web
www.noelblakeman.com

Address
Noel Blakeman
10 Bishops Meadow
Long Buckby
Northampton NN6 7WG

Noel Blakeman

Sculpture

Noel Blakeman designs and produces contemporary functional sculptures using metal as the main medium.
Noel is inspired by the complicated mathematical formulae that are often present in the natural world – from the Fibonacci series to Phi (the Golden Ratio) – and uses them in each piece.
Projects include public and corporate commissions as well as work with community and education groups.

Avon steel cut-out silhouettes

Allium sculpture

Colour changing fibre optic tree chandelier

Contact
Ruth Moilliet
m: 07973 908839
sculpture@ruthmoilliet.com

Web
www.ruthmoilliet.com

Address
Ruth Moilliet
2 Springfield Road
Ramsbottom
Bury BL0 9SU

Ruth Moilliet

Sculpture

Ruth Moilliet produces bespoke limited edition artworks for the public, private and corporate sectors.

Sculptures range from small detailed pieces to large eye-catching structures that are suitable for long-term display.

A team of specialists works with Ruth to provide computer-aided design, fabrication, specialist finishing techniques and structural advice. A delivery and installation service is also available.

Allium stainless steel seedhead sculpture

Pollination stainless steel sculpture – Birmingham

Dandelion Clock stainless steel sculpture

Contact
Kate Thomson
t: 0131 667 3532
kate@ukishima.net

Web
www.ukishima.net

Address
Ukishima Sculpture Studio
192/3 Causewayside
Edinburgh EH9 1PN

Ukishima Sculpture Studio

Public sculpture

Ukishima Sculpture Studio explores local stories and aspirations as well as symbolic connections found in nature. The studio has created site-specific sculptures in natural granite and marble stone for public sites worldwide.

Seating and paving are often incorporated into the designs to create harmonious spaces with a tangible sense of place. These spaces can be used as rest stops or open-air community meeting and event locations; places where people can connect with their social, natural and built environment.

River Spirit sculpture – Oatlands Square, Glasgow

River Spirit sculpture in grey, black and red granite – Oatlands Square, Glasgow

River Spirit sculpture – Oatlands Square, Glasgow

GILLIAN FORBES
STONECARVER

Contact
Gillian Forbes
t: 01577 830754
gillian@forbesstonecarver.com

Web
www.forbesstonecarver.com

Address
Gillian Forbes
The Workshop
Pathgreen Cottage
Path of Condie
Forgandenny PH2 9DW

Awards
Queen Elizabeth Scholarship Trust Award
JD Fergusson Arts Award

Gillian Forbes

Stone carving

Gillian Forbes specialises in commissioned pieces
for individuals and organisations.
Projects include signage, public art, letter cutting,
memorials and sculpture using predominantly
British stone – slate, sandstone and granite.
The preservation and promotion of hand-carving
skills in Scotland is fundamental to the pieces.

Canongate Wall – Scottish Parliament, Edinburgh

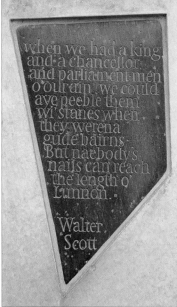

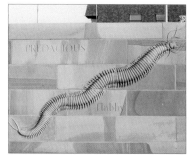
See Wall TERN Art Project – Morecambe

Detail of niche carving in Mouselow sandstone

Detail of Easdale slate panel in Canongate Wall

FIONA & ALEC PEEVER
LETTERING AND SCULPTURE

Contact
Fiona and Alec Peever
t: 01993 868012
peeverstudio@aol.com

Web
www.fionapeever.com
www.alecpeever.com

Address
Lettering & Sculpture Ltd
Studio Barn
Hunts Copse
Wilcote Riding
Wilcote
nr Finstock
Chipping Norton OX7 3DX

Operational area
Worldwide

Lettering & Sculpture Ltd

Letter carving and sculpture

Lettering & Sculpture designs and produces
contemporary sculpture and hand-carved
lettering in stone. Projects are undertaken for
large and small public and private collections.
Work includes lettering for paving, monuments,
garden features and public art.
The company also specialises in bespoke sculpted
commemorative plaques and architectural
carving.
• **Services**
Services range from concept and creation
through to delivery and installation, with projects
completed throughout the UK and overseas.

Composition and manufacture
Traditional craft skills are combined with
contemporary techniques and modern materials
to create innovative works of art.

Projects
Recent commissions include: sculptural works
and hand-carved stone plaques, Oxford
University; Winchester College; Kew Bridge
Pumping Station development project, St James's;
Ashmolean Museum, Oxford; Chichester
Cathedral; and Highgate School, London.

New gargoyles – Bodleian Library

Reflective Forms sculpture

Hand-carved lettering

Auguries of Innocence sculpture

Robbie Schneider

Lettering sculpture

Robbie Schneider is a designer and sculptor specialising in carved and fabricated inscriptions and architectural lettering in stone, wood and metals. All lettering is designed specifically for each project, material, purpose and site.
Public and private commissions are undertaken in close collaboration with clients.
Projects include: a commemorative limestone panel set into green slate, Church of St Edmund the King, London; a 30m sandstone inscription set into paving, Dysart, Fife.

Commemorative limestone church panel – London

30m sandstone inscription – Dysart High Street, Fife

Bronze panel with raised lettering

Contact
Robbie Schneider
t: 01764 656071
m: 07736 669321
robbie@robbieschneider.co.uk

Web
www.robbieschneider.co.uk

Address
Robbie Schneider
West Glen Turret Farmhouse
Crieff PH7 4JR

Afilliations
Royal British Society of Sculptors
Letter Exchange
Scottish Lettercutters Association

Operational area
UK

Contact

Gary Drostle
m: 07719 529520
arts@drostle.com

Web

www.drostle.com

Address

Drostle Public Arts Ltd
F2 Old Europa Gym Centre
Europa Trading Estate
Fraser Road
Erith DA8 1QL

Affiliations

British Association for Modern Mosaics (BAMM)
International Contemporary Mosaicists (AIMC)
Society of American Mosaic Artists (SAMA)

Awards

2016 National Railways Heritage Craft Skills award
2015 Prix Picassiette, Chartres, France
2014 Mosaic of the Year, BAMM
2014 Mosaic Arts International, Houston TX
2013 Mosaic Arts International, Washington WA

Drostle Public Arts Ltd

Mosaics and murals

Gary Drostle has been producing site-specific artworks since 1985. He specialises in large-scale hand-crafted murals and mosaics, aiming to produce art that is complementary to the surrounding landscape and architecture, and that can be appreciated as modern landmarks.

• **Murals**
Mural work ranges from domestic trompe l'oeil to historical panoramas for public sites. The murals are undertaken in Keim mineral paints, artists' acrylics, enamels, buon fresco or ceramic on-glaze colours. They can be painted onto cement render, plaster, MDF panels, canvas, metal or glazed tile.

• **Mosaics**
Mosaics are usually made off site using the traditional reverse technique. Materials include handmade Venetian glass smalti, 24-carat gold smalti, vitreous glass, iridised glass, frost-proof ceramic, stone, marble or mixed media.

Sitework

Once fabricated, mosaics are installed by Gary Drostle himself and his team. All installation operatives are CSCS accredited.

Accreditation

Floor mosaics have been tested to conform to UKSRG and BS 7976-2 for slip resistance.

2008 MAI, Miami – Best Architectural Award

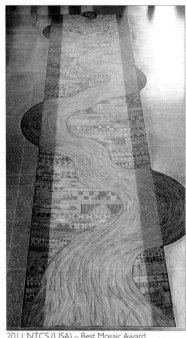

2011 NTCS (USA) – Best Mosaic Award

Gary Drostle at work – Municipal Hall, Puente Alto, Santiago, Chile

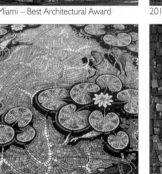

Lily Pond – Oxfordshire

Paul Robeson portrait

2016 Saxon grave mosaic – Cambridge

2016 National Railways Heritage Craft Skills Award

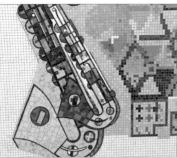

Paolozzi mosaics – Tottenham Court Road

Centaur, after Rubens, Venetian smalti

Brook Street Capers Mural – Chester

Movement & Vitality – The University of Iowa

2014 Prix Picassiette winner – Chartres, France

Kaleidoscope mosaic – Transport for London

2013 Mosaic Arts International – Best in Show

1997 Croydon Design Awards – Landscape Section winner

Contact
Diane McCormick
t: 028 8673 7008
info@dianemccormick.co.uk

Web
www.dianemccormick.co.uk

Address
Diane McCormick
16 Brookend Road
Ardboe
Dungannon BT71 5BR

Awards
Best Example of Integrating Artworks into a Building
Project 2008, NI War Museum, Belfast – Arts
Council

Operational area
UK and Ireland

Diane McCormick

Ceramics

Diane McCormick designs and creates site-specific artworks in ceramics, glass, enamel and perspex. Numerous public and private commissions have been undertaken throughout the UK and Ireland.

Design services

For healthcare environments, Diane can work in collaboration with patients, staff and visitors using poetry, words, images and photos.
Diane's work combines strong patterns with fine detail and craftsmanship.

Enamel and glass birds wall installation – NI Hospice

Ceramic design for courtyard walls – Linn Dara

Trace, porcelain artwork – Ulster Hospital

Large perspex screens – Ulster Hospital

Hawthorn perspex screen – Ulster Hospital

Contact
Helen Michie
t: 01687 470322
helenmichie@oneuk.com

Web
www.helenmichieceramics.co.uk

Address
Helen Michie
Marnoch
Roshven
Lochailort PH38 4NB

Helen Michie

Ceramic and mosaic artwork

Helen Michie designs and produces site-specific outdoor artworks for both private clients and public organisations. These include stoneware ceramic sculptures and installations, as well as mosaic wall features and sculptures.
Combining years of experience as ceramicist, community artist and Arts Co-ordinator, Helen can work with a wide range of clients to create bespoke artworks for a variety of locations and purposes.

Mosaic entranceway – Glenuig Community Hall

Sculpture commission

Interpretive mosaic – Shin Falls

Stoneware garden wall feature

Good Directions

CLOCKS · CUPOLAS · GRP STRUCTURES · WEATHERVANES · FINIALS

Contact
Sales
t: 01489 797773
sales@good-directions.co.uk

Web
www.good-directions.co.uk

Address
Good Directions Ltd
Time House
19 Hillsons Road
Botley SO30 2DY

Accreditation
ISO 9001

Country of manufacture
UK

Additional entries
Co-ordinated street furniture ➤ 309
Seats and benches ➤ 336
Litter bins ➤ 358
Planters ➤ 379

Good Directions Ltd

Exterior clocks

Good Directions is a UK manufacturer with a worldwide reputation for the design and manufacture of clock features.
Designs can include dial illumination, electronic bell chiming, bell striking, signage and company logos.

• Exterior clocks
The company produces a large range of dial designs, clock mechanisms and automated control systems.

• Bezel and projecting clocks
Single-sided bezel clocks are produced for surface mounting. Double-sided drum clocks are fitted with brackets for projecting or hanging.

• Pillar clocks
Pillar clocks are free-standing and can be co-ordinated with other street furniture.

• Clock towers
A range of GRP clock towers can be fitted with up to four exterior clocks.

• Floral clocks
Hands and mechanisms that are suitable for planted clock dials up to 5m in diameter are available. These can be used in parks and open spaces.

Four suspended clocks with colour-changing LED lighting

Bespoke square clock for tennis courts

Bespoke floral clock

George pillar clock with commemorative plaque

Big Ben replica clock for Harrods signature room

Brad Dillon Sundials

Armillary spheres and sundials

Brad Dillon Sundials has 25 years' experience in manufacturing a range of armillary spheres, walldials and horizontal sundials for public spaces and private clients.

Dials are made from bronze, brass, stainless steel and slate.

The company's experienced craftsmen use water jet cutting, laser etching, traditional engraving, traditional rivet fixing and tig welding techniques. As well as a standard product range, the company can work with customers' own designs to create site-specific products.

3m sundial – Cemetery Park, St Austell

800mm bronze armillary sphere sundial

1.2m stainless steel armillary sphere sundial – Schaeffler UK, Pontypridd, South Wales

Bronze walldial with declination lines

800mm bronze armillary sphere – Dumfries House

14" bronze horizontal dial on Haddonstone plinth

Soane Mouth of Truth Fountain

Victorian Jardiniere

Haddonstone Ltd

Garden ornament

Haddonstone Ltd manufactures ornamental and architectural stone pieces to any shape or size. The company is a founder member of the United Kingdom Cast Stone Association (UKCSA) and distributes worldwide.

Standard designs include planters, sundials, statues, fountains, garden furniture and architectural stonework. Custom designs to individual requirements are a speciality.

Materials include dry cast *Haddonstone®*, wet cast *TecStone®* and *GRC TecLite®*.

Contact
Sales
t: 01604 770711
f: 01604 770027
info@haddonstone.co.uk

Web
www.haddonstone.com

Address
Haddonstone Ltd
The Forge House
East Haddon
Northampton NN6 8DB

CPD
The history of cast stone; latest manufacturing methods; and traditional and innovative applications

Country of manufacture
UK, USA

Additional entries
Architectural cast stone ➤ 409

Self-circulating *Neapolitan Fountain* with *Pavilion* behind

Soane Caryatid statue – Chelsea 2014

Obelisk – RHS Rosemoor

Capability Brown bust

Haddonstone offers an engraving service

Art deco and cubist inspired planters

FOUNTAINS DIRECT

Contact
Nick Roberts (sales)
Gordon Murray (technical)
t: 01932 336338
nick@fountainsdirect.com
gordon@fountainsdirect.com

Web
www.fountainsdirect.com

Address
Fountains Direct Ltd
21 Trade City
Avro Way
Brooklands Business Park
Weybridge KT13 0YF

Operational area
Worldwide

Country of manufacture
UK, Germany

Additional entries
Millstone and boulder fountains ➤ 449

Fountains Direct Ltd

Fountains and water displays

Fountains Direct Ltd offers a complete service for the design, creation, installation and maintenance of all kinds of public, commercial and garden water displays.

• Design services
Fountains Direct's team of specialists combines creative CAD, technical expertise and water engineering skills, enabling the company to design turnkey projects. The company is often consulted early in the development of new projects, and can suggest design alterations that lead to cost savings and performance improvements.

• Installation services
Fountains Direct is regularly involved in the installation, commissioning and maintenance of its water features.
The company undertakes all mechanical and electrical work, as well as plumbing, GRP/metal fabrication, and waterproofing. A supervise-only installation service is also available.

• Fountain equipment
Fountains Direct uses and supplies OASE's range of European-manufactured products including nozzles, pumps, lighting, control systems and accessories.

Composition and manufacture

Equipment is manufactured from stainless steel, bronze or cast iron. Products have excellent corrosion resistance.

Projects

- Al Maryah Island, Abu Dhabi.
- Amburan Villas, Azerbaijan.
- Bangalore Airport, India.
- Western Green Spine, Qatar.
- Nwanbia Road, Uyo, Nigeria.
- Fulham Reach, London.
- Aberfeldy New Village, London.
- Bournville Village, Birmingham.
- Kew Bridge Road, London.
- One Tower Bridge, London.
- Prime Four BP, Aberdeen.
- V&A, Dundee.
- Battersea Power Station, London.

Lisburn, Northern Ireland

Milton Keynes

Sowwah Square, Abu Dhabi

Enfield Library

Williamson Square, Liverpool

Paradise Street, Liverpool

Falkirk Wheel

St Edmunds

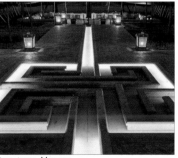

Azzaytouna, Morocco

Eurocentral, Glasgow

Fountains & Features Ltd

Water Feature Design, Installation and Maintenance

Contact
Andrew Harrison
t: 0161 870 3550
sales@fountainsandfeatures.co.uk

Web
www.fountainsandfeatures.co.uk

Address
Fountains & Features Ltd
Unit 3
Meridian Business Centre
King Street
Oldham OL8 1EZ

Operational area
Worldwide

Water features and fountains

Fountains & Features undertakes many forms of water feature including fountains, reflection pools, cascades, waterfalls, water walls, rills, jets, monoliths, plaza features, streams, formal pools, lakes and ponds. Well thought-out designs with eye-catching elements can enhance residential, commercial, municipal or private projects.

• Bespoke fountain design and installation
Fountains & Features provides a comprehensive service from concept and design to installation and handover. This includes mechanical, hydraulic and electrical aspects, as well as waterproofing, lighting, water treatment, misting, fabrication, paving and stone masonry. A design-only package is also offered, along with advice on water feature feasibility studies and concept design.

• Maintenance
An experienced team of engineers can support clients with ongoing maintenance for new and existing water features, from regular weekly or monthly maintenance visits to one-off services.

• Refurbishment and restoration
Refurbishment and restoration of water features that have fallen into disrepair is also carried out. Services include mechanical and electrical aspects, cleaning, and repair and restoration of stone and ironwork. Water treatment systems can be modernised to conform to current requirements.

Raised pool and decorative feature – Liverpool Hope University

Millstone – Aberdeen Royal Infirmary

Pool and jet feature – Battersea Reach

Plaza feature – Doncaster

Plaza feature – Redcar

Cascading rill and jet feature – Woolwich

Water wall – Fulham Reach

Water table – Farnborough Business Park

Arching fountain jets – Chelmsford

Lakes & Fountains

Fountains and water features

Lakes & Fountains specialises in the design, construction, installation and maintenance of bespoke water features for commercial sites, the public sector and private clients, including retail developments, the leisure industry, hotels, golf courses, parks, city gardens and private estates.

• Bespoke fountains and water features
The company can source any kind of fountain or water feature, including fountains, waterfalls, modern designs such as cascading pools, and sculptural water features. Materials include stone, steel, bronze and copper.

Contact
t: 07884 374995
enquiries@lakesandfountains.co.uk

Web
www.lakesandfountain.com

Address
Lakes & Fountains
The Clays
Merrydown Lane
Chineham RG24 8LU

Operational area
Worldwide

Bespoke water feature – commercial site

Water feature – private client

Lake and water feature – private estate

Fountain

Lake with water features

Illuminated fountain

Bespoke water feature

Lakes & Fountains designs, constructs, installs and maintains bespoke water features

Giles Rayner

Water sculpture

Giles Rayner creates unique high-quality water sculptures for private and commercial clients. The use of water adds energy and focus to the designs.

Work undertaken and media used

Giles specialises in metalwork including copper, bronze and stainless steel, often at a large scale, to create imaginative and timeless pieces.

Design services

Giles offers a consultative approach, including concept designs, construction, installation and maintenance.
Sculptures can vary from 1 to 12m in height. Most are bespoke but an extensive portfolio is also available to choose from.
Sculptures are created to complement the surrounding landscape and architecture.

Projects

• The Beauty of Mathematics Show Garden – RHS Chelsea 2016.
• Public commission – City of Muscat, Oman, 2016.
• Water feature – Lakeside Shopping Centre, Essex, 2016.

Contact
Giles Rayner
t: 01453 835201
m: 07989 320335
giles@gilesrayner.com

Web
www.gilesrayner.com

Address
Giles Rayner
Westend
Avening
nr Tetbury GL8 8ND

Blade bronze sculpture – Ireland

Serpent stainless steel sculpture – Scotland

Lasso stainless steel sculpture – Kent

Whirlpool copper (reinforced) sculpture – Oxfordshire

Contact
Nick Roberts (sales)
Gordon Murray (technical)
t: 01932 336338
nick@fountainsdirect.com
gordon@fountainsdirect.com

Web
www.fountainsdirect.com

Address
Fountains Direct Ltd
21 Trade City
Avro Way
Brooklands Business Park
Weybridge KT13 0YF

Operational area
Worldwide

Country of manufacture
UK, Germany

Additional entries
Fountains and water displays ➤ 444

Fountains Direct Ltd

Millstone and boulder fountains

Fountains Direct Ltd supplies millstone and boulder fountain kits.

• Millstone fountains
Millstone fountains provide attractive, relatively inexpensive features that are easy to maintain. Self-contained, the packages allow water to be introduced into an environment without the need to install space-consuming water surfaces. Externally they can be used to great effect in courtyards, patios and gardens. Internally they can be used in hotels, offices, leisure centres and hospitals to liven up foyers and entrance areas.

• Boulder fountains
Boulder fountains are similar to the millstone fountains, using a large boulder in place of a millstone. They form an attractive, self-contained feature that can be easily installed and maintained in external and internal locations in hotels, offices, leisure centres, hospitals, courtyards, patios and gardens.

Composition and manufacture
Millstones are made from aerated, lightweight concrete as standard, or in natural stone to order.
All boulders are natural stone, sourced from standard quarry stocks.

Millstone fountain – Eastleigh crematorium

Millstone kit in raised planter

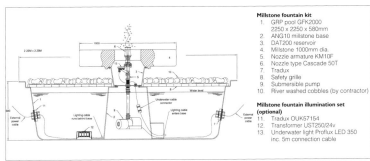

Millstone fountain kit
1. GRP pool GFK2000 2250 x 2250 x 580mm
2. ANG10 millstone base
3. DAT200 reservoir
4. Millstone 1000mm dia.
5. Nozzle armature KM10F
6. Nozzle type Cascade 50T
7. Tradux
8. Safety grille
9. Submersible pump
10. River washed cobbles (by contractor)

Millstone fountain illumination set (optional)
11. Tradux OUK57154
12. Transformer UST250/24v
13. Underwater light Proflux LED 350 inc. 5m connection cable

Drawing available from www.fountainsdirect.com as a dwg or PDF file

Boulder fountain – Bristol Parkway North

Boulder fountain

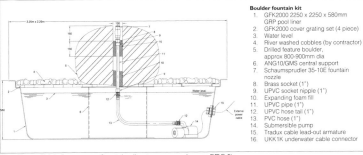

Boulder fountain kit
1. GFK2000 2250 x 2250 x 580mm GRP pool liner
2. GFK2000 cover grating set (4 piece)
3. Water level
4. River washed cobbles (by contractor)
5. Drilled feature boulder, approx 800-900mm dia
6. ANG10/GMS central support
7. Schaumsprudler 35-10E fountain nozzle
8. Brass socket (1")
9. UPVC socket nipple (1")
10. Expanding foam fill
11. UPVC pipe (1")
12. UPVC hose tail (1")
13. PVC hose (1")
14. Submersible pump
15. Tradux cable lead-out armature
16. UKK1K underwater cable connector

Drawing available from www.fountainsdirect.com as a dwg or PDF file

London Swimming Pool Company Ltd

Outdoor swimming pools and spas

The award-winning London Swimming Pool Company (LSPC) has been designing, building and refurbishing luxury pools, spas and wellness facilities for over 30 years. LSPC's portfolio includes bespoke pools built from traditional materials, and Berndorf Bäderbau's prefabricated stainless steel pool materials.

When completed, LSPC Servicing provides regular servicing and maintenance to keep clients' pools and spas in peak condition.

Contact
t: 020 8605 1255
enquiries@londonswimmingpools.com

Web
www.londonswimmingpools.com

Address
London Swimming Pool Company Ltd
Unit 1, Shannon Commercial Centre
Beverley Way, New Malden KT3 4PT

Accreditation
CHAS

Affiliations
SPATA

Awards
UK Pool & Spa Awards 2016 – Winner, Residential Indoor Pool of the Year; Gold Standard, Residential Outdoor Pool of the Year
UK Pool & Spa Awards 2015 – Energy Efficiency Award
SPATA 2015 – Gold Award, Subterranean Pool
SPATA 2015 – Gold Award, Sustainability Award
SPATA 2015 – Gold Award, Luxury Spa
SPATA 2015 – Bronze Award, Moving Floor Pool

Award-winning pool refurbishment

Berndorf Baderbäu stainless steel private pool – Vienna, Austria (photo Matthias Malpricht)

Bespoke stainless steel pool built in just a few months – Surrey

Hot and cold plunge pools – Notting Hill, London

Family pool – Berkshire

Berndorf Baderbäu private stainless steel pool – Bavaria, Germany (photo Matthias Malpricht)

RECREATION

Playgrounds   452-477

Inclusive play products to suit all abilities and educational needs.

Modular and stand-alone playground equipment in timber, metal and plastics including: multi-play towers, adventure platforms and play houses; swings, spinners, climbing nets, ladders, trampolines, roundabouts and springers; play trees and logs.

Imaginative and sensory play: outdoor musical instruments and sound sculptures; interactive activity panels; sand and water play.

Outdoor games and fitness   478-481

Multi-games areas, fitness trail equipment and outdoor gyms for communities, schools and colleges.

Ball courts, goal ends, tennis nets and table tennis tables.

Skate parks and parkour schemes.

Fitness trail equipment, workout stations and outdoor gym equipment.

Safer surfacing   482-487

Rubber wet-pour, rubber crumb, expanded polypropylene and synthetic grass surfacing for absorbing impact and minimising injury risks in recreational areas in schools, nurseries and activity parks.

Sports surfaces and equipment   488-496

Artificial sports pitches, including drainage, base construction, lighting and fencing systems for rugby, football, hockey, netball, cricket, athletics, tennis and multi-use sports pitches.

Natural grass sports pitch and cycle trail construction, including drainage and irrigation, for school, community and professional use.

Sands for the amelioration and top dressing of sports pitches, golf bunkers and equestrian arenas.

Sports equipment – goals, nets, wickets, throwing cages, long jump runs and pits; and line marking services.

Sports fencing   497-503

Perimeter fencing systems for ball courts and multi-use games areas with associated accessories including rebound boards and goal ends.

Spectator railings for sports pitches, running tracks, velodromes and viewing enclosures.

Sports shelters   504

Shelters, domes and structures for covering pitches, pools, MUGAs, coaching areas, driving ranges, outdoor gyms and grandstands.

EXTERNAL WORKS ONLINE

For detailed information supported by case studies, downloads and tools to help you make faster and better decisions ...
☞ www.externalworks.co.uk

SEE ALSO
Irrigation 506, **Turf** 507, **Grass seed** 513

Contact
t: 01483 813834
eibe@eibe.co.uk

Web
www.eibe.co.uk

Address
eibe Play Ltd
eibe House
Forsyth's Home Farm
A3 Bypass Road
Hurtmore
Surrey GU8 6AD

Accreditation
ISO 9001
ISO 14001
CHAS
Constructionline

Affiliations
Association of Play Industries (API)
International Association of Amusement Parks and Attractions (IAAPA)
International Play Association (IPA)
Federation of the European Play Industry (FEPI)
Royal Society for the Prevention of Accidents (RoSPA)

Awards
Green Apple World Ambassador 2016
Green Apple Built Environment Award
Green Apple Environmental Best Practice Award
Eagle Radio Biz Green Award

Operational area
Worldwide

eibe Play Ltd

Play equipment

Tracing its roots back to 1438, eibe Play has evolved into a contemporary, dynamic business that produces imaginative and thought-provoking play spaces for children of all ages.
Innovative play equipment and bespoke designs are offered, with product ranges manufactured from high-quality and sustainable materials.
• **Outdoor and indoor play equipment**
Standard or bespoke designs and equipment are provided for any project, from exciting outdoor spaces with pirate ships and challenging rope swings, to themed indoor adventure zones.
• **Online shop**
The entire eibe catalogue can be browsed on the company's website: www.eibe.co.uk.

Services

Services include personal advice and consultation, individual planning of each playground space to suit individual requirements, and generating both supply-only and installation quotations. Large 3D designs can be provided to showcase the potential of each project.

Projects

Projects include: Peppa Pig World®, Paultons Park; Legoland; Kew Gardens; ThomasLand®, Drayton Manor; Hootz House Pensthorpe Nature Reserve; and Southwater Country Park.

Cheltenham Borough Council – Pittville Park

Legoland Windsor Hotel

Forestry Commission – Dalby Forest

Lyme Regis Town Council – Anning Road

Rhondda Cynon Taf County Borough Council – Lido Ponty

Southampton City Council – Houndwell Park

Pensthorpe Nature Reserve – Hootz House

Amazonia – Bolton Shopping Centre

massey&harris.

Contact

David Pilgrim
t: 0161 480 5243
f: 0161 476 0151
info@masseyandharris.com

Web

www.masseyandharris.com
www.mhschools.co.uk

Address

Unit 5, The Hollygate
Albert Street
Stockport SK3 0BD

Accreditation

Working towards:
ISO 9001:2008
ISO 14001:2004
OHSAS:18001

Massey & Harris (Engineering) Ltd

Playground equipment

Massey & Harris has over 70 years' experience in producing exciting, challenging and reliable playground equipment. The company is a privately owned independent manufacturer.

• **Product range**
Massey & Harris equipment is designed and manufactured to conform to British Standards EN 1176 and 1177.
A wide range of standard products is offered including swings, play units and roundabouts. The company produces specialist steel slides for playgrounds and interiors, wheelchair accessible roundabouts and play units, and equipment for schools including outdoor classrooms.

• **Bespoke items**
Bespoke items, including architectural work and canopies, can be designed and manufactured.

Technical support

Massey & Harris provides in-house design and support from initial design ideas to 3D CAD and manufacturing data.

Projects

• 'High Five' Adventure[3] with 4.5m tunnel slide, Aberdeenshire.
• Piccadilly Gardens, Manchester city centre.
• Bramhall Hall play area, Stockport.

'High Five' Adventure[3] with 4.5m tunnel slide – Aberdeen

Gullwing seesaw

Junior goal end

Wide stainless steel slide and roll over rings

Stainless steel slide and *Tulip* spinner

Timber and steel play fort

2.2m wheelchair accessible roundabout

6m hexagonal outdoor classroom

TIPO canopy

Feature timber and stainless steel roundabout

2.5m giant spinning disc

Nessie nest swings

Bespoke stainless steel slides

Pentagonal Funtasia play unit

Oak monolith climbing walls

Football roundabout

Urban stainless steel play feature

2.5m nest swing

Stainless steel sand digger

Contact
t: 01442 265489
info@monsterplay.co.uk

Web
www.monsterplay.co.uk

Address
Monster Play @ Caloo Ltd
Unit 12, Boxted Farm
Berkhamstead Road
Hemel Hempstead HP1 2SG

Accreditation
ISO 9001:2008
CHAS
Constructionline

Operational area
UK

Additional entries
Outdoor fitness equipment ➤ 481
Safer surfacing ➤ 482

Monster Play @ Caloo Ltd

Playground equipment

Monster Play @ Caloo supplies playground equipment, ranging from traditional play to innovative new units. All equipment complies with BS EN 1176.

A range of stainless steel and aluminium equipment is available for very challenging environments.

• **Infant play equipment**

Stimulating play equipment for infants includes slides, springers and swings. Small multiplay units and themed play units encourage social interaction and development.

• **Junior play equipment**

FSC timber, recycled steel and plastic play units for young children can include climbing nets, swings, aerial runways and trampolines. Roundabouts can be DDA compliant.

• **Youth play equipment**

Skate parks, multi-use games areas, goal units and shelters are available to provide an outdoor space for teenagers.

Design services

Monster Play provides a free site survey and design service throughout the UK, including 3D illustrations and technical plans to help clients envisage their projects.

Coaster boat playhouse

Cantilever basket swing

Themed play units

Skate park

Rabbit springer

ManDDAla roundabout

Younger years play units

Music play panels

Timber trail

Play units for older children

Natural multiplay unit

Inka adventure play

Clamber Stack

Fire engine playhouse

Climbing net

Feature play unit

Innovative seesaw

Contact
Marketing
t: 0115 982 3980
marketing@proludic.co.uk

Web
www.proludic.co.uk

Address
Proludic Ltd
The Play Hub
Bradmore Business Park
Loughborough Road
Bunny
Nottingham NG11 6QA

Accreditation
ISO 9001
ISO 14001
Constructionline
CHAS
Investors in People
CPD certified

Affiliations
Association of Play Industries (API)

Metropolis themed tower

The Sand Factory

Proludic Ltd

Play and sport equipment

Proludic has 25 years' experience in the design and creation of freely accessible play and sports areas. The company's creativity, knowledge and experience enable it to propose unique and innovative design solutions to meet the needs of users and those responsible for maintaining play and sports facilities.

- **Origin multi-play equipment**
Origin is a Robinia wood multi-play and trim trail equipment range, suitable for natural settings.
- **Ixo multi-play equipment**
Ixo multi-play equipment is inspired by modern architecture and is suitable for junior age children.
- **The Sand Factory sandpit equipment**
The Sand Factory reinvents the traditional sand pit by creating modular elements that teach children the value of sand play.
- **Climbing nets**
Climbing structures allow children to test their balance, agility and co-ordination. Products are available in varying heights.
- **Trim trails**
Trim trails provide a succession of activity-based equipment that can be timed or practiced as ability levels dictate.
- **Traditional play equipment**
Traditional play equipment includes swings, slides, roundabouts and springers. Products are available in either timber or metal to suit the environment.
- **Inclusive play equipment**
Inclusive play equipment is suitable for children of all abilities. More specficially the range caters for children with autism alongside visual, hearing, motor or learning impairments.
- **Dynamic Sports equipment**
The *Dynamic Sports* range has been developed for teenagers to replicate exhilarating extreme sports like windsurfing.
- **Street Workout fitness equipment**
Street Workout urban sport equipment allows users to build muscles and practice gymnastics. Exercises can be completed on different bars, for example pull ups, dips, push ups and squats.
- **Proludic Urbanix fitness equipment**
Proludic Urbanix is innovative outdoor gym equipment that uses hydraulic pistons to offer users 8 levels of resistance for a more progressive workout.

Design services
Proludic offers bespoke design solutions where standard equipment choices are not appropriate.

Projects
- *Proludic Urbanix* outdoor gym – Kingston Road, Leatherhead.
- Bespoke inclusive multi-play ship – Markeaton Park, Derby.
- *Metropolis* themed tower and play area – Central Park, Havering.

Bespoke design – themed play equipment

Grafic Games Medieval tower

Vertical World climbing unit

Dynamic Sports – Rodeo Board

Rotating equipment – *Roll Up*

Proludic *Urbanix* stair climber

Dippy the Dolphin traditional springer

Inclusive *Talk Tubes*

Street Workout

Inclusive roundabout

Origin Robinia multi-play equipment

Trampolines

Climbing net

Traditional swings

Trim trail

Contact

Michelle Ruther
t: 0114 282 3474
f: 0114 282 3463
michelle@timberplay.com

Web
www.timberplay.com

Address
Timberplay Ltd
Aizlewoods Mill
Nursery Street
Sheffield S3 8GG

Accreditation
ISO 9001:2008
ISO 14001:2004
CHAS

Affiliations
Association of Play Industries; Constructionline

Additional entries
Play equipment ➤ 475

Timberplay Ltd

Play equipment

Timberplay Ltd supplies play equipment from Bavarian play specialists Richter Spielgeräte GmbH for children of all ages and abilities. The equipment is suitable for parks, playgrounds, leisure attractions, schools, community spaces and shopping centres.

Timberplay's Landscape Design department can work with landscape architects to create play spaces to meet site-specific requirements. Timberplay uses timber from sustainable sources.

• Combination structures

Combination structures can be designed to suit any application. Large towers, platforms and huts can be combined with swings, slides, inclined nets, bridges, ladders, balancing beams, ramps, ropes, fireman's poles or climbing trunks.

• Adventure play

An extensive adventure play range includes giant *Pyramid Towers* that can be used to create focal points in adventure play areas. Cableways, high-energy swings, roundabouts and rockers deliver challenges for children across a wide age range. Bespoke *Climbing Forests*, huge climbing structures and the *Timberwood Tangle* stimulate older children. Trim trail options include *Totter Beams*, rotating balance beams, *Jumping Discs*, balancing ropes, seesaws and boats.

• Sand and water play

Steel playground pumps and troughs can be mixed with water channels, dams and water wheels to create distinctive sand and water play combinations. *AQuadrat* is a standalone combination of pumps, channels and dams. The *Forest Fountain* comprises pumps and vertical timbers with different spray heads and is particularly popular during warmer months.

• Teen play

Teen play equipment promotes group play and friendly competition, offering older children more of a challenge and creating social meeting spaces. Products include the *Queen Swing*, tractor tyre swings, balancing ropes, climbing walls, climbing structures and meeting and hang-out shelters.

• Bespoke play

Bespoke play is particularly suitable within leisure attractions. However, sometimes specific play themes can be detrimental to the play value. Timberplay can work closely with designers and managers to create equipment that does not compromise on play value.

Projects

• 'Children's Wonderland' Princess Diana Memorial Playground, Kensington Gardens.
• Little Wormwood Scrubs, Dalgano Gardens, London.
• Heartlands, Redruth, Cornwall.
• Tumbling Bay play area, Queen Elizabeth Olympic Park.
• Jubilee Gardens, London.

Timber play house

Sand and water play with the *Forest Fountain*

A variety of pumps engage and delight children

Climbing structures offer a range of physical and imaginative play opportunities, and encourage interaction

Seesaw carousel play equipment for teenagers

Climbing Forests encourage exciting and challenging physical activity

The high-energy *Queen Swing* at Victoria Park, London

Water play provides stimulation for all children

Water play allows children to interact

Sand and water play is perfect for younger children

Contact
t: 01933 665151
enquiries@timotayplayscapes.co.uk

Web
www.timotayplayscapes.co.uk

Address
Timotay Playscapes
14 Hinwick Road
Wollaston NN29 7QT

Accreditation
ISO 9001
ISO 14001

Affiliations
Association of Play Industries (API)
Register of Play Inspectors International Ltd (RPII)
Royal Society for the Prevention of Accidents (RoSPA)
Association of Professional Landscapers (APL)
British Association of Landscape Industries (BALI)
Contractors Health & Safety Assessment Scheme (CHAS)

Awards
Best Community Garden Winner – Association of Professional Landscapers Awards 2016

Operational area
UK

Additional entries
Landscaping services ➤ 51

Timotay Playscapes
Playground equipment

Established in 1985, Timotay Playscapes manufactures award-winning educational, bespoke and engaging playgrounds and playground equipment. Applications include family attractions, community play areas, schools, nurseries and SEN settings.
The company can design and build bespoke playgrounds specifically for children with special needs. Projects have included early years settings, nurseries and children hospitals. Gardens can feature tactile surfacing, sensory zones, shades, orientation signage, and sensory planting.

Composition and manufacture
All of Timotay Playscapes' play equipment is manufactured in the UK from FSC timbers. The company only uses sustainable materials.

Accreditation
All play equipment is safety tested and complies with BS EN 1176.

Services provided
Timotay Playscapes works with clients to tailor solutions to their briefs and objectives. The company's services range from consultation, through to bespoke play products created by experienced playground designers, to installation.

Play equipment is made from FSC timber

Illustration of small play area

FSC timber outdoor classroom for primary school

Water play area

Play equipment can be created to suit available space

Play equipment is made to clients' briefs

Winner of APL 2016 Best Community Garden – Kings Hedges School, Cambridge

Play equipment complies with BS EN 1176

Key stage 1 play equipment

Cycle track with bridge – Kings Hedges School

Bespoke play area

Bespoke playground for primary school

Visualisations of play areas are provided

Contact
Stuart Wetherell (Sales Director)
t: 01536 517028
sales@wicksteed.co.uk

Web
www.wicksteed.co.uk

Address
Wicksteed Playgrounds
Digby Street
Kettering NN16 8YJ

Accreditation
ISO 9001:2008 – FM 01642
ISO 14001:2004 – EMS 544458
CHAS, CCS, Constructionline
Exor (Services) Ltd – Gold – AH1461
SMAS

Affiliations
Association of Play Industries (API)
SAPCA – Principal Contractor

Additional entries
Bespoke play equipment ➤ 476

Wicksteed Playgrounds

Playground equipment

Wicksteed Playgrounds has almost 100 years' experience in the design, manufacture and installation of play and sports products. The company's service ranges from supplying standalone units to designing entire landscaped sites incorporating fully bespoke play elements.

• **Play products**
Wicksteed's range of play equipment is very broad, and includes products suitable for children aged as young as 3 up to more physically challenging units for teenagers and adults.
Several multiplay ranges are available, on a variety of themes, including castles, forests and jungles, pirates and space. They include products made primarily in timber or metal.
Various types of slide, roundabout and swing are available, as well as musical, sand and water play products. Complementary furniture, shelters, fencing, gates and signage are also available.

• **Sports equipment**
Sport and fitness equipment includes *Fitness Legacy Zone*, a professionally developed range for teenagers and adults from 14 years upwards. Other products include the *Fantasy Funrun* and *Xerscape* fitness equipment ranges, high-level and low-level timber fitness trails, as well as MUGAs, goal ends and skate park units.

XS modular play system, with low-level chill-out areas and more challenging elements – Cann Hall Park

Fitness Legacy Zone – Shaftesbury Rec Ground

Crusader rope end swing

Hurricane Swing with button seats – Waltham Forest

Castle-themed multiplay unit – Crathes

Large *Fitness Legacy Zone* outdoor gym area – Sandwell Valley, West Bromwich

King Kong multiplay unit for toddlers

Inclusive *Swirl Roundabout* – Highams Park, London

Gwydyr multiplay structure from the *Forest* range – Ryton Pools Country Park

Twin *Tree House* units – St Thomas C of E School

Memory Swing

Complete play scheme – Bannerfield Park, Selkirk

Bespoke mound with stepping logs, tunnels and slides – Emslie Horniman's Pleasance park, London

Young Explorer multiplay unit – Mewsbrook Park

Bespoke mound with slide – Walton Hall Park

Acoustic Arts

Outdoor musical instruments and sound sculptures

Acoustic Arts offers a range of high-quality outdoor instruments and bespoke musical sculptures for educational, recreational and therapeutic settings.

The robust timber and steel constructions are hand-built and tuned by UK craftsmen.

The interactive designs are accessible to all abilities and promote social and physical interaction.

Products are BS EN 1176 compliant.

Contact
John Walls
t: 0117 935 2034
info@acousticarts.org.uk

Web
www.acousticarts.org.uk

Address
Acoustic Arts
The Old Laundry
Kingswood Estate
Bristol BS15 8DB

Country of manufacture
UK

Bell Drum

Frame Chimes and Pipe Drums

Bespoke music area for children with autism – Prior's Court School, Berkshire

Spiral Scraper

Tone Wheel

Bespoke xylophone sculpture – Horniman Museum, London

Contact
t: 01308 425100
sales@hucknetting.co.uk

Web
www.huck-net.co.uk

Address
Huck Nets (UK) Ltd
Gore Cross Business Park
Corbin Way
Bradpole
Bridport DT6 3UX

Accreditation
ISO 9001:2008

Affiliations
Association of Play Industries (API)
Federation of Sport and Play (FSPA)

Additional trading names
Huck Play
HuckTek
All Play Ireland
Edwards Sports Products
William James

Huck Nets (UK) Ltd

Rope play equipment

Huck Nets offers a diverse range of rope play
equipment that can be used to create adventure
play landscapes. The products are found in
schools, nurseries, parks, public playgrounds and
day care centres around the UK. They are
designed and manufactured by Huck Seiltechnik
in Germany.

• Rope play equipment

Products include rope pyramids, group swings,
jungle bridges, climbing nets and trampolines that
are suitable for all ages and abilities, including
special educational needs.

The *Spider* series of rope climbing pyramids have
a central steel pole and either 4, 6 or 8 guy lines.
The largest is 8.3m high.

The *Black Forest* range includes the *Double Birds
Nest Tower*. It sits over 6.5m high and is suitable
for large play areas. It features a connecting
bridge, climbing nets, slides, climbing ladders and
net tunnels.

Design services

A dedicated team is available for the design and
installation of new playgrounds, and can create
the best possible play experience at a particular
site. With their child-focused approach they
ensure that schemes are innovative, educational,
challenging, stimulating, age-appropriate and fun.

Cheops Pyramid Maxi

Long Swing Frame in Douglas fir

Spider 6-rope climbing pyramid

Trampoline 2000

Dragon Rope End Swinger

Quad Toddler Swing

Mini M Swing nest seat

Black Forest Tower Duo

Contact

Edinburgh Office
t: 0131 445 7989

Nottingham Office
t: 0115 969 9859

info@jupiterplay.co.uk

Web

www.jupiterplay.co.uk

Address

Edinburgh Office
Jupiter Play & Leisure Ltd
14 Swanston Steading
109 Swanston Road
Edinburgh EH10 7DS

Nottingham Office
23 Rectory Road
West Bridgford
Nottingham NG2 6BE

Awards

Nancy Ovens Trust
Street Design Awards 2011 – Highly Commended
Innovation in Playground Design 2015 – Best
Bespoke Outdoor Playground Equipment Award

Operational area

UK

Accreditation

ISO 9001:2008
CHAS
Constructionline
SMAS Workplace

Affiliations

Association of Play Industries (API)

Jupiter Play & Leisure Ltd

Design-led play spaces

Jupiter Play is an independent play and sport design consultancy. The company supplies innovative outdoor equipment brands from around the world.

Innovation is a core value of the company, supporting new designers and technologies in the play and sport industry, with the aim of inspiring people of all ages to be active and make the most of their community spaces.

Product range

The Jupiter Play range is extensive with brands being represented under 6 core themes: Interactive, Inclusion, Nature, Urban, Active and Bespoke. Whether the requirement is for a soft design aesthetic requiring natural materials, such as robinia or oak, or a more urban setting with steel products, there is a very wide selection to choose from. Examples include bespoke robinia play equipment, MUGAs and gyms, inclusive design and the interactive products like the *Sutu* football wall or *Fono* DJ booth.

Design services

The design team can advise on how to develop a sport or play project, without the constraints of being tied to one brand of equipment. Full bespoke design services are offered, allowing any playground idea to be made into reality.

FHS *Mikado Tower*

Galopin *Ecopark* nature trail

Galopin *Little Facades FAC04*

Bespoke FHS ship – Hudson Way, Taunton Deane

Inclusive Play *IP21 Lollipop*

Yalp *Sutu Interactive* football wall

Galopin *Scienta Water Play*

Galopin *Cubic Multi Play*

Learning Through Play

Contact
Roy Nicholls
t: 01474 569576
info@learningthroughplay.net

Web
www.learningthroughplay.net

Address
Learning Through Play
Hartshill Nursery, Thong Lane
Shorne, Gravesend DA12 4AD

Accreditation
CHAS, Constructionline, Exor

Affiliations
British Association of Landscape Industries (BALI)

Operational area
London, South East England

Additional entries
Landscape services ➤ 48

Bespoke playgrounds

Learning Through Play, a division of Baylis Landscape Contractors, provides a bespoke design and build playground service for schools and nurseries. Projects are undertaken within London and South East England, to extend curricula learning from inside the classroom to outside.
Natural and long-lasting materials are used to create unique themed learning and play experiences. Products are independently inspected for safety on completion.

Work undertaken

All aspects of the external playground environment are catered for. Easily managed packages can include fencing and gates, artificial grass and rubber surfaces for games and play areas, play equipment and features, outdoor class rooms, amphitheatres and shade structures.

Consultation

Learning Through Play works closely with clients to create designs that realise their vision. Projects frequently involve collaboration with pupils and teachers, from concept to installation, to make the whole project a learning experience.

Adventure Zone

Adventure Fort

Problem-solving stream

Talk Tube and den-making *Tee Pees*

Music Zone

Forest School

Mini sports pitch

Adventure Island

Adventure Mine – interior

Contact
Robert Wilkins
t: 01277 849990
f: 01277 849991
robertw@ruskins.co.uk

Web
www.ruskins.co.uk

Address
Ruskins Trees and Landscapes Ltd
The Rose Garden, Warley Street,
Great Warley, Brentwood CM13 3JH

Accreditation
ISO 9001:2008, ISO 14001:2004,
OHAS 18001:2007, CHAS

Affiliations
British Association of Landscape Industries (BALI)

Additional entries
Tree and hedge moving ➤ 530
Tree root investigation ➤ 532
Tree and shrub supply and planting ➤ 541

Ruskins Trees and Landscapes

Play trees and logs

Ruskins supplies and installs tree trunks and logs
for natural playgrounds and recreational areas.
• **Natural climbing structures**
Whole trees and trunks with major branches can
be supplied and installed to create natural
climbing structures, with holds added as required.
• **Stepping logs and balance beams**
Trunks, logs and large branches with etched
surfaces to reduce slipperiness are supplied and
installed to create stepping logs, log rings and
balancing beams.

Materials

Play trees and play logs are of durable hardwood,
primarily oak and sweet chestnut, and need not
be treated. They can be supplied with bark or
with bark removed.
Selections can be made from a large reserve to
suit client and site requirements.
All play trees and play logs are sourced from
sustainable sources in England.

Installation

Ruskins is expert at handling large trees and
locating trees into areas with difficult access.

Operational area

Projects are undertaken throughout the UK.

Play tree in-situ – Ruskins is expert at handing large trees and locating trees into areas with difficult access

Balance beams with etched surfaces

Natural play logs for creative play

Climbing logs for vertical insertion and adding of holds

Stepping log with etched surface to reduce slip risk

Enhanced cobweb of play trees

Vertical play trees

Adventure Play Equipment

Contact
Jonathan Bhowmick
t: 01462 817538
jonathan@setterplay.co.uk

Web
www.setterplay.co.uk

Address
Setter Play Equipment
Unit 6A
Shefford Mill
Stanford Road
Shefford SG17 5NR

Accreditation
ISO 9001:2008
CHAS

Affiliations
Association of Play Industries (API)

Additional entries
Shelters and canopies ➤ 386

Setter Play Equipment

Play equipment

Setter is a family-run business producing adventure play equipment for nurseries, schools and recreation grounds.

Modular play equipment ranges from low-level adventure trail units to tower systems.

Units incorporate platforms that can be reached by mini rock walls, wobble bridges, monkey bars, nets and rope ladders, together with slides, poles, steps and ramps.

Individual items of play equipment can also be provided, as well as seating and shelters.

Fair Bear single tower unit

Super Spiffy non-prescriptive climber

A castle can be used to create a focal point at the top of a mound

Custom *Timber Tree House* multi-play unit

Klink three-tower unit

SOVEREIGN
Bringing imagination into play

Contact
Darran Hine, Sales Director
t: 01702 291129
f: 01702 290092
info@sovereign.gb.com

Web
www.sovereignplayequipment.co.uk

Address
Sovereign Design Play Systems Ltd
40 Towerfield Road
Shoeburyness
Southend-on Sea SS3 9QT

Staff/turnover
80 people

Accreditation
ISO 14001
ISO 9001
Constructionline
Contractors Health & Safety Assessment Scheme
(CHAS)
Forest Stewardship Council (FSC)

Affiliations
Register of Play Inspectors International (RPII)
TÜV Rheinland UK
British Holiday & Home Parks Association

Operational area
UK

Country of manufacture
UK

Sovereign Design Play Systems

Imaginative outdoor play areas

Sovereign has completed over 10,000 outdoor play area installations for schools, councils, and commercial and private clients across the UK. The company delivers the whole package, from design and manufacture to installation and aftersales support. It designs play equipment and facilities for children of all ages, ensuring the highest level of safety with maximum play value. All materials come from sustainable sources and meet with the relevant guidelines.

Sovereign offers a free, no-obligation, consultancy and design service to show what can be achieved.

Colourful toadstools provide seating for younger children

Play ships encourage interactive play

Colourful pencils break up school playgrounds

Trail equipment aids balance and co-ordination

Play towers encourage interactive play

Activity panels can be installed in grass or tarmac

Play towers and mounds encourage interactive play

Shades provide shelter throughout the year

Multi-use games areas (MUGAs) are suitable for netball, cricket, hockey, basketball and football

Playground markings encourage imaginative play

Contact

Andrew Lofting
t: 01227 463606
t: 0800 803 0038
info@ssp-uk.co.uk

Web
www.ssp-uk.co.uk

Address
SSP. Specialised Sports Products Ltd
Unit 3, Heppington Barn
Street End/Faussett Hill
Lower Hardes
Canterbury CT4 7AL

Affiliations
Sport and Play Contractors Association (SAPCA)

Operational area
UK

Additional entries
Safer surfacing ➤ 486

SSP. Specialised Sports Products Ltd

Playground equipment and services

SSP. Specialised Sports Products consults with school teachers, PTAs, councils, architects and construction companies to provide play facilities. An extensive range of play equipment for all ages is available, as well as sun shades, permanent and portable sports enclosures, playground marking in numerous colours and designs, fencing, and safety and sports surfacing.

A turnkey service is offered throughout the UK from groundworks through to completion.

Tower climbing frame

Climbing wall and *Mezzo Clamber Stack* climbing frame installed on artificial surfacing

Clamber Stack Midi climbing frame

Wet pour surfacing in school playground

Play mound with slide and underground tunnel

Play equipment is available for all age groups

Climbing frame with net

Contact

Sales/technical
t: 01977 653200
f: 01977 653222
info@sutcliffeplay.co.uk

Scotland
Joe Duffy, Sutcliffe Play Scotland
t: 01382 562351
f: 01382 561590
info@sutcliffeplayscotland.co.uk

North & South East England
Sutcliffe Play Ltd
t: 01977 653200
f: 01977 653222
info@sutcliffeplay.co.uk

South West England
Roy Allcock, Sutcliffe Play South West
t: 01202 621528
f: 01202 621538
sales@sutcliffeplaysw.co.uk

Ireland
Brian McKee, All Play
t: 028 9756 5129
f: 028 9756 1915
sales@all-play.com

Web
www.sutcliffeplay.co.uk

Address
Sutcliffe Play Ltd
Waggon Lane
Upton
Pontefract WF9 1JS

Accreditation
ISO 9001:2000
ISO 14001:2004
Investors in People
BS 4800
EN 1176

Affiliations
Association of Play Industries (API)
Federation of the European Play Industry (FEPI)
Royal Society for the Prevention of Accidents
(RoSPA)

Operational area
Worldwide

Country of manufacture
UK

Sutcliffe Play Ltd

Play equipment

Sutcliffe Play Ltd is an international supplier of child-centred, design-led playground equipment, and is committed to improving the quality of children's play. A British manufacturer, and employee owned, the company offers equipment that is designed to be challenging and allows children to take risks in a safe environment. Sutcliffe offers a complete package, from free consultation and site survey through to design, landscaping, supply and installation, as well as inspection and maintenance.

• **Inclusive play**
Sutcliffe Play is an industry leader in designing equipment for children of all abilities, not just the able-bodied. The company's inclusive designs allow children of all abilities to play together on the same playground equipment.

• **Snug**
Snug is an innovative approach to play equipment, which changes the psychology of the playground. It consists of a family of large-scale, modular play elements that children can use separately or together in any combination, creating a dynamic, exciting playscape where they can have fun, explore and learn. Teachers can also use *Snug* as a creative learning resource across the curriculum. Requiring no installation, the *Snug* elements are soft, tactile, durable and waterproof.

Orchard timber range

Snug playground equipment

Themed play range

Inclusive playground equipment

Essentials Oyster Roundabout

Pod Youth Shelter

Timberplay Ltd

Play equipment

Contact
Michelle Ruther
t: 0114 282 3474
f: 0114 282 3463
michelle@timberplay.com

Web
www.timberplay.com

Address
Timberplay Ltd
Aizlewoods Mill
Nursery Street
Sheffield S3 8GG

Accreditation
ISO 9001:2008
ISO 14001:2004
CHAS

Affiliations
Association of Play Industries; Constructionline

Additional entries
Play equipment ➤ 460

Timberplay Ltd supplies play equipment from the pioneering Bavarian play specialists Richter Spielgeräte GmbH for children of all ages and abilities. The equipment is suitable for parks, playgrounds, leisure attractions, schools, community spaces, hospitals and shopping centres. Timberplay only uses timber from sustainable sources.

• **Early years play**
Early years play equipment includes *Stroking Animal Stones*, the *Swinging Horse*, *Dwarf Castle*, the *Duck Family, Tractor and Trailer, Standing and Resting Sheep* and the *Peter Horse and Cart*. Small, two-storey and combination play structures are also available.

• **Acoustic play**
Acoustic play products include *Sound Cushions* and *Dance Chimes*, which let children create tuneful melodies through play. *Sound Rollers* and *Musical Path* create a pleasant acoustic backdrop for any play area.

• **Inclusive play (special needs)**
Inclusive play equipment is specifically designed to accommodate wheelchair users and children with sensory impairment. Wheelchair seesaws and carousels are suitable for children with physical limitations and can also be used by children with other special needs.

Sound Cushions

Developing co-ordination with *Balance Blocks*

Stone Xylophone helps to develop the senses

Wind Pipes

Rotating Discs create optical illusion patterns

Playing with the senses with *Scent Organ*

Contact

Stuart Wetherell (Sales Director)
t: 01536 517028
sales@wicksteed.co.uk

Web

www.wicksteed.co.uk

Address

Wicksteed Playgrounds
Digby Street
Kettering NN16 8YJ

Accreditation

ISO 9001:2008 – FM 01642
ISO 14001:2004 – EMS 544458
CHAS, CCS, Constructionline
Exor (Services) Ltd – Gold – AH1461
SMAS

Affiliations

Association of Play Industries (API)
SAPCA – Principal Contractor

Additional entries

Playground equipment ➤ 464

Wicksteed Playgrounds

Bespoke play equipment

Wicksteed Playgrounds has almost 100 years' experience in the design, manufacture and installation of play and sports products.

Design services

Wicksteed's expertise includes the creativity to design complete new schemes and create entire landscaped play sites. Bespoke elements can be added to most of the standard products. Free consultation is offered prior to any job.

Bespoke dragon head slide and climber – Cambridgeshire

Bespoke shark's head – Fishersgate Rec, Worthing

Bespoke dragon head slide – Cambridge

Treetops Tower – Walton Hall Park, Warrington

Bespoke galleon play structure – Oban

Bespoke net and slides – Calderglen Country Park

Bespoke toddler multiplay unit with gnomes motifs

Bespoke *Young Explorer* multiplay unit

M&M Timber Ltd

PlayGuard playground timber

M&M Timber is a leading supplier of playground timber with over 30 years' experience in sourcing, manufacturing and supplying products. *PlayGuard* timber delivers an innovative natural solution for playgrounds, educational and leisure applications. It is suitable for a wide range of venues including schools, play areas, parks and sports zones.

Palisade fencing manufactured using UK sourced pine is available for securing play areas.

Composition and manufacture

PlayGuard is manufactured using high quality Radiata pine which has inherent low-split properties. It is kiln-dried and pressure-treated with *Tanalith E* wood preservative for durability and long service life.

Accreditation

M&M Timber hold a WPA Benchmark Certificate to offer *PlayGuard 15* for 15 years desired service life. For bespoke projects the option of a 30-year warranty is available.

Services

As well as a standard range of *PlayGuard* playground timber, a bespoke service is available for companies who design and build custom-made play equipment.

Contact
Sales Team
t: 0333 003 5133
sales@mmtimber.co.uk

Web
www.mmtimber.co.uk

Address
M&M Timber Ltd
Hunt House Sawmills
Clows Top
Nr Kidderminster DY14 9HY

Affiliations
BALI

Additional entries
Unilog Pro retaining walls ➤ 41

Play equipment built with *PlayGuard* timber

Play equipment built with *PlayGuard* timber

Bespoke service available for play equipment companies

Case Studies

Premium Paving & Flagstones at Greystones Marina

The challenge was to transform Greystones Harbour into a vibrant community focal point, offering not just a social amenity to residents but also a tourist attraction...

aG acheson + glover

External seating for Myatts Field regeneration

Awarded best regeneration project for the second year running at the London Evening Standard New Homes Award, the £174M Myatts Field North regeneration scheme...

Furnitubes

Find solutions

Find out how experts can help you tackle your challenges and bring added value to your projects by reading their case studies.
There's a wealth of experience and expertise to tap into on the EXTERNAL WORKS website ...

EW INDEX **EXTERNAL WORKS**
better decisions for better environments

👉 **www.externalworks.co.uk**

AMV Playground Solutions

Outdoor sports and playground equipment

AMV Playground Solutions has been designing, manufacturing and installing vandal-resistant outdoor sports and playground equipment for over 30 years.

The company's experienced product design and projects team can work alongside architects, contractors and local authorities to create solutions to suit any age group, ability or budget.

Product range

Products include multi-sport goal units, multi-use games areas (MUGAs), activity trim trails, netball and basketball posts, outdoor table tennis, steel tennis nets, outdoor fitness equipment, climbing walls and a range of playground equipment. Bespoke canopies and shelters are also produced.

Accreditation

Steel structures are certified to BS EN 1090.

Installation

AMV offers a UK-wide installation service. The company can also provide associated markings, artificial grass and safety surfacing on the projects it delivers.

Contact
t: 01704 740323
f: 01704 895392
sales@amvplaygrounds.co.uk

Web
www.amvplaygrounds.co.uk

Address
AMV Playground Solutions
Unit D
Abbey Lane Enterprise Park
Abbey Lane
Burscough L40 7SR

Accreditation
CHAS
Constructionline
ISO 9001:2008

Operational area
UK

Multi-use games area (MUGA) goals and fencing

Playground shelters and markings

Steel tennis nets and multi-sport goal

Clear traverse climbing wall

Heavy-duty outdoor table tennis

Fitness trail equipment

Vandal-resistant steel trim trail

Ball court for school

Park Leisure

Sports and play equipment

Park Leisure specialises in steel ball courts, skate park equipment, parkour schemes and urban play equipment. The company's plant in Kent allows for short lead times, customisation of products and fully bespoke solutions.

• **MUGAs/ball courts**

3 specifications are available.

Sport Zone is a heavy-duty ball court fitted with an industry-leading noise reduction system to minimise sound, and a mesh formation that offers a true rebound.

Game Zone is a mid-range hybrid ball court. It offers a mix of heavy-duty *Sport Zone* panels and lighter duty *Play Zone* super rebound panels.

Play Zone ball courts are suitable for projects with lower budgets that do not require a high specification, while still offering high strength and sound-dampening fixings.

• **Parkour schemes**

Concrete and heavy-duty steel are used to achieve durable urban designs.

• **Skate equipment**

Urban Ramps skate park equipment is made entirely from heavy duty steel and is extremely durable, flexible and robust.

• **Play equipment**

A range of steel play equipment includes the *Kidabout* wheelchair accessible roundabout.

Contact
t: 01233 840141
enquiries@parkleisure.com

Web
www.parkleisure.com

Address
Park Leisure Ltd
Pivington Mill
Pluckley
Ashford TN27 0PG

Accreditation
ISO 9001
ISO 14001

Affiliations
CHAS
SMAS

Operational area
UK, International

Country of manufacture
UK

Ball court for school

Ball court

Parkour scheme

Skate park

Contact

t: 01296 614448
info@safeandsoundplaygrounds.co.uk

Web
www.safeandsoundplaygrounds.co.uk

Address
Safe and Sound Playgrounds
Unit 9A, Triangle Business Park
Wendover Road
Stoke Mandeville HP22 5BL

Accreditation
CHAS

Affiliations
RoSPA
SAPCA

Operational area
UK

Safe & Sound Playgrounds

Multi-use games areas (MUGAs)

Safe & Sound Playgrounds' multi-use games areas are built to withstand years of repeated high impact use and comply with BS EN 15312. They can be built to virtually any size and specification. Surfaces can be tarmac, synthetic turf or polymeric. Polymeric surfaces provide a resilient, all-weather surface with excellent grip and a high degree of absorbency, reducing the risk of injury. Individual sport pitches and courts can be marked out. Gates can be positioned anywhere around the perimeter. MUGAs are made from hot-dip galvanised steel and are powder-coated.

Multi-use games area

Optional basketball hoops can be included

Goal units are available in a range of colours

A range of fencing options is offered

Individual goal unit

Multi-use games areas can be customised for the space available

Contact

t: 01442 265489
info@caloo.co.uk

Web

www.caloo.co.uk

Address

Caloo Ltd
Unit 12, Boxted Farm
Berkhamstead Road
Hemel Hempstead HP1 2SG

Accreditation

ISO 9001:2008
CHAS
Constructionline

Operational area

UK

Additional entries

Playground equipment ➤ 456
Safer surfacing ➤ 482

Caloo Ltd

Outdoor fitness equipment

Caloo has over 20 years' experience in supplying outdoor fitness equipment to schools, councils and other organisations.

Products include outdoor gyms, multi-active games areas, skate parks and table tennis tables.

• Outdoor gym equipment

Outdoor gym equipment is available in bundles or as individual units. Equipment is designed to extend exercise opportunities to the wider community. A range of calisthenics street workout units is also available.

• Multi-active games areas

Multi-active games areas can transform outdoor activity areas. Durable and flexible, they provide multiple activities built in and around a single structure. Pre-configured designs are available, or bundles can be custom-built for specific sites.

• Table tennis tables

Table tennis tables have rounded corners that comply with health and safety standards worldwide. Anti-glare surfaces and a robust build ensure that tables stay resistant to vandalism and environmental factors.

Accreditation

Outdoor gyms include products independently certified by TÜV SÜD to BS EN 16630.

Education Outdoor Gym Bundle

Outdoor gym equipment is available in different colours

Slim Diabolo table tennis table with rounded corners

Rider individual gym unit

Community outdoor gym bundle

5-panel multi-active games area

Calisthenics street workout units

www.caloo.co.uk

Contact
t: 01442 265489
info@caloo.co.uk

Web
www.caloo.co.uk

Address
Caloo Ltd
Unit 12, Boxted Farm
Berkhamstead Road
Hemel Hempstead HP1 2SG

Accreditation
ISO 9001:2008
CHAS
Constructionline

Operational area
UK

Additional entries
Playground equipment ➤ 456
Outdoor fitness equipment ➤ 481

Caloo Ltd

Safer surfacing
Caloo offers safer surfacing to suit all requirements that is BS EN 1177 certified. The company is experienced in the installation of surfacing in playgrounds, multi-use games areas (MUGAs) and recreational areas.

Product range
- Bonded rubber mulch.
- Grassmats.
- Acrylic coating.
- SuDS bonded surfacing.
- Synthetic grass.
- Resin bound gravel.
- Thermoplastic line markings.
- Play surface markings.
- Wet pour surfacing.
- Edging and pathways.

Design services
Caloo works with clients to help find the most appropriate surfacing for specific project requirements and budgets. This includes assessing free-fall heights, and advising on surfacing options including colours, dependent on the surfacing selected and technical specifications.

Installation
Caloo installs safer surfacing systems throughout the UK.

Colourful wet pour play surfacing in playground

Grassmats installed in playground

Bonded rubber mulch in play area

Bonded rubber mulch

Synthetic grass

Wet pour surfacing can be used to create colourful games in playgrounds

Resin bound gravel

Wet pour surfacing

Synthetic grass for outdoor fitness area

Acrylic coating on multi-use games area

Acrylic coatings installed at athletics track and games area

Grassmats

SuDS bonded drainage solution

nottssport////:
Synthetic Surfacing

Contact
t: 01455 883730
f: 01455 883755
info@nottssport.com

Web
www.nottssport.com

Address
Notts Sport Ltd
Innovation House
Magna Park
Lutterworth LE17 4XH

Accreditation
England Hockey Official Facilities Partner
ECB Approved Pitch Supplier
ECB Code of Conduct
ICC Development Programme Europe Official Partner

Operational area
Europe, North America, Asia

Additional entries
Artificial sports surfaces ➤ 490

Notts Sport Ltd

Safer surfacing: ChildsPlay®

Notts Sport Ltd has over 30 years' experience in designing, supplying and advising upon artificial surfaces. The company can provide surfaces for a number of different activity areas, from children's playgrounds to sports pitches and tennis courts. *ChildsPlay®* safer surfacing not only protects children, but also plays an important role in enhancing the design and overall appearance of play areas. A range of standard surface designs is offered, or bespoke designs can be created. *ChildsPlay®* systems suit a range of environments, from slip-resistant, mud-free recreational areas through to under climbing frames, swings and other equipment. Systems offer critical fall height protection of up to 3m.

• **ChildsPlay® Active synthetic turf system**
The exclusive *ChildsPlay® Active* system combines opportunities for sport, play and education in a single space. It provides a multi-purpose outdoor classroom that will not overstretch budgets. The system is designed to stimulate learning, meeting elements of Upper Foundation Stages and Key Stages 1 and 2 through imaginative free play, as well as supporting structured activities.

Composition and manufacture
Unique *NottsBase® EPP* tiles provide a specialist base layer that can be used in some *ChildsPlay®* systems. Tiles are moulded from expanded polypropylene (EPP), and have an array of hemispheres on the underside, which provides better dispersal of impact energy than flat tiles.

Finish and appearance
ChildsPlay® surfaces can incorporate a large range of colours. These can be used to denote zones for formal or free play, mark out areas suitable for children of different ages and abilities, create paths and circuits, or create patterns and games.

Installation and maintenance
ChildsPlay® is a versatile surfacing system that can be installed over existing asphalt, concrete, soil or stone. It is suitable for use on flat surfaces, or over irregular mounds or slopes.

Colourful design for children's play area

Educational mat

Children's play area

Designs stimulate learning

Sports pitch

ChildsPlay® safer surfacing

Kickabout area

playrite
Specialist
Surfaces for Sport and Leisure

Contact
Chris Pickles
t: 01924 412488
cpickles@playrite.co.uk

Web
www.playrite.co.uk

Address
Playrite
Wellington Mills
Liversedge WF15 7FH

Accreditation
ISO 9001; ISO 14001

Affiliations
Sports & Play Construction Association (SAPCA)

Operational area
Worldwide

Country of manufacture
UK

Additional entries
Artificial sports surfaces ➤ 491

Playrite
Playground safety surfacing

Playsafe is an impact-absorbing playground safety system that is manufactured in the UK.
Five levels of critical fall height provide the right levels of safety for installed play equipment. With surfacing suitable for early years through to key stages 1 and 2, *Playsafe* systems can be specified to suit specific needs and budgets without compromising on safety.

Product range
• **Playsafe 12 surfacing**
Critical fall height up to 120cm.
Suitable for early years level children.
• **Playsafe 17 surfacing**
Critical fall height up to 170cm.
Suitable for foundation level children.
• **Playsafe 20 surfacing**
Critical fall height up to 200cm.
Suitable for key stage 1 children (age 5–7).
• **Playsafe 27 surfacing**
Critical fall height up to 270cm.
For high equipment including swings and slides.
Suitable for key stage 2 children (age 8–11).
• **Playsafe 30 surfacing**
Critical fall height up to 300cm.
For under high climbing frames and tower units.
Suitable for key stage 2 children onwards.

Finish and appearance
Playsafe systems are completed with *Matchwinner Velour* – a low maintenance, vandal resistant, sand-dressed top surface.
The range is available in 14 bright colours: Yellow, Green, Sporting Green, Autumn Green, Red, Burgundy, Ochre, Lavender, Marine, Navy, Black, Terracotta, Orange and Platinum Grey.
Vibrant designs with educational shapes and patterns can be created using laser cutting technology.

Accreditation
Playsafe surfaces are tested to BS EN 1177 standards.

Playsafe impact-absorbing playground safety system

Vibrant designs with educational shapes and patterns

Playsafe critical fall heights: 1.2, 1.7, 2.0, 2.7, 3.0m

Nearlygrass artificial grass for landscaping

Playsafe surfaces are completed with *Matchwinner Velour*, a low maintenance, sand-dressed top surface

Playsafe is available in 14 bright colours

SPECIALISED SPORTS PRODUCTS

SSP. Specialised Sports Products Ltd

Safer surfacing

SSP. Specialised Sports Products Ltd advises upon, designs and supplies outdoor play, safety and sports surfaces for children.

SSP Wet Pour Rubber dual layer, porous surfacing has an EPDM rubber wearing course and is used in playgrounds and sports facilities. A choice of colours and thicknesses is available.

SSP Artificial Grass simulates natural turf and is suitable for-all weather play and sports surfaces. A shockpad underlay offers impact absorbency.

Contact
Andrew Lofting
t: 01227 463606
t: 0800 803 0038
info@ssp-uk.co.uk

Web
www.ssp-uk.co.uk

Address
SSP. Specialised Sports Products Ltd
Unit 3, Heppington Barn
Street End/Faussett Hill
Lower Hardes
Canterbury CT4 7AL

Affiliations
Sport and Play Contractors Association (SAPCA)

Operational area
UK

Additional entries
Playground equipment and services ➤ 473

Wet pour surface with games

Artificial grass surfacing

Wet pour sports surface

Wet pour surface

Pop up Olympics sports court, London

Multi-use games area surfacing

Wet pour rubber rainbow surface

TVS Play Surfaces

Shock-absorbent safety surfacing

TVS Play Surfaces, part of the TVS Group, specialises in impact protection systems for playgrounds and multi-sports areas.

• **Impact protection for playgrounds**

Impact protection tiles are made from recycled rubber bonded with polyurethane elastomer. Critical fall height is determined by the Head Injury Criteria (HIC) method and tiles are compliant with impact protection standards EN 1177:2008 and ASTM F 1292:2009.

Tiles are highly resilient, unharmed by weathering and cost-effective to install. The tiles are suitable for under outdoor playground equipment for fall heights from 0.6–3.0m eg under swings, climbing frames, tree-houses, see-saws and slides, as well as beneath outdoor fitness equipment. Adjacent tiles are inter-connected with pre-inserted pins ensuring the surface remains safe and secure.

• **Surfacing systems for multi-sports areas**

Sports pavement slabs have excellent abrasion resistance and outstanding ball rebound properties conforming to DIN 18032 Part 2. High elasticity provides cushioning for ligaments and joints. Successful applications include paved areas for football, basketball, street hockey, volleyball and generation-spanning activity parks.

Contact
Jason Lewis-Lamb
t: 01706 260220
f: 01706 260240
jason@tvs-group.co.uk

Web
www.TVS-Group.co.uk

Address
TVS Group
Low Bay
Commerce Street
Carrs Industrial Estate
Haslingden
Rossendale BB4 5JT

Operational area
International

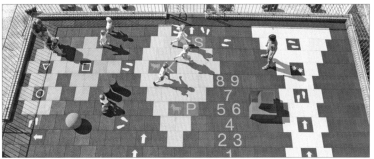

Customisable impact protection tiles are suitable for any size or shape of playground equipment

Tiles require no heavy mixing machinery or paving units and can be installed in any area

Tiles can be used to create colourful and unique designs for play areas

Sports surfacing can be used for multi-use games areas, and tiles can be installed in play areas

Tiles in play park

Modular tiles are easy to install

Contact

Amanda Banks
t: 01642 488328
a.banks@cls-headoffice.co.uk

Web
www.cleveland-land-services.co.uk

Address
CLS Sports
Park Farm
Dunsdale
Guisborough TS14 6RQ

Accreditation
ISO 9001:2008, Investors in People, CHAS,
Constructionline

Affiliations
SAPCA
LDCA
IOG
Sport England Framework Partners

Additional entries
Natural sports field construction ➤ 493

CLS Sports

Sport England endorsed all-weather sports facilities

CLS Sports is a division of Cleveland Land Services Ltd and provides a complete in-house service for the design, construction and maintenance of all-weather sports facilities.

Design services
CLS Sports advises clients on the correct system depending on the sporting use. Each synthetic grass surface has its own specific design criteria and construction system, cost and playing characteristics.

Construction services
Finished surfaces are laid by in-house teams, who also provide all supporting services – earth moving, drainage, base construction, floodlighting and fencing. Laser-controlled equipment ensures that surfaces are installed to design parameters.

Maintenance services
CLS sports carries out maintenance work to ensure the safety of synthetic sports and play surfaces, retaining quality and appearance, and prolonging life.
Work is undertaken on all types of surfaces, including full-size synthetic turf sports pitches and cricket wickets, macadam MUGAs and tennis courts, and polymeric sport and play surfaces.

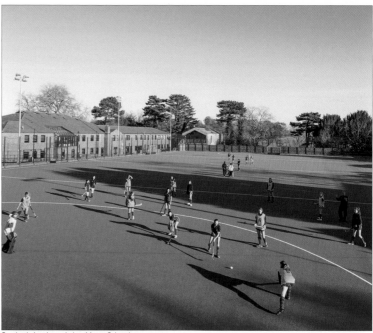

Synthetic hockey pitch – Yarm School

Synthetic hockey pitch built to FIH standards

Synthetic football pitch

Synthetic hockey pitch and MUGA with cricket practice nets – Yarm School

3G synthetic pitch – Consett Football Club

Macadam MUGA – Kettlethorpe High School

10-bay synthetic cricket wicket training facility

Hunter Construction (Aberdeen) Ltd

Artificial sports surfaces

Hunter Construction, formed in 1972, is a specialist in the design, construction and management of synthetic sports surfacing. Surfaces range from third generation FIFA- and IRB-compliant football and rugby pitches, to FIH approved hockey surfaces and polymeric running tracks.

Accreditation

The company operates systems with compliance to ISO 9001:2015 and ISO 14001:2015.

Technical support

Hunter Construction's experienced and professionally qualified staff offer support with budget costing, the preparation of business cases, and the specification of appropriate and durable sports surface solutions.

The company manages all stages of a project including planning, statutory consents, geotechnical studies, design and on-site delivery. Advice can be provided on all ancillary project aspects such as floodlighting and fencing.

Installation and maintenance

Projects are undertaken throughout Scotland. A full aftercare, planned and preventative maintenance and renovation service is available.

Contact
Mark Oakley
t: 01467 627290
f: 01467 625791
mark.oakley@hunter-construction.co.uk

Web
www.hunter-construction.co.uk

Address
Hunter Construction (Aberdeen) Ltd
Centaur House
Camiestone Road
Thainstone Business Park
Inverurie AB51 5GT

Accreditation
ISO 9001:2015
ISO 14001:2015
Achilles BuildingConfidence
Constructionline
ConstructionSkills
Contractors Health and Safety Scheme (CHAS)

Affliations
Civil Engineering Contractors Association (CECA)
Sports and Play Construction Association (SAPCA)

Operational area
Scotland and Northern England

Synthetic pitch – Forfar Athletic FC stadium

Tennis court installation

Running track – Aberdeen Sports Village

Running track installation – Greenock

3G synthetic pitch

Synthetic pitch installation

Laser controlled paver

Synthetic pitch – Mineralwell Park, Stonehaven

Installation in progress

nottssport///:
Synthetic Surfacing

Contact
t: 01455 883730
f: 01455 883755
info@nottssport.com

Web
www.nottssport.com

Address
Notts Sport Ltd
Innovation House
Magna Park
Lutterworth LE17 4XH

Accreditation
England Hockey Official Facilities Partner
ECB Approved Pitch Supplier
ECB Code of Conduct
ICC Development Programme Europe Official Partner

Operational area
Europe, North America, Asia

Additional entries
Safer surfacing: ChildsPlay® ➤ 484

Notts Sport Ltd

Artificial sports surfaces

Notts Sport Ltd has 30 years' experience in designing, supplying and advising on artificial surfaces. Activity areas range from sports pitches to children's play areas. The company has worked with sports associations, local authorities, universities, schools and clubs.

- **Hockey surfaces**

Notts Sport is the only Official Facilities Partner and Official Club Weekend Partner of England Hockey. A wide range of IHF (International Hockey Federation) compliant pitches are available via the company's manufacturing partners. A comprehensive choice of solutions can be tailored to meet each customer's individual requirements for new build, conversion and refurbishment projects.

- **Multi-sports surfaces**

VHAF® NottsSward® 1300 turf carpet is suitable for sports such as football, tennis, hockey and basketball. It provides a comfortable and consistent surface for players of all ages and standards of play. It is attractive, durable, vandal resistant and provides rapid drainage.

- **Cricket pitches**

Artificial cricket pitches and practice lanes are used for matchplay and coaching. They are suitable for all ages and standards. Four products are ECB approved.

The exclusive *PowerPlay Instant Cricket Mat* can be used on almost any existing artificial turf surface. It opens up opportunities for all year round play for clubs and schools in urban areas.

- **Fast Track Funding initiative**

The company's unique initiative arranges funding for artificial sports surfacing projects. Clients repay funding over 5 or 7 years via an operating lease agreement. Notts Sport works at risk to secure all consents and to put funding in place.

Synthetic multi-sports pitch

Hockey pitch

Multi-sports pitch

PowerPlay Instant Cricket Mat

Cricket pitch

Cricket pitch

3G football pitch

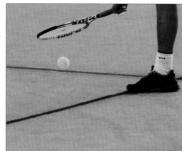
Multi-sports pitch

Hockey pitch

Contact
Chris Pickles
t: 01924 412488
cpickles@playrite.co.uk

Web
www.playrite.co.uk

Address
Playrite
Wellington Mills
Liversedge WF15 7FH

Accreditation
ISO 9001
ISO 14001

Affiliations
Sports & Play Construction Association (SAPCA)
Institute of Groundsmanship (IOG)

Operational area
Worldwide

Additional entries
Playground safety surfacing ➤ 485

Playrite

Artificial sports surfaces

Playrite has manufactured high quality synthetic surfaces for schools and sports clubs since 1991. Specific ranges are manufactured for: multi-use games areas; football, hockey and rugby pitches; tennis courts; netball courts; cricket surfaces; and bowling greens.

- **Multi-use games areas**

Four highly accredited surfaces are available that are suitable for a wide range of sports and extracurricular activities.

- **Football**

Conqueror 3G surfaces offer exceptional ball bounce and roll characteristics, a high level of ball control, and maximum comfort underfoot.

Composition and manufacture

Products are formulated for specific sports applications in a variety of grades to suit performance and budgetary requirements. Playrite is the only UK manufacturer of needlepunch, woven and tufted synthetic turf surfaces. All products come with manufacturer and UV warranties.

Accreditation

Products conform to BS EN 15330. Many have been accredited to FIH and International Tennis Federation standards, as well as the IATS FIFA 1 star equivalent.

Playrite manufactures four premium grade MUGA surfacing systems for a wide range of sports

Playrite surfaces conform to BS EN15330

Conqueror

Conqueror

Conqueror

Matchplay 2 has a high porosity rating, ITF pace rating 3, and meets AENA national netball standards

Conqueror

Verde Sports (Cricket) Ltd

Synthetic turf cricket facilities

Verde Sports supplies and fits synthetic turf systems for cricket facilities. These give schools, local authorities and clubs lower maintenance surfaces than conventional pitches, and offer safe, consistent performance. Two types of base design are offered, both approved by the ECB.

• Test Match base design

Test Match systems have a hard porous aggregate laid over a consolidated stone base. This gives the pitch playing characteristics that alter with the climate and the compaction of the base. Rolling compacts the base to increase pace and bounce, while watering softens it to achieve the opposite effect. A geotextile lining and *AP10 Shockpad* reduce maintenance and improve longevity.

• Premier base design

Premier systems have factory formed underlays laid over a stone base. These spreads the load, minimising variations in base compaction and increasing ball bounce. They limit the effects of changes in climate, and provide high consistency.

Design services

Verde Sports draws on the 30 years' experience of its director Peter Dury. A former ECB non-turf pitch consultant, Peter advises on the design of new facilities and renovation of existing pitches.

Contact
Peter Dury
t: 0115 846 5732
verdesports.cricket@ntlworld.com

Web
www.verdesportscricket.com

Address
Verde Sports (Cricket) Ltd
Gabbotts Farm Barn
Bury Lane
Withnell
Chorley PR6 9SW

Accreditation
England and Wales Cricket Board (ECB) Approved
Pitch System Supplier for Test Match and Premier

Synthetic turf systems for cricket facilities

Match pitch facility

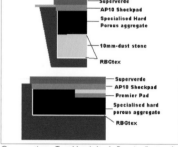
Cross-sections: *Test Match* (top); *Premier* (bottom)

CLS Sports

Natural sports field construction

CLS Sports, a division of Cleveland Land Services Ltd, offers a complete design and build package for natural sports and amenity areas. The service covers all aspects of construction, drainage, attenuation, irrigation and maintenance, and is tailored to suit the client's budget.

Design services

CLS Sports designs natural playing surfaces that are tailored to each sport's specific needs. Schemes can range in size from a single pitch to a multi-pitch sports complex.
Drainage systems are designed to ensure that a playing surface remains in best condition.

Construction services

Following site survey and clearance, finished surfaces are laid by in-house teams. In the case of amenity/sport areas, grass is sown using seed drills developed specifically for sports fields. CLS has invested in drainage equipment and is able to carry out both primary and secondary drainage to precise standards.

Maintenance services

Specialist equipment can be used to improve pitches that have deteriorated, including surface renovation, vertidraining and top dressing. Regular maintenance schedules are also offered.

Contact
Amanda Banks
t: 01642 488328
a.banks@cls-headoffice.co.uk

Web
www.cleveland-land-services.co.uk

Address
CLS Sports
Park Farm, Dunsdale
Guisborough TS14 6RQ

Accreditation
ISO 9001:2008, Investors in People, CHAS, Constructionline

Affiliations
SAPCA, LDCA, IOG
Sport England Framework Partners for 'the design and construction of artificial sports surfaces'

Additional entries
Sport England endorsed all-weather sports facilities
➤ 488

Multi-tiered pitch construction – Russell Foster Football Centre

Rockliffe Hall training pitches, Middlesborough FC

Drainage installation – South Shields Football Club

Mastenbroek sports drainage chain trencher

Installation of sand slits using Koro topdrain

Spreading root zone – Mowden Park, Darlington RFC

Installing deep sand slits

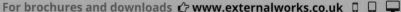

Contact

Richard Ward
t: 01277 890274
f: 01277 890322
richardward@hughpearl.co.uk

Web

www.hughpearl.co.uk

Address

Hugh Pearl (Land Drainage) Ltd
New Farm
Bobbingworth
Ongar CM5 0DJ

Accreditation

ISO 9001:2008, Constructionline, CHAS

Affiliations

Land Drainage Contractors Association, Institute of
Groundsmanship, RSPB, Essex Wildlife Trust

Additional entries

Lakes and watercourses ➤ 47

Hugh Pearl (Land Drainage) Ltd

Natural sports field construction

With 60 years' experience, Hugh Pearl's team can undertake the construction, refurbishment and maintenance of natural sports pitches. Hard and soft landscaping, track, path, cycle and mountain bike trail installation services are also provided. Clients include local authorities, sports clubs, schools and colleges and private individuals.
The company has in-house earth moving and levelling machinery, laser controlled trenchers and a full range of ancillary sports turf equipment for sand slitting, sand banding, verti-draining, sand top-dressing, seeding and fertilising operations.

New playing field construction

Sand slitting at Twickenham Stadium

Sand banding for London Borough of Barnet

Mountain bike trails at Hadleigh Country Park

Mastenbroek 10/12D *Sportsfield* trencher on Wanstead Flats

Patersons Quarries Ltd

Contact
Sales
t: 01236 433351
f: 01236 425172
sales@patersonsquarries.co.uk

Web
www.patersonsquarries.co.uk

Address
Patersons of Greenoakhill Ltd
Gartsherrie Road
Coatbridge ML5 2EU

Accreditation
ISO 9001:2000

Affiliations
Concrete Block Association (CBA)
Concrete Society
Freight Transport Association (FTA)
Quarry Products Association (QPA)

Fife Silica Sands (a division of Patersons of Greenoakhill Ltd)

Sand

Fife Silica Sands extracts flint silica sand from Burrowine Moor Quarry near Alloa for container glass production. The company also offers specialist sands for both horticultural and sports applications. The FS9 grade of sand (1mm–0.125micron) is widely used in soil amelioration, top dressing and bunkers. Fife Silica also produces an outdoor and indoor equestrian arena sand. Due to their cleanliness, both sands are also suitable for use in children's play areas.

Flint silica sand from Burrowine Moor Quarry, Alloa

Equestrian arena sand

Flint silica sand used in a playground

Golf course application

Contact

Julie Brewster (sales)
t: 01635 867537
f: 01635 864588
julie@sportsmark.net

Mike Pocklington (technical)
t: 01635 867537
f: 01635 864588
mike@sportsmark.net

Web
www.sportsmark.net

Address
Sportsmark™ Group Ltd
18 St Georges Place
Semington
Trowbridge BA14 6GB

Additional entries
Road studs and markings ➤ 132

Sportsmark™ Group Ltd

Sports equipment

Established over 50 years ago, Sportsmark™ Group supplies premium-quality equipment for all kinds of sports.

The majority of products supplied are UK manufactured. They include goals, nets, cricket wickets and cages, training equipment, boot-wipers, and groundsman's equipment.

• Installation and construction

Whilst Sportsmark™ can install most types of equipment, when it comes to construction the company's expert crews concentrate on a focused number of areas.

These are: bowling green construction and refurbishment; cricket wickets and cages; long jump run-ups and pits; throwing cages; and sports hall fit-outs.

• Court marking

Sportsmark™ has over 50 years' experience in marking sports courts.

These services can be carried out indoors in sports halls, or outdoors on playgrounds and ball courts.

The company also offers a full tennis court cleaning, colour coating and line painting service.

Throwing cages

Cricket wickets and cages

Long jump run-ups and pits

Sports court marking

Contact

t: 01709 763410
sales@vicasl.co.uk

Web
www.vicasl.co.uk

Address
Vica SL Ltd
Aizlewood Mill
Nursery Street
Sheffield S3 8GG

Accreditation
Constructionline
CHAS

Country of manufacture
UK

Additional entries
Sports fencing ➤ 503

Vica SL Ltd

Goal ends

Vica SL produces a range of goal ends with a 25-year guarantee.

The *Heavy Duty Goal* and *Ball Wall* are ideal for unmanaged parks, or areas that are susceptible to vandalism and heavy usage.

The *School Goal* and *School Goal End* are designed specifically for schools. They feature a small goal and a reduced height basketball hoop. Target panels make it a competitive game for children. Steel is hot dip galvanised to EN ISO 1461 and powder-coated to BS EN 13438:2013.

3m square *Heavy Duty Goal*

School Goal is available in any RAL colour

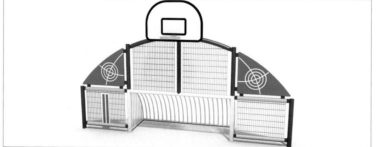
School Goal End with ball target panels

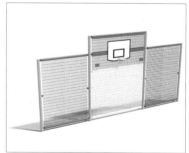
Ball Wall with heavy-duty noise reduction panels

Contact
Adam Savage
t: 01782 319264
f: 01782 599724
sales@barkersfencing.com

Web
www.barkersfencing.com

Address
Barkers Engineering Ltd
Etna Works
Duke Street
Fenton
Stoke-on-Trent ST4 3NS

Accreditation
ISO 9001:2000

Additional entries
Mesh fencing systems ➤ 166
Railings ➤ 177
Steel palisade fencing ➤ 181
High-security fencing systems ➤ 185
Sliding gates and swing gates ➤ 200

Barkers Fencing

Sports fencing

Barkers Fencing manufactures rigid mesh sports fencing systems for low and medium impact uses. Typical applications include multi-use games areas (MUGAs), football pitches, rugby pitches, hockey pitches, tennis courts and skate parks.
• **Sports Bronze fencing**
Sports Bronze is designed for use in schools, urban sports grounds, health clubs and professional sports environments.
• **Sports Bronze Rebound fencing**
Sports Bronze Rebound has a 1.2m integrated rebound panel with extra horizontal double wires at the bottom to cope with heavy use football and hockey applications.
• **Goal ends**
Barkers manufactures standard and bespoke goal ends and recesses. Products are available powder coated in different colours to highlight goal ends.
• **Sports equipment and accessories**
A full range of high quality sports equipment is offered, including: basketball hoops and boards; tennis posts and nets; five-a-side and full size football goals; badminton posts and nets; volleyball posts and nets; netball hoops and posts; trampolines; and other products.

Sports Bronze MUGA system

Sports Bronze Rebound fencing

Sports Bronze Rebound fencing

Goal end with basketball hoop

CLD Fencing Systems

CLD
Fencing
Systems

Contact
Specification Department
t: 01270 764751
f: 01270 757503
info@cld-fencing.com

Web
www.cld-fencing.com

Address
CLD Fencing Systems
Unit 11, Springvale Business Centre
Millbuck Way
Sandbach CW11 3HY

Accreditation
ISO 9001:2008
LPS 1175
Secured by Design
NBS
BIM

Additional entries
General purpose fencing ➤ 168
Security fencing systems ➤ 169
UniGril rigid fencing systems ➤ 170
Zoological fencing systems ➤ 171
Bespoke laser-cut fencing ➤ 172
Stone Fence™ walling systems ➤ 172
Gates and access control systems ➤ 201
Sports Rail™ spectator fencing ➤ 499

Perimeter fencing systems for sports pitches and MUGAs

CLD manufactures steel rigid mesh and double wire panel fencing systems for sports pitches and multi-use games areas. Systems are available in heights up to 6m for professional, amenity and school sports facilities.

Dulok Rebound™ has dense double steel wire panels that absorb the shock of small or large balls and return them to play.

Polypropylene mesh *Ballstop Netting™* is used to extend fence heights to improve ball retention, particularly with the *Dulok Sports™* system.

Securus SR1 fencing – Etihad training complex

Dulok Rebound™ double wire sports panel fencing system for multi-use game areas

Rigid weld mesh panels at sports facility

Corporate and advertising banners on sports pitch rigid welded mesh perimeter fence

Polypropylene mesh *Ballstop Netting™*

Dulok Rebound™ double wire panel fencing system

Dulok Sports™ double wire panel fencing system

Fencing protects school play area

Contact

Specification Department
t: 01270 764751
f: 01270 757503
info@cld-fencing.com

Web
www.cld-fencing.com

Address
CLD Fencing Systems
Unit 11, Springvale Business Centre
Millbuck Way
Sandbach CW11 3HY

Accreditation
ISO 9001:2008
LPS 1175
Secured by Design
NBS
BIM

Additional entries
General purpose fencing ➤ 168
Security fencing systems ➤ 169
UniGril rigid fencing systems ➤ 170
Zoological fencing systems ➤ 171
Bespoke laser-cut fencing ➤ 172
Stone Fence™ walling systems ➤ 172
Gates and access control systems ➤ 201
Perimeter fencing systems for sports pitches and MUGAs ➤ 498

CLD Fencing Systems

Sports Rail™ spectator fencing

Sports Rail™ is a steel tubular handrail system used to protect players and spectators around the perimeter of running tracks, velodromes, school playgrounds, football, rugby and hockey pitches, and spectator enclosures.
• Quick and easy clamp system.
• Standard heights: 990, 1190, 1390mm.
• Choice of flat or profiled welded mesh infill.
• Solid panels for messaging and advertising.
• Polyester powder coated as standard.
• Standard colours: Green RAL 6005 and Black RAL 9005; full range of RAL colours available.

Sports Rail™ spectator railings – velodrome, York

Sports Rail™ spectator railings with flat mesh panel infill

Sports Rail™ spectator railings with infill – Manchester FC Etihad Training Complex

Sports Rail™ spectator railings

Railings around spectator enclosure

Sports Rail™ spectator railings – Brighton Velodrome

ZAUN

Contact
Steve Roberts
t: 01902 796696
sales@zaun.co.uk

Web
www.zaun.co.uk

Address
Zaun Ltd
Steel Drive
Wolverhampton WV10 9ED

Accreditation
ISO 9001:2008, Secured by Design, CHAS

Affiliations
FCA, UVDB, PSSA, Constructionline

Additional entries
Perimeter fencing ➤ 164
Architectural fencing ➤ 173
Railings ➤ 175
Security fencing ➤ 182
DBS acoustic fencing system ➤ 198
Gates and access control ➤ 211

Zaun Ltd

Sports fencing systems

Zaun manufactures a wide range of sports fencing suitable for schools, colleges and sporting facilities. The company specialises in the production of customised systems for particular requirements.

• **Multi-use games fencing**
Colosseum multi-use games courts include football and basketball playing areas and are designed for playability and safety in different sports. They have an attractive, functional curved design.
Sports Barn is a covered multi-use games area that is playable in all weathers and provides a safe, secure environment.

• **Ball court fencing**
Ball court fencing is constructed with a twin-wire welded mesh, resulting in good vandal resistance and through-visibility.

• **Wire mesh rebound panels**
Wire mesh panels are an alternative to traditional wooden boards. They are vandal resistant, give good visibility and are less noisy during play.

• **Hockey fencing**
Hockey fencing uses mesh to replace wooden boards, resulting in a cheaper and quieter system.

• **Tennis fencing**
Advantage Tennis is a double-wire mesh panel system with apertures that are designed to ensure a tennis ball cannot pass through.

Cranked top extensions for enhanced ball retention

Rebound panels – an alternative to wooden boards

Transition panels

Zaun sports fencing clad with *Duo* mesh in one single height 3m panel

Hockey fencing has an all-in-one panel construction

Colosseum goal ends

Goal/basketball unit

Hi-Sec can feature bespoke images/messages

Multisport fencing with curved corner panels

Sports Barn multi-use games areas provide indoor conditions for outdoor sports

Junior Goal basketball/goal unit

Recessed goal with over-panel and basketball hoop

Spectator rails

Colosseum multi-use games area fencing

Laser-cut shapes can be incorporated

Radiused corner unit

Rubber inserts minimise noise

Contact

Chris Boskandji/Kevin O'Grady
t: 01302 364551
heras.sales@herasuk.co.uk

Web
www.herasuk.co.uk

Address
Heras UK Fencing Systems
Herons Way
Carr Hill
Doncaster DN4 8WA

Accreditation
ISO 9001:2008
Constructionline
UVDB Standard

Additional entries
Perimeter mesh fencing and gates ➤ 167
Self-adjusting railing systems ➤ 180
High-security perimeter protection ➤ 186
Gates and entrance control ➤ 209

Heras UK Fencing Systems

Sports fencing and MUGAs

Heras UK Fencing Systems offers specialist fencing systems for use with multisports courts.

• Sports fencing systems
Systems can be made solely from standard *Pallas* welded mesh panels, or can incorporate *Multimesh* rebound panels at the bottom section. *Multimesh* panels are designed to withstand impact and provide a uniform bounce. This makes them ideal for sports applications, particularly hockey, football and basketball. Where a fence divides two courts, panels can be fitted to both sides of the posts, providing a rebound surface for each court.

• Accessories
For hockey applications, a timber board can be fitted to the bottom of the fence to provide additional protection. FA goal recesses, radius corners and basketball hoops are available, as well as spectator railing and gates.

Dimensions

The overall fence may be 3, 4 or 5m high, and the height can be varied around the court. For example, the height may be 3m around the sides, rising to 5m behind each goal.
Single gates are normally 1.2m wide and 2m high, and double gates are normally 3m wide and 3m high.

Radius corner

Multimesh ball court with height change

Multimesh ball court with double skin

Multimesh ball court with kickboards

3D single pitch

FA goal recess with *Pallas* sports mesh

Spectator rail and double skinned *Pallas* sports mesh

Contact
t: 01709 763410
sales@vicasl.co.uk

Web
www.vicasl.co.uk

Address
Vica SL Ltd
Aizlewood Mill
Nursery Street
Sheffield S3 8GG

Accreditation
Constructionline
CHAS

Country of manufacture
UK

Additional entries
Goal ends ➤ 496

Vica SL Ltd

Sports fencing

Vica SL produces a range of fencing systems specifically for sports applications.

• **Primary fencing system**
Primary has an adapted 868 panel with a solid flat bar replacing the end wire, increasing the panel rigidity. Durable, laser-cut, noise-absorbing fixing lugs with circular tubes make the system more visually appealing. It has a 6-year guarantee.

• **Premier fencing system**
Premier has an adapted 868 panel with the same modifications as *Primary*. In addition it has strainer tubes along the top and bottom of each panel and larger posts, making it resilient against heavy use and vandalism. It has a 12-year guarantee.

• **Elite fencing system**
Elite is a heavy-duty system most suited to unmanaged public spaces and is completely different to 868 fencing. It is a flat bar system with twisted bar giving it very high rigidity and strength. Heavy-duty posts and strainer tubes make the system extremely vandal-proof. It has a 30-year guarantee.

Independent noise tests show that Vica's systems are 50% quieter than standard 868 fencing. All systems are hot dip galvanised to EN ISO 1461 by an ISO 9001 certified galvaniser and powder-coated to BS EN 13438:2013. They are available in any RAL colour and panel size.

Sports fencing is available in any RAL colour and panel size

Sports fencing with basketball hoop

Sports fencing with goal end and basketball hoop

Sports fencing with integrated goal end and basketball hoop

Sports fencing is galvanised and powder-coated

Contact
David Ruffell
Business Development Manager
t: 0117 370 7710
david@rocklyn.co.uk

Web
www.rocklynsports.co.uk

Address
Rocklyn Sports
Dirac Crescent
Bristol & Bath Science Park
Emersons Green, Bristol BS16 7FR

Accreditation
ISO 9001:2008
OHSAS 18001:2010
SafeContractor
Constructionline
CE Marking

Additional entries
Cycle parking ➤ 251
Shelters, canopies and covered walkways ➤ 393

Rocklyn Sports

Sports shelters

Rocklyn Sports is a leading manufacturer and supplier of sports equipment. Clients include sports clubs and councils in the UK and Ireland.
• **Standard products**
Standard products include air domes, multi-use games areas (MUGAs), sports shelters, permanent sports structures, sports surfacing, outdoor gym equipment and grandstand seating.
• **Bespoke products**
The company utilises 3D design capabilities and the skills of its designers and fabricators to create custom-made products to clients' requirements.

Air Dome over tennis courts

Permanent structure over swimming pool

Driving Range golf shelter

Boundary MUGA with permanent sports cover

Covered MUGA

Troop dug-out shelter

Permanent sports structure

Air Dome – Castlebar Tennis Club

Aurora cycle shelter

SOFTSCAPE

Irrigation   506
Irrigation for playing fields, racecourses, amenity landscapes, parks and gardens.

Turf growers   507-512
Cultivated turf for landscape and sports applications including big roll systems.

Grass seed specialists   513-516
Grass seed for amenity areas, fine landscape areas, specific types of sports pitch, golf courses, road verges, shaded sites, coastal locations and wildflower meadows.
Slow-release fertilisers and root growth stimulants.

Wildflowers   517-519
Pre-seeded wildflower matting; wildflower turf; wildflower plugs, bulbs and seed mixes for river banks, hedgerows, coastal areas and meadows.

Mulches and root barriers   520
Rubber mulches for playgrounds, pathways and gardens.
Root barriers for suppressing weeds and containing tree roots.

Urban tree care   521-529
Urban tree planting systems. Root bridges for existing trees, geocellular structural cells for new tree planting, structural tree soil, irrigation and ventilation systems.
Tree grilles, tree guards and permeable tree pit paving.
Tree anchoring, rootball fixing, root protection and irrigation systems.

Arboricultural services   530-532
Tree planting, moving and aftercare. Tree and vegetation clearance.
Air spade and tree root investigation services.

Trees, hedging and topiary   533-543
Trees – standard, specimen, semi-mature and unusual forms. Hedging and topiary.

Shrubs and climbers   543-545
Shrubs and climbers for amenity and landscape projects.

Herbaceous perennials   546-548
Container-grown herbaceous plants for rapid impact. Sedum ground cover matting.

Aquatic plants   549
Wetland plants, marginals, water lillies and oxygenators.

Hardy exotics   550
Hardy exotics in contrasting foliage sizes and textures.

EXTERNAL WORKS ONLINE

For detailed information supported by case studies, downloads and tools to help you make faster and better decisions ...
☞ www.externalworks.co.uk

Contact
t: 01903 278240
f: 01903 278245
info@ttirrigation.co.uk

Web
www.ttirrigation.co.uk

Address
Topturf Irrigation
Unit L, Rudford Industrial Estate
Ford
Arundel BN18 0BF

Awards
Hunter Trailblazer Award
Otterbine Contractor of the Year 2006–2010;
2012–2015

Operational area
UK

Topturf Irrigation

Irrigation

Topturf Irrigation is a family-run company that has become one of the leading irrigation companies in the UK and Europe.

• Irrigation systems

Working to the highest industry standards, the company specialises in design, supply and build of irrigation systems. Topturf's skilled engineers operate four fully-stocked vans to provide service support for new and existing irrigation systems.

• Pumping plant systems

Topturf can also design, build and supply single and multi-pump plant systems utilising *Lowara* and *Grundfos* pumps with *Aqualectra* controls. In addition, full service and repair support is provided for all types of pumping plant.

Projects

Topturf offers bespoke services throughout the UK, and has also completed projects in Europe and Africa. Clients range from private landowners to large multi-nationals in a variety of industries, including:

• Golf courses
• Sports stadia
• Racecourses
• Parks and gardens
• Business and retail parks
• Recreational facilities

Lythe Hill Hotel and Spa

Private garden

Pressure gauge

Southampton Football Club

Pump set – AELTCC

Old Thorns Golf and Country Club

Otterbine Equinox aerator with lights

Contact
Chris Carr
t: 0800 061 2805
f: 01842 827911
chris@harrowdenturf.co.uk

Web
www.harrowdenturf.co.uk

Address
Harrowden Turf Ltd
Corkway Drove
Hockwold
Thetford IP26 4JR

Affiliations
British Association of Landscape Industries (BALI)
Turfgrass Growers Association (TGA)

Operational area
England, Wales, Scotland

Additional entries
MeadowMat wildflower matting ➤ 517
Enviromat sedum matting ➤ 546

Harrowden Turf Ltd
Cultivated turf

Harrowden Turf is one of the largest producers of amenity turfgrass in the UK.

The company delivers competitively priced landscape supplies, including turf, lawn feeds, seeds and lawn soil/top dressings, all across the UK mainland.

Two grades of turf are available:

Premier is a hard-wearing ryegrass mix grown to TGA standard. It establishes quickly into any well prepared soil and forms a beautiful verdant lawn.

Standard is a basic-quality turf best suited to budget and commercial applications.

Premier cultivated turf

Standard cultivated turf

Premier turf being installed in big roll format

Forms a beautiful verdant lawn

County Turf Ltd

Turf growers

County Turf produces turf for sports and landscaping projects across the UK and Europe. It also holds the UK and European licence for the hybrid systems of *Eclipse Stabilised Turf* and *Hero Hybrid Grass*. Turf is produced on over 1600 acres using innovative technologies.

• Growing conditions

County Turf grows its turf on some of the coarsest sand root-zones in the country, without using netting. It is carefully irrigated to ensure optimum growing conditions throughout the year. Special harvesting equipment is used to protect the sward during transport and relaying.

Distribution

Turf is available in 1m² standard rolls, *Big Rolls* in 0.75 and 1.25m widths, and 40mm thick for instant play surfaces. All turf can be provided with laying equipment and forklift off-load facilities. A fleet of lorries offers year-round nationwide delivery, and laying teams provide full installation.

Projects

Projects have included Olympic Stadium (London 2012), Leicester Tigers, Hampden Park (Glasgow 2014 Commonwealth Games), Croke Park Stadium, Lord's Cricket Ground, Nya Ullevli Stadium (Gothenburg), Leicester City FC, Skibo Castle golf course and Castle Stuart golf course.

Contact
Sales Team
t: 01724 855000
f: 01724 282777
info@countyturf.co.uk

Web
www.countyturf.co.uk

Address
County Turf Ltd
Low Santon Farm
Appleby
Scunthorpe DN15 0DF

Staff/turnover
25 people/£3m per year

Affiliations
Turf Growers' Association (TGA)
Turfgrass Producers International (TPI)
Sports Turf Research Institute (STRI)
Institute of Groundsmanship (IOG)

Operational area
UK, Europe

COUNTY TURF LTD TURF GRADES	
GRADE	**APPLICATION**
Hybrid Systems	Instant play/high wear areas
County Greens	Golf and bowling greens
County USGA Greens	Instant greens
Lawnscape	Prestige landscaping, golf tees and ornamental lawns
Greenscape	Landscape and amenity projects
County Shade	Shade and drought tolerant
Sports Greenscape	Hardwearing sports areas and instant play pitches
County Stadia	Stadium pitches and sports fields
RTF	Drought prone areas
Fibre Reinforced	Grass car parks and sports pitches up to 40mm thick
Washed Turf	Available in all grades for projects that require quick rooting and clean surfaces
Revetting Turf	Bunker constructions

Washed Turf creates a high-quality landscaped lawn

Hard-wearing play area

Hybrid turf

Hybrid system

Landscaping – Goodwood Winners' Enclosure

Hybrid system close up

Washed Turf – Lord's Cricket Ground

Washed Turf

Official natural sports turf supplier (Olympic venues) – London 2012 Olympic Games

La Moye Golf Course, Jersey

Forest Pines Golf Course

Hybrid system installed – Griffin Park, Brentford FC

Carnegie Links, Skibo Castle

Croke Park Stadium, Dublin

2014 Commonwealth Games, Hampden Park

Hybrid system installation – Leicester Tigers, Welford Road Stadium

Contact
Alex Edwards, Stephen Edwards
t: 01759 321000
f: 01759 380130
alex@inturf.co.uk
stephen@inturf.co.uk

Web
www.inturf.com

Address
Inturf
The Chestnuts
Wilberfoss
York YO41 5NT

Affiliations
Turfgrass Growers Association (TGA)
British Association of Landscape Industries (BALI)
British and International Golf Greenkeepers'
Association (BIGGA)
Institute of Groundsmanship (IOG)

Inturf

Cultivated turf

Inturf (the trading name of Turfgrass Services International Ltd) is a well-established business, operating since 1985. The company has a reputation for its cultivated turf products, highly skilled installation services and innovative achievements with turfing systems.

Big roll systems can be used, and equipment hired, by companies undertaking the work. Inturf has developed custom growing for special uses, such as sports stadia, tennis courts, golf courses and prestigious landscaping projects. Hundreds of hectares are cultivated all year round to provide a uniform, consistent supply. Visitors are welcome to inspect the turf at the nurseries by appointment.

Inturf also delivers CPD seminars for landscape architects and sports field professionals, and is a well-established supplier of high-quality topsoil and *TerraCottem* soil conditioner.

Growing conditions and techniques

The soil used for growing turf is light, sandy loam, well suited to sports and landscaping applications. For special requirements, such as reinforced landscapes, amenity areas and certain sports applications, Inturf sources and imports appropriate soil types and rootzones, and spreads them on designated areas at the nurseries. The turf is then custom-grown to maturity.

Turf grades

Inturf Masters is a traditional mixture of four fescue grasses.
Inturf Classic Landscape contains super fine dwarf perennial ryegrass and complementary grasses.
Inturf Classic Sport uses perennial ryegrass for areas subject to heavy wear.
Fibre Reinforced Turf is a highly durable mixture of grasses grown on a reinforced rootzone.
RTF rhizomatous tall fescue is drought tolerant and deeper rooting than other grasses, and is suitable for embankments and coastal locations.
Really Tough Turf contains perennial ryegrass, tufted hair grass and tall fescue and lends itself well in most situations.

Carnoustie Golf Course

War graves commission – France

Big rolls of turf enable quick and efficient installation

Rhizomatous Tall Fescue (RTF) is drought tolerant

Really Tough Turf installed in a park

Fibre Reinforced Turf close up

Gibraltar Commonwealth Park

Fine leaved *Masters Turf*

Golf greens turf

Quality seed and soil types are used to produce turf

Automated production

Gibraltar Commonwealth Park

Lindum

Cultivated turf

Lindum specialises in producing turf and innovative grass products for the landscaping, sporting and civil engineering industries.
Lindum's turf is used across the UK in parks and gardens; and retail, office and building developments; as well as at visitor attractions and stately homes.
Over 25 years of growing experience ensures that Lindum turf is of consistently high quality, strong, and stays looking good with easy care.

• Growing conditions

Landscaping turf is grown on stone-free sandy loam soils to TGA standards and BS 3969.
Expertise in nutrition and irrigation ensures constant quality and rapid establishment.
All varieties used are named cultivars, highly rated by the STRI for wear and disease tolerance, recovery and appearance.
All turf is free from netting. It is available in small 1m² or large 28m² rolls.

• Turf grades

LT7 Festival is a hard-wearing, attractive landscape turf that is easy to maintain.
LT6 Sporturf uses the toughest ryegrasses for sports pitches and high-wear landscaping areas.
LT4 Smooth Stalk has a fine appearance for ornamental lawns.
LT2 Low Maintenance contains Crested Hairgrass and is ideal for drought-prone areas and banks.

• Other turf products

Lokturf™ is suitable for grass roads, overflow car parking, paths and heavy-wear areas.
Grassfelt™ is suitable for unusual landscape features, steep banks and erosion control.
Wildflower turf is suitable for environmental enhancement and green roofs.
Washed turf is suitable for rapid establishment and for high-sand rootzones.

Delivery

Delivery is available nationwide, with flexible load sizes and a range of vehicle options, depending on site access.

Hardwearing landscaping turf for public realm design

Landscaping turf for heavy foot traffic area at zoo

Lokturf™ installed for heavy foot traffic in public park

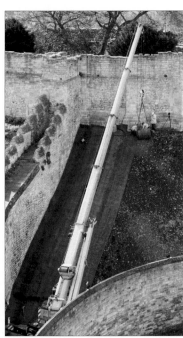
Solutions and advice is offered for landscape design

LT6 Sporturf used for a hard-wearing lawn

LT6 Sporturf – Ascot Racecourse

LT7 Festival – residential development

Contact

Paul Hadley
t: 01386 791102
m: 07990 507729
phadley@dlf.co.uk

Phil Seedhouse
t: 01386 791102
m: 07778 786470
pseedhouse@dlf.co.uk

Web

www.dlf.co.uk

Address

DLF Seeds Ltd
Thorn Farm
Inkberrow
Worcester WR7 4LJ

amenity@dlf.co.uk

Additional entries

Sports seed specialist ➤ 515

DLF Seeds Ltd

Amenity seed specialist

DLF is a leading breeder and producer of amenity grass seed and wild flower mixtures.

• **Grass seed mixtures**

Masterline is a comprehensive amenity grass seed range covering all lawn, landscape, sports and environmental needs. It uses only STRI tested cultivars from in-house breeding programmes. *Masterline* includes new *4turf*™ ryegrass technology for improved quality and reduced maintenance costs, and *MicroClover* seed mixtures for a lower carbon footprint.

Gromax biostimulant seed coating improves establishment and is standard on all mixtures.

• **Wildflower seed mixtures**

Pro Flora offers a wide range of site-specific wildflower mixtures. All wildflowers are from UK native stock and are produced in the UK.

• **Special mixtures**

DLF provides advice and produces mixtures to meet client needs.

Technical data

Mixtures are produced in a purpose-built, dedicated amenity seed production facility under a strict quality assurance system.

Purity and germination certificates and COSHH data sheets are available upon request.

PM51 with *Double 4turf*™ perennial rye

Pro Flora Native Wildflower meadow mixtures

Promaster 85 low-maintenance road verge

Promaster 70 Universal

Contact

Richard Brown
t: 01522 868714
f: 01522 868095
lincoln@germinal.com

Web
www.germinalamenity.com

Address
Germinal GB Ltd
Camp Road
Witham St Hugh
Lincoln LN6 9QJ

Accreditation
DEFRA-licensed laboratory testing

Affiliations
British Association of Landscape Industries (BALI)
Institute of Groundsmanship (IOG)
British and International Golf Greenkeepers
Association (BIGGA)
British Society of Plant Breeders (BSPB)
Sports and Play Construction Association (SAPCA)
IBERS research centre, Aberystwyth University
Turf Grass Association (TGA)

Seed lots tested for purity and germination

Germinal GB Ltd

Grass seed, fertilisers, wildflowers and wetting agents

Germinal, formerly British Seed Houses, is a privately owned company established in 1825. It is the only company selling British-bred turf grasses direct to the end user. The range includes professional grass seed mixtures and fertilisers for greenkeepers, groundsmen, landscape contractors and landscape architects. Applications include golf courses, sports fields and landscaping.

• **Grass seed mixtures**
Germinal's *Grade 'A'* range of landscaping, sports and golf mixtures comprises seed mixes from carefully maintained cultivars that are rigorously tested for purity and germination. These mixtures are used by some of the UK's top groundsmen, greenkeepers and landscape professionals.

• **Wildflower mixtures**
The company offers the *Regional Environmental (RE)* and *General Landscaping Wild Flora (WF)* ranges. Most mixes feature only UK-native wild flora but, to meet demand, two mixtures have been created that include non-native species: *WF17 Cultivated Annuals* gives a display throughout summer where maximum visual impact is required.
WF19 Pollinators' Paradise is highly attractive to bees and other pollinators.
All mixtures that contain flowers have been deemed 'Perfect for Pollinators' by the Royal Horticultural Society (RHS).

• **Sustainable slow-release fertilisers**
With standard compound fertilisers, it is generally accepted that 60% of nitrogen is lost through leaching and volatilisation into the atmosphere, so a high spreading rate is required to compensate. *Floranid* slow-release fertilisers incorporate IBDU nitrogen (isobutylidene diurea), which has very limited cold water solubility and can be fully utilised by the grass without leaching. It can be spread at lower rates and less frequently than other fertilisers, saving man hours and preventing damage to the environment.

• **Agrosil LR phosphate**
Phosphate has a strong stimulating effect on root growth and is highly beneficial to the establishment of all plants including grass, trees and shrubs. However, it is quickly fixed in the soil and becomes unavailable to plants.
Agrosil LR keeps phosphate completely available and carries it down to a depth of 30cm. It improves soil structure and promotes greater drainage, gas exchange and good health in even the poorest soils, as well as sandy rootzones, compost and manufactured soils. The silicate gels of *Agrosil LR* absorb heavy metals such as lead or cadmium so they can no longer be taken up by the plant, enabling growth on contaminated sites. *Agrosil LR* also facilitates growth on road verges that are subject to large quantities of salt.

Grade 'A' landscape mixture for every application

Flower mixtures for maximum visual impact

UK native wildflower mixtures

Grade 'A' mixture for sports

Exclusive UK-bred varieties

Grade 'A' mixtures for golf

Johnsons Sports Seed

Sports seed specialist

Johnsons Sports Seed offers dedicated sports turf seeds that combine market-leading cultivars and *ProNitro* 4th generation nutrient seed coating technology, that delivers faster establishment and offers greater value for money.

For over 190 years these mixtures have helped to produce high quality sports turf.

Mixtures are available for golf, football, rugby, tennis, cricket and racecourse applications.

Seed mixtures are produced in a dedicated production facility and all products are independently tested.

Breeding and mixture trials of all species are carried out and evaluated in the UK.

Technical support

A team of national technical representatives delivers advice on mixture and cultivar selection, and undertakes field support.

Customers can visit the UK research and demonstration site.

Projects

4turf™ *Tetraploid* ryegrasses were used for the 2016 European Championship pitches in France. *J Premier Pitch* has been used by Leicester City FC IOG Grounds Team of the Year 2015; and BT Murrayfield Stadium, a 2015 Rugby World Cup host and IOG Groundsman of the Year 2015.

Contact

Derek Smith (Amenity Sales Manager)
m: 07778 859905
dsmith@dlf.co.uk

John Hughes (Technical Sales Manager, North West)
m: 07801 459625
jhughes@dlf.co.uk

Roger Peacock (Technical Sales Manager, North East)
m: 07801 459623
peacock@dlf.co.uk

Craig Spooner (Technical Sales Manager, South East)
m: 07824 906933
cspooner@dlf.co.uk

Ian Barnett (Technical Sales Manager, South West)
m: 07814 669085
ibarnett@dlf.co.uk

Web

www.johnsonssportsseed.co.uk

Address

Johnsons Sports Seed / DLF Seeds Ltd
Thorn Farm
Inkberrow
Worcester WR7 4LJ

t: 01386 791102
amenity@dlf.co.uk

Additional entries
Amenity seed specialist ➤ 513

J Premier Pitch – Leicester City Football Club, IOG Football Grounds Team of the Year 2015

J Fescue – Royal Lytham Golf Club

J Premier Wicket – Hampshire Cricket Club

New *ProNitro* 4G seed coat technology

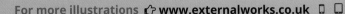

Phoenix Amenity Supplies Ltd

Amenity grass seed

Phoenix Amenity is an independent, family owned seed and soft landscaping supply company. It provides a comprehensive range of grass seed mixtures, technical advice and a personal service to the landscaping and sports amenity sector. High quality grass seed mixtures are available for all situations.

• Standard mixtures

Landscaping seed mixtures are offered for hard wearing areas.
Fine fescue seed mixtures provide high quality grass for fine turf landscaping.
Low maintenance seed mixtures are suitable for verges, embankments and reduced maintenance landscaping.
Specialist landscape seed mixtures are available for road verges, shaded areas and coastal areas.
Reclamation sites mixtures are designed to increase fertility in poor soils.
Sports field maintenance and construction mixtures are available for both summer and winter sports.
Rye and non-rye golf course fairways mixtures and fine greens seed mixtures are offered.

• Bespoke mixtures

The company can advise upon and produce mixtures to customers' specifications.

Contact
t: 01684 212020
f: 01684 578424
sales@phoenixamenity.co.uk

Web
www.phoenixamenity.co.uk

Address
Phoenix Amenity Supplies Ltd
The Bakery
Old Vicarage
Hanley Castle WR8 0BJ

Affiliations
British Association of Landscape Industries (BALI)
Flora Locale

Operational area
UK

Additional entries
Wildflower seed mixtures ➤ 519

Embankment grass seed mix

Universal grass seed mix

Premier grass seed mix

Mixtures are offered for sports fields

Harrowden Turf Ltd

MeadowMat wildflower matting

Contact
Chris Carr
t: 0800 061 2805
f: 01842 827911
chris@harrowdenturf.co.uk

Web
www.meadowmat.com

Address
Harrowden Turf Ltd
Corkway Drove
Hockwold
Thetford IP26 4JR

Affiliations
British Association of Landscape Industries (BALI)

Operational area
England, Wales, Scotland

Additional entries
Cultivated turf ➤ 507
Enviromat sedum matting ➤ 546

MeadowMat wildflower matting

MeadowMat wildflower matting is grown in Norfolk by turfgrass producer, Harrowden Turf.

• Standard MeadowMat
MeadowMat consists of over 30 species of native perennial wildflowers and grasses. It is delivered to site with the plants growing strongly and ready to root into prepared impoverished soil. Installed like turf, it forms a dense mat of vegetation that suppresses annual weed seeds in the soil. *MeadowMat* emulates a species-rich meadow. Plants are chosen to provide nectar for butterflies and shelter for amphibians and small mammals.

• MeadowMat for Birds and Bees
MeadowMat for Birds and Bees consists of plant species specially selected for their value to pollinating insects and for their architectural seed heads, which will offer up winter bird feed.

Installation and maintenance
Management is simple and minimal. Once established, *MeadowMat* only needs to be cut back once a year. Clippings should be removed and composted or used to make hay.

Delivery
MeadowMat can normally be delivered within three working days. The minimum order for standard seed mixes is 1m². Bespoke seed mixes can be grown for a minimum quantity of 500m².

MeadowMat consists of more than 30 species of native perennial wildflowers and grasses

MeadowMat is delivered with plants already growing

MeadowMat for Birds and Bees consists of plant species specially selected for their value to pollinating insects

MeadowMat can be installed at any time of year

MeadowMat is a quick and easy way to establish a wildflower meadow in a garden

MeadowMat wildflower matting

Lindum
taking grass a step further

Contact
Stephen Fell
t: 01904 448675
f: 01904 448713
lindum@turf.co.uk

Web
www.turf.co.uk

Address
Lindum
West Grange
Thorganby
York YO19 6DJ

Affiliations
British Association of Landcape Industries (BALI)
Sports Turf Research Institute (STRI)
Turfgrass Growers Association (TGA)

Additional entries
Turf reinforcement ➤ 26
Green roofs ➤ 29
Cultivated turf ➤ 512

Lindum

Wildflower turf

Lindum offers pre-grown wildflower turf for use in parks, gardens and golf courses.

Lindum wildflower turf mats are a balanced mixture of wildflowers, grasses, herbs and perennial plants. Plants are grown in a moisture-retentive felt and sown at the correct density for optimum establishment to give a high proportion of flowers, and therefore interest, colour and biodiversity. Mats are easy to lay and can be rolled out on flat surfaces, or pegged to steep slopes for bank stabilisation.

• Lindum Wildflower turf

Lindum Wildflower turf is a mixture of wildflowers, herbs and flowering perennials.

Developed to respond to more varied and extreme climatic conditions, the plants in the mix are chosen for their visual attractiveness and drought tolerant properties. It also benefits wildlife by providing valuable nectar sources, attracting butterflies, bees and other insects.

The plants in flower can vary during the season and from year to year as the mixture adapts to the soil type, rainfall and temperature. The soil in which the plants are established determines the type of wildflowers that will flourish.

• Bespoke mixtures

Special mixtures to suit individual soil types can be grown to order for large-scale areas.

Lindum Wildflower turf making an impact in a garden

Lindum Wildflower turf replaces traditional borders

Wildflower turf enhances public parks

Lindum Wildflower turf – RHS Harlow Carr

Wildflower turf mats on a bank

Ready-established wildflower plants in felt mat

Wildflower turf adds colour and biodiversity to a site

BritishFlora

Native wildflowers

BritishFlora offers a complete range of native flora with full British provenance.
Wildflowers, grasses and sedges, marginals and aquatics are grown on a purpose-built nursery. BritishFlora has used its experience of wildflower establishment and habitat creation to develop its own site-specific wildflower seed mixes. Commercial quantities of native plants are produced for a diverse range of applications such as remediation, reed beds, wildlife habitat creation and green roofs.

Contact
t: 01684 212027
f: 01684 578424
info@britishflora.co.uk

Web
www.britishflora.co.uk

Address
BritishFlora
The Bakery
Old Vicarage
Hanley Castle WR8 0BJ

Affiliations
British Association of Landscape Industries (BALI)
Flora Locale

Operational area
UK

Country of manufacture
UK

Bumblebee Mix

Wildflowers on a river bank

Iris pseudacorus

BFS6 Hedgerow & Shade Wildflower Mix

Phoenix Amenity Supplies Ltd

Wildflower seed mixtures

Phoenix Amenity is an independent, family owned seed and soft landscaping supply company. It provides a comprehensive range of ecologically designed wildflower seed mixtures, technical advice and a personal service to the landscaping and sports amenity sectors, local authorities and conservation groups.
A member of Flora locale, the company provides high quality wildflower seeds, bulbs and plugs. Bespoke mixtures can be advised upon and produced to customers' specifications.

Contact
t: 01684 212020
f: 01684 578424
sales@phoenixamenity.co.uk

Web
www.phoenixamenity.co.uk

Address
Phoenix Amenity Supplies Ltd
The Bakery
Old Vicarage
Hanley Castle WR8 0BJ

Affiliations
British Association of Landscape Industries (BALI)
Flora Locale

Operational area
UK

Additional entries
Amenity grass seed ➤ 516

Mixtures are available for coastal areas

Wildflower mixtures suit conservation areas

Special mixtures are available on request

Flora Mix	Category	Ref
80% Low Maintenance Grasses and 20% Flora Blend	Dry/Sandy Soil Mix	PFS1
	Dry/Semi Acidic Soil Mix	PFS2
	Neutral/Damp Soil Mix	PFS3
	Heavy/Clay Soil Mix	PFS4
	Wetland Pond Edge Mix	PFS5
	Hedgerow and Shade Mix	PFS6
	Calcareous Soil Mix	PFS7
	Economy Meadow Mix	PFS8
	Country Meadow Mix	PFS9
	Species Rich Meadow Mix	PFS10
	Coastal Area Mix	PFS11
	Green Roof Mix	PFS12
100% Wildflower Seeds	Wildlife Mix	PFS13
	Cornfield Annual Mix	PFS14
	Old Arable Cornfield Mix	PFS15
	Butterfly Meadow Mix	PFS16
	Bumble Bee Conserv. Mix	PFS17
Urban Wildflower Mixtures	Purple Glade, perennials	PFS18
	Golden Summer, perennials	PFS19
	Golden Summer, annuals	PFS20
	Contrasting annuals	PFS21
	Ground Cover, annuals	PFS22

Contact
Adrian Smallridge
t: 023 9220 0606
mail@meonuk.com

Clinton Humphris
t: 028 3085 0049
mail@meonireland.com

Web
www.meonuk.com

Address
Meon Ltd
Railside
Northarbour Spur
Portsmouth PO6 3TU

Additional entries
DekorGrip Resin Bound surfacing ➤ 99
DekorGrip Tree Surround surfacing ➤ 529

Meon Ltd

DekorGrip Rubber Mulch

DekorGrip Rubber Mulch is made from 100% premium recycled tyres and free from fibres and wires. It provides fade-resistant, easy to manage play and landscape areas all year round.
The porous system allows excellent drainage and does not absorb water, therefore it dries quickly and will not freeze or attract animals and insects.
A bound in solution, it prevents material migration, avoiding annual replacement costs.
Meon provides support and training on all *DekorGrip* systems, including *Rubber Mulch*.

DekorGrip Rubber Mulch – school playground

DekorGrip Rubber Mulch – picnic area

DekorGrip Rubber Mulch – pathway

DekorGrip Rubber Mulch – garden

Contact
David Poole/Ryan Markham
t: 01233 720097
f: 01233 720098
sales@hy-tex.co.uk

Web
www.hy-tex.co.uk

Address
Hy-Tex (UK) Ltd
Aldington Mill, Mill Lane, Aldington
Ashford TN25 7AJ

Accreditation
ISO 9001

Affiliations
BALI

Additional entries
Silt and run-off pollution control ➤ 10
Biodegradables ➤ 26
Vertical green wall planters ➤ 376

Hy-Tex (UK) Ltd

Root barriers

Root Barrier C3 protects structures and services from tree root damage and controls the spread of invasive plant species such as Japanese knotweed, giant hogweed, mares tail and bamboo.
Typical applications include tree pits, foundations and service channels.

Properties
Made from triple coated and twin reinforced polyethylene, *Root Barrier C3* offers the strength and durability of a ground engineering fabric and the puncture resistance of a geomembrane.
The fabric conforms to all the criteria required by the Environment Agency code of practice and offers a cost-effective and quick alternative to the excavation and transportation off site of soil infested with invasive weeds.
Root Barrier C3 has a life expectancy of over 50 years, which is an important recommended requirement by the Environment Agency because the Japanese knotweed rhizome can remain dormant for at least 20 years.
The fabric is UV stabilised and highly resistant to natural acids, alkalis, bacteria and fungi.

Dimensions
Root Barrier C3 can be supplied in rolls up to 4x100m long to reduce laps.

Root Barrier C3 horizontal knotweed barrier

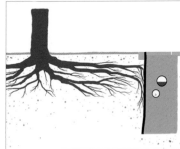
Root Barrier C3 as vertical tree root barrier

Root Barrier C3 invasive weed containment cell

Root Barrier C3 knotweed containment cell lining

GREEN GRID SYSTEMS
INNOVATIVE TREE ROOT PROTECTION

Contact
Colin Holmes
t: 01962 882020
sales@greengridsystems.com

Web
www.greengridsystems.com

Address
Green Grid Systems
The Nursery
Littleton Lane
Winchester SO21 2LS

CPD
Protecting existing tree root systems and
maximising development opportunities

Operational area
UK

Green Grid Systems

Tree root bridges for existing trees

Green Grid's *RootBridge* is designed to protect
tree root systems where new developments such
as walkways, steps and car parking areas are
planned close to existing trees.
With a low structure height from 75mm, it
requires minimal excavation and can easily be
retrofitted.
Once installed, it protects the existing root range
from harmful pressures which can lead to soil
compaction, loss of aeration, drainage problems
and, ultimately, the death of the tree.
The system meets both local authority demands
for no-dig tree root protection and engineers'
demands for a reliable solution.

System overview
RootBridge is a modular steel lattice construction
that sits on screwed-in foundations. The
foundation screws are inserted between the
roots up to approximately 2m into the soil. Any
subsequent loads are absorbed by the structure
rather than the tree roots. The structure is strong
enough to withstand pressure from tree roots.

Dimensions
RootBridge is a modular system that can be used
to construct any size of root bridge.
Longitudinal beams: 2x1m and 1x1m lengths.
Grids: 1x1m. Foundational screws: 2m long.

RootBridge installed in park

RootBridge protects existing tree roots near steps

RootBridge on public walkway

RootBridge maximises space use near trees

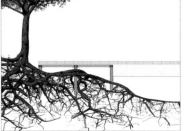
Longitunal beams supported on foundational screws

RootBridge used in car parking area

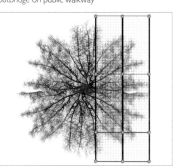
RootBridge RB52S – 500x200cm

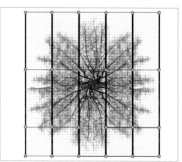
RootBridge RB551S – 500cm² with 100cm² opening

RootBridge can be installed as a half root bridge

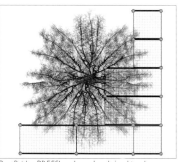
Paving materials can be overlaid after installation

RootBridge RB55SL – shaped and sized to plan

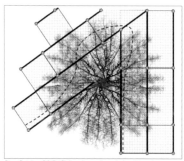
RootBridge RB54SX – shaped and sized to plan

GreenBlue Urban Ltd

Urban tree and landscape products

Founded in 1992, GreenBlue Urban is a specialist in tree pit products. The company has researched and analysed infrastructure challenges and the causes of premature mortality, to devise solutions to establish and integrate trees in urban spaces.

• ArborSystem urban tree pit package
ArborSystem is an integrated tree pit package that brings together the key products for successful design and simplifies the installation process.
It combines root management units, structural soil components, aeration, irrigation, a grille and a vertical guard in a single package.
ArborSystem's integrated system ensures product compatibility at the design stage. Time spent on specifying, quoting and ordering is reduced. The system can be adapted to suit differing location and budget constraints. It also demonstrates to clients a professional, long-term approach to tree planning and management issues.

Technical support
GreenBlue offers support from design to installation, including an on-site support service.

Projects
ArborSystem has been proven in many demanding locations, such as in central London.

Contact
Shane Frost (UK office)
t: 01580 830800
enquiries@greenblueurban.com

Alwyn White (Ireland office)
t: 028 7134 5620
info@greenleafireland.com

Web
www.greenblue.com
www.greenleafireland.com

Address
GreenBlue Urban Ltd
Northpoint
Junction Road
Bodiam TN32 5BS

Operational area
International

Additional entries
RootSpace™ soil support system ➤ 523

ArborSystem – central London

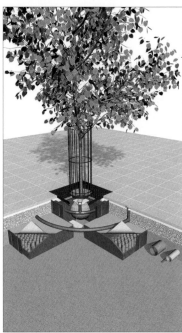
ArborSystem cutaway diagram

ArborSystem – *Rootcells* in place

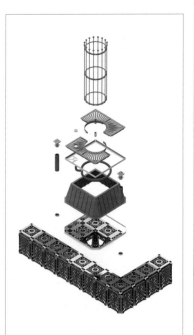
ArborSystem construction diagram

ArborSystem – ventilation and protection

ArborSystem – completed system

Contact
Shane Frost (UK office)
t: 01580 830800
enquiries@greenblueurban.com

Alwyn White (Ireland office)
t: 028 7134 5620
info@greenleafireland.com

Web
www.greenblue.com
www.greenleafireland.com

Address
GreenBlue Urban Ltd
Northpoint
Junction Road
Bodiam TN32 5BS

Operational area
International

Additional entries
Urban tree and landscape products ➤ 522

RootSpace™ 600 Upright vertical panel

Installation of RootSpace™ 600 Upright vertical panel

GreenBlue Urban Ltd

RootSpace™ soil support system

GreenBlue Urban, an industry leader in tree pit design and root protection products, offers *RootSpace™* soil support systems. They are designed to provide the maximum possible soil and rooting volume for trees. A large volume of uncompacted, good quality soil is required for the successful establishment and long-term health of a tree, but this is not normally available in a paved area.

They integrate with the *Arborsystem* family of products including: *Arborvent* irrigation/aeration vents; *RootDirector* root management units; *RootForm* root guides; *Arborflow 100* tree drainage systems; and *Arborguy* tree guying systems.

• **RootSpace 600 Upright**
RootSpace 600 Upright is an interlocking, high-strength vertical panel designed to be quickly installed and connected to neighbouring panels so that extensive structures can be rapidly built. Their open structure is fast to fill and the void provides more soil for the tree, while not impacting on utility pipes.

• **RootSpace Airflow lid**
Patented *Rootspace™ Airflow* quick release top lids encourage movement of air, allowing the soil to breathe. A central aperture is designed to collect debris and diffuse water flow into the soil zone, reducing the potential for erosion.

• **RootSpace 600 Infill**
RootSpace™ 600 Infill is an optional side panel that provides increased stability against lateral ground movements. It can be used around the perimeter of the installation where there is a likelihood of subterranean ground settlement after planting.

Composition and manufacture
RootSpace™ 600 Upright and *Airflow* lids are made from interlocking, recycled plastic panels which give very high structural strength. Their open lattice structure requires a low amount of plastic to manufacture, reducing cost.

Sitework
RootSpace™ panels are economic to transport and fast to install, reducing labour costs.

RootSpace™ 600 Upright vertical panel, RootSpace™ 600 Infill and RootSpace™ Airflow quick release top

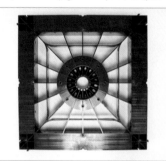
RootSpace™ Airflow quick release top

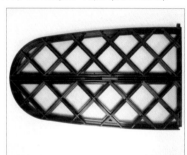
RootSpace™ 600 Infill panel

RootSpace™ 600 Upright vertical panel

Installation of structural soil fill

Installation of RootSpace™ Airflow quick release tops

Contact
t: 01423 332114
f: 01423 332101
info@gtspecifier.co.uk

Web
www.gtspecifier.co.uk

Address
Green-tech Ltd
Rabbit Hill Business Park
Great North Road
Arkendale
Knaresborough HG5 0FF

Accreditation
ISO 9001:2008, ISO 14001:2004

Affiliations
BALI, APL, Constructionline, HTA

CPD
ArborRaft tree planting system
The Green-tree Guide to Good Soil
Effective tree and plant irrigation
Tree anchoring systems

Operational area
International

Additional entries
Green roofs ➤ 30
Laser-cut tree grilles ➤ 525
Urban tree irrigation ➤ 525

gt Specifier
Urban tree planting systems

gtSpecifier products provide protection for newly planted trees even in the most challenging urban environments.

• Tree planting system
The *ArborRaft System* is a geocellular system that spreads the load of surfacing materials and vehicle movements around a tree's rooting area.
ArborRaft units are locked together to form a raft system that sits over the tree pit providing load-bearing support. This eliminates over compaction of the rooting area within the pit and maintains the ideal growing environment for tree roots to establish and mature.
The open structure of the individual units also acts as an air gap diverting root growth away from the pavement towards nutrient-rich soil.
It is a tried and tested system that has successfully been installed into projects across the UK and Europe.
Units are manufactured from recycled materials.

• Structural soil
ArborRaft Soil has been specially developed for the UK market to work as a rootzone with the *ArborRaft System*. Extensively tested, *ArborRaft Soil* ensures optimum moisture, aeration and nutrient content, whilst maintaining a stable soil layer.
The growing media provides an open structure for the free-flow of water, oxygen and nutrients.

ArborRaft prevents compaction and root damage without restricting natural tree root growth

The *ArborRaft System* supports loads preventing compaction of growing media in the rootzone

ArborRaft Soil works as a rootzone

Individual *ArborRaft* unit

ArborRaft units are simple to lock together

ArborRaft can be designed to fit any tree pit size

Specially designed *ArborRaft Soil*

gt Specifier

Laser-cut tree grilles

Laser-cut steel tree grilles are a new addition to the *Dales Collection* of tree grilles and guards. They are designed to add a contemporary aesthetic to urban projects.

Four designs are each available in corten, stainless or mild steel. Mild steel grilles can be powder-coated. Custom designs can be made to order. The grilles are supplied in two halves or four quarters for assembly within a fixing frame.

Sizes range from 800 to 2500mm.

Optional extras include irrigation holes, wording, uplighters and co-ordinating tree guards.

Laser-cut steel tree grids are produced in 4 finishes

Geo tree grille in corten steel

Planet tree grille in stainless steel

Flare tree grille in mild steel

Branch tree grille with powder coated finish

Contact

t: 01423 332114
info@gtspecifier.co.uk

Web
www.gtspecifier.co.uk

Address
Green-tech Ltd
Rabbit Hill Business Park, Great North Road,
Arkendale, Knaresborough HG5 0FF

Accreditation
ISO 9001:2008, ISO 14001:2004

Affiliations
BALI, APL, Constructionline, HTA

Operational area
International

Additional entries
Green roofs ➤ 30
Urban tree planting systems ➤ 524
Urban tree irrigation ➤ 525

gt Specifier

Urban tree irrigation

gtSpecifier offers specialist irrigation solutions to ensure urban trees receive the very best start and continued support for the life of the tree.

Mona Tree Irrigation Systems ensure that water and nutrients are delivered in the right quantity to tree roots, resulting in improved root development and optimal growth.

Mona Relief Vente is a decorative cast aluminium irrigation unit designed for urban environments. The unit is compatible with standard relief tubing and the gtSpecifier range of tree grilles. Bespoke text is available.

Mona Relief Vente cast aluminium tree irrigation unit

The *Mona Tree Irrigation System* ensures that water and nutrients are delivered to the root of the tree

Contact

t: 01423 332114
info@gtspecifier.co.uk

Web
www.gtspecifier.co.uk

Address
Green-tech Ltd
Rabbit Hill Business Park, Great North Road,
Arkendale, Knaresborough HG5 0FF

Accreditation
ISO 9001:2008, ISO 14001:2004

Affiliations
BALI, APL, Constructionline, HTA

CPD
Effective tree and plant irrigation

Additional entries
Green roofs ➤ 30
Urban tree planting systems ➤ 524
Laser-cut tree grilles ➤ 525

Additional entries
Protective post and rail ➤ 219
Bollards ➤ 235
Cycle parking ➤ 249
Signage and wayfinding ➤ 264
Illumination ➤ 272
Co-ordinated street furniture ➤ 278
Protective street furniture ➤ 280
Co-ordinated street furniture ➤ 282
Seats and benches ➤ 320
Litter bins ➤ 357
Planters ➤ 378

Marshalls plc

Tree protection

Marshalls tree grilles enable green infrastructure to be combined with hard landscaping. They provide room for water irrigation while protecting the tree roots, allowing trees to be added to landscapes without the risk of root growth damaging surrounding paving.

Tree grilles are available in materials including aluminium, concrete, cast iron, steel, stainless steel, ferrocast polyurethane and slimline concrete in modern or traditional styles.

The tree grilles complement a wide variety of Marshalls street furniture and paving products.

Escofet Cerda tree grille

Escofet Carmel tree surround

Monoscape Treepave concrete tree grille

Ferrocast 58 Series tree grille with *Tegula* paving

Ollerton M3 stainless steel tree grille and guard with co-ordinating M3 street furniture

Contact
Murielle Jayer
t: 01737 762300
f: 01737 773395
info@platipus-anchors.com

Web
www.platipus-anchors.com

Address
Platipus® Anchors Ltd
Kingsfield Business Centre
Philanthropic Road
Redhill RH1 4DP

Accreditation
ISO 9001:2008

Affiliations
BALI
Society of Garden Designers
Association of Professional Landscapers

CPD
Modern developments in tree anchoring and irrigation

Operational area
Worldwide

Country of manufacture
UK

Additional entries
Mechanical earth anchoring ➤ 43

Systems are suitable for urban planting

Platipus® Anchors Ltd

Tree anchoring and irrigation

An ISO 9001:2008 accredited company, Platipus® Anchors Ltd designs and manufactures tree anchoring systems for the landscape industry. Platipus invented the first tree anchoring system, with no unsightly stakes or guy wires, more than 30 years ago. Due to continuous innovation, the company has developed a range of solutions for all planting situations with trees up to 20m high.

• **Rootball fixing system – Plati-Mat®**
The *Platipus®* rootball fixing system, including *Plati-Mat®*, is a popular method of securing rootballed, containerised and airpot-grown semi-mature trees. Its benefits include ease and speed of installation, planting at the nursery line, a lack of unsightly timber stakes or guy wires, more secure fixing and better root establishment. The system naturally degrades after 3–5 years to allow unrestricted root growth.

• **D-MAN® system – Plati-Mat®**
The award-winning *D-MAN®* is a strong, compact and lightweight system primarily designed to replace the traditional deadman where there are buried services or shallow soils. *D-MAN®* can be used individually or in multiples and units simply lock/unlock together. It has a distinctive letterbox style wire tendon anchor point and a unique cup for water storage. Units are easily stackable for building up large planting areas and can be used to protect roof planting from damage. *D-MAN®* is made from recycled plastic and is completely nestable, allowing for compact transportation.

• **Piddler® tree irrigation system**
Drought stress remains one of the biggest contributors to high mortality rates of transplanted trees in the first few years of establishment. *Piddler®* is a special membrane that delivers water and air directly to a tree's rootzone, helping to ensure tree growth and sustainability. *Piddler®* supplies water evenly all around the rootball, drenching the soil laterally. Unlike traditional systems, *Piddler®* reduces waste and keeps water from evaporating, running off and escaping in to the bottom of the tree pit. Quick to assemble and tailor to size, it is used for all rootball diameters. Its lightweight design also allows significant freight cost savings over traditional pipe systems.

• **Eyebolt system – Plati-Mat®**
Platipus also provides a solution to resolve challenging planting situations such as roof gardens, containers, solid bases and unusual urban sites. This tree anchoring system includes eyebolts, securely expanded into the concrete.

• **Permanent anchoring**
In addition to its standard *Plati-Mat®* solutions, Platipus® Anchors can also provide permanent tree anchoring systems, using stainless steel accessories. They are available in a range of options to suit applications such as podiums, roof gardens, bridges, concrete planters and jetties.

Rootball fixing kit – *Plati-Mat®*

Rootball fixing system – *Plati-Mat®*

D-MAN® award-winning fixing system – *Plati-Mat®*

Rootball fixing with *Piddler®* tree irrigation system

Commonwealth Park, Gilbraltar

Eyebolt fixing system – *Plati-Mat®*

Roof garden, Great Ormond Street Hospital

Systems produce an aesthetically pleasing finish

![SureSet Permeable Paving]

Contact
t: 01985 841180
mail@sureset.co.uk

Web
www.sureset.co.uk

Address
SureSet UK Ltd
32 Deverill Road Trading Est, Sutton Veny BA12 7BZ

Accreditation
CHAS; CPD Certified; ISO 9001; ISO 14001

Affiliations
Builders and Contractors Guild; English Historic
Towns Forum; British Association of Landscape
Industries (BALI); Building Register; Landscape
Institute; Confederation of Construction Specialists;
The Guild of Builders and Contractors
Considerate Contractors Scheme

Additional entries
Surface drainage ➤ 74
Spectrum glass bound surfacing ➤ 96
SureSet permeable bound surfacing ➤ 97

SureSet UK Ltd

Permeable tree pit surfacing

SureSet is a resin bound, permeable tree pit paving that provides an attractive, sustainable, eco-friendly, low-maintenance surfacing. It is guaranteed for 18 years.

Tree pits are often a target for casually discarded litter, requiring disproportionate time and effort to keep clean. *SureSet* is an attractive, cost-effective alternative to metal grilles that is less likely to be vandalised and provides better drainage.

SureSet is suitable for Sustainable Drainage Systems (SuDS), which enhance the environment by reducing the risk of flooding.

SureSet allows for tree movement and growth. It also enables air and water to freely permeate to the roots of a tree through the interconnecting voids between each stone particle. This prolongs the life of trees and can eliminate the need to install or maintain a watering tube.

Composition and manufacture

SureSet uses flexible resin technology with aggregates in 6 or 10mm sizes.

Installation and maintenance

SureSet is installed using a low-energy, cold-applied laying method. It is virtually maintenance free, requiring only an occasional brush or power-wash.

SureSet permeable tree pit paving provides an attractive, low-maintenance alternative to tree grilles

SureSet uses flexible resin technology

SureSet is installed with a cold-applied laying method

SureSet is permeable, meaning that a tree watering tube may not be required

SureSet can use 6 and 10mm aggregates

Meon Ltd

DekorGrip Tree Surround surfacing

DekorGrip Tree Surround surfacing protects trees and their roots. A resin bound aggregate, this system is usually made with a larger stone than traditional resin bound surfacing. As the stone is bound together very little material is migrated away from the tree pit making it maintenance-free, and avoiding nuisance to pedestrians from loose stones.

The *DekorGrip Tree Surround* system is also SuDS-compliant and water still reaches the bed of the tree and its roots.

DekorGrip Tree Surround – hospital

DekorGrip Tree Surround with built-in tree beds

DekorGrip Tree Surround – hospital, Portsmouth

DekorGrip Tree Surround

DekorGrip Tree Surround in a pavement

Ruskins
Trees
and Landscapes

Contact

Robert Wilkins
t: 01277 849990
f: 01277 849991
robertw@ruskins.co.uk

Web

www.ruskins.co.uk

Address

Ruskins Trees and Landscapes Ltd
The Rose Garden, Warley Street,
Great Warley, Brentwood CM13 3JH

Accreditation

ISO 9001:2008, ISO 14001:2004,
OHAS 18001:2007, CHAS

Affiliations

British Association of Landscape Industries (BALI)

Additional entries

Play trees and play logs ➤ 470
Tree root investigation ➤ 532
Tree and shrub supply and planting ➤ 541

Ruskins Trees and Landscapes

Tree and hedge moving

Ruskins is expert at moving large trees, shrubs and established hedges. Customers include local authorities, golf courses, developers, horticultural organisations and private individuals.

• Tree moving

Using tree spades to plant large trees is cost effective. Ruskins has operated a fleet of tree spades since 1985, including the biggest in the UK – the *Stocker 8 Tree Spade* – which can transplant trees up to 20cm trunk diameter. Trees that are too large to be moved by tree spades can still be moved using a rootball, frame and crane technique. With larger trees, root preparation in advance of transplanting is vital. With all transplanted specimens aftercare is required until root systems are re-established.

• Hedge moving

Hedges can be moved without height reduction.

Operations

Work is undertaken throughout the UK.
All staff are CSCS and RWSA accredited and work in established, experienced teams.
When space is limited on site, Ruskins can store and care for specimens, returning and planting them when the site is ready. The optimum time to transplant is from October to March.

Stocker 8 Tree Spade ready to take tree to new location

Stocker 8 2.16m-diameter, eight-bladed tree spade

100 year old hedge, 10 years after transplanting

Mature pine moving

Stocker 8 Tree Spade cradle open, ready to close around the tree

Practicality Brown Ltd

Tree moving

Practicality Brown has over 35 years' experience in moving and transplanting trees, specialising in moving trees with girths ranging from 20–50cm. Clients include park managers, property developers, private estates, landowners, golf and sports clubs.

Equipment and resources

Practicality Brown operates its own tree spade machines, including an *Optimal 1100* mounted on a *Kramer 520* compact loader, and a *Big John* 1.6m 4×4 truck-mounted tree spade.

Machines can be supplied with 'flotation tyres' for work on sensitive ground.

Machinery is operated by experienced, trained operators who are backed up by a skilled planting team, if required, for securing the trees or assisting with planting.

Operational area

Projects are undertaken for private and commercial organisations throughout the UK.

Contact
t: 01753 652022
f: 01753 653007
TreeMoving@pracbrown.co.uk

Web
www.pracbrown.co.uk

Address
Practicality Brown Ltd
Swan Road
Iver SL0 9LA

Accreditation
ISO 9001, ISO 14001, Achilles CoRE

Affiliations
CHAS, SMAS, Constructionline, FCA, Confor

Additional entries
Tree and vegetation clearance ➤ 531
Instant hedges ➤ 542
Semi-mature and specimen trees ➤ 542

Experts with specialised equipment

Optimal 1100 mounted on a compact loader

Big John 1.6m 4×4 truck-mounted tree spade

Practicality Brown Ltd

Tree and vegetation clearance

Practicality Brown has been operating for over 35 years as a specialist contractor offering tree and vegetation clearance services to the forestry, utility and construction markets.

Services

- Mechanised 'no-burn' tree clearance.
- Whole tree chipping.
- Tree stump removal.
- Forestry mulching.
- Habitat mitigation.
- Tree surgery.

With an extensive range of in-house specialists, both man-power and machinery, all work is carried out to stringent compliance measures.

Operational area

Practicality Brown's tree clearance division operates UK wide, offering a fast and efficient service with a large fleet of tree clearance equipment.

Projects

- M25 widening.
- A421/M1 to Bedford.
- A46 Nottingham to Newark Road.
- Norwich North Distributor Road.
- Centre Parcs.

Contact
t: 01753 652022
f: 01753 653007
TreeClearance@pracbrown.co.uk

Web
www.pracbrown.co.uk

Address
Practicality Brown Ltd
Swan Road
Iver SL0 9LA

Accreditation
ISO 9001, ISO 14001, Achilles CoRE

Affiliations
CHAS, SMAS, Constructionline, FCA, Confor

Additional entries
Tree moving ➤ 531
Instant hedges ➤ 542
Semi-mature and specimen trees ➤ 542

Practicality Brown specialises in mechanised no-burn tree and vegetation clearance

Owns a large fleet of tree clearance machinery

AHWI RT400 tracked mulcher

Contact

Robert Wilkins
t: 01277 849990
f: 01277 849991
robertw@ruskins.co.uk

Web

www.ruskins.co.uk

Address

Ruskins Trees and Landscapes Ltd
The Rose Garden, Warley Street, Great Warley
Brentwood CM13 3JH

Accreditation

ISO 9001:2008, ISO 14001:2004,
OHAS 18001:2007, CHAS

Affiliations

British Association of Landscape Industries (BALI)

Additional entries

Play trees ➤ 470
Tree and hedge moving ➤ 530
Tree and shrub supply and planting ➤ 541

Ruskins Trees and Landscapes

Tree root investigation

Ruskins tree root investigation services are
conducted using air spades. Investigations can
often prove that roots are not present, allowing
development plans to proceed.

• **Air spades services**

Air spades remove soil from around roots
without damaging them, enabling:
- The presence and importance of roots
  to be determined.
- Trenches to be dug through the root systems
  of protected trees.
- Locations to be found for piles that avoid roots.
- Soil de-compaction and root aeration.
- Removal of soil placed above root systems.
- Service locations to be identified.
- Roots to be pruned in accordance with
  good arboricultural practice.
- Root health checks.

Operations

Work is undertaken throughout the UK.
Operations can include the removal and
reinstallation of hard surfaces.

Service trench 1m off mature *London Plane*

Services installed 1m from mature *London Plane*

Air Spade root investigation

Air Spade root-friendly excavation

Trench excavated to reveal roots

Todds Nursery Ltd

Trees and hedging

Todds Nursery is a family-run company led by a father-son collaboration. With over 44 years of experience in the industry, the team has gained a reputation for delivering top quality and innovative services, supplying some of the largest and most prestigious projects in UK landscaping.

Nursery stock

Todds Nursery is among the largest growers of field and container grown stock. The wholesale nursery supplies the trade from 72 hectares of production in Bedfordshire.

A wide range of varieties is grown and supplied, from 14–16cm girth, up to extra large semi-mature trees of 100cm girth plus.

A large range of multi-stemmed plants and a selection of 'instant hedging' is also available.

Projects

- Heathrow Airport Terminals 3 and 5.
- The Royal Bank of Scotland World HQ.
- London 2012 Olympic Games.
- Glaxo Smith Kline Stevenage & Brentford.
- The British Museum.

Delivery

Todds Nursery supplies landscape professionals, developers and estates managers throughout the UK and Europe.

Contact
Jon Todd/Will Todd
t: 01462 813390
info@toddsnursery.co.uk

Web
www.toddsnursery.co.uk

Address
Todds Nursery Ltd
The Garden House
Southill Park
Southill
Biggleswade SG18 9LL

Operational area
UK, Europe

5–6m high *Ginko biloba 'Fagistiata Blagon'*

40–45cm girth *Acer x Freemanii*

35–40cm girth pleached *Tilia*

2m high *Photinia x fraseri 'Red Robin'* instant hedging

60–70cm girth field grown *Pinus sylvestris*

7–8m high field grown multi-stem *Betula*, mixed varieties

LAPPEN
DIE BAUMSCHULE

Contact
Georg Engelke
t: 00 49 2157 818 153

Hans Drath
t: 00 49 2157 818 108

info@lappen.de
f: 00 49 2157 818 180

Web
www.lappen.de

Address
Lappen Nurseries, Herrenpfad 14,
D-41334 Nettetal-Kaldenkirchen, Germany

Staff/turnover
120 people
£12m per year

Accreditation
Zertifizierte Markenbaumschule – Quality certificate
of the Association of German Nurseries

Operational area
Worldwide

Fairground – Hanover, Germany

Lappen Nurseries

Tree stock

Lappen Nurseries is a traditional, family-owned company that was established in 1894.
On an area of more than 630 hectares in Nettetal-Kaldenkirchen and in the neighbouring city Venlo in the Netherlands, the nursery grows an assortment of avenue and specimen trees, as well as feathered trees and multi-stem plants, specimen shrubs, conifers and topiary plants in different varieties and sizes.
Lappen's high-quality stock features a variety of homogeneous plants in a range of sizes, from small to large stem girths.

Technical support
• Specification aids
Besides supplying high-quality plant stock, Lappen provides the market with high-profile planning aids, such as the dendrological photo-atlas *Flora*, as well as the company's full-colour catalogue.
Flora contains pictures of 341 plants in a 30x20cm ringbinder format. This format makes it easier for architects and designers to present an individual selection of plants to clients. Plant descriptions in German, English, French and Dutch are found on the back of each photograph, as are recommended pH values for every plant described. *Flora* is continuously expanded with new sets of photos, which can be ordered via the company's website.
Lappen's 2015 catalogue has been revised and features more than 1000 pages, including over 3500 colour photographs.
The Lappen catalogue gives a general idea of the nursery's range of products, as well as detailed descriptions of plants and their suitability. Available in five languages, it is divided into sections for: deciduous plants (including climbing plants), rhododendrons and azaleas, roses, conifers, topiary plants, bamboos, fruit plants, and a detailed section on herbaceous perennials. Up-to-date information is also available on Lappen's website.
• Contract growing
Contract growing is frequently undertaken, and can involve long-term growing over several years.
• Nursery visits and consultancy
Nursery visits are common and welcomed by the company. Professional advice is given over the telephone or by email or post, and photographs are supplied on request, also by email or post.

Projects
Lappen has completed many projects throughout the UK and Europe, including: Thames Barrier Park, London; Thames Valley Park, Reading; The London Eye and Jubilee Garden, London; Merry Hill Shopping Centre, Dudley; Green Park, Reading; Heathrow Terminal 5, London; city centre regeneration, Sheffield; Campus Park, University of Birmingham; and Regent's Place, London.

Parc du 21 juillet – Brussels, Belgium

Brussels, Belgium

Provident Bank – Heinsberg, Germany

Olpe, Germany

Place de la Republique – Metz, France

Krymskaja Naberezhnaja – Moscow, Russia

Metz, France

IGA 2013 – Hamburg, Germany

The Telegraph Garden – Chelsea Flower Show 2014, Gold medal winner

Erfurt, Germany

LORENZ VON EHREN
THE NURSERY. SINCE 1865

Contact
Peter Flügge (sales)
t: 00 49 40 761 08-126
f: 00 49 40 761 08-100
Peter@LvE.de

Sebastian Beindorff (UK contact)
m: 07815 912785
Sebastian@LvE.de

Web
www.LvE.de

Address
Lorenz von Ehren Nurseries
Maldfeldstrasse 4
D-21077 Hamburg
Germany

Accreditation
Deutsche Markenbaumschule

Affiliations
Bund Deutscher Baumschulen (BdB) – German
Nurseries Association

Lorenz von Ehren

Specimen plants

Established in 1865, Lorenz von Ehren is founded
on five generations of experience in the
production of trees and shrubs. The company's
nurseries in Hamburg and Bad Zwischenahn
cover 550 hectares in total.
Lorenz von Ehren is committed to fulfilling its
customers' requirements through continuous
innovation and development.
Lorenz's plants are used throughout Europe to
enhance schemes and projects on a regional
scale, as well as in cities, streets and gardens.

Nursery stock

A complete range of plants, including specimen
trees and shrubs, topiary, ground cover plants
and mediterranean plants, is available.
Nursery stock includes avenue trees, deciduous
and coniferous specimen trees with a girth from
16–18cm, mature trees with a girth up to 140cm
and heights up to 15m, specimen shrubs,
evergreens and topiary.
The company's website offers videos and an
online catalogue detailing the entire plant range.

Delivery

The company can process orders efficiently and
swiftly, with dispatch of plants to site within days
once an order has been confirmed.

Aerial view of production field

Show garden – Hamburg

Acer freemanii 'Autumn Blaze' 300–400cm wide, 600–700cm high

Pinus sylvestris and *Taxus baccata*, pyramids

Larix kaempferi 'Pendula' 400–500cm wide, 350–400cm high

Pinus parviflora, bonsai

Pinus sylvestris, multi-stem, umbrella shape, 6.3t

Contact
Paul Anderson
t: 0161 440 8060
sales@ladybrooknursery.com

Web
www.ladybrooknursery.com

Address
Ladybrook Nursery
Lytham Drive
off Seal Road
Bramhall
Stockport SK7 2LD

Additional entries
Topiary and hedging ➤ 539
Specimen shrubs ➤ 544
Herbaceous plants ➤ 547

Ladybrook Nursery
Trees and conifers

Established in 1971, Ladybrook Nursery is a wholesale grower and supplier of specimen plants to designers, contractors, developers and estates managers in the private and public sectors.

- **Deciduous trees**

Ornamental specimen and semi-mature amenity trees range from 8–10 to 20–25cm girth.
Forms include standard, half standard, feathered and screening trees. *Betula jacquemontii* is grown to 5m and *Amelanchier lamarckii* to 4m.

- **Conifers and evergeens**

Over 70 varieties of conifers and evergreens are container-grown in 7.5–500 litre pots. Large numbers are available in the 2–4m range.

- **Growing conditions and techniques**

All trees are grown to the company's own size and quality specifications, which enable them to thrive when planted out. All plants have been containerised for over 12 months.
Green credentials include the use of peat-reduced composts, biological pest control, slow release fertilisers and a lean irrigation program.

Services
- Plant selection and technical advice.
- Online stock list, with photos on request.
- Competitive quotes by email or post.
- European stock sourcing, collection & delivery.
- Nationwide delivery for large orders.

Pleached trees, stems to 200cm – *Camellia, Carpinus, Fagus, Quercus Ilex, Ligustrum, Photinia Red Robin*

Specimen trees from 8–10 to 20–25cm girth

Conifers are grown in 7.5–500 litre pot sizes

Container-grown ornamental specimen trees

Screening trees provide structure and privacy

35 varieties of container-grown conifer

Trees are containerised in peat-reduced compost for over 12 months

European stock sourcing, collection and delivery

Contact
Paul Anderson
t: 0161 440 8060
sales@ladybrooknursery.com

Web
www.ladybrooknursery.com

Address
Ladybrook Nursery
Lytham Drive
off Seal Road
Bramhall
Stockport SK7 2LD

Additional entries
Trees and conifers ➤ 538
Specimen shrubs ➤ 544
Herbaceous plants ➤ 547

Ladybrook Nursery

Topiary and hedging

Established in 1971, Ladybrook Nursery is a wholesale grower and supplier of specimen plants to designers, contractors, developers and estates managers in the private and public sectors.

• Topiary
Over 20 varieties of topiary are grown in a wide range of forms including ball, ball on stem, cone, half-standard, pleached, pyramid, spiral, square and round columns. Pot sizes range from 25–285 litres for the largest specimens.

• Hedging
Many shrubs and conifers are available for hedging, including *Thuya, Taxus, Ilex, Buxus, Prunus Rotundifolia* and *Prunus Angustifolia*.

• Growing conditions and techniques
Plants are grown to the company's own size and quality specifications, which enable them to thrive when planted out. Many are pruned twice a year to produce dense, bushy specimens.
Green credentials include the use of peat-reduced composts, biological pest control, slow release fertilisers and a lean irrigation program.

Services
- Plant selection and technical advice.
- Online stock list, with photos on request.
- European stock sourcing, collection & delivery.
- Nationwide delivery for large orders.

Dense, bushy topiary

Clipped specimen topiary for Japanese styled garden

Buxus sempervirens

Pyramid topiary, *Carpinus bet. piramide* 150

Topiary can create immediate impact

Topiary held in stock

Ball on stem topiary

Spiral topiary

Contact
Nick Coslett
t: 01233 813340
f: 01233 813071
sales@palmstead.co.uk

Web
www.palmstead.co.uk

Address
Palmstead Nurseries Ltd
Harville Road, Wye, Ashford TN25 5EU

Awards
Winner – Supplier of the Year, APL Awards 2016
Winner – UK Grower Awards 2012

Accreditation
Certified Supplier of perennial plants and shrubs
(Olympic Park) to the London 2012 Games

Additional entries
Shrubs ➤ 545
Perennials ➤ 548
Hardy exotics ➤ 550

Palmstead Nurseries Ltd

Trees and hedging

Established in 1968, Palmstead occupies a 53ha
site near Wye in Kent. Over 200,000 field-grown
plants are produced annually. Trees to 20cm+
girth, and hedging up to 250cm tall is grown in
the field, as well as in containers up to 90 litre, all
using a peat-free growing medium.
Production involves regular transplanting and
undercutting, and carbohydrate loading of field
trees to stimulate root growth.
Palmstead is a wholesale supplier to the
landscape and amenity markets, local authorities
and leading garden designers.

Nursery reservoir and propagation house

Betula jacquemontii

Betula multistems

Field-grown *Pinus nigra*

Trees being carefully handled on site

Taxus topiary

Prunus laurocerasus hedging

600cm Italian *Cupressus*

Contact
Robert Wilkins
t: 01277 849990
f: 01277 849991
robertw@ruskins.co.uk

Web
www.ruskins.co.uk

Address
Ruskins Trees and Landscapes Ltd
The Rose Garden, Warley Street,
Great Warley, Brentwood CM13 3JH

Accreditation
ISO 9001:2008, ISO 14001:2004,
OHAS 18001:2007, CHAS

Affiliations
British Association of Landscape Industries (BALI)

Additional entries
Play trees and play logs ➤ 470
Tree and hedge moving ➤ 530
Tree root investigation ➤ 532

Ruskins Trees and Landscapes

Tree and shrub supply and planting

Ruskins has specialised in the supply and planting
of large trees, shrubs and hedges since 1986.
• **Supply and planting service**
Any commercially grown specimen tree or shrub
can be sourced and selected from a network of
leading European growers which Ruskins has
established over the past 25 years.
Semi-mature and specimen trees and shrubs are
also held at the company's nursery.
• **Planting only service**
Ruskins is skilled at handling and planting large
trees, including trees in challenging locations.
Services provided include unloading, positioning
and planting. A collation service is offered
whereby specimens are cared for then delivered
to site to an agreed schedule. This service is often
used when a site is unsuitable for delivery by
articulated lorry.
• **Large living Christmas trees**
Large living Christmas trees are available for hire.
Hired trees, which range in heights from 6–10m,
are delivered at the start of the festive period,
retrieved in early January, cared for, then
re-supplied to the client the following year.

Operational area

Services are provided for residential, commercial
and local authority clients across the UK.

Large specimen trees

Living Christmas trees are available for hire

Betula pendula, 60–70cm girth

Planting a tree with 120cm girth

Pleached trees

Practicality Brown Ltd

Instant hedges

Practicality Brown is the premier supplier of the mature *Elveden Instant Hedge™* – a fully formed hedge which is sold by the linear metre and not as individual plants.
Completed projects include the supply of many instant hedges for award-winning RHS Flower Show gardens.
Individual specimens for hedging and screening are also supplied up to 6m high.

Product lines
Stock supplied for commercial and residential projects includes evergreen hedging for screening and deciduous hedges for seasonal interest.
• **Instant deciduous hedge species**
Berberis thunbergii, Fagus sylvatica, Crataegus monogyna, Carpinus betula, Fagus sylvatica 'Purpurea' and Native Mix.
• **Instant evergreen hedge species**
Buxus sempervirens, Prunus laurocerasus, Ilex aquifolium, Prunus lusitanica, Photinia fraseri, Thuja occidentalis Yellow Ribbon, Taxus baccata and Ligustrum ovalifolium.

Dimensions
Elveden Instant Hedge™ is supplied in heights from 1.2m to 1.8m, typically 50cm widths, and in 2.5m lengths which are prepared to order.

Contact
t: 01753 652022
f: 01753 653007
hedge@pracbrown.co.uk

Web
www.pracbrown.co.uk

Address
Practicality Brown Ltd
Swan Road
Iver SL0 9LA

Accreditation
ISO 9001, ISO 14001, Achilles CoRE

Affiliations
CHAS, SMAS, Constructionline, FCA, Confor

Additional entries
Tree and vegetation clearance ➤ 531
Tree moving ➤ 531
Semi-mature and specimen trees ➤ 542

Elveden Instant Hedge™ – Fagus sylvatica

Elveden Instant Hedge™ – Prunus laurocerasus

Elveden Instant Hedge™ – Fagus sylvatica, in Autumn

Practicality Brown Ltd

Semi-mature and specimen trees

Practicality Brown is an instant landscape specialist and has been supplying high quality semi-mature trees and hedges since 1989.

Product lines
Stock covers evergreen and deciduous trees for a wide range of applications, with a combination of home grown and outsourced specimen and semi-mature trees for sale. The extensive range includes all the main indigenous UK species.

Dimensions
Tree sizes can be supplied in a range of sizes:
• Clear stemmed trees
Girth measurement of 18–100cm, measured around the tree stem at 1m high.
• Feathered evergreen trees
Heights of 2–12m.

Services
Tree moving and planting are available if required.

Nursery visits
Practicality Brown's tree nursery in Iver showcases specimen trees and large, top quality containerised trees. Viewings are available, by arrangement.

Contact
t: 01753 652022
f: 01753 653007
trees@pracbrown.co.uk

Web
www.pracbrown.co.uk

Address
Practicality Brown Ltd
Swan Road
Iver SL0 9LA

Accreditation
ISO 9001, ISO 14001, Achilles CoRE

Affiliations
CHAS, SMAS, Constructionline, FCA, Confor

Additional entries
Tree and vegetation clearance ➤ 531
Tree moving ➤ 531
Instant hedges ➤ 542

Containerised trees at the nursery in Iver

Clear stemmed trees in girths of 18–100cm

Feathered trees in heights of 2–12m

Dingle Nurseries Ltd

Trees and hedging

Established in 1968, Dingle Nurseries extends to around 160 acres, growing a full range of high-quality plants for the amenity and wholesale nursery market. Located just outside Welshpool, 130 acres are dedicated to open-ground production. An additional 30 acres are used for container-grown stock.

The company's tree stock consists of semi-mature trees, feathered trees, conifers up to 7m and standard trees. Shrubs and climbers are also provided.

Projects
- Kingsway regeneration, Newport.
- Taff Bargoed Trail, South Wales.
- Corporation Park restoration, Blackburn.
- Stanley Park restoration, Preston.
- Tesco new stores and refurbishments.
- Prescott regeneration, Liverpool.
- New Met Office, Exeter.
- SAS Base, Hereford.
- Breme Technology Park, Worcestershire.
- Imperial Park, Bristol.
- New power station, Northern Ireland.
- NFU offices, Royal Showground.
- National Maritime Museum, Swansea.
- Whitby Abbey.

Contact
t: 01938 552587
f: 01938 554734
info@dinglenurseries.co.uk

Web
www.dinglenurseries.co.uk

Address
Dingle Nurseries Ltd
Frochas, Welshpool, Powys SY21 9JD

Affiliations
Horticultural Trades Association (HTA)

Awards
Chelsea Flower Show
Shrewsbury Flower Show
Tatton Park

Additional entries
Shrubs and climbers ➤ 543

130 acres of open-ground production are kept

3x tr budded ornamentals grown on wide spacing

Feathered tree production

30 acres are used for container-grown stock

Dingle Nurseries Ltd

Shrubs and climbers

Established in 1968, Dingle Nurseries extends to around 160 acres, growing a full range of high-quality plants for the amenity and wholesale nursery market. 130 acres are dedicated to open-ground production. An additional 30 acres are used for container-grown stock.

The company's shrubs and climbers stock consists of seedlings and transplants, herbaceous plants and specimen shrubs. Semi-mature trees, feathered trees, conifers up to 7m and standard trees are also provided.

Projects
- Kingsway regeneration, Newport.
- Taff Bargoed Trail, South Wales.
- Stanley Park restoration, Preston.
- Tesco new stores and refurbishments.
- Prescott regeneration, Liverpool.
- New Met Office, Exeter.
- SAS Base, Hereford.
- Breme Technology Park, Worcestershire.
- Imperial Park, Bristol.
- New power station, Northern Ireland.
- NFU offices, Royal Showground.
- National Maritime Museum, Swansea.
- Whitby Abbey.
- Bradley Stoke School, South Gloucestershire.

Contact
t: 01938 552587
f: 01938 554734
info@dinglenurseries.co.uk

Web
www.dinglenurseries.co.uk

Address
Dingle Nurseries Ltd
Frochas, Welshpool, Powys SY21 9JD

Affiliations
Horticultural Trades Association (HTA)

Awards
Chelsea Flower Show
Shrewsbury Flower Show
Tatton Park

Additional entries
Trees and hedging ➤ 543

Bradley Stoke School

Seedlings, transplants, herbaceous plants and shrubs

2 and 3 litre container production

Ladybrook Nursery

Specimen shrubs

Established in 1971, Ladybrook Nursery is a wholesale grower and supplier of specimen plants to designers, contractors, developers and estates managers in the private and public sectors.

- **Container-grown specimen shrubs**

Ladybrook grows over 160 varieties of specimen shrub. This extensive choice is available both within the 5–15 litre containers, and for large specimens, from 25–500 litres. The shrubs can be used to create immediate impact and structure in public realm, commercial and residential projects.

- **Growing conditions and techniques**

All shrubs are grown to the company's own size and quality specifications, which enable them to thrive when planted out. Shrubs are containerised for over 12 months. Many are pruned twice a year to produce dense, bushy specimens.

- **Sustainability**

Green credentials include the use of peat-reduced composts, biological pest control, slow release fertilisers and a lean irrigation program.

Services

- Plant selection and technical advice.
- Online stock list, with photos on request.
- Competitive quotes by email or post.
- European stock sourcing, collection & delivery.
- Nationwide delivery for large orders.

Contact
Paul Anderson
t: 0161 440 8060
sales@ladybrooknursery.com

Web
www.ladybrooknursery.com

Address
Ladybrook Nursery
Lytham Drive
off Seal Road
Bramhall
Stockport SK7 2LD

Additional entries
Trees and conifers ➤ 538
Topiary and hedging ➤ 539
Herbaceous plants ➤ 547

Over 160 varieties of semi-mature shrubs stocked in container sizes ranging from 5–500 litres

Shrubs give impact and structure to projects

Many shrubs are pruned twice a year

Plants are grown to Ladybrook's size specifications

Plant selection and expert technical advice provided

Nationwide delivery for large orders

Palmstead Nurseries Ltd

Shrubs

Palmstead Nurseries Ltd is a wholesale supplier focusing on the landscape and amenity markets, local authorities and leading garden designers. The company offers trade sales, a well stocked cash-and-carry and discounted online sales. The website also allows specifiers to view live stock availability.

Palmstead hold successful soft landscaping workshops and masterclasses. Details of the current programme of events are on the company's website.

Contact
Nick Coslett
t: 01233 813340
f: 01233 813071
sales@palmstead.co.uk

Web
www.palmstead.co.uk

Address
Palmstead Nurseries Ltd
Harville Road, Wye, Ashford TN25 5EU

Awards
Winner – Supplier of the Year, APL Awards 2016
Winner – UK Grower Awards 2012

Accreditation
Certified Supplier of perennial plants and shrubs
(Olympic Park) to the London 2012 Games

Additional entries
Trees and hedging ➤ 540
Perennials ➤ 548
Hardy exotics ➤ 550

A leading producer of nursery stock

Palmstead Nurseries workshop seminar

Over one million containers are produced annually

Nursery

Part of Palmstead's production area with full rainwater harvesting

ASGD garden centred around bowl and axis

Contact
Chris Carr
t: 0800 061 2807
f: 01842 827911
chris@harrowdenturf.co.uk

Web
www.enviromat.co.uk

Address
Harrowden Turf Ltd
Corkway Drove
Hockwold
Thetford IP26 4JR

Affiliations
British Association of Landscape Industries (BALI)
Turfgrass Growers Association (TGA)

Operational area
England, Wales, Scotland

Additional entries
Cultivated turf ➤ 507
MeadowMat wildflower matting ➤ 517

Harrowden Turf Ltd

Enviromat sedum matting

Harrowden Turf's *Enviromat* sedum matting provides low maintenance ground cover for dry, sunny areas. It can be installed onto banks, low-traffic areas and roofs for instant visual effect. Wildlife-friendly sedum plants flower for up to 8 months of the year providing a colourful display which is highly attractive to pollinating insects such as butterflies and bees.

Enviromat is an easy to install vegetation blanket with at least 85% plant coverage.

Kits for domestic pitched and flat green roofs are available, with installation instructions.

Enviromat sedum matting on a green roof

Enviromat sedum matting with spring flowers

Enviromat ground cover – Legoland, Windsor

Enviromat sedum matting attracts pollinating insects

Enviromat green roof on a gazebo

Enviromat sedum matting

Contact
Paul Anderson
t: 0161 440 8060
sales@ladybrooknursery.com

Web
www.ladybrooknursery.com

Address
Ladybrook Nursery
Lytham Drive
off Seal Road
Bramhall
Stockport SK7 2LD

Additional entries
Trees and conifers ➤ 538
Topiary and hedging ➤ 539
Specimen shrubs ➤ 544

Ladybrook Nursery

Herbaceous plants

Established in 1971, Ladybrook Nursery is a wholesale grower and supplier of specimen plants to designers, contractors, developers and estates managers in the private and public sectors.

• **5 litre specimen plants**
Ladybrook grows over 160 varieties of herbaceous plant, 60 ornamental grasses and 15 ferns. These plants can be used to create immediate impact and structure in the public realm, commercial and residential projects, and are often specified for show homes and gardens.

• **Growing conditions and techniques**
All plants are grown to the company's own size and quality specifications, and containerised for over 12 months, enabling them to thrive when planted out.

• **Sustainability**
Green credentials include the use of peat-reduced composts, biological pest control, slow release fertilisers and a lean irrigation program.

Services
• Plant selection and technical advice.
• Online stock list, with photos on request.
• Competitive quotes by email or post.
• European stock sourcing, collection & delivery.
• Nationwide delivery for large orders.

Agastache Black Adder

Crocosmia Lucifer

Thilactrum

Herbaceous plants give impact and structure

Plants are grown to Ladybrook's size specifications

Hemerocallis Red Rum

Verbascum

Expert plant selection and technical advice

Over 160 herbaceous varieties in 5 litre pots

 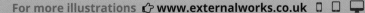

Contact
Nick Coslett
t: 01233 813340
f: 01233 813071
sales@palmstead.co.uk

Web
www.palmstead.co.uk

Address
Palmstead Nurseries Ltd
Harville Road, Wye, Ashford TN25 5EU

Awards
Winner – Supplier of the Year, APL Awards 2016
Winner – UK Grower Awards 2012

Accreditation
Certified Supplier of perennial plants and shrubs
(Olympic Park) to the London 2012 Games

Additional entries
Trees and hedging ➤ 540
Shrubs ➤ 545
Hardy exotics ➤ 550

Palmstead Nurseries Ltd

Perennials

Palmstead continues to develop its perennial range, which comprises of over 35% of production across 1200 species and varieties. Complex plant lists can be supplied to commercial schemes and garden designers. Complex projects delivered on target include the Olympic Park World Gardens, Barbican Roof Garden and Sackler Gallery. The company offers a well-stocked cash and carry, with live stock availability and discounted ordering online. Workshop and masterclass events are held regularly. See website for details and booking.

Serpentine Sackler Gallery, London

Beech Gardens, Barbican, London

Palmstead perennials for Barbican Beech Gardens

Palmstead perennials for a Huf House garden

Plants in award-winning garden for Stoke-on-Trent City Council – Chelsea Flower Show 2014

Palmstead perennials for the Olympic Delivery Authority

Contact
Robert Toal
t: 01625 875333
info@aqualifeltd.co.uk

Web
www.aqualifeltd.co.uk

Address
Aqualife Water Plants & Landscapes Ltd
Lockstock Nursery
Lockstock Hall Road
Poynton SK12 1DP

Awards
RHS Tatton Park Flower Show Awards 2011,
2012, 2013
RHS Chelsea Flower Show 2009

Operational area
Europe

Aqualife Water Plants & Landscapes Ltd

Aquatic plants

Aqualife is an aquatic nursery based in Cheshire specialising in the production of high-quality water plants and aquatic landscaping.
Plants are delivered nationwide to a variety of customers, including garden designers, local authorities, landscape contractors, architects, developers, water plant retailers and private customers, for the creation of high-quality ponds, lakes and marsh gardens.

Nursery stock

Aqualife's specialist aquatic nursery is stocked with a large collection of water plants, including over 400 species of wetland plants, marginals, moisture loving plants, water lilies and oxygenators.
All are of the highest quality and sizes range from plugs plants up to large specimen plants, which provide an instant effect for landscapers.

Technical support

Contract growing is undertaken for medium to large scale projects – lakes, ponds, rivers, estuaries, canals and wetlands – where volumes of plants are delivered within specified deadlines. Aqualife also offers design, plant selection advice and construction, drawing on its experience of native and ornamental water work constructions.

High-quality water plants for landscapers, plant retailers and private customers

Aqualife can work on any stage of a project

Offers a large collection of ornamental water lilies

Specialised planting for fisheries and reserves

Conservation planting for wetland habitats

Stock includes 400+ species of wetland plants, marginals, moisture loving plants, water lilies and oxygenators

Palmstead Nurseries Ltd

Hardy exotics

Palmstead Nurseries grows and stocks an established range of hardy exotic plants. Successful planting schemes can incorporate contrasting foliage sizes and textures. Palmstead's team can assist clients with plant selection at its cash and carry in Wye. A handbook of exotic plants can be downloaded from the company's website.

Contact
Nick Coslett
t: 01233 813340
f: 01233 813071
sales@palmstead.co.uk

Web
www.palmstead.co.uk

Address
Palmstead Nurseries Ltd
Harville Road, Wye, Ashford TN25 5EU

Awards
Winner – Supplier of the Year, APL Awards 2016
Winner – UK Grower Awards 2012

Accreditation
Certified Supplier of perennial plants and shrubs
(Olympic Park) to the London 2012 Games

Additional entries
Trees and hedging ➤ 540
Shrubs ➤ 545
Perennials ➤ 548

Melianthus major

Agave neomexicana

Trachycarpus fortunei palms available in many sizes

Agave havardiana

Beschorneria yuccoides

A big thank you to all the companies who invested time and effort to showcase their core strengths and capabilities.

If this print edition helps you make better decisions about who to work with for your projects, please mention "EXTERNAL WORKS" to companies sourced from this book.

ADVERTISERS

Featured companies   551–562

Address and contact details with index of illustrated entries in this edition.

Marketing opportunities   563–564

Next print edition. Website, bulletin and direct marketing opportunities.

DESKTOP | TABLET | MOBILE

Find a lot **MORE INFORMATION** on all the products and companies featured in this edition on the **EXTERNAL WORKS** website ...

- Detailed factual descriptions
- Key data and fast facts
- More illustrations
- Downloads and videos
- Related products and case studies

And workflow tools designed to save you time and effort ...

- Compare similar
- Review alternatives
- Copy specifications
- Save for later
- Email enquiries

EW INDEX **EXTERNAL WORKS**
better decisions for better environments
www.externalworks.co.uk

A

ABG Ltd
E7 Meltham Mills Road, Holmfirth
HD9 4DS.
tel: 01484 852096
fax: 01484 851562
info@abgltd.com
www.abg-geosynthetics.com
25   Reinforced natural grass rootzones
28   Green and blue roofs
31   Webwall flexible retaining wall system
68   Cellular SUDS paving
68   Geocomposite drainage

Acheson + Glover Ltd
4 Marlin Office Village, 1250 Chester
Road, Castle Vale, Birmingham
B35 7AZ.
tel: 0121 747 0202
specifications@ag.uk.com
www.ag.uk.com
32   Concrete retaining walls
106   Concrete paving flag systems
116   Concrete block paving systems

**ACO Water Management – a division of ACO
Technologies plc**
ACO Business Park, Hitchin Road, Shefford
SG17 5TE.
tel: 01462 816666
fax: 01462 815895
technologies@aco.co.uk
www.aco.co.uk
54   Interceptors
63   Stormwater control

Acoustic Arts
The Old Laundry, Kingswood Estate,
Britannia Road, Bristol BS15 8DB.
tel: 0117 935 2034
info@acousticarts.org.uk
www.acousticarts.org.uk
466   Outdoor musical instruments and sound
          sculptures

Addagrip Terraco Ltd
Addagrip House, Bell Lane Industrial Estate,
Uckfield TN22 1QL.
tel: 01825 761333
sales@addagrip.co.uk
www.addagrip.co.uk
73   Resin bound SUDS porous surfacing
92   Resin bound porous surfacing
93   Addastone resin bonded decorative
          surfacing

Alfresco Floors Ltd
Unit 6, Teddington Business Park, Station Road,
Teddington TW11 9BQ.
tel: 020 8977 0904
fax: 020 8977 0825
info@alfrescofloors.co.uk
www.alfrescofloors.co.uk
117   Outdoor floor tiles

All Urban Ltd
Aizlewood's Mill, Nursery Street,
Sheffield S3 8GG.
tel: 0114 282 1283
fax: 0114 282 3463
info@allurban.co.uk
www.allurban.co.uk
274   Santa & Cole lighting
324   Contemporary seating
390   Youth shelters

Alpha Rail Ltd
Nunn Brook Rise, County Estate, Huthwaite,
Nottingham NG17 2PD.
tel: 01623 750214
websales@alpharail.co.uk
www.alpharail.co.uk
174   Railings
412   Architectural metalwork

Althon Ltd
Vulcan Road South, Norwich NR6 6AF.
tel: 01603 488700
fax: 01603 488598
sales@althon.co.uk
www.althon.co.uk
58   Precast headwalls
60   Flow control
82   Channel drainage

Amberol Ltd
The Plantation, King Street, Alfreton
DE55 7TT.
tel: 01773 830930
fax: 01773 834191
sales@amberol.co.uk
www.amberol.co.uk
346   Litter, dog waste and grit bins
347   Recycling bins
372   Self-watering planting baskets
373   Self-watering planting systems

AMV Playground Solutions
Unit D, Abbey Lane Enterprise Park,
Abbey Lane, Burscough L40 7SR.
tel: 01704 740323
fax: 01704 895392
sales@amvplaygrounds.co.uk
www.amvplaygrounds.co.uk
478   Outdoor sports and playground equipment

Anderton Concrete Products
Units 1 & 2, Cosgrove Business Park,
Anderton Wharf, Soot Hill, Anderton
CW9 6AA.
tel: 01606 535300
fax: 01606 75899
structural@andertonconcrete.co.uk
www.andertonconcrete.co.uk
33   Retaining wall systems

Andrea Geile Sculpture
17 Clarence Street, Edinburgh
EH3 5AE.
tel: 0131 556 0251
info@andreageile.co.uk
www.andreageile.co.uk
426   Sculpture

Antique Bronze Ltd
44 Hillway, Holly Lodge Estate,
London N6 6EP.
tel: 020 8340 0931
fax: 020 8340 0743
info@antiquebronze.co.uk
www.antiquebronze.co.uk
413   Conservation and restoration

Aqualife Water Plants & Landscapes Ltd
Lostock Nursery, Lostock Hall Road, Poynton
SK12 1DP.
tel: 01625 875333
info@aqualifeltd.co.uk
www.aqualifeltd.co.uk
549   Aquatic plants

Architectural Street Furnishings Ltd
Priory Road, off Armytage Road,
Brighouse HD6 1PY.
tel: 01484 401414
fax: 01484 721398
info@asfco.co.uk
www.asfco.co.uk
216   Post and rail systems
225   Bollards
277   Bespoke street furniture
325   Seats and benches
414   Bespoke metalwork

Artform Urban Furniture Ltd
Adlington Business Park, London Road,
Adlington SK10 4NL.
tel: 0800 542 8118
enquiries@artformurban.co.uk
www.artformurban.co.uk
284   Co-ordinated street furniture
326   Seats and benches

ArtParkS International Ltd
Sausmarez Manor, Sausmarez Road, St Martins,
Guernsey GY4 6SG.
tel: 01481 235571
fax: 01481 235572
peter@artparks.co.uk
www.artparks.co.uk
424   Sculpture commissions

AUTOPA Limited
Cottage Leap, Rugby CV21 3XP.
tel: 01788 550556
fax: 01788 550265
info@autopa.co.uk
www.autopa.co.uk
212   Rising arm barriers
213   Telescopic posts and automatic
          bollards
214   Height restrictors and swing gates
217   High visibility protection
221   Traffic flow plates and speed ramps
226   Bollards
228   Parking posts
242   Cycle shelters and compounds
244   Cycle stands
268   Illuminated bollards
283   Street furniture
391   Shelters, canopies and walkways

Avon Barrier Corporation Ltd
149 South Liberty Lane, Ashton Vale Trading
Estate, Bristol BS3 2TL.
tel: 0117 953 5252
fax: 0117 953 5373
sales@avon-barrier.co.uk
www.avon-barrier.co.uk
208   Gates, barriers and access control systems
232   High-security bollards

B

Bailey Streetscene
Adlington Business Park, London Road,
Adlington SK10 4NL.
tel: 01625 855900
sales@baileystreetscene.co.uk
www.baileystreetscene.co.uk
286   Co-ordinated street furniture
392   Shelters and canopies

BandB Innovations Ltd
2 Dovecot Workshops, Barnsley Park,
Cirencester GL7 5EG.
tel: 01285 740488
bins@bandbinnovations.co.uk
bandbinnovations.co.uk
233   Removable and static bollards
353   Litter bins

Barkers Fencing
Etna Works, Duke Street, Fenton,
Stoke-on-Trent ST4 3NS.
tel: 01782 319264
fax: 01782 599724
sales@barkersfencing.com
www.barkersfencing.com
166   Mesh fencing systems
177   Railings
181   Steel palisade fencing
185   High-security fencing systems
200   Sliding gates and swing gates
497   Sports fencing

Barlow Tyrie Ltd
Springwood Industrial Estate, Rayne Road,
Braintree CM7 2RN.
tel: 01376 557600
fax: 0870 460 1100
info@teak.com
www.teak.com
327   Outdoor seating

Baylis Landscape Contractors Ltd
Hartshill Nursery, Thong Lane, Shorne,
Gravesend DA12 4AD.
tel: 01474 569576
info@baylislandscapes.co.uk
www.baylislandscapes.co.uk
48   Landscape services

BBS Granite Concepts Ltd
Kimcote Court, Walton Road, Kimcote,
Lutterworth LE17 5RU.
tel: 01455 559474
fax: 01455 554118
sales@bbsgraniteconcepts.com
www.bbsnaturalstone.com
119   Natural stone suppliers

BCM GRC Ltd
Unit 22, Civic Industrial Park,
Whitchurch SY13 1TT.
tel: 01948 665321
fax: 01948 666381
info@bcmgrc.com
www.bcmgrc.com
59 GRC headwalls/retaining structures

Benchmark Design Ltd
Cheriton House, Barnham Lane, Walberton,
Arundel BN18 0AZ.
tel: 01243 545926
fax: 01243 545453
info@benchmark-ltd.co.uk
www.benchmark-ltd.co.uk
288 Co-ordinated street furniture
314 Contemporary shaped seating
344 Picnic tables
354 Contemporary litter bins
374 Planters

Benkert Street Furniture Ltd
Unit 1A, Southern Cross Business Park,
Bray, Ireland.
tel: 0808 101 1590
malcolm@benkert.biz
www.benkertstreetfurniture.co.uk
306 Contemporary street furniture

BikeAway Ltd
Bell Close, Newnham Industrial Estate,
Plympton, Plymouth PL7 4JH.
tel: 01752 202116
info@bikeaway.com
www.bikeaway.com
246 Cycle stands and lockers

Bituchem Asphalt Ltd
Laymore Road, Forest Vale Industrial Estate,
Cinderford GL14 2YH.
tel: 01594 826768
fax: 01594 826948
mark@bituchem.com
www.bituchem.com
94 Natural and coloured macadam surfaces:
    Natratex, Colourtex

BPI Recycled Products
College Road, Dumfries DG2 0BU.
tel: 0333 202 6800
fax: 01773 533862
plaswoodsales@bpipoly.com
www.plaswoodgroup.com
142 Plaswood boardwalks and decking

Brad Dillon Sundials
High Noon, Ladock, Truro TR2 4PW.
tel: 01726 252970
brad@armillaryspheres.co.uk
www.braddillonsundials.co.uk
442 Armillary spheres and sundials

Branson Leisure Ltd
Fosters Croft, Foster Street,
Harlow CM17 9HS.
tel: 01279 432151
sales@bransonleisure.co.uk
bransonleisure.com
328 Seats and benches
345 Picnic suites

BritishFlora
The Bakery, The Old Vicarage, Haney Castle,
Worcester WR8 0BJ.
tel: 01684 212027
fax: 01684 578424
info@britishflora.co.uk
www.britishflora.co.uk
519 Native wildflowers

Buzon UK Ltd
Unit 6, Teddington Business Park, Station Road,
Teddington TW11 9BQ.
tel: 020 8614 0874
fax: 020 8977 0825
sales@buzonuk.com
www.buzonuk.com
152 Paving support pedestals

C

Caloo Ltd
Unit 12, Boxted Farm, Berkhamsted Road,
Hemel Hempstead HP1 2SG.
tel: 01442 265489
fax: 0845 055 8219
info@caloo.co.uk
www.caloo.co.uk
481 Outdoor fitness equipment
482 Safer surfacing

Cambridge Direct Tree Seeding Ltd
Hilton House, 37 Hilton Street, Over,
Cambridge CB24 5PU.
tel: 01954 232350
fax: 01954 231313
iain@cdts.info
www.cdts-ltd.co.uk
44 Hydroseeding

Candela Light Ltd
319 Long Acre, Waterlinks Nechells,
Birmingham B7 5JT.
tel: 0121 678 6700
fax: 0121 678 6701
sales@candela.co.uk
www.candela.co.uk
269 Illuminated bollards and bulkheads
275 Road, street and amenity lighting

Cheviot Trees Ltd
Newton Brae, Foulden,
Berwick-upon-Tweed TD15 1UL.
tel: 01289 386664
fax: 01289 386750
sales@etsluk.com
www.etsluk.com
193 Acoustic barriers: Green Barrier™

Chris Brammall Ltd
Low Mill Business Park, Morecambe Road,
Ulverston LA12 9EE.
tel: 01229 588580
chris@chrisbrammall.com
www.chrisbrammall.com
158 Bridges
415 Bespoke architectural and sculptural
     metalwork
425 Sculpture

Chris Nangle Furniture
Unit 8, Site A Rednal Industrial Estate,
West Felton SY11 4HS.
tel: 01691 611864
info@chrisnanglefurniture.co.uk
www.chrisnanglefurniture.co.uk
298 Co-ordinated street furniture
335 Bespoke seating

CLD Fencing Systems
Unit 11, Springvale Business Centre,
Millbuck Way, Sandbach CW11 3HY.
tel: 01270 764751
fax: 01270 757503
sales@cld-fencing.com
www.cld-fencing.com
168 General purpose fencing
169 Security fencing systems
170 UniGril rigid fencing systems
171 Zoological fencing systems
172 Bespoke laser-cut fencing
172 Stone Fence™ walling systems
201 Gates and access control systems
498 Perimeter fencing systems for sports pitches
     and MUGAs
499 Sports Rail™ spectator fencing

Clearstone Paving Ltd
Unit 5A, Valley Farm Business Park,
Reeds Lane, Sayers Common, Hassocks
BN6 9JQ.
tel: 01273 358177
new@clearstonepaving.co.uk
www.clearstonepaving.co.uk
98 Resin-bound surfacing

Cleveland Sitesafe Ltd
Riverside Works, Dockside Road,
Middlesbrough TS3 8AT.
tel: 01642 244663
fax: 01642 244664
sales@cleveland-sitesafe.ltd.uk
www.cleveland-sitesafe.ltd.uk
402 Modular leisure buildings

CLS Sports
Park Farm, Dunsdale, Guisborough
TS14 6RQ.
tel: 01642 488328
a.banks@cls-headoffice.co.uk
www.cleveland-land-services.co.uk
488 Sport England endorsed all-weather sports
     facilities
493 Natural sports field construction

Colas Ltd
Wallage Lane, Rowfant, Crawley RH10 4NF.
tel: 01326 375660
fax: 01326 375167
colas.cornwall@colas.co.uk
www.colas.co.uk
120 Coarse grained, silver-grey granite products
     from Carnsew Quarry

Component Developments
Halesfield 10, Telford TF7 4QP.
tel: 01952 588488
sales@componentdevelopments.com
www.componentdevelopments.com
83 Channel and slot drainage

Coralie Turpin Artist
Studio 48, Yorkshire Artspace, Persistence
Works, 21 Brown Street, Sheffield S1 2BS.
tel: 07946 424602
turpinthomson@gmail.com
www.coralieturpin.co.uk
  426 Large-scale public art

CORE Landscape Products
Units 1–3 Calves Lane Farm, Bellswood Lane,
Iver SL0 0LU.
tel: 0800 118 2278
sales@corelp.co.uk
www.corelp.co.uk
  20 Tree root protection and ground
      reinforcement
  69 Porous gravel/resin bound surfacing

Cotswold Estates & Gardens Ltd
Baunton Lane, Cirencester GL7 7BG.
tel: 01285 654766
fax: 01285 654499
info@estatesandgardens.co.uk
www.estatesandgardens.co.uk
  49 Landscape services

County Turf Ltd
Low Santon Farm, Appleby,
Scunthorpe DN15 0DF.
tel: 01724 855000
fax: 01724 282777
info@countyturf.co.uk
www.countyturf.co.uk
  508 Turf growers

Creative Spiral
Pontprenddu, Llandissilio,
Clunderwen SA66 7TT.
tel: 01437 563308
gideon@creativespiral.co.uk
www.creativespiral.co.uk
  427 Public sculpture

CTS Bridges Ltd
Abbey Road, Shepley, Huddersfield HD8 8BX.
tel: 01484 606416
fax: 01484 608763
enquiries@ctsbridges.co.uk
www.ctsbridges.co.uk
  137 Decking and landscape structures
  156 Bridges

Cycle-Works Ltd
8–9 Rodney Road, Portsmouth PO4 8BF.
tel: 023 9281 5555
fax: 023 9281 5544
info@cycle-works.com
www.cycle-works.com
  252 Secure cycle parking

D

David A Annand (Sculptor)
Pigscrave Cottage, The Wynd, Kilmany,
Cupar KY15 4PU.
tel: 01382 330714
david@davidannand.com
www.davidannand.com
  427 Public art

David Backhouse Sculptures
Yew Trees, Langford Place,
Lower Langford, Bristol
BS40 5BT.
tel: 01934 863049
jennieweston@yahoo.co.uk
www.backhousesculptures.com
  428 Sculpture

David Watkinson Sculpture
Stockheld Crossing, Stockheld Lane, Scholes,
Leeds LS15 4NG.
tel: 0113 265 7984
david@davidwatkinsonsculpture.co.uk
www.davidwatkinsonsculpture.co.uk
  428 Kinetic sculpture

Derbyshire Specialist Aggregates
Arbor Low Works, Long Rake, Youlegreave,
Bakewell DE45 1JS.
tel: 01629 636500
fax: 01629 636425
sales@derbyaggs.com
www.derbyshireaggregates.com
  130 Resin bound, bonded, decorative and
      landscape aggregates

Diane McCormick Ceramics
16 Brookend Road, Ardboe,
Dungannon BT71 5BR.
tel: 028 8673 7008
info@dianemccormick.co.uk
www.dianemccormick.co.uk
  440 Ceramics

Dingle Nurseries Ltd
Frochas, Welshpool SY21 9JD.
tel: 01938 552587
fax: 01938 554734
info@dinglenurseries.co.uk
www.dinglenurseries.co.uk
  543 Trees and hedging
  543 Shrubs and climbers

DLF Seeds Ltd
Thorn Farm, Inkberrow, Worcester
WR7 4LJ.
tel: 01386 791102
fax: 01386 792715
amenity@dlf.co.uk
www.dlf.co.uk
  513 Amenity seed specialist

DP Structures Ltd
Unit 12, Dale Mill, Hallam Road,
Nelson BB9 8AN.
tel: 01282 697563
enquiries@dpstructures.co.uk
www.dpstructures.co.uk
  416 Bespoke architectural metalwork

DP Studio
Unit 12, Dale Mill, Hallam Road,
Nelson BB9 8AN.
tel: 01282 697563
enquiries@dpstructures.co.uk
www.dpstudio.co.uk
  420 Bespoke metalwork

Drostle Public Arts Ltd
F2 Old Europa Gym Centre, Europa Trading
Estate, Fraser Road, Erith DA8 1QL.
tel: 07719 529520
arts@drostle.com
www.drostle.com
  438 Mosaics and murals

Dunhouse Quarry Co. Ltd
Dunhouse Quarry Works, Cleatlam,
Darlington DL2 3QU.
tel: 01833 660208
fax: 01833 660748
enquiries@dunhouse.co.uk
www.dunhouse.co.uk
  122 Natural stone suppliers

E

East Midlands Landscaping Ltd
The Knoll, Leicester Road, Earl Shilton,
Leicester LE9 7TJ.
tel: 01455 850250
info@eastmidlandslandscaping.co.uk
www.eastmidlandslandscaping.co.uk
  52 Soft landscaping services

eibe Play Ltd
eibe House, Forsyths Home Farm, A3 By-pass
Road, Hurtmore, Godalming GU8 6AD.
tel: 01483 813834
fax: 01483 813851
eibe@eibe.co.uk
www.eibe.co.uk/en_GB
  452 Play equipment

Ekkehard Altenburger
APT Studios Deptford, 6 Creek Side,
Deptford, London SE8 4SA.
tel: 07788 458902
e@altenburger.co.uk
www.altenburger.co.uk
  429 Sculpture

Elcot Environmental
Kingsdown Lane, Blunsdon, Swindon
SN25 5DL.
tel: 01793 700100
enquiries@elcotenviro.com
www.elcotenviro.com
  46 Japanese knotweed control

Elefant Gratings
Enterprise Drive, Four Ashes,
Wolverhampton WV10 7DF.
tel: 01902 797110
sales@elefantgratings.com
www.elefantgratings.com
  154 External flooring: gratings and planks
  400 Plant housing and storage compounds

Emma Stothard Sculptor
Unit 5A, Enterprise Way, Whitby YO22 4NH.
tel: 01947 605706
sculpture@emmastothard.com
www.emmastothard.com
  429 Sculpture

Entry Parking Posts
Norton Reach, Norton Green Lane, Knowle,
Solihull B93 8PL.
tel: 01564 773188
entryparkingpost@aol.com
www.entryparkingposts.net
  215 Access control
  224 Direction and speed restrictors

Environmental Street Furniture Ltd
Valley Business Centre, 67 Church Road,
Newtownabbey, Belfast BT36 7LS.
tel: 0845 606 6095
sales@worldofesf.com
www.worldofesf.com
  307 Co-ordinated street furniture
  313 External seats and benches
  351 Litter bins

Erlau AG
Units 10–14, John Wilson Business Park,
Thanet Way, Whitstable CT5 3QT.
tel: 07423 431510
Paul.Strong@rud.co.uk
www.erlauuk.co.uk
  290 Co-ordinated street furniture

ESE World Ltd
Beacon House, Reg's Way, Bardon Hill,
Coalville LE67 1GH.
tel: 01530 277900
fax: 01530 277911
sales@eseworld.co.uk
www.eseworld.co.uk
  350 Solar energy compaction bins
  351 Underground waste systems

EverEdge®
PO Box 333, Market Drayton
TF9 4WL.
tel: 01630 657629
info@everedge.co.uk
www.everedge.co.uk
  88 Steel landscape edging

F

Factory Furniture Ltd
5 Pioneer Road, Faringdon SN7 7BU.
tel: 01367 242731
hello@factoryfurniture.co.uk
www.factoryfurniture.co.uk
  292 Contemporary street furniture
  329 Seats and benches
  355 Litter bins
  375 Tree planters

Fibaform Products Ltd
22 Lansil Industrial Estate, Caton Road,
Lancaster LA1 3PQ.
tel: 01524 60182
fax: 01524 389829
sales@fibaform.co.uk
www.fibaform.co.uk
  396 Bespoke prefabricated cabinets, kiosks and
      buildings

Fife Silica Sands (a division of Patersons of Greenoakhill Ltd)
Gartsherrie Road, Coatbridge ML5 2EU.
tel: 01236 433351
fax: 01236 425172
sales@patersonsquarries.co.uk
www.patersonsquarries.co.uk
    495   Sand

Fitzpatrick Woolmer Design & Publishing Ltd
Unit 7, Lakeside Park, Neptune Close,
Rochester ME2 4LT.
tel: 01634 711771
fax: 01634 711761
info@fwdp.co.uk
www.fwdp.co.uk
    253   Creative sign solutions

Forma Landscapes
The Mill House, Wattisfield Road,
Walsham le Willows, Bury St Edmunds
IP31 3BD.
tel: 0333 123 7373
info@formalandscapes.com
formalandscapes.com
    330   Scandinavian outdoor seating

Fountains & Features Ltd
Unit 3, The Meridian Centre, King Street,
Oldham OL8 1EZ.
tel: 0161 870 3550
sales@fountainsandfeatures.co.uk
www.fountainsandfeatures.co.uk
    446   Water features and fountains

Fountains Direct Ltd
21 Trade City, Avro Way, Brooklands Business
Park, Weybridge KT13 0YF.
tel: 01932 336338
sales@fountainsdirect.com
www.fountains-direct.co.uk
    444   Fountains and water displays
    449   Millstone and boulder fountains

Frontier-Pitts Ltd
Crompton House, Crompton Way,
Manor Royal Industrial Estate, Crawley
RH10 9QZ.
tel: 01293 548301
fax: 01293 560650
sales@frontierpitts.com
www.frontierpitts.com
    204   Gates and barriers

Furnitubes International Ltd
Meridian House, Royal Hill, Greenwich,
London SE10 8RD.
tel: 020 8378 3261
fax: 020 8378 3250
esibook@furnitubes.com
www.furnitubes.com
    218   Railings and guardrails
    230   Bollards
    241   Cycle parking
    260   Signage
    308   Co-ordinated street furniture
    316   Seating
    331   Bespoke seating
    356   Litter bins

FWDesign Ltd
The Design Hub, 41 Brookley Road,
Brockenhurst SO42 7RB.
tel: 020 7928 0412
enquire@fwdsignsolutions.com
www.fwdsignsolutions.com
    261   Signage and wayfinding systems

G

Germinal GB Ltd
Camp Road, Witham St Hughs,
Lincoln LN6 9QJ.
tel: 01522 868714
fax: 01522 868095
lincoln@germinal.com
www.germinal.com/amenity
    514   Grass seed, fertilisers, wildflowers and
           wetting agents

Giles Rayner ARBS
Farm Hill House Studio, Westend, Avening,
Tetbury GL8 8ND.
tel: 01453 835201
giles@gilesrayner.com
www.gilesrayner.com
    448   Water sculpture

Gillian Forbes Stonecarver
The Workshop, Pathgreen Cottage, Path of
Condie, Forgandenny, Perth PH2 9DW.
tel: 01577 830754
gillian@forbesstonecarver.com
www.forbesstonecarver.com
    436   Stone carving

Glasdon UK Ltd
Preston New Road, Blackpool FY4 4UL.
tel: 01253 600410
fax: 01253 792558
sales@glasdon-uk.co.uk
www.glasdonlitterbins.com
    352   Litter and recycling bins

Global Stone (Colchester) Ltd
Tey Gardens, Church Lane, Little Tey,
Colchester CO6 1HX.
tel: 0845 606 0240
fax: 01206 213229
info@globalstonepaving.co.uk
globalstonepaving.co.uk
    118   Porcelain paving tiles

GMJ Woodcarving
Flat 1, 114 Salisbury Road, Moseley,
Birmingham B13 8JZ.
tel: 07963 193944
info@gmjwoodcarving.co.uk
www.gmjwoodcarving.co.uk
    430   Wooden sculptures

Good Directions Ltd
Time House, 19 Hillsons Road, Botley,
Southampton SO30 2DY.
tel: 01489 797773
fax: 01489 796700
sales@good-directions.co.uk
www.good-directions.co.uk
    441   Exterior clocks

Goose Street Furniture Ltd
Britannia House, Junction Street,
Darwen BB3 2RB.
tel: 01254 700213
enquiries@goosefootuk.com
www.goosefootuk.com
    294   Standard and bespoke furniture

GoPlastic Ltd
Waverley, St Martins Road, Caerphilly
CF83 1EJ.
tel: 029 2086 4095
info@goplastic.co.uk
www.goplastic.co.uk
    143   Recycled plastic profiles for decks,
           boardwalks, jetties and bridges
    189   Recycled plastic fencing
    234   Recycled plastic bollards
    332   Recycled plastic seating

Gramm Barrier Systems Ltd
18 Clinton Place, Seaford BN25 1NP.
tel: 01323 872243
fax: 01323 872244
steve@grammbarriers.com
www.grammbarriers.com
    194   Acoustic barriers

Grass Concrete Ltd
Duncan House, 142 Thornes Lane, Thornes,
Wakefield WF2 7RE.
tel: 01924 379443
fax: 01924 290289
info@grasscrete.com
www.grasscrete.com
    21   Grass pavers and erosion control
    30   Overlay paving system for extensive or
           intensive green roofs
    34   Retaining walls

Green Grid Systems
The Nursery, Littleton Lane,
Winchester SO21 2LS.
tel: 01962 882020
sales@greengridsystems.com
www.greengridsystems.com
    521   Tree root bridges for existing trees

Greenbarnes Ltd
Unit 7, Barrington Court, Ward Road,
Buckingham Road Industrial Estate,
Brackley NN13 7LE.
tel: 01280 701093
fax: 01280 702843
sales@greenbarnes.co.uk
www.greenbarnes.co.uk
    254   Signing systems

GreenBlue Urban Ltd
Northpoint, Compass Park, Junction Road,
Bodiam, Robertsbridge TN32 5BS.
tel: 01580 830800
enquiries@greenblueurban.com
www.greenblue.com
    522   Urban tree and landscape products
    523   RootSpace™ soil support system

Greenfix Soil Stabilisation & Erosion Control Ltd
Old Manor Farm Yard, Beckford Road, Ashton
under Hill, Evesham WR11 7SU.
tel: 01608 666027
sales@greenfix.co.uk
www.greenfix.co.uk
    12   Geoweb® cellular confinement
    27   Erosion control mats and blankets
    35   Earth retention structures

Gridforce
Industrial Estate South, Park Road, Calverton,
Nottingham NG14 6BP.
tel: 0115 965 7303
fax: 0115 965 5151
sales@gridforce.co.uk
www.gridforce.co.uk
    16   Ground reinforcement
    70   Surface drainage

Gripsure UK Ltd
Unit 2, Rockhill Business Park, Bugle PL26 8RA.
tel: 01726 844616
info@gripsure.co.uk
www.gripsure.co.uk
    150   Non-slip timber decking

gtSpecifier
Rabbit Hill Business Park, Great North Road,
Arkendale, Knaresborough HG5 0FF.
tel: 01423 332114
fax: 01423 332101
info@gtspecifier.co.uk
www.gtspecifier.co.uk
    30   Green roofs
    524   Urban tree planting systems
    525   Laser-cut tree grilles
    525   Urban tree irrigation

H

Haddonstone Ltd
The Forge House, East Haddon,
Northampton NN6 8DB.
tel: 01604 770711
info@haddonstone.co.uk
www.haddonstone.com
    409   Architectural cast stone
    443   Garden ornament

Hahn Plastics Ltd
Old Pilkington Tiles Site, Rake Lane, Swinton,
Manchester M27 8LJ.
tel: 0161 850 1965
sales@hahnplastics.co.uk
www.hahnplastics.com
    41   Ecocrib retaining wall system
    190   100% recycled plastic fencing
    408   Recycled plastic palisade profiles

Handspring Design Ltd
Ecclesall Woods Sawmill, Abbey Lane,
Sheffield S7 2QZ.
tel: 0114 221 7785
graeme@handspringdesign.co.uk
handspringdesign.co.uk
    343   Bespoke timber seats and benches
    395   Bespoke timber shelters
    406   Timber engineering

The biggest and best landscaping event...

just keeps getting bigger...

and better...

Established as the essential trade event, **LANDSCAPE** attracts garden designers, architects, landscape contractors, local authority landscaping professionals, facilities managers and interior designers from all over the UK and beyond.

Landscape
IT'S INDOORS MEETS OUTDOORS

For more information and for stand bookings contact us

t: +44(0)20 7821 8221
e: info@landscapeshow.co.uk
🐦: @landscapeevent
www.landscapeshow.co.uk

Hardscape Resourcing Limited
Westleigh Hall, Wakefield Road, Denby Dale,
Huddersfield HD8 8QJ.
tel: 01484 860044
sales@hrlonline.co.uk
hrlonline.co.uk
  71 Permeable paving in grass and gravel
  90 Landscape edgings and perimeters
 101 Gravel stabilisation grids for naturally
     permeable paving

Harrowden Turf Ltd
Corkway Drove, Hockwold, Thetford
IP26 4JR.
tel: 0800 061 2805
fax: 01842 827911
chris@harrowdenturf.co.uk
www.harrowdenturf.co.uk
 507 Cultivated turf
 517 MeadowMat wildflower matting
 546 Enviromat sedum matting

Harry Gray Sculptor
The Carving Workshop, 53A St Philips Road,
Cambridge CB1 3DA.
tel: 07880 813526
hg@harrygray.co.uk
www.harrygray.co.uk
 418 Architectural metalwork
 430 Artworks for public spaces

Heald Ltd
Northfield, Atwick Road, Hornsea
HU18 1EL.
tel: 01964 535858
fax: 01964 532819
sales@heald.uk.com
www.heald.uk.com
 206 Hostile vehicle mitigation and
     traffic control solutions

Helen Michie Ceramics & Mosaic
Marnoch, Roshven, Lochailort PH38 4NB.
tel: 01687 470322
helenmichie@oneuk.com
www.helenmichieceramics.co.uk
 440 Ceramic and mosaic artwork

Heras UK Fencing Systems
Herons Way, Carr Hill, Doncaster
DN4 8WA.
tel: 01302 364551
heras.sales@herasuk.co.uk
www.heras.co.uk
 167 Perimeter mesh fencing and gates
 180 Self-adjusting railing systems
 186 High-security perimeter protection
 209 Gates and entrance control
 502 Sports fencing and MUGAs

Hoppings Softwood Products plc
The Woodyard, Epping Road,
Epping CM16 6TT.
tel: 01992 578877
fax: 01992 561385
info@hoppings.co.uk
www.qualitydecking.co.uk
 144 Q-Shades decking
 145 Anti-slip decking
 190 Q-Garden treated pine screening

Howarth Timber
Prince Edward Works, Pontefract Lane,
Cross Green, Leeds LS9 0RA.
tel: 0330 119 3119
info@howarth-timber.co.uk
www.howarth-timber.co.uk
 146 Trex® Transcend composite decking

HRL Ventraco Limited
Westleigh Hall, Wakefield Road, Denby Dale,
Huddersfield HD8 8QJ.
tel: 01484 863880
sales@colchem.co.uk
www.colchem.co.uk
 103 Decorative in situ concrete pavements

Huck Nets (UK) Ltd
Gore Cross Business Park, Corbin Way,
Bradpole, Bridport DT6 3UX.
tel: 01308 425100
fax: 01308 458109
sales@hucknetting.co.uk
www.huck-net.co.uk
 467 Rope play equipment

Hugh Pearl (Land Drainage) Ltd
New Farm, New House Lane, Bobbingworth,
Ongar CM5 0DJ.
tel: 01277 890274
fax: 01277 890322
richardward@hughpearl.co.uk
www.hughpearl.co.uk
  47 Lakes and watercourses
 494 Natural sports field construction

Hunter Construction (Aberdeen) Ltd
Centaur House, Camiestone Road,
Thainstone Business Park, Inverurie AB51 5GT.
tel: 01467 627290
fax: 01467 625791
mark.oakley@hunter-construction.co.uk
www.hunter-construction.co.uk
 489 Artificial sports surfaces

Hydro International
Shearwater House, Clevedon Hall Estate,
Victoria Road, Clevedon BS21 7RD.
tel: 01275 878371
fax: 01275 874979
enquiries@hydro-int.com
www.hydro-int.com
  61 Stormwater flow control
  62 Stormwater treatment

HydroBlox Ltd
Franklin House, 4 Victoria Avenue,
Harrogate HG1 1EL.
tel: 020 3189 1468
sales@hydrobloxinternational.co.uk
www.hydrobloxinternational.co.uk
  67 Surface and sub-surface drainage

Hydron Protective Coatings Ltd
Unit 7, Phoenix Road Industrial Estate,
Phoenix Road, Wednesfield,
Wolverhampton WV11 3PX.
tel: 01902 450950
fax: 01902 451050
enquiries@hydronpc.co.uk
www.hydronpc.co.uk
 135 Protective coatings

Hy-Tex (UK) Ltd
Aldington Mill, Mill Lane, Aldington,
Ashford TN25 7AJ.
tel: 01233 720097
fax: 01233 720098
sales@hy-tex.co.uk
www.hy-tex.co.uk
  10 Silt and run-off pollution control
  26 Biodegradables
 376 Vertical green wall planters
 520 Root barriers

I

Ian Marlow Sculptor ARBS
Ebenezer Chapel, Buckland Dinham,
Frome BA11 2QT.
tel: 01373 471711
ian@marlowsculpture.co.uk
www.marlowsculpture.co.uk
 431 Sculpture

Iles Waste Systems
Valley Mills, Valley Road, Bradford BD1 4RU.
tel: 01274 728837
fax: 01274 734351
wastesystems@trevoriles.co.uk
www.ileswastesystems.co.uk
 348 Litter bins
 349 Recycling bins

IMAG Ltd
1 Fountain Street, Congleton CW12 4BE.
tel: 01260 278810
fax: 01260 278331
imag.ltd@btconnect.com
www.imag.co.uk
 126 Natural stone suppliers

Inturf
The Chestnuts, Wilberfoss, York YO41 5NT.
tel: 01759 321000
fax: 01759 380130
alex@inturf.co.uk
www.inturf.com
 510 Cultivated turf

IOTA Garden and Home Ltd
Wick Road, Wick St Lawrence,
Weston-super-Mare BS22 7YQ.
tel: 01934 522617
fax: 01934 522107
info@iotagarden.com
www.iotagarden.com
 360 Planters

Ivan Black Sculpture
Whitewell in the Ruins, Penally,
Tenby SA70 7RY.
tel: 01834 870087
info@ivanblack.co.uk
www.ivanblack.com
 431 Kinetic sculpture

J

Jacksons Fencing
Stowting Common, Ashford TN25 6BN.
tel: 0800 096 6360
fax: 01233 750403
info@jacksons-fencing.co.uk
www.jacksons-fencing.co.uk
 178 Perimeter security
 179 Railings
 191 Timber fencing and gates
 195 Acoustic barriers
 210 Gates, barriers and access control

James Price Blacksmith Ltd
The Workshop, Highbridge Lane,
East Chiltington, Lewes BN7 3QY.
tel: 01273 890398
info@blacksmithdesigner.com
www.blacksmithdesigner.com
 423 Bespoke metalwork

Jankowski Weathervanes
Unit 6, Cain Valley Trading Estate,
Lanffyllin SY22 5DD.
tel: 07929 566342
stan@panjankowski.com
www.panjankowski.com
 422 Weathervanes and garden art

Jenny Pickford
12c Shucknall Court, Weston Beggard,
Hereford HR1 4BH.
tel: 07985 246056
info@jennypickford.co.uk
www.jennypickford.co.uk
 421 Artist blacksmith

Johnsons Sports Seeds
Thorn Farm, Inkberrow, Worcester WR7 4LJ.
tel: 01386 791102
fax: 01386 792715
amenity@dlf.co.uk
www.johnsonssportsseed.co.uk
 515 Sports seed specialist

Jon Mills Ltd
Robertson Yard, 42A Robertson Road,
Brighton BN1 5NJ.
tel: 01273 235810
jon@metaljon.com
www.metaljon.com
 423 Bespoke metalwork

Joseph Ingleby
Glasgow Sculpture Studios, The Whisky Bond,
2 Dawson Road, Glasgow G4 9SS.
tel: 0141 337 2184
joe@josephingleby.com
www.josephingleby.com
 432 Public sculpture

Jupiter Play & Leisure Ltd
14 Swanston Steading, 109 Swanston Road,
Edinburgh EH10 7DS.
tel: 0131 445 7989
fax: 0131 445 7980
info@jupiterplay.co.uk
www.jupiterplay.co.uk
 468 Design-led play spaces

K

Keith McCarter FRBS
10 Coopersknowe Crescent,
Galashiels TD1 2DS.
tel: 01896 751112
keith@keith-mccarter.com
www.keith-mccarter.com
   432 Sculpture

Keller
Oxford Road, Ryton-on-Dunsmore,
Coventry CV8 3EG.
tel: 024 7651 1266
fax: 024 7630 5230
derek.taylor@keller.co.uk
www.keller.co.uk
   42 Ground engineering

Kent Stainless (Wexford) Ltd
Ardcavan, Wexford, Ireland.
tel: 0800 376 8377
fax: 00 353 53 914 1802
info@kentstainless.com
www.kentstainless.com
  131 Lift-assist manholes
  132 Heelproof ventilation access
        grilles
  239 In-ground units
  262 Wayfinding signage
  383 Planters

KFS Enterprises Ltd
1 Possil House, 23 Copse Hill,
London SW20 0NB.
tel: 07576 581872
neil@kfsent.com
www.puczynski.pl
  313 Co-ordinated street furniture

Kinley Systems Ltd
Northpoint, Compass Park,
Staplecross TN32 5BS.
tel: 01580 830688
sales@kinley.co.uk
www.kinley.co.uk
   91 Landscape edging: ExcelEdge®
  147 Decking and paving
  383 Perimeta planter systems

L

Ladybrook Nursery
Lytham Drive, off Seal Road, Bramhall,
Stockport SK7 2LD.
tel: 0161 440 8060
sales@ladybrooknursery.com
www.ladybrooknursery.com
  538 Trees and conifers
  539 Topiary and hedging
  544 Specimen shrubs
  547 Herbaceous plants

Lakes & Fountains
The Clays, Merrydown Lane,
Chineham RG24 8LU.
tel: 07884 374995
enquiries@lakesandfountains.co.uk
www.lakesandfountain.com
  447 Fountains and water features

The Land Design Partnership Ltd
Unit 1, Dairy Lane Farm, Chainhurst, Marden,
Tonbridge TN12 9SS.
tel: 01622 820522
rob@ldp.uk.com
www.ldp.uk.com
   50 Landscape services

Landmark
32 Henry Road, Barnet EN4 8BD.
tel: 0808 129 3773
fax: 0808 129 3774
enquiries@madebylandmark.com
madebylandmark.com
  263 Visitor signage

Landscape Show Ltd
28 Churton Street, London SW1V 3XG.
tel: 020 7821 8221
info@landscapeshow.co.uk
www.landscapeshow.co.uk
  562 Landscape Show

Lang+Fulton
Unit 2b, Newbridge Industrial Estate,
Newbridge, Edinburgh EH28 8PJ.
tel: 0131 441 1255
fax: 0131 441 4161
sales@langandfulton.co.uk
langandfulton.co.uk
  153 External floor gratings and treads
  160 Louvred fences: Italia and Delta
  162 Grating fences
  176 Railings: Modena, Siena and Rimini
  203 Gates
  398 Bin stores, plant housings
        and compounds

Langley Design
Unit L (Gate 1), Chelworth Industrial Estate,
Cricklade, Swindon SN6 6HE.
tel: 01793 759461
fax: 01793 759642
info@langleydesign.co.uk
www.langleydesign.co.uk
  248 Cycle parking
  296 Co-ordinated street furniture
  333 Outdoor seats and benches

Lappen Nurseries
Herrenpfad 14, D-41334 Nettetal, Germany.
tel: 00 49 2157 818 153
GEngelke@lappen.de
www.lappen.de/en
  534 Tree stock

Learning Through Play
Hartshill Nursery, Thong Lane, Shorne,
Gravesend DA12 4AD.
tel: 01474 569576
info@learningthroughplay.net
www.learningthroughplay.net
  469 Bespoke playgrounds

Lettering & Sculpture Ltd
Manor Farm, 1 Witney Road,
Witney OX29 7TZ.
tel: 01993 868012
peeverstudio@aol.com
www.alecpeever.com
  436 Letter carving and sculpture

Lindum
West Grange, Thorganby, York
YO19 6DJ.
tel: 01904 448675
fax: 01904 448713
lindum@turf.co.uk
turf.co.uk
   26 Turf reinforcement
   29 Green roofs
  512 Cultivated turf
  518 Wildflower turf

Livingreen Design Ltd
24/6 Dryden Road, Bilston Glen
Industrial Estate, Loanhead, Edinburgh
EH20 9HX.
tel: 0131 440 9804
fax: 0131 440 9805
tony.sawyer@livingreendesign.com
www.livingreendesign.com
  196 Greenscreen acoustic barriers
  362 Planters for roof gardens
  364 Feature planters

Logic Street & Park Furniture Ltd
Royce House, Royce Avenue,
Cowpen Industrial Estate, Billingham
TS23 4BX.
tel: 01642 373400
enquiries@logic-sf.co.uk
www.logic-sf.co.uk
  318 External benches and seating
  334 Ullswater timber seating
  377 Planters

London Swimming Pool Company Ltd
Unit 1, Shannon Commercial Centre,
Beverley Way, New Malden KT3 4PT.
tel: 020 8605 1255
enquiries@londonswimmingpools.com
www.londonswimmingpools.com
  450 Outdoor swimming pools and spas

Lorenz von Ehren
Maldfeldstrasse 4, D-21077 Hamburg,
Germany.
tel: 00 49 40 761 08 126
fax: 00 49 40 761 08 100
Peter@LvE.de
lve-baumschule.de
  536 Specimen plants

Lumena Lights Ltd
Centre 33, Long March, Daventry
NN11 4NR.
tel: 01327 871161
sales@lumenalights.com
www.lumenalights.com
  270 Illuminated bollards

M

m-tec
Britannia House, Junction Street,
Darwen BB3 2RB.
tel: 01254 773718
fax: 01254 783287
info@m-tec.uk.com
www.m-tec.uk.com
  410 Specialist metal fabricator

M&M Timber Ltd
Hunt House Sawmills, Clows Top,
Kidderminster DY14 9HY.
tel: 0333 003 5133
fax: 01299 832536
sales@mmtimber.co.uk
www.mmtimber.co.uk
   41 Unilog Pro retaining walls
  477 PlayGuard playground timber

Macs Automated Bollard Systems Ltd
Unit 8.1b, Tameside Business Park,
Windmill Lane, Denton M34 3QS.
tel: 0161 320 6462
fax: 0161 320 6463
enquiries@macs-bollards.com
www.macs-bollards.com
  238 Automatic rising bollards

Magma Safety Products Ltd
Unit 1, Sawston Park, London Road,
Pampisford, Cambridge CB22 3EE.
tel: 01223 836643
fax: 01223 834648
info@magmasafety.co.uk
www.magmasafety.co.uk
  136 Anti-slip surfaces

Mallon Foundry
22 High Street, Moneymore,
Magherafelt BT45 7PD.
tel: 07899 913537
Charlie@mallonfoundry.com
www.mallonfoundry.com
  433 Sculpture

Mansfield Sand Company
Two Oaks Quarry, Coxmoor Road,
Kirkby in Ashfield, Mansfield NG18 5BW.
tel: 01623 707555
fax: 01623 707579
louise.barrington-earp@mansfield-sand.co.uk
www.mansfield-sand.co.uk
   22 Fibre-reinforced rootzones

Marion Smith, Sculptor
Auchendownie, Leven KY8 5QH.
tel: 07870 957971
info@marionsmithsculptor.co.uk
www.marionsmithsculptor.co.uk
  433 Sculpture

Marley Eternit
Lichfield Road, Branston,
Burton-on-Trent DE14 3HD.
tel: 01283 722588
info@marleyeternit.co.uk
www.marleyeternit.co.uk
  138 Anti-slip timber deck boards:
        JB Antislip Plus® and JB CitiDeck®

Marshalls plc
Landscape House, Premier Way,
Lowfields Business Park, Elland
HX5 9HT.
tel: 0870 444 6217
fax: 0870 442 7725
esi.marshalls@web-response.co.uk
www.marshalls.co.uk/commercial
   76 Priora permeable block paving
   80 Linear drainage systems
   84 Combined kerb & drainage systems
   86 Kerb systems
  104 Concrete paving systems
  112 Concrete block paving and setts
  124 Natural stone
  219 Protective post and rail
  222 Traffic calming systems
  235 Bollards
  249 Cycle parking
  264 Signage and wayfinding
  272 Illumination
  278 Co-ordinated street furniture
  280 Protective street furniture
  282 Co-ordinated street furniture
  320 Seats and benches
  357 Litter bins
  378 Planters
  526 Tree protection

Massey & Harris (Engineering) Ltd
Unit 5, The Hollygate, Albert Street,
Stockport SK3 0BD.
tel: 0161 480 5243
fax: 0161 476 0151
info@masseyandharris.com
www.masseyandharris.com
  454 Playground equipment

Melissa Cole Artist Blacksmith
Moonraker Farm, Bottlesford,
Pewsey SN9 6LU.
tel: 07711 325209
melissa@melissacole.co.uk
www.melissacole.co.uk
  422 Ironwork and sculpture

Meon Ltd
Railside, Northarbour Spur,
Portsmouth PO6 3TU.
tel: 023 9220 0606
mail@meonuk.com
www.meonuk.com
   99 DekorGrip Resin Bound surfacing
  520 DekorGrip Rubber Mulch
  529 DekorGrip Tree Surround surfacing

metroSTOR®
Wootton Lane, Wootton, Canterbury
CT4 6RP.
tel: 0845 075 0760
enquiries@metrostor.eu
www.metrostor.eu
  395 Outdoor storage systems

Michael Cooper Sculptor
Grange Farm, Radnage,
High Wycombe HP14 4ED.
tel: 01494 482226
michael@michaelcoopersculptor.com
www.michaelcoopersculptor.co.uk
  434 Sculpture and carvings

Modular Wall Systems (UK) Ltd
Unit 2, Rugby Street, Hull HU3 4RB.
tel: 0800 915 5429
info@modularwall.co.uk
www.modularwall.co.uk
   36 Retaining walls
  188 Boundary fence walls
  197 Acoustic barriers

Monster Play @ Caloo Ltd
Unit 12, Boxted Farm, Berkhamsted Road,
Hemel Hempstead HP1 2SG.
tel: 01442 265489
info@monsterplay.co.uk
www.caloo.co.uk
  456 Playground equipment

N

Neptune Street Furniture
Time House, 19 Hillsons Road, Botley,
Southampton SO30 2DY.
tel: 01962 777799
fax: 01962 777723
enquiries@neptunestreetfurniture.co.uk
www.neptunestreetfurniture.co.uk
  309 Co-ordinated street furniture
  336 Seats and benches
  358 Litter bins
  379 Planters

Noel Blakeman
10 Bishops Meadow, Long Buckby,
Northampton NN6 7WG.
tel: 01327 843995
studio@noelblakeman.com
www.noelblakeman.com
  434 Sculpture

Notts Sport Ltd
Innovation House, Magna Park,
Lutterworth LE17 4XH.
tel: 01455 883730
fax: 01455 883755
info@nottssport.com
www.nottssport.co.uk
  484 Safer surfacing: ChildsPlay®
  490 Artificial sports surfaces

O

Omos Ltd
Unit 1–3, Military Road Industrial Park,
Naas, County Kildare, W91 TX28,
Ireland.
tel: 0870 471 3557
fax: 00 353 4589 9803
alastair@omos.ie
www.omos.ie
  310 Street furniture
  337 Seating
  359 Litter bins
  380 Planters

OSC Sales Ltd
The Forge, Wheelers Lane, Linton
ME17 4BN.
tel: 0800 652 2203
fax: 0845 241 9863
sales@oscsales.com
www.oscsales.co.uk
  151 Self-drilling screws

The Outdoor Deck Company
Unit 6, Teddington Business Park, Station Road,
Teddington TW11 9BQ.
tel: 020 8977 0820
fax: 020 8977 0825
sales@outdoordeck.co.uk
www.outdoordeck.co.uk
  150 Timber decking

Outdoor Design
Unit 1, Block A, Ford Airfield Industrial Estate,
Ford, Arundel BN18 0HY.
tel: 01903 716960
info@outdoordesign.co.uk
www.outdoordesign.co.uk
  366 Bespoke planters
  417 Bespoke metal fabrication for
       landscape and garden designers

P

Palmstead Nurseries Ltd
Harville Road, Wye, Ashford
TN25 5EU.
tel: 01233 813340
fax: 01233 813071
sales@palmstead.co.uk
www.palmstead.co.uk
  540 Trees and hedging
  545 Shrubs
  548 Perennials
  550 Hardy exotics

Park Leisure Ltd
Pivington Mill, Pluckley TN27 0PG.
tel: 01233 840141
enquiries@parkleisure.com
www.parkleisure.com
  479 Sports and play equipment

Phi Group
Hadley House, Bayshill Road,
Cheltenham GL50 3AW.
tel: 01242 707600
southern@phigroup.co.uk
www.phigroup.co.uk
   37 Retaining structures

Phoenix Amenity Supplies Ltd
The Bakery, Old Vicarage,
Hanley Castle WR8 0BJ.
tel: 01684 212020
fax: 01684 578424
sales@phoenixamenity.co.uk
www.phoenixamenity.co.uk
  516 Amenity grass seed
  519 Wildflower seed mixtures

Platipus® Anchors Ltd
Kingsfield Business Centre, Philanthropic Road,
Redhill RH1 4DP.
tel: 01737 762300
fax: 01737 773395
info@platipus-anchors.com
www.platipus-anchors.com
43 Mechanical earth anchoring
527 Tree anchoring and irrigation

Playrite
Wellington Mills, Liversedge
WF15 7FH.
tel: 01924 412488
fax: 01924 412337
info@playrite.co.uk
www.playrite.co.uk
485 Playground safety surfacing
491 Artificial sports surfaces

Polypipe Civils
Charnwood Business Park,
North Road, Loughborough
LE11 1LE.
tel: 01509 615100
fax: 01509 610215
civils@polypipe.com
www.polypipe.com
55 Ridgistorm-XL
56 Component chambers
64 Permavoid
65 Polystorm

Pomery Natural Stone Ltd
Little Heathers, Outlands Lane,
Curdridge SO30 2HD.
tel: 01489 789444
sales@pomery.co.uk
www.pomery.co.uk
87 Natural stone kerbs
87 Tactile paving, natural stone
127 Natural stone specialists
343 Natural stone seating

Pop UP Power® Ltd
PO Box 1447, Ilford IG2 6GT.
tel: 020 8227 0208
info@popuppower.co.uk
www.popuppower.co.uk
240 Retractable power units

The Pot Company
Maynards Farm, Lamberhurst Quarter,
Tunbridge Wells TN3 8AL.
tel: 01892 890353
sales@thepotco.com
www.thepotco.com
368 Planters

Practicality Brown Ltd
Swan Road, Iver SL0 9LA.
tel: 01753 652022
fax: 01753 653007
sales@pracbrown.co.uk
www.pracbrown.co.uk
531 Tree moving
531 Tree and vegetation clearance
542 Instant hedges
542 Semi-mature and specimen trees

Procter Contracts
11 Pantglas Industrial Estate, Bedwas,
Caerphilly CF83 8XD.
tel: 029 2000 5884
esi@proctercontracts.co.uk
www.procterbros.co.uk/contracts
187 High-security fencing systems
202 Automatic gates

Proludic Ltd
The Play Hub, Bradmore Business Park, Bunny,
Nottingham NG11 6QA.
tel: 0115 982 3980
info@proludic.co.uk
www.proludic.co.uk
458 Play and sport equipment

Public Spaces
Unit 1A, Southern Cross Business Park,
Bray, Ireland.
tel: 0808 101 1590
malcolm@benkert.biz
www.publicspaces.eu
338 External furniture/urban elements

Q

Queensbury Shelters Ltd
Fitzherbert Road, Farlington,
Portsmouth PO6 1SE.
tel: 023 9221 0052
fax: 023 9221 0059
sales@queensburyshelters.co.uk
www.queensburyshelters.co.uk
250 Cycle storage solutions
384 Passenger shelters
385 Walkways and canopies

R

RMB Hydroseeding
Lower Wick Farm, Lower Wick,
Dursley GL11 6DD.
tel: 01453 511365
fax: 01453 511364
info@hydroseeding.co.uk
www.hydroseeding.co.uk
45 Hydroseeding

Road Maintenance Services Ltd
Mowpen Brow, High Legh,
Knutsford WA16 6PB.
tel: 01925 752165
fax: 01925 757098
enquiries@rms-ltd.com
www.rms-ltd.com
100 Impressions natural surfaces

Robbie Schneider Lettering Sculptor
West Glen Turret Farmhouse, Crieff PH7 4JR.
tel: 07736 669321
robbie@robbieschneider.co.uk
www.robbieschneider.co.uk
437 Lettering sculpture

Rocklyn Engineering Ltd
Dirac Crescent, Bristol & Bath Science Park,
Emersons Green, Bristol BS16 7FR.
tel: 0117 370 7710
info@rocklyn.co.uk
www.rocklyn.co.uk
251 Cycle parking
393 Shelters, canopies and covered walkways

Rocklyn Sports
Dirac Crescent, Bristol & Bath Science Park,
Emersons Green, Bristol BS16 7FR.
tel: 0117 370 7710
info@rocklyn.co.uk
www.rocklynsports.co.uk
504 Sports shelters

Round Wood of Mayfield Ltd
Round Wood, Newick Lane,
Mayfield TN20 6RG.
tel: 01435 867072
fax: 01435 864708
sales@roundwood.com
www.roundwood.com
148 Hardwood timber decking
401 Oak-framed buildings

RPC Contracts
Quarryfields, Ruthin LL15 2UG.
tel: 01824 709102
fax: 01824 709105
contracts@rpcltd.co.uk
www.rpcltd.co.uk
38 Retaining structures

RPC Environmental
Quarryfields, Ruthin LL15 2UG.
tel: 01824 709102
fax: 01824 709105
contracts@rpcltd.co.uk
www.rpcltd.co.uk
14 Erosion control systems

RPC Paving
Quarryfields, Ruthin LL15 2UG.
tel: 01824 702493
fax: 01824 704527
enquiries@rpcpaving.co.uk
www.rpcltd.co.uk
107 Decorative paving flags and kerbs

Ruskins Trees and Landscapes Ltd
The Rose Garden, Warley Street, Great Warley,
Brentwood CM13 3JH.
tel: 01277 849990
fax: 01277 849991
info@ruskins.co.uk
www.ruskins.co.uk
470 Play trees and play logs
530 Tree and hedge moving
532 Tree root investigation
541 Tree and shrub supply and planting

Russetts Developments Ltd
27–29 Burners Lane, Kiln Farm,
Milton Keynes MK11 3HA.
tel: 0870 770 2800
fax: 0870 770 2801
info@russetts.co.uk
www.russetts.co.uk
11 Flexible sheet membranes

Ruth Moilliet Sculpture
2 Springfield Road, Ramsbottom, Bury BL0 9SU.
tel: 07973 908839
sculpture@ruthmoilliet.com
www.ruthmoilliet.com
435 Sculpture

S

S2T Grass Reinforcement
125 High Road, North Weald,
Epping CM16 6EA.
tel: 01992 522797
fax: 01992 878176
info@perfo.co.uk
www.perfo.co.uk
23 Self-anchoring grass and ground
reinforcement tiles

Safe & Sound Playgrounds
Unit 9A, Triangle Business Park,
Wendover Road, Stoke Mandeville HP22 5BL.
tel: 01296 614448
info@safeandsoundplaygrounds.co.uk
www.safeandsoundplaygrounds.co.uk
480 Multi-use games areas (MUGAs)

Sarum Hardwood Structures Ltd
Unit 1B, Chilbolton Down Farm,
Stockbridge SO20 6BU.
tel: 01264 811600
fax: 01264 810600
info@sarumhardwood.co.uk
www.sarumhardwood.co.uk
158 Bridges
220 N1 timber highway parapets

SDS Limited
Clearwater House, Castlemills,
Biddisham BS26 2RE.
tel: 01934 751303
fax: 01934 751304
info@sdslimited.com
www.sdslimited.com
66 Surface water management

Setter Play Equipment
Unit 6A, Shefford Mill, Stanford Road,
Shefford SG17 5NR.
tel: 01462 817538
jonathan@setterplay.co.uk
www.setterplay.co.uk
471 Play equipment

Setter Shelters
Unit 6A, Shefford Mill, Stanford Road,
Shefford SG17 5NR.
tel: 01462 817538
jonathan@setterplay.co.uk
www.settershelters.co.uk
386 Shelters and canopies

Shelley Signs Ltd
54 Cartmel Drive, Harlescott,
Shrewsbury SY1 3TB.
tel: 01743 460996
sales@shelleysigns.co.uk
www.shelleysigns.co.uk
265 Signs and panels

Sign 2000 Ltd
Units 3 & 4, Deacon Trading Estate,
209–211 Vale Road, Tonbridge
TN9 1SU.
tel: 01732 772000
info@sign2000.co.uk
sign2000.co.uk
  256 Architectural signs
  266 Corporate branding signs

Signscape AND Signconex Ltd
Pear Tree Industrial Estate, Bath Road,
Upper Langford, Bristol BS40 5DJ.
tel: 01934 852888
fax: 01934 852816
sales@signscape.co.uk
www.signscape.co.uk
  258 Wayfinding signs and information
       displays

Silva Timber Products Ltd
Unit 4, Albright Road, Widnes
WA8 8FY.
tel: 0151 495 3111
enquiries@silvatimber.co.uk
www.silvatimber.co.uk
  140 Timber decking and cladding
  192 Timber fencing and screens

Sovereign Design Play Systems Ltd
40 Towerfield Road, Shoeburyness,
Southend-on-Sea SS3 9QT.
tel: 01702 291129
fax: 01702 290092
info@sovereign.gb.com
www.sovereignplayequipment.co.uk
  472 Imaginative outdoor play areas

Sportsmark™ Group Ltd
18 St Georges Place, Semington,
Trowbridge BA14 6GB.
tel: 0800 019 7733
fax: 01635 864588
info@sportsmark.net
www.sportsmark.net
  132 Road studs and markings
  496 Sports equipment

SSP. Specialised Sports Products Ltd
Unit 3, Heppington Barn,
Street End/Faussett Hill,
Lower Hardes, Canterbury CT4 7AL.
tel: 01227 463606
info@ssp-uk.co.uk
www.ssp-uk.co.uk
  473 Playground equipment and services
  486 Safer surfacing

Steintec®
730 London Road, West Thurrock
RM20 3NL.
tel: 01708 860049
fax: 01780 860893
info@steintec.co.uk
www.steintec.co.uk
  133 Early trafficking mortars
  134 Specialist mortars for pavement
       construction
  134 Paving cleaning and protection

Street Design Ltd
Unit 47, Hayhill Industrial Estate,
Barrow upon Soar, Loughborough LE12 8LD.
tel: 01509 815335
fax: 01509 815332
sdl@street-design.com
www.street-design.com
  311 Co-ordinated street furniture
  339 Seating
  370 Planters

Street Furnishings Ltd
Festival House, Mumbery Hill, Wargrave,
Reading RG10 8EE.
tel: 0118 940 4717
fax: 0118 940 3216
mail@streetfurnishings.co.uk
www.streetfurnishings.co.uk
  236 Bollards
  276 Solar sign lighting systems and reflective
       bollards

Street Furniture Works Ltd
3rd Floor, 7 Nova Scotia Place, Spike Island,
Bristol BS1 6XJ.
tel: 0117 403 3604
sales@streetfurnitureworks.info
www.streetfurnitureworks.info
  300 Street furniture

Streetlife
Herengracht 36, Leiden 2312LD,
The Netherlands.
tel: 00 31 71 524 6846
fax: 00 31 71 524 6849
streetlife@streetlife.nl
www.streetlife.nl/en
  302 Co-ordinated street furniture

Suregreen Ltd
2 Croft Way, Eastways Industrial Estate,
Witham CM8 2FB.
tel: 01376 503869
fax: 01376 503563
sales@sure-green.com
www.sure-ground.com
  24 Permeable grass and gravel ground
      reinforcement

SureSet UK Ltd
32 Deverill Road Trading Estate, Sutton Veny,
Warminster BA12 7BZ.
tel: 01985 841180
fax: 01985 841260
mail@sureset.co.uk
www.sureset.co.uk
  74   Surface drainage
  96   Spectrum glass bound surfacing
  97   SureSet permeable bound surfacing
  528 Permeable tree pit surfacing

Sutcliffe Play Ltd
Waggon Lane, Upton, Pontefract WF9 1JS.
tel: 01977 653200
fax: 01977 653222
info@sutcliffeplay.co.uk
www.sutcliffeplay.co.uk
  474 Play equipment

T

TenCate Geosynthetics (UK) Ltd
PO Box 773, Telford TF7 9FE.
tel: 01952 588066
fax: 01952 588466
Service.uk@tencate.com
www.tencate.com
  8   Woven geotextiles
  9   Non-woven geotextiles
  15 Reinforcement and erosion control

Terram
Blackwater Trading Estate,
The Causeway, Maldon
CM9 4GG.
tel: 01621 874200
fax: 01621 874299
info@terram.com
www.terram.com
  13 Geocells
  18 GrassProtecta reinforcement mesh
  19 Porous paving for reinforcement
  72 Porous paving for SUDS

Timberplay Ltd
Aizlewood's Mill, Nursery Street, Sheffield
S3 8GG.
tel: 0114 282 3474
fax: 0114 282 3463
info@timberplay.com
www.timberplay.com
  460 Play equipment
  475 Play equipment

Timotay Landscapes Ltd
14 Hinwick Road, Wollaston,
Wellingborough NN29 7QT.
tel: 01933 665151
enquiries@timotaylandscapes.co.uk
www.timotaylandscapes.co.uk
  51 Landscape services

Timotay Playscapes
14 Hinwick Road, Wollaston,
Wellingborough NN29 7QT.
tel: 01933 665151
enquiries@timotayplayscapes.co.uk
www.timotayplayscapes.co.uk
  462 Playground equipment

Tobermore
2 Lisnamuck Road, Tobermore,
Magherafelt BT45 5QF.
tel: 028 7964 2411
fax: 028 7964 4145
sales@tobermore.co.uk
www.tobermore.co.uk
  39   Concrete retaining walls
  75   Permeable concrete block paving
  108 Concrete flag paving
  114 Concrete block paving

Todds Nursery Ltd
The Garden House, Southill Park,
Southill, Biggleswade
SG18 9LL.
tel: 01462 813390
info@toddsnursery.co.uk
www.toddsnursery.co.uk
  533 Trees and hedging

TOPP & Co.
Unit 5, The Airfield Industrial Estate,
Tholthorpe, York YO61 1ST.
tel: 01347 833173
enquiry@toppandco.com
www.toppandco.com
  419 Architectural metalwork

Topturf Irrigation
Unit L, Rudford Industrial Estate,
Ford, Arundel BN18 0BF.
tel: 01903 278240
fax: 01903 278245
info@ttirrigation.co.uk
www.ttirrigation.co.uk
  506 Irrigation

Tradstocks Ltd
Dunaverig, Thornhill, Stirling
FK8 3QW.
tel: 01786 850400
fax: 01786 850404
info@tradstocks.co.uk
www.tradstocks.co.uk
  128 Natural stone processor

Trans-European Stone Ltd
4th Floor, Park House,
22 Park Street, Croydon
CR0 1YE.
tel: 020 8243 8905
info@t-estone.co.uk
t-estone.co.uk
  129 Natural stone supplier

Trueform
Pasadena Trading Estate,
Pasadena Close, Hayes
UB3 3NQ.
tel: 020 8561 4959
fax: 020 8848 1397
sales@trueform.co.uk
www.trueform.co.uk
  267 Signs, wayfinding and digital displays
  388 Shelters, canopies and walkways

TVS Play Surfaces
Low Bay, Commerce Street,
Carrs Industrial Estate, Haslingden
BB4 5JT.
tel: 01706 260220
jason@tvs-group.co.uk
www.TVS-Group.co.uk
  487 Shock-absorbent safety surfacing

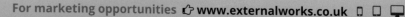

U

Ukishima Sculpture Studio
192/3 Causewayside, Edinburgh EH9 1PN.
tel: 0131 667 3532
kate@ukishima.net
www.ukishima.net
435 Public sculpture

URBASTYLE®
Severn House, Hazell Drive,
Newport NP10 8FY.
tel: 07890 585768
uk@urbastyle.com
www.urbastyle.com
109 Silkstone Fasonado paving
237 Architectural concrete bollards
312 Architectural concrete street furniture
340 Architectural concrete benches and seats
381 Architectural concrete planters

V

Verde Sports (Cricket) Ltd
Gabbotts Farm Barn, Bury Lane, Withnell,
Chorley PR6 8SW.
tel: 0115 846 5732
verdesports.cricket@ntlworld.com
www.verdesportscricket.com
492 Synthetic turf cricket facilities

Vica SL Ltd
Aizlewood Mill, Nursery Street,
Sheffield S3 8GG.
tel: 01709 763410
fax: 01709 763411
sales@vicasl.co.uk
www.vicasl.co.uk
496 Goal ends
503 Sports fencing

W

Westminster Stone Co Ltd
Shaw's Estate, Sodylt, Ellesmere
SY12 9EL.
tel: 01978 710685
ask@westminsterstone.com
www.westminsterstone.com
111 Paving flags
111 National Trust Landscape Collection

Wicksteed Playgrounds
Digby Street, Kettering
NN16 8YJ.
tel: 01536 517028
sales@wicksteed.co.uk
www.wicksteed.co.uk
464 Playground equipment
476 Bespoke play equipment

William Bain Fencing Ltd
Lochrin Works, 7 Limekilns Road, Blairlinn
Industrial Estate, Cumbernauld G67 2RN.
tel: 01236 457333
fax: 01236 451166
sales@lochrin-bain.co.uk
www.lochrin-bain.co.uk
184 High-security perimeter systems

Woodberry of Leamington Spa
Bericote Wood Yard, Bericote Road,
Leamington Spa CV32 6QP.
tel: 01926 889922
fax: 01926 430044
mail@woodberryofleamingtonspa.com
www.woodberryofleamingtonspa.com
341 Seats and benches

WoodBlocX
Munro Sawmills, Old Evanton Road,
Dingwall IV15 9UN.
tel: 0800 389 1420
fax: 01349 864508
admin@woodblocx.co.uk
woodblocx-landscaping.co.uk
40 Modular timber retaining walls
382 Modular timber planters

Woodscape Ltd
1 Sett End Road West, Shadsworth Business
Park, Blackburn BB1 2QJ.
tel: 01254 685185
fax: 01254 671237
sales@woodscape.co.uk
www.woodscape.co.uk
149 Hardwood decking, raised decks and
boardwalks
304 Co-ordinated street furniture
342 Hardwood seating
407 Landscape structures

Z

Zaun Ltd
Steel Drive, Wolverhampton WV10 9ED.
tel: 01902 796699
fax: 01902 796698
sales@zaun.co.uk
www.zaun.co.uk
164 Perimeter fencing
173 Architectural fencing
175 Railings
182 Security fencing
198 DBS acoustic fencing system
211 Gates and access control
500 Sports fencing systems

Zenith Canopy Structures Ltd
Units 1 & 2, Stokes Farm, Binfield Road,
Wokingham RG40 5PR.
tel: 0118 978 9072
info@zenithcsl.com
www.zenithcsl.com
394 Modular canopy shelters